# Concise Textbook of Physiology for Dental Students

# Concise Textbook of Physiology for Dental Students

*Hema Pispati*

YMCA Library Building, Jai Singh Road, New Delhi 110 001

Oxford University Press is a department of the University of Oxford. It furthers the University's objective of excellence in research, scholarship, and education by publishing worldwide in

Oxford New York

Athens Auckland Bangkok Bogota Buenos Aires Cape Town Chennai Dar es Salaam Delhi Florence Hong Kong Istanbul Karachi Kolkata Kuala Lumpur Madrid Melbourne Mexico City Mumbai Nairobi Paris São Paolo Shanghai Singapore Taipei Tokyo Toronto Warsaw

with associated companies in Berlin Ibadan



Published in India
By Oxford University Press, New Delhi



First published 2001



ISBN 019 565 2096

Typeset by Eleven Arts, Keshav Puram 110 035
Printed in India by Rashtriya Printers
Published by Manzar Khan, Oxford University Press
YMCA Library Building, Jai Singh Road, New Delhi 110 001

# Preface

In my twenty years of teaching first year dental (BDS) students, I have realized that there are hardly any textbooks of physiology available exclusively for dental students who, therefore, have to rely on larger textbooks meant for MBBS students. Due to the limited time available to dental students during the academic year, it becomes difficult for them to select relevant aspects of basic physiology and imbibe the fundamentals of these.

The aim of this book is to provide a knowledge of basic physiology in a concise form. I have dealt with all the topics in the syllabus laid down by the Dental Council of India and simplified them with suitable tables, diagrams and flow charts. The basic functions of the different systems of the body, and their control and clinical importance have been emphasized. Some of the basic facts have been arranged in the form of lists for the convenience of the students.

This book should be useful not only for dental students, for whom it is meant, but also for those in paramedical courses, such as physiotherapy, occupational therapy and speech therapy, and for postgraduate dental (MDS) students as well. It may serve as a handy reference book for postgraduate medical students who wish to take entrance examinations for admission to various medical courses.

I am grateful to Dr (Mrs) M.P. Sharma, Professor and head of the Department of Physiology, T.N. Medical College and Nair Hospital, Mumbai, for her encouragement, and to many of my colleagues for their cooperation. I would also like to thank Oxford University Press, New Delhi, for its cooperation and keen interest in the publication of this book. Thanks also to Miss Christine Rebello for her dedicated secretarial help.

The greatest reward any author can get is feedback, good or bad, from the readers. Teachers and students of physiology may notice some lacunae or shortcomings in this book and their suggestions on how to improve it are most welcome.

Dr (Mrs) H.P. Pispati

# Contents

# Introduction to Physiology

Physiology is the study of the mechanisms by which different structures in the body function and interact.

A knowledge of the normal is essential before an understanding of the abnormal (disease) is possible.

In the wider subject of general biology, there are single-cell organisms, for example the amoeba, which are capable of living an independent life. However, the cells of the human body are not capable of an independent existence and are the structural units of the total complex human organism.

## ORGANIZATION OF THE BODY

The *cell* is both the structural and functional unit of the body. There are great variations in the appearance and consistency of different cells, and all parts of the body are aggregates of many of these units.

During the early stages of the development of an embryo, all cells look alike. Soon, they begin to undergo changes in their structure. This process is called differentiation. As differentiation occurs, groups of cells become specialized in function, that is, they perform mainly one type of physiological activity. Such differentiation and specialization result in the formation of the tissues of the body.

A *tissue* may be defined as the organization of like cells, performing a special bodily function, bound together with intercellular substance and bathed in interstitial fluid.

There are four types of primary tissue:

1. Epithelial: This tissue forms the covering of the body, the lining of its parts and also, the secreting portions of glands.
2. Connective: This forms the supporting framework of the body and binds the parts together.

   The vascular and lymphatic tissues transport substances throughout the body and provide the cell's immediate environment.
3. Muscular: Muscular tissue performs work by its ability to shorten or contract.
4. Nervous: This carries impulses to all parts of the body, thus coordinating various functions. Its specialized properties of irritability and conductivity help carry impulses.

Two or more tissues grouped together, performing a highly specialized function, form an *organ*, for example the stomach, heart and lungs.

The stomach is made of all types of tissues. Its covering and lining are formed by epithelial tissue, and its wall by connective and muscular tissues. Nervous tissue is distributed throughout its structure.

Groups of organs that act together to perform highly complex and specialized functions are called *systems*. For example, the entire process of digestion takes place through the coordinated activity of the organs of the digestive system.

The following nine body systems are commonly recognized:

1. Skeletal
2. Muscular
3. Circulatory
4. Respiratory
5. Digestive
6. Excretory
7. Endocrine
8. Nervous
9. Reproductive

The musculoskeletal system is concerned with movements in the external environment, that is, communication with the outside world. The circulatory and lymphatic systems are concerned with internal transportation, the respiratory system with the intake of oxygen and elimination of carbon dioxide, the digestive system with the intake of raw material (food), the excretory system with the elimination of waste products, the endocrine and nervous systems with communication within the body, and the reproductive system with propagation of the species.

No one system can function in isolation and each system is constantly influenced by environmental conditions. The science of human physiology, therefore, involves the study of the interrelationship between different organs and organ systems, which is necessary for the survival of the body as a whole. Adaptation to the external environment and maintenance of the internal environment (homeostasis) are the basic features of life. The internal environment is constituted by extracellular fluid (ECF), which surrounds the tissue cells. The volume, osmotic pressure, temperature, pH and electrolyte concentration of ECF must be maintained within a normal range for the optimum functioning of cells. Failure of homeostatic mechanisms results in abnormal function.

SECTION

# I

# General Physiology

CHAPTER 1

# The Cell

Under a light microscope, a cell is seen to consist of the cytoplasm within which is the nucleus. The cell membrane and the complex nature of the cytoplasm and nucleus can be seen under an electron microscope.

The cell membrane separates the cytoplasm from the extracellular fluid (ECF). The cytoplasm consists of intracellular fluid (ICF), in which several structures are dispersed. These structures can be classified into the following three groups:

1. The organelles: These are the basic structures in the cell. They have an outer membrane and contain several enzymes which take part in the metabolic activities of the cell. Some examples of organelles are the mitochondria, endoplasmic reticulum and Golgi apparatus.
2. The inclusions: These are temporary components of some cells, and may or may not have a covering membrane. Carbohydrates, proteins, lipids and pigments are a few examples.
3. Other components: These form a supportive network in the cytoplasm and include centrioles, microtubules and microfilaments. They do not have an outer covering membrane and are not directly concerned with cell metabolism.

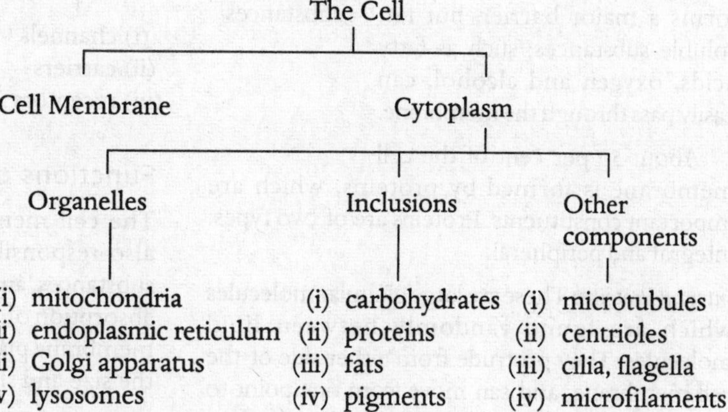


## CELL MEMBRANE

### Structure

The cell membrane is fluid in nature and basically a lipid bilayer. The lipid molecules are phospholipids and cholesterol. Each layer of the cell membrane consists of lipid molecules, which are shaped like clothespins. The globular part of the molecule is water-soluble (hydrophilic) and is made of the phosphate moiety of phospholipid or the hydroxyl radical of cholesterol. The slender part is water-insoluble (hydrophobic) and is made of the fatty acid or steroid radical of cholesterol. Lipid

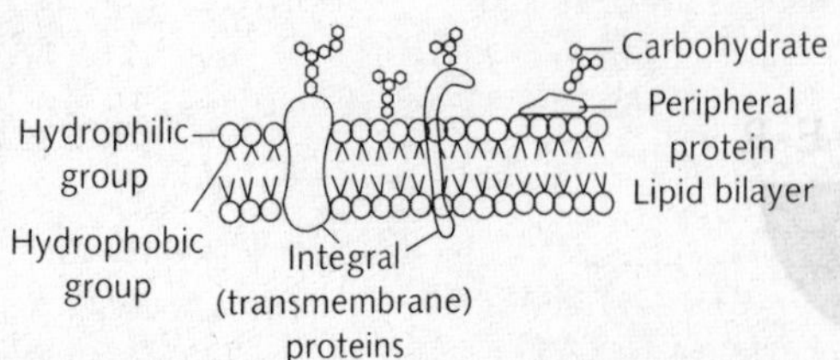


**Fig. 1.1:** Diagrammatic representation of structure of cell membrane

molecules are arranged in such a way that their hydrophilic ends are directed outwards on either side of the cell membrane, and the hydrophobic ends are directed towards the centre of the membrane (Fig. 1.1). Water-soluble molecules, such as glucose and ions, cannot pass through the lipid bilayer, which forms a major barrier, but fat-soluble substances, such as fatty acids, oxygen and alcohol, can easily pass through the membrane.

About 50 per cent of the cell membrane is formed by proteins, which are important constituents. Proteins are of two types: integral and peripheral.

*Integral Proteins:* These are large globular molecules which are found randomly between lipid molecules. They protrude from either side of the cell membrane, and can move from one point to another within it. Their functions are listed below.

1. Some act as channels for the diffusion of water-soluble substances across the cell membranes (cell pores). Some substances are allowed greater diffusion than others (selective diffusion).
2. Some act as carriers, facilitating diffusion.
3. Some act as receptor proteins for binding of hormones and neurotransmitters.

*Peripheral Proteins:* These are attached to integral proteins and are present on the inner surface of the cell membrane. They act as enzymes, modifying the cellular processes.

The carbohydrates present in the cell membrane are arfached either to lipid molecules (glycolipids) or protein molecules (glycoproteins), and protrude outside the cell membrane. Their functions are listed below.

1. Some act as receptors for the binding of hormones.
2. Some act as antigens.
3. Some influence membrane permeability.

The structure of other membranes within the cell is basically similar to that of the outer membrane.

Components of the Cell Membrane and their Functions

- Lipids
  - barrier for water-soluble substances
- Proteins
  - Integral
    - (i) channels
    - (ii) carriers
    - (iii) receptors
  - Peripheral
    - enzymes
- Carbohydrates
  - (i) receptors
  - (ii) antigens
  - (iii) influence cell permeability

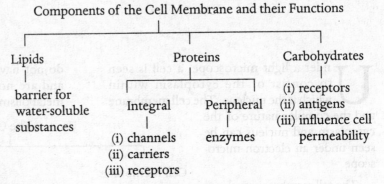

## Functions of cell membrane

The cell membrane provides protection. It is also responsible for the selective transport of substances, and for gaseous exchange as well. The absorption of nutrients is regulated by it. The cell membrane plays an important role in maintaining the size and shape of the cell.

# THE CYTOPLASM

## The organelles

### The Mitochondria

These are cylindrical bodies with two membranes. The inner membrane is folded to form shelves (Fig. 1.2). This increases the inner surface area for enzyme action. Its cavity contains enzymes for the citric acid (Kreb's) cycle and for fatty acid (β) oxidation. Enzymes involved in oxidative phosphorylation, generating ATP (adenosine triphosphate), are present on the inner membrane. The function of the mitochondria is, therefore, to produce ATP, which is

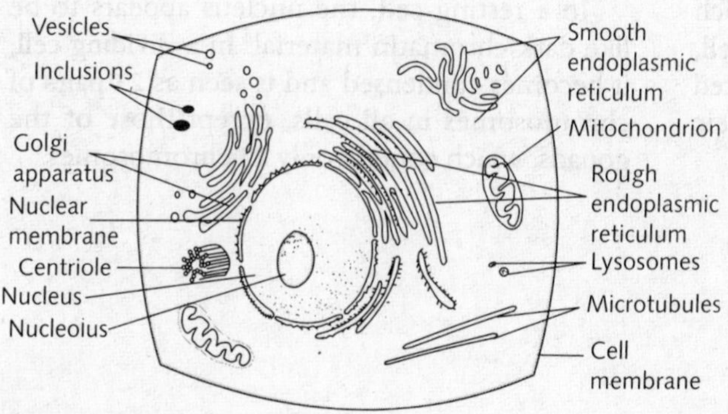


**Fig. 1.2:** Structure of a cell

an immediate source of energy for cellular activity.

The number and site of mitochondria vary in different cells according to their energy requirement and the site of intense activity.

### The Endoplasmic Reticulum

This is a network of membranous tubules and vesicles containing fluid. It has a vast surface area, on which various enzymes are attached.

The endoplasmic reticulum is of two types, rough and smooth, depending on the presence or absence, respectively, of ribosomes (small particles containing ribonucleic acid—RNA) on its surface.

The following are the functions of the rough endoplasmic reticulum:

1. Synthesis of carbohydrates, proteins and lipids, including steroid hormones and enzymes.
2. Transport of these synthesized substances from one part of the cell to another.

The smooth endoplasmic reticulum has the following functions:

1. Synthesis of steroid hormones, for example, in the adrenal cortex and testes, and various enzyme reactions in liver cells.
2. Release and uptake of calcium ions in skeletal and cardiac muscles during contraction.

### The Golgi Apparatus

This consists of a few flat vesicles stacked one above the other. It is involved in the secretory process and is located between the nucleus and secretory surface. The functions of the Golgi apparatus are the concentration and packaging of secretory proteins into membrane-bound vesicles or lysosomes. Another function is the glycosylation of protein to form glycoproteins.

### Lysosomes

These contain various enzymes capable of digesting carbohydrates, proteins, fats and nucleic acids. They are surrounded by a membrane which prevents these enzymes from acting on the intracellular organelles. The lysosomes destroy engulfed foreign bodies like bacteria and, therefore, help in phagocytosis.

## Cytoplasmic inclusions

These are temporary components of cytoplasm. They contain glycogen, protein, lipid droplets, and pigment, such as melanin.

## Other components (cytoskeleton)

*Microtubules:* These are rigid, tube-like bodies which give shape to the cell and are involved in intracellular transport.

*Centrioles:* These are two short cylindrical structures located near the nucleus. Their walls contain microtubules. The centrioles are concerned with the movement of chromosomes during cell division.

*Cilia and flagella:* These are the motile processes extending from the surface of the cell, and contain microtubules.

*Microfilaments:* These are the five protein filaments in the cytoplasm made up of actin. In the muscle cells they contain myosin also. Both actin and myosin are contractile proteins.

## THE NUCLEUS

The nucleus is surrounded by a double layer of membrane, which has pores through which protein molecules can pass. The space between the membranes is continuous with the lumen of the endoplasmic reticulum.

The nucleus contains nucleoli, which are rich in protein. It controls all the activities of the cell, including reproduction. This control is mediated via genes, which are made of deoxyribonucleic acid (DNA).

In a resting cell, the nucleus appears to be like dark chromatin material. In a dividing cell, it becomes condensed and is seen as 23 pairs of chromosomes in all cells, except those of the gonads, which contain only 23 chromosomes.

CHAPTER

# Transport Through the Cell Membrane

The mechanisms of transport involved in the movement of various substances across the cell membrane may be classified into three types:

1. Passive transport
2. Active transport
3. Transport of macromolecules

## PASSIVE TRANSPORT

Passive transport is characterized by the movement of molecules across the cell membrane, along the concentration and electrical gradient. There is no expenditure of energy involved in this form of transport, which is of two types:

1. Diffusion, which may be simple or facilitated, and
2, Osmosis.

### Diffusion

Diffusion is the movement of molecules from one compartment to another due to random molecular movement.

**Simple Diffusion**

This is the diffusion of molecules or ions through the membrane, without the help of carrier protein. Simple diffusion is affected by physical and biological factors.

The physical factors include the concentration or chemical gradient, that is, the difference in the concentration of substances across the cell membrane. The movement of molecules occurs from an area of higher concentration to one of lower concentration, and the higher the gradient, the higher the rate of diffusion.

The cross-sectional area of the membrane through which diffusion occurs is another physical factor. The greater the area, the greater the rate of diffusion. The thickness of the diffusion membrane is another factor. The greater the thickness, the lower the rate of diffusion.

The other physical factors are the electrical gradient and the temperature. Positively charged ions move towards an area with negative charge. The higher the temperature, the greater the rate of diffusion.

The biological factor is the permeability of the biological membrane to a particular substance. It depends on lipid solubility and water solubility.

*Lipid solubility*: Lipids and lipid-soluble substances, such as $O_2$, $N_2$, alcohol and steroids, diffuse across the lipid bilayer with great ease.

*Water solubility*: Water and water-soluble substances diffuse across the membrane through protein channels dispersed among the lipid molecules. The factors determining their diffusion include the size of the molecules, the number of protein channels, selective permeability and 'gating' of these channels.

As for the size of the molecule, diffusion of water-soluble substances, such as urea, glucose, $Na^+$ and $K^+$, is inversely proportionate to their molecular sizes. The greater the number of protein channels, the higher the rate of diffusion. As regards selective permeability, the specific protein channels for different substances have been identified, such as those for $Na^+$, $K^+$, $Ca^+$ and $Cl^-$.

The gating of protein channels can be described as follows. The opening of the protein channel can be controlled by conformational change in the protein. A part of the protein molecule acts like a gate and closes the opening, while lifting of the gate opens the channel (Fig. 2.1).

The opening and closing of the gate is controlled by the following two mechanisms:

1. Voltage gating: A change in the electrical potential across the cell membrane controls the opening or closure of some channels, such as $Na^+$ channels. A decrease in the membrane potential (by about 15 mV) opens the $Na^+$ channels in excitable tissues, such as nerves and muscles.
2. Ligand gating: Binding of the protein channel with another molecule, such as a hormone or neurotransmitter, opens some channels. An example is the opening of the $Na^+$ channels by acetylcholine at the neuromuscular junction.

**Facilitated Diffusion**

This is the diffusion of large water-soluble molecules such as glucose and amino acids, that is, the protein molecule within the cell membrane. Molecules are transported merely by

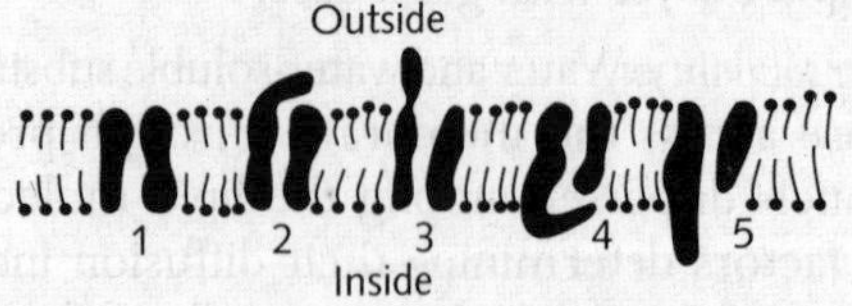


**Fig. 2.1:** Gating of protein channels—1. Ungated channel 2. Gated $Na^+$ channel, gate closed 3. Gated $Na^+$ channel, gate open 4. Gated $K^+$ channel, gate closed 5. Gated $K^+$ channel, gate open

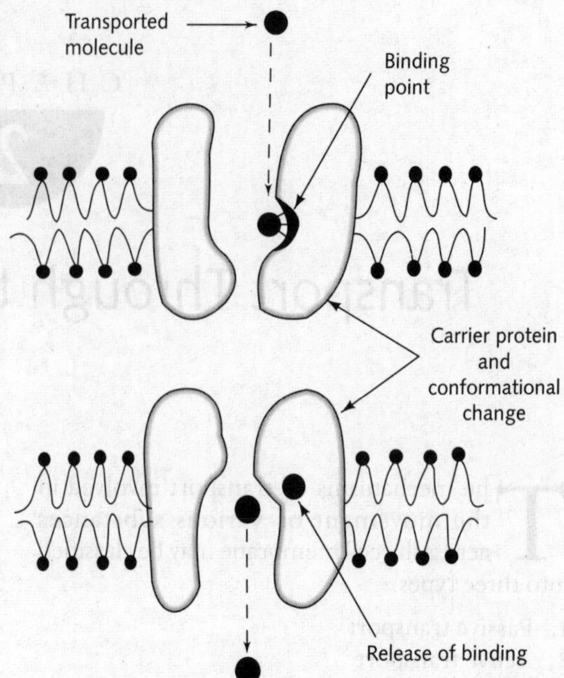


**Fig. 2.2:** Postulated mechanism for facilitated diffusion

a configurational change in the protein molecule (Fig. 2.2).

The characteristics of facilitated diffusion are specificity, saturation and competition.

*Specificity*: The carrier proteins are highly specific for different molecules.

*Saturation*: There is a limit beyond which a substance cannot be carried, even if its concentration is increased. When the maximum limit is reached, the carrier system is said to be saturated, that is, when all the specific carrier sites on the cell membranes are occupied and the system operates at a maximum capacity (Fig. 2.3).

*Competition*: If two molecules are carried by the same carrier, an increase in the concentration of one molecule may decrease the transport of the other molecule.

The rate of carrier-mediated transport depends on the rate at which carrier protein undergoes conformational change, that is, becomes available for the next molecule to pick up and bind with it.

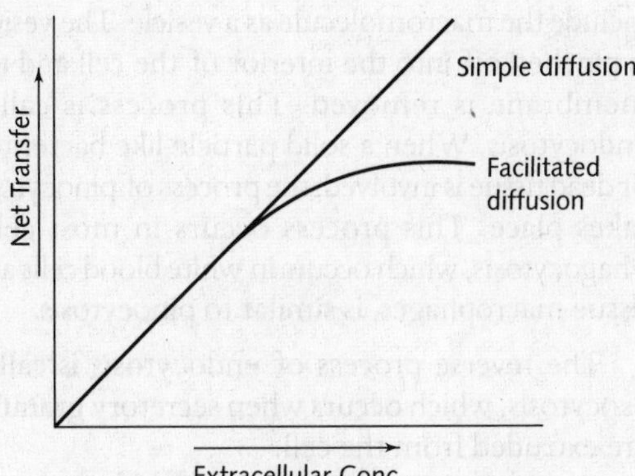


**Fig. 2.3:** Difference between simple diffusion and facilitated diffusion: Effect of saturation of the carrier

## Osmosis

Osmosis is the passive diffusion of water molecules (solvent) from an area with a lower concentration of solutes to an area with a higher concentration of solutes. The minimum pressure required to prevent diffusion of the solvent is called osmotic pressure.

The osmotic pressure varies directly according to the concentration of osmotically active particles in a solution. One osmole is equal to the total number of particles in one gram molecular weight of the nondissociable solutes per litre of water. In the case of physiological fluids, the term 'milliosmole' (0.001 osmole) is used. Normal extra- and intracellular fluids have an osmolality of about 300 osmoles/kg. A fluid with an osmolality similar to that of plasma is called isotonic. One with an osmolality less than that of plasma is called hypotonic, and higher, hypertonic.

## ACTIVE TRANSPORT

Active transport is characterized by the movement of molecules across the cell membrane against an electrochemical gradient. A carrier is involved, and the transport of molecules occurs faster than expected due to facilitated diffusion.

Active transport entails the expenditure of energy by transport proteins. ATPase activity is incorporated in the transport proteins involved in such transport. This activity converts ATP into ADP (adenosine diphosphate).

Since carrier proteins are involved, the active transport system, too, shows specificity, saturation and competition. Sugars, amino acids, $Na^+$, $K^+$, $H^+$, $Cl^-$ and I are transported by the active mechanism.

### Sodium–potassium pump

The sodium–potassium pump is present in the cell membrane (Fig. 2.4). It maintains the $Na^+$ and $K^+$ concentration difference across the cell membrane. It extrudes three $Na^+$ ions out of the cell and at the same time, pumps two $K^+$ ions into the cell.

The sodium–potassium pump is an electrogenic pump and also helps maintain the electrochemical potential difference across the cell membrane. In

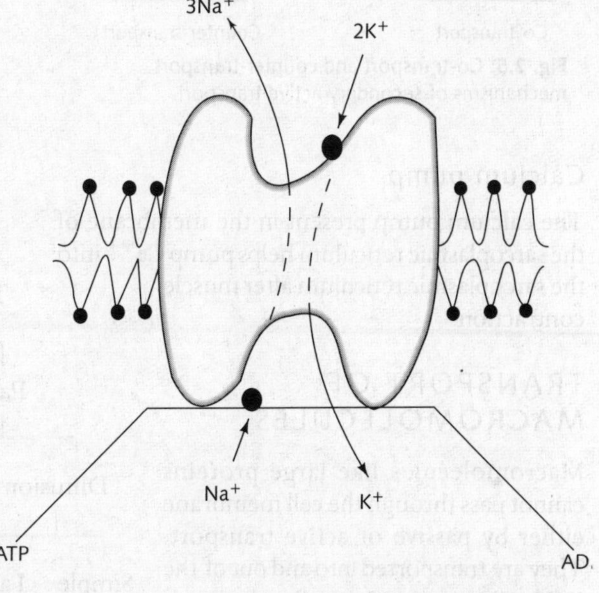


**Fig. 2.4:** Functional characteristics of the $Na^+$–$K^+$ pump

addition, it helps control the osmotic properties of living cells and, therefore, the cell volume.

## Co-transport and counter-transport

The transfer of many other substances by the active transport mechanism depends on the activity of the $Na^+$–$K^+$ pump. This is called secondary active transport, and can be of two types: co-transport and counter-transport.

When the transport of one substance is linked with that of another in the same direction, it is called co-transport. An example is the transport of glucose and $Na^+$ across the luminal membrane of the intestinal epithelium.

When the transport of one substance is linked with that of another in the opposite direction, it is called counter-transport. The $Na^+$–$K^+$ exchange or $Na^+$–$H^+$ exchange in the epithelium of renal tubules are examples of counter-transport (Fig. 2.5).

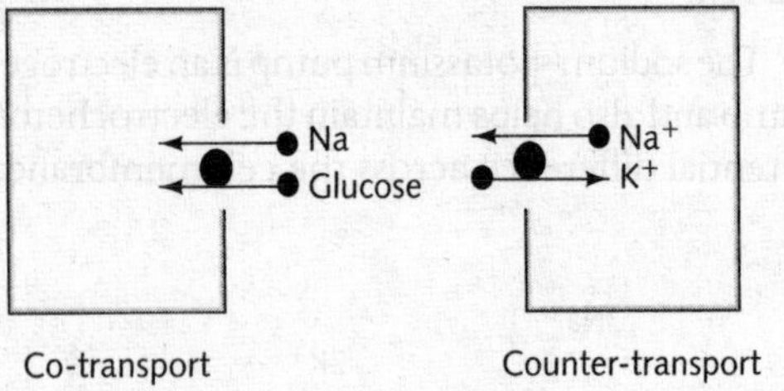


**Fig. 2.5:** Co-transport and counter-transport mechanisms of secondary active transport

## Calcium pump

The calcium pump present in the membrane of the sarcoplasmic reticulum helps pump $Ca^{++}$ into the sarcoplasmic reticulum after muscle contraction.

# TRANSPORT OF MACROMOLECULES

Macromolecules like large proteins cannot pass through the cell membrane either by passive or active transport. They are transported into and out of the cell by the mechanisms of endocytosis and exocytosis, respectively.

When a macromolecule comes in contact with the cell membrane, the latter gets invaginated to include the macromolecule as a vesicle. The vesicle is pinched off into the interior of the cell and the membrane is removed. This process is called endocytosis. When a solid particle like bacterium or dead tissue is involved, the process of pinocytosis takes place. This process occurs in most cells. Phagocytosis, which occurs in white blood cells and tissue macrophages, is similar to pinocytosis.

The reverse process of endocytosis is called exocytosis, which occurs when secretory granules are extruded from the cell.

## Transport through cellular sheaths

Such transport occurs by diffusion and active transport on one side and facilitated diffusion and co- or counter-transport on the other (Fig. 2.6).

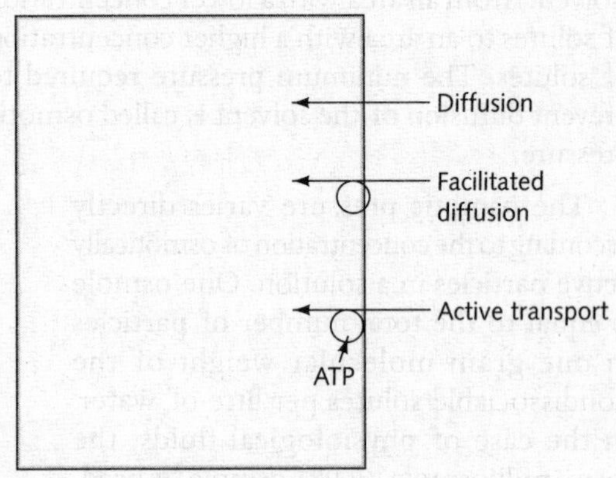


**Fig. 2.6:** Transport through cell membrane

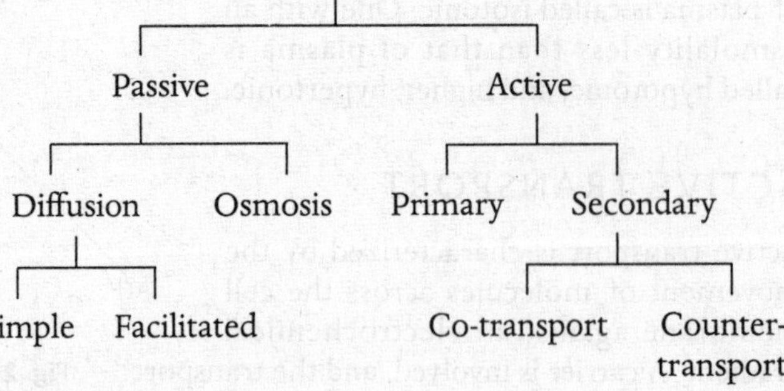

CHAPTER

3

# Bioelectric Phenomenon

All living cells show a bioelectric phenomenon due to the electric potential across the cell membrane (transmembrane potential). This includes the (i) resting membrane potential (RMP) and (ii) action potential (AP).

## RESTING MEMBRANE POTENTIAL (RMP)

The RMP is the difference in electrical potential across the cell membrane when the cell is at rest.

The interior of a cell is negative with respect to the exterior. This can be demonstrated by inserting a microelectrode into the cell, placing another electrode on the external surface and connecting them to a galvanometer or cathode ray oscilloscope (CRO) (Fig. 3.1).

The RMP varies from –60 to –90 mV. The RMP of a myelinated nerve and that of a skeletal muscle cell is –90 mV, and that of the cardiac muscle –60 mV.

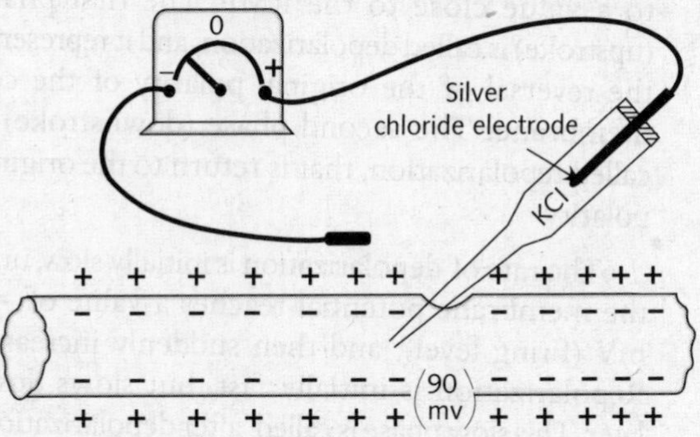


Fig. 3.1: Measurement of the membrane potential of nerve fibre using a microelectrode, at rest

The basis of the RMP is diffusion of $K^+$ and presence of $Na^+$–$K^+$ pump. This pump is of fundamental importance in maintaining the difference in the concentration of electrolytes between the ECF and ICF.

Concentration of important ions in body fluids

| Ions | ICF | ECF |
|---|---|---|
| $Na^+$ | 14 meq/l | 145 meq/l |
| $K^+$ | 140 meq/l | 4 meq/l |
| $Cl^-$ | 4 meq/l | 120 meq/l |
| $Protein^-$ | 155 meq/l | – |
| $HCO_3^-$ | 10 meq/l | 28 meq/l |

Thus, the ECF contains more $Na^+$ and $Cl^-$, while the ICF contains more $K^+$ and $protein^-$ ions (nondiffusible anions). These are separated by a selectively permeable cell membrane, which allows diffusion of ions to a certain extent. The factors affecting net diffusion are (i) the concentration gradient, (ii) the electric gradient, (iii) the pressure gradient, and (iv) the permeability of the cell membrane.

**Membrane Potential Caused by Diffusion**

*Diffusion of $Na^+$*: Due to the concentration

gradient, $Na^+$ diffuses into the cell but the membrane is less permeable to it.

*Diffusion of $K^+$*: Due to the concentration gradient, $K^+$ diffuses out of the cell, the membrane being highly permeable to it. At resting state the permeability to $K^+$ is a hundred times more than that to $Na^+$.

The relation between the diffusion potential and the difference in concentration can be determined by the Nernst equation:

$$\underset{(mV)}{\text{EMF}} = -61 \log_{10} \frac{\text{Conc(I) i.e., inside}}{\text{Conc(O) i.e., outside}}$$

For $Na^+$: $\dfrac{14 \text{ meq/l}}{145 \text{ meq/l}}$ = conc. difference

Nernst potential = $(-61) \times \log_{10} 0.1 = +61$ mV

For $K^+$: $\dfrac{140 \text{ meq/l}}{4 \text{ meq/l}}$ = conc. difference

Nernst potential = $(-61) \times \log_{10} 35 = -94$ mV

The Goldman, Hodgkin, Katz equation takes into consideration the permeability concentration and charges of various ions such as $Na^+$, $K^+$ and $Cl^-$. Therefore, according to it, RMP = –86 mV.

**Membrane Potential Caused by Active Transport**

The $Na^+$–$K^+$ pump in the cell membrane is electrogenic, requires energy, and presence of a carrier. It pumps three $Na^+$ ions outside the cell and two $K^+$ ions inside the cell.

Due to one less positive ion in the interior and more negative ions, especially proteins, the ICF is always negative with respect to the ECF.

RMP due to $Na^+$–$K^+$ pump = –4 mV
RMP in large skeletal muscle and nerve fibres = (–86) + (–4) = –90 mV

In small nerve and skeletal muscle fibres and many neurons in the central nervous system, the RMP is –40 mV to –60 mV.

**Basis and Importance of RMP**

The basis of the RMP is 1) the existence of the $Na^+$–$K^+$ pump, 2) the fact that the membrane permeability to the $K^+$ ions to the outside is a hundred times greater than that to the $Na^+$, 3) the large amount of protein anions within the cell. The cell membrane acts as a charged capacitor.

## ACTION POTENTIAL (AP)

At rest, the cell membrane is said to be polarized when its outer surface carries a positive charge with respect to the inner surface.

When the RMP is being recorded on the cathode ray oscilloscope, if the cell membrane is stimulated a short distance away, a potential difference develops between the stimulated part and the resting part. If the stimulus is inadequate, only a local excitatory state is produced, but if it is adequate, an action potential is observed on the oscilloscope (Fig. 3.2).

The AP is a pulse-like electric change that propagates along the cell membrane of an excitable cell when an adequate stimulus is applied to it.

The point of stimulation is seen on the CRO as a mild deflection of the baseline, called the stimulus artefact, due to leakage of electric current from the stimulating to the recording electrode. This is followed by a short isoelectric period known as the latent period. The latent period indicates the time taken by the current to travel from the stimulating to the recording electrode. It varies directly with the distance between them and indirectly with the velocity of its conduction.

The record then suddenly shoots up from a potential of –70 mV (RMP) to +35 mV, followed by a quick reversal of the membrane potential to a value close to the RMP. The first phase (upstroke) is called depolarization, and it represents the reversal of the original polarity of the cell membrane. The second phase (downstroke) is called repolarization, that is return to the original polarity.

The rate of depolarization is initially slow, until the membrane potential reaches a value of –55 mV (firing level), and then suddenly increases. Repolarization is initially fast, but slows down later. This slow phase is called 'after depolarization'.

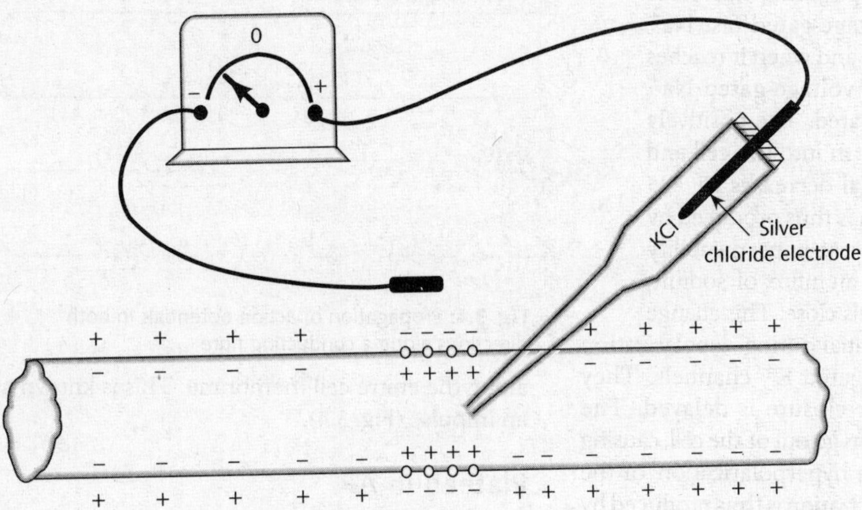


**Fig. 3.2:** Method of recording and a record of action potential in the nerve and muscle

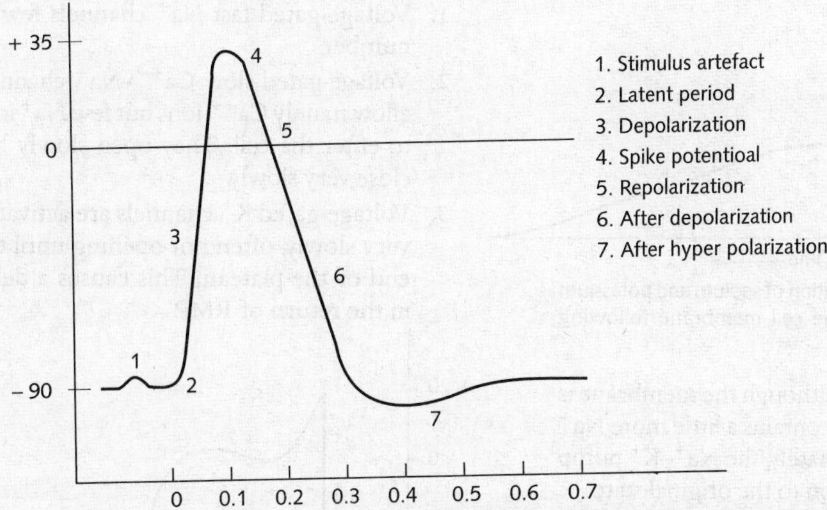


1. Stimulus artefact
2. Latent period
3. Depolarization
4. Spike potentioal
5. Repolarization
6. After depolarization
7. After hyper polarization

The peak value of the AP record is known as spike potential.

Repolarization is followed by a prolonged period of mild hyperpolarization, called 'after hyperpolarization'. Finally, the RMP is restored.

## Ionic basis of AP

The cell membrane excitable cell has various types of channels for the transport of ions. These are characteristic for different cells and produce different patterns of action potential for example:

1. Voltage-gated fast sodium channels in skeletal muscle, myelinated nerve and cardiac muscle.
2. Voltage-gated slow $Ca^{++}$–$Na^{+}$ channels in heart and smooth muscles.
3. Voltage-gated potassium channels in all the excitable cells.
4. $Na^{+}$–$K^{+}$ pump.

As the membrane potential decreases from –90 mV, the voltage-gated fast $Na^+$ channels open partially, and when it reaches –55 mV (firing level), voltage-gated $Na^+$ channels are fully activated. The positively charged sodium ions rush into the cell and the membrane potential decreases to +35 mV. The depolarization is thus produced by a sudden but brief increase in permeability to $Na^+$ ions, leading to an influx of sodium after which the channels close. This change in the membrane potential during depolarization opens up the voltage-gated $K^+$ channels. They open slowly and their closure is delayed. The positively charged $K^+$ ions go out of the cell, causing repolarization and 'after hyperpolarization' of the membrane. The repolarization is thus produced by an increase in the permeability of the cell membrane to $K^+$ ions, leading to a $K^+$ efflux (Fig. 3.3).

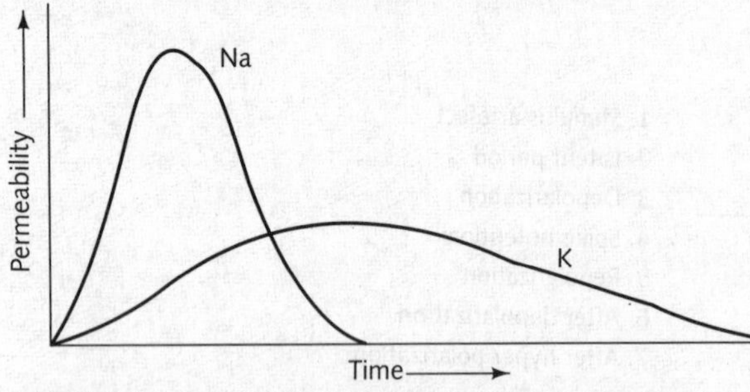


**Fig. 3.3:** Graphical representation of sodium and potassium permeability changes in the cell membrane following stimulation

At the end of an AP, although the membrane is polarized again, the cell contains a little more $Na^+$ and a little less $K^+$. Ultimately, the $Na^+$–$K^+$ pump restores the concentration to the original state.

## Propagation of AP

Action potential originated at any point on an excitable cell membrane usually causes the adjacent points on the membrane to get excited. This results in its propagation. The mechanism is known as 'formation of local circuits of current'. Local circuits are formed between depolarized and adjacent repolarized areas, causing more areas to be depolarized. Hence the depolarization spreads

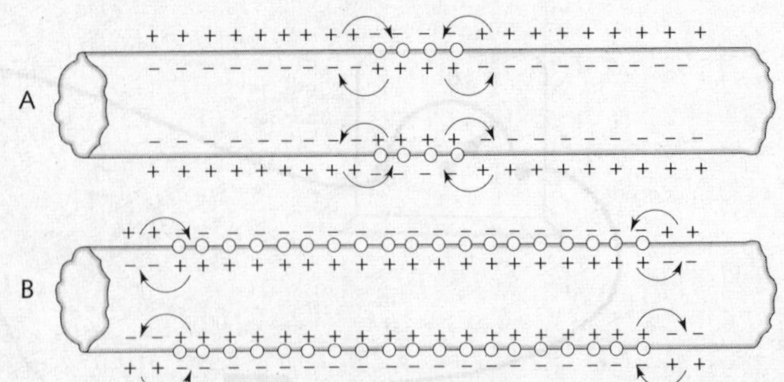


**Fig. 3.4:** Propagation of action potentials in both directions along a conducting fibre

along the enitre cell membrane. This is known as an impulse (Fig. 3.4).

## Plateau in AP

The period of depolarization is prolonged in heart muscle, resulting in a plateau (Fig. 3.5).

The causes of this are as follows:

1. Voltage-gated fast $Na^+$ channels few in number.
2. Voltage-gated slow $Ca^{++}$–$Na^+$ channels allow mainly $Ca^{++}$ ions but few $Na^+$ ions to enter the cell. They open slowly but close very slowly.
3. Voltage-gated $K^+$ channels are activated very slowly, often not opening until the end of the plateau. This causes a delay in the return of RMP.

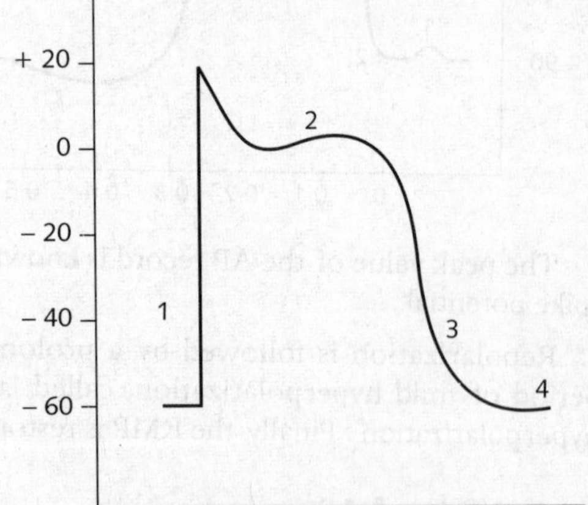


**Fig. 3.5:** Phases of cardiac action potential: 1. depolarization, 2. plateau phase, 3. late repolarization, 4. baseline

CHAPTER

# Body Fluids

Approximately 60 per cent of the total body weight consists of water. An average adult weighing 70 kg contains about 40 l of water, of which about 25 l can be found inside the cells (ICF) and 15 outside (ECF). The ECF consists mainly of blood plasma (3.5 l), tissue or interstitial fluid (10.5 l) and small amounts of fluid, present as cerebrospinal fluid, in the eyeballs and joint spaces.

## MAINTENANCE OF HYDROGEN ION CONCENTRATION OF BLOOD

The $H^+$ ion concentration of the body fluids is expressed by the symbol 'pH'.

$$pH = \log \frac{1}{H^+}$$

The pH of water is 7, and that of arterial blood 7.4. An increase in the $H^+$ ion concentration (decreased pH) is called acidosis, while a decrease (increased pH) is called alkalosis.

An arterial blood pH of below 7 or above 8 is incompatible with life. Hence, the blood pH is maintained around 7.4.

The $H^+$ ion concentration of blood is maintained by acid–base buffers and $H^+$ secretion by the kidneys.

## Acid–base buffers

### Bicarbonate Buffer

This is usually a combination of weak acid and its salt, with a strong base. An example is $H_2CO_3$ and $NaHCO_3$. If a strong acid is added to it, the following reaction takes place.

$$HCl + NaHCO_3 \rightarrow H_2CO_3 + NaCl$$

Thus, a strong acid is converted to a weak acid.

If a strong base is added to it, the following reaction occurs:

$$NaOH + H_2CO_3 \rightarrow NaHCO_3 + H_2O$$

Thus, a strong base is converted into a weak base.

Hence, when a moderate amount of a strong acid or base is added to the acid–base buffer system, marked changes in the $H^+$ ion concentration are prevented as a weak acid or weak base dissociates poorly into $H^+$ or $OH^-$ ions.

### Haemoglobin and Plasma Proteins

Proteins are amphoteric in nature, that is, they have both an acid (COOH) and a basic ($NH_2$) radical, which can neutralize a strong base or acid that is added to it.

### Phosphate Buffer

This consists of $NaH_2PO_4$ (acidic phosphate) and $Na_2HPO_4$ (basic phosphate).

$$Na_2HPO_4 + HCl \rightarrow NaH_2PO_4 + NaCl$$

$$NaH_2PO_4 + NaOH \rightarrow Na_2HPO_4 + H_2O$$

**Henderson–Hasselbach Equation**

This equation expresses the mathematical relationship between the pH of the solution and the ratio of the concentrations of the acidic and basic elements of each buffer system.

$$pH = PK + \log \frac{base}{acid}$$

PK = ionization constant

The pH will increase if the concentration of the base increases or that of the acid decreases. The pH will decrease if the concentration of the base decreases or that of the acid increases.

The efficiency of the buffer system is at its best when its PK is the same as the pH of the solution in which it is acting.

The bicarbonate buffer system is not so efficient since its PK (6.1) is far from the pH of plasma (7.4). However, it is still very important as both its components can be regulated in the body, for example, carbonic acid ($CO_2$) is regulated by the respiratory system, while the bicarbonate concentration is regulated by the kidneys.

The plasma proteins, and particularly haemoglobin, are the most efficient in blood since their concentration in blood is high (7 gdl and 15 gdl, respectively), and their PK (7) is very close to the pH of plasma.

The phosphate buffer system is the least effective in blood because although its PK (6.8) is close to 7.4, its concentration in plasma is poor. The phosphates are important buffers in the kidney since their concentration is increased in renal tubular fluid.

The phosphates and proteins also constitute important buffers in intracellular fluid as their concentrations are high within the cell.

In respiratory acidosis and alkalosis, almost all the buffering is intracellular. In metabolic acidosis and alkalosis, about 50 per cent of buffering is intracellular.

The three major buffer systems—bicarbonate, protein and phosphate—exert a mutual buffering action on each other.

The extracellular and intracellular buffer systems act fast and form the first line of defence against changes in the $H^+$ ion concentration. The respiratory system forms the second line of defence and can correct the pH partially. The kidneys form the last defence but at the end, excrete all the excess acid and alkali that is added to the body fluid, bringing its pH back to exactly normal.

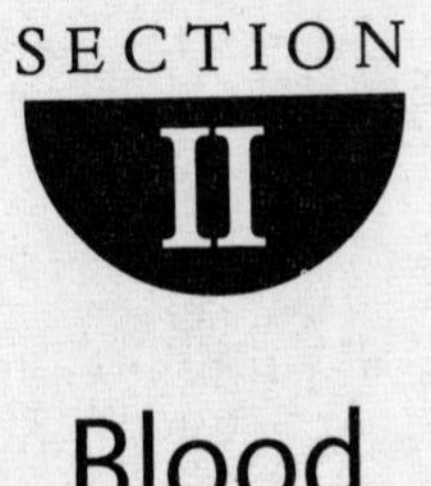

# Blood

CHAPTER

5

# Functions and Composition

Blood is the medium of life. It is defined as a fluid connective tissue, flowing in the blood vessels.

Blood is reddish due to the presence of haemoglobin. Its volume in a normal healthy adult is 5 l. The specific gravity of whole blood is 1.055, the range being 1.052 to 1.060. The specific gravity of cells is 1.090, and that of plasma 1.032. The pH of blood is 7.4, which is slightly alkaline, and this level is maintained. The fluidity of blood is maintained only as long as it circulates in the blood vessel. When removed from a vein and kept in a test-tube, it becomes a solid mass within minutes by a process known as coagulation (clotting) of blood.

## FUNCTIONS OF BLOOD

The functions of blood are dependent on the function of the cardiovascular system, which keeps it circulating throughout the body. The functions are listed below.

*Transport of respiratory gases*: Blood carries oxygen from the lungs to the tissues, and carbon dioxide from the tissues to the lungs.

*Transport of nutrients*: The end-products of digestion which are absorbed from the gastro-intestinal tract, for example, glucose, amino acids and fatty acids, are carried to (i) the tissues for energy, growth and repair, and (ii) the liver for storage.

*Transport of substances*: Hormones, enzymes, vitamins and essential chemical substances are transported by blood to various tissues.

*Transport of waste products*: Metabolic end-products such as urea, uric acid and creatinine are carried to the excretory organs, for example, the kidneys.

*Maintenance of acid–base balance*: Haemoglobin, plasma proteins, bicarbonate and phosphate buffers in the blood are responsible for this.

*Maintenance of water balance*: The water content of the tissues and different body fluid compartments is maintained as water can move from blood into extracellular spaces through the capillary membrane.

*Maintenance of body temperature*: Blood contains a large amount of water, which has the following physical properties:

1. High specific heat—maximum amongst all liquids. Therefore, it can store and lose heat without any change in temperature.
2. High thermal conductivity. Therefore, the heat produced in active structures like the liver and muscles is quickly distributed throughout the body.
3. High latent heat of vaporization. Therefore, increased body temperature, which increases sweating, increases heat loss from the body. Thus, the quick distribution of heat and its loss through the skin and lungs prevents

sudden changes in body temperature.

*Regulation of blood pressure*: The blood pressure is maintained by adjustments in the volume of blood. For example, increased blood pressure causes increased movement of water from the blood in the capillaries into tissue spaces.

*Protection of body from infection*: White blood cells have a phagocytic action, by which they destroy bacteria. Moreover, the immune bodies produced by these cells protect the individual from foreign substances.

*Haemostasis*: Clotting of blood, which is caused by various clotting factors present in it, prevents further haemorrhage when a blood vessel is injured. This arrest of haemorrhage is called haemostasis.

## COMPOSITION

Blood consists of plasma and formed elements suspended in it.

Plasma, a clear yellowish fluid, is blood minus the formed elements. Plasma minus the clotting factors (mainly fibrinogen) is serum. Serum is released due to the shrinkage of blood after clotting.

The formed elements are:

1. Red blood cells (RBCs) or erythrocytes,
2. White blood cells (WBCs) or leucocytes, and
3. Platelets or thrombocytes.

Blood is more viscous than water due to the presence of blood cells.

Blood can be separated into plasma and formed elements by taking blood mixed with anticoagulant in a special haematocrit tube and centrifuging it at a high speed (3000 revolutions per minute) for 30 minutes. The formed elements settle at the bottom and clear plasma floats on top.

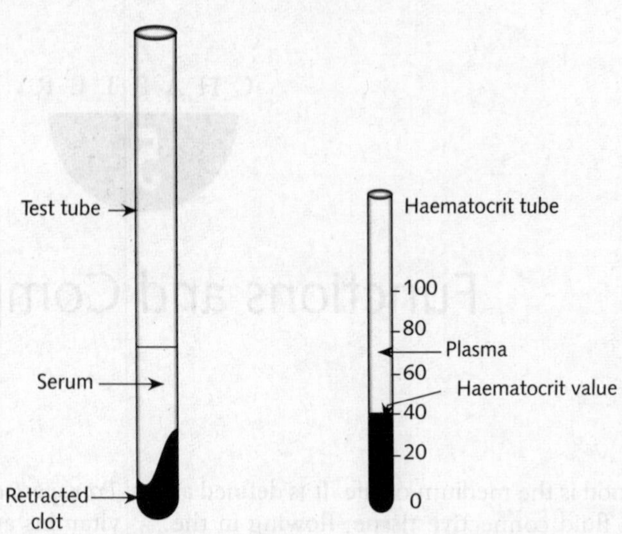


**Fig. 5.1:** Determination of packed cell volume (PCV)

The volume of cells expressed as a percentage of the total volume of blood is known as the packed cell volume (PCV). The PCV is approximately 45 per cent in males and 42 per cent in females. When expressed as a ratio of cells to plasma volume, for example., 45:55, it is called haematocrit (Fig. 5.1).

### Composition of Plasma

Plasma contains water (90–91%) and solids (9–10%). The solids include plasma proteins (7%), organic and inorganic substances (2%) and other substances (1%). The organic substances include urea, uric acid, creatinine (NPN), glucose, lactic acid, amino acid, fatty acid and cholesterol. The inorganic substances are various ions, for example $Na^+$, $K^+$, $Ca^{++}$, $Mg^{++}$, $Cl^-$, $HCO_3$, $PO_4$ and $SO_4$.

The other substances include vitamins, hormones, bilirubin pigment and trace elements, for example iron, copper and zinc.

#### Plasma Proteins

The plasma proteins are the major solid constituent of plasma. They form about 7.5 per cent of the total weight of plasma. The different types of plasma

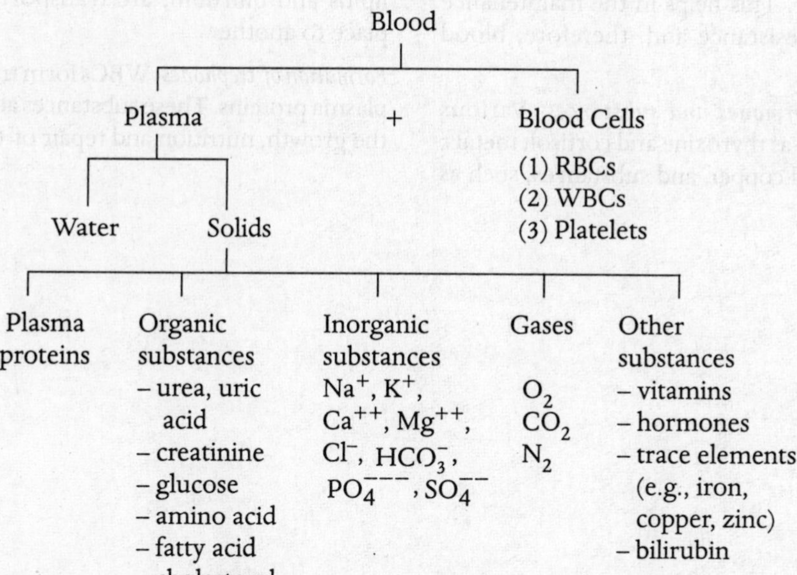


proteins can be separated by electrophoresis. The different types are:

1. Albumin (4.5–5.5 g/dl)
2. Globulin (2.5–3 g/dl)
3. Fibrinogen (0.25–1 g/dl)
4. Prothrombin (0.025–0.05 g/dl)

Albumin can be further separated into the alpha, beta and gamma types.

The albumin molecule is small, compact and ellipsoid. Therefore, it is the first protein molecule to escape through urine in any kidney disease. Normally, there is no albumin in urine, so its detection in urine forms a very sensitive kidney function test. The globulin molecule is larger and globular than the albumin molecule, and the fibrinogen molecule is the largest and most irregular.

The albumin: globulin ratio (A:G ratio) is approximately 2:1 and remains constant in good health. Albumin is formed only in the liver but globulin is formed in other organs, too, by reticuloendothelial cells. In liver disease, the formation of albumin decreases while that of globulin continues, causing a reversal of the ratio. Therefore, the measurement of the A:G ratio is an important liver function test.

Plasma proteins have the following functions:

*Exertion of colloid osmotic pressure*: This controls the exchange of fluid between blood and tissue fluid. Albumin contributes 80 per cent of the pressure because of its small size and large number.

*Protection against infection*: Gamma globulin forms antibodies.

*Clotting of blood*: Fibrinogen, prothrombin and other coagulation factors take part in the process of clotting.

*Protein reserve*: During starvation, tissues draw proteins from plasma.

*Acid–base balance*: Proteins act as buffers because they are amphoteric in nature, and hence, can combine with acidic and basic ions.

*Maintenance of erythrocyte sedimentation rate* (ESR): Fibrinogen and globulin increase the ESR, while albumin decreases it. The determination of the ESR has diagnostic and prognostic value.

*Carriage of $CO_2$*: $CO_2$ combines with proteins to form carbamino compounds.

*Viscosity*: Fibrinogen contributes the most to viscosity due to the large size and irregular shape of the molecule. This helps in the maintenance of peripheral resistance and, therefore, blood pressure.

*Transport of hormones and substances*: Various hormones, such as thyroxine and cortisol, metals, such as iron and copper, and substances, such as lipids and bilirubin, are transported from one place to another.

*Formation of trephones*: WBCs form trephones from plasma proteins. These substances are required for the growth, nutrition and repair of tissues.

CHAPTER

6

# Red Blood Cells

Each red blood cell (RBC) is a biconcave, non-nucleated disc, pale-buff in colour. Its mean diameter is 7.2 microns, surface area 120 square microns and volume 83 cubic microns. The thickness at the periphery is 2 microns and at the centre, 1 micron. This shape allows moderate swelling of the cell without stretching the cell membrane and also provides a large surface area for efficient gas diffusion throughout the cell (Fig. 6.1).

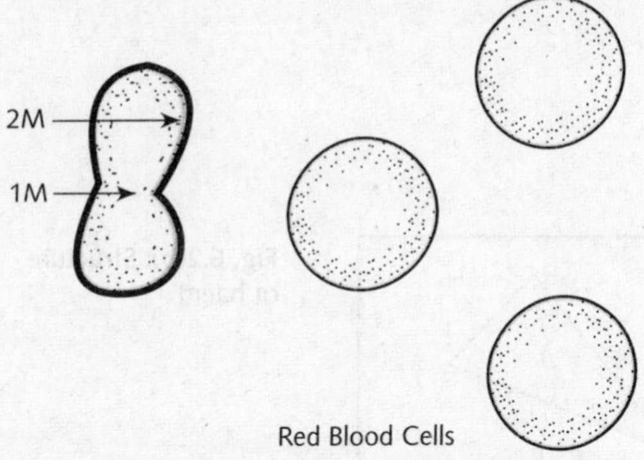


**Fig. 6.1:** Red blood cells

The normal RBC count is 4–5 million/mm$^3$. In males, the range is 4.8–6 million/mm$^3$, the average being about 5.5 million/mm$^3$. In females, the range is 4.2–5.5 million/mm$^3$, with an average of about 4.8 million/mm$^3$.

Several physiological factors cause variations in the RBC count. As age advances, the RBC count decreases. In newborns, it is 6–7 million/mm$^3$ while in old age, it decreases as the red bone marrow is replaced by the yellow bone marrow. Males have a higher RBC count than females because the male sex hormone, testosterone, stimulates the formation of RBC.

The RBC count increases after muscular exercise due to the release of epinephrine, which causes contraction of the spleen. It increases at high altitudes as well, due to low oxygen tension in the atmosphere.

The red cell membrane is freely permeable to water. It contains a $Na^+$–$K^+$ pump, the energy for which is derived from glycolysis in red cells. The red cell membrane contains a specific glycoprotein, which differs from person to person and forms the basis of blood groups.

## HAEMOGLOBIN

Haemoglobin (Hb), an iron-containing red pigment, is the most important constituent of the RBC and forms about 35 per cent of its volume. It is a conjugated protein with a molecular weight of 68,000.

Haemoglobin has an iron-containing compound, haem, which is a pigment, and globin, which is a simple protein. Each Hb molecule has four subunits, each of which contains iron-containing porphyrin. Porphyrin is made of four pyrrole rings, which are attached to one iron atom. The iron atom in each subunit of haem is in ferrous form ($Fe^{++}$) and has a 'bond' available for loose union with an oxygen molecule. The globin molecule is made of four polypeptiole chains, two alpha (α) chains (141 amino acids) and two beta (β) chains (146 amino acids). The sequence of amino acids differs in both types of chains. The Hb present in an adult is called HbA ($\alpha_2\beta_2$) (Figs 6.2a and 6.2b).

The mean Hb concentration of blood in adult males is 15 g/dl, the range being 13–18 g/dl, and in adult females 14 g/dl, the

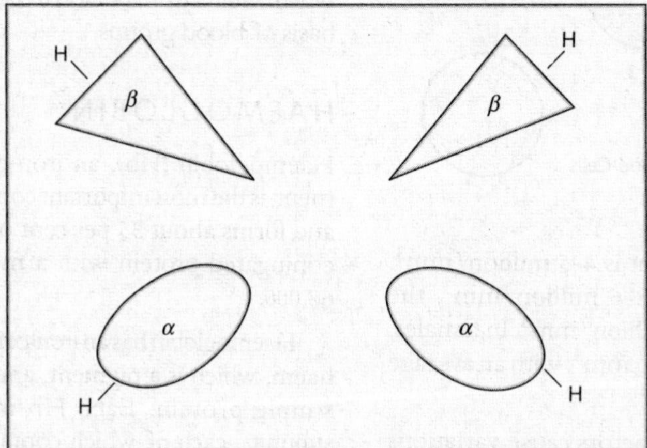


**Fig. 6.2(a):** Structure of haemoglobin (H=Haem)

Pyrrole Ring

Haem

**Fig. 6.2(b):** Structure of haem

range being 12–16 g/dl. The Hb concentration of blood is higher at birth but falls to about 10 g/dl by the end of the third month. (This is due to the destruction of RBCs producing physiological jaundice of the newborn).

An important property of the Hb molecule is that it can form a loose, irreversible compound with oxygen, oxyHb, which is bright red. Each Hb molecule can take up four oxygen molecules. In oxyHb, iron remains in the $Fe^{++}$ form and is not converted to the $Fe^{+++}$ form. Hence, this process is called oxygenation.

$$\underset{\text{(oxygenated) Hb}}{HbO_2} \rightleftharpoons \underset{\text{(deoxygenated) reduced Hb}}{Hb + O_2}$$

Each gram of Hb carries 1.34 ml of oxygen when it is fully saturated with oxygen. Thus, 100 ml of arterial blood carries about 20 ml of oxygen ($O_2$-carrying capacity).

In the tissues, oxyHb dissociates into deoxygenated Hb, which is dark red, and oxygen, which is released.

Thus, the most important function of Hb is to carry oxygen from the lungs to the tissues. It is also involved in the transport of $CO_2$ from the tissues to the lungs. $CO_2$ is transported in combination with the globin part of Hb by renous blood. Hb constitutes the most important acid–base buffer system of blood. It has six times the buffering capacity of plasma proteins.

Normally, Hb remains within the RBC and is not filtered by the kidneys. Hence, it appears in urine only when there is excessive destruction of RBCs (haemolysis).

## Foetal haemoglobin

During foetal life, the red cells contain a different type of Hb, HbF. It differs from HbA only in the globin part. It contains two alpha and two gamma chains ($\alpha_2\gamma_2$). The gamma chain contains some amino acids which are different from those of the beta chain. Hence, the affinity of HbF for oxygen is markedly increased, which helps in the transport of $O_2$ during foetal life.

## Carboxyhaemoglobin

When carbon monoxide (CO) is inhaled, it gets attached to Hb at the same site where $O_2$ is normally attached, resulting in the formation of carboxyHb. Hb has a twenty times greater affinity to CO than to $O_2$, and carboxyHb cannot take part in the transport of $O_2$. As a result, hypoxia occurs. CarboxyHb can be converted to normal Hb by the inhalation of pure oxygen.

## Methaemoglobin

The iron present in Hb in the ferrous ($Fe^{++}$) form is oxidized by certain drugs to the ferric ($Fe^{+++}$) form, resulting in the formation of methaemoglobin, a brown pigment. Methaemoglobin cannot unite reversibly with $O_2$. Therefore, when a large amount of it is present, the patient suffers from oxygen deficiency. The administration of methylene blue or ascorbic acid (reducing agents) can reconvert it to normal Hb.

Spectroscopic examination of blood helps diagnose the presence of carboxyHb and methaemoglobin.

## Haemoglobinopathies

The red cells of certain individuals contain abnormal types of Hb. This is determined genetically. Thalassaemia and sickle-cell anaemia are two types of haemoglobinopathy.

*Thalassaemia*: This is characterized by the persistence of HbF ($\alpha_2\gamma_2$) even in post-natal life. Such red cells are rapidly destroyed (haemolysed).

*Sickle-cell anaemia*: This condition is characterized by the presence of HbS (amino acid valine replaces glutamic acid at the sixth position beta chain). When it is deoxygenated, it forms long crystals, giving the red cells the shape of a sickle, hence the name. These red cells are more prone to rapid destruction.

# HAEMOPOIESIS

Haemopoiesis is the formation of blood cells. In the first three months of intrauterine life, it occurs in the area vasculosa of the yolk sac, that is, intravascularly, by the proliferation of the endothelial cells of the capillaries. From the third to fifth month, it occurs in the liver and spleen of the foetus. From the fifth to ninth month of foetal life, the bone marrow takes over the function of haemopoiesis and continues to form blood cells after birth.

In children, most of the marrow is markedly cellular and appears red. Therefore, haemopoiesis occurs in all the bones. As the child grows, red bone marrow is gradually replaced by yellow bone marrow, which consists of adipose tissue. In an adult, red bone marrow is present at the following sites, at which haemopoiesis also occurs:

1. the ends of the long bones, for example, the humerus and tibia;
2. the flat bones, for example, the sternum, ribs and skull;
3. the irregular bones, for example, the vertebrae, wrist and ankle bones; and
4. the short bones, for example, metacarpal and metatarsal.

In situations like hypoxia (lack of $O_2$), which requires rapid erythropoiesis, yellow marrow is converted to red marrow and, therefore, acts as a reserve for increased blood formation.

The red marrow contains common progenitor (pleuripotent) cells, which give rise to various types of blood cells. These can be seen in stained smears of red bone marrow obtained from the sternum or iliac bone. Some of them migrate to other areas and produce lymphocytes. Others (uncommitted stem cells) are converted to the erythroid line of cells, the myeloid line of cells or platelet-forming cells by a process of commitment. Certain humoral substances push the uncommitted stem cells into their respective lines of development (Fig. 6.3).

## ERYTHROPOIESIS

This is the process of the formation or genesis of RBCs. By this process, the RBC count is maintained at a constant, which is necessary for adequate transport of $O_2$ to the tissues.

### Stages of erythropoiesis

The pleuripotent haemopoietic stem cell and the earliest cell committed to the red cell series (proerythroblast) are microscopically similar.

*Proerythroblast:* The proerythroblast is a large cell, with a diameter of 15–20 microns. It has a big nucleus, with many nucleoli. The cytoplasm is basophilic (blue) and forms a thin rim at the periphery. The cell divides actively and passes through the following stages, in which its size goes on decreasing.

*Early normoblast*: This is of smaller size, and the nucleus is more dense. The chromatin shows nodes of condensation, and the nucleoli decrease in number and disappear. The cytoplasm is basophilic and mitosis occurs.

*Intermediate normoblast*: This is even smaller, and the nucleus shifts to one side. For the first time, the cytoplasm contains Hb and, therefore, becomes polychromatophilic (partly blue and partly red), that is, it takes both acidic and basic stains.

*Late normoblast*: This is smaller still. The nucleus is small, round and deeply stained (pyknotic), and disappears, that is, it is extruded from the cell. The cytoplasm is red as it carries the full quota of Hb. It loses its capacity to divide.

*Reticulocyte*: The size of the cell is smaller than in the last stage. There is no nucleus, and remnants of the disintegrated nucleus form the RNA reticulum, which can be stained with a supravital stain, hence the name.

In an adult, 1 per cent of the reticulocytes are present in peripheral blood, while the rest are mature RBCs. The number of reticulocytes increases when erythropoiesis is accelerated, for example, in anaemic patients under treatment.

*Mature RBC*: This is the smallest cell. The nucleus is absent and the cytoplasm is orange-pink due to the accumulation of Hb.

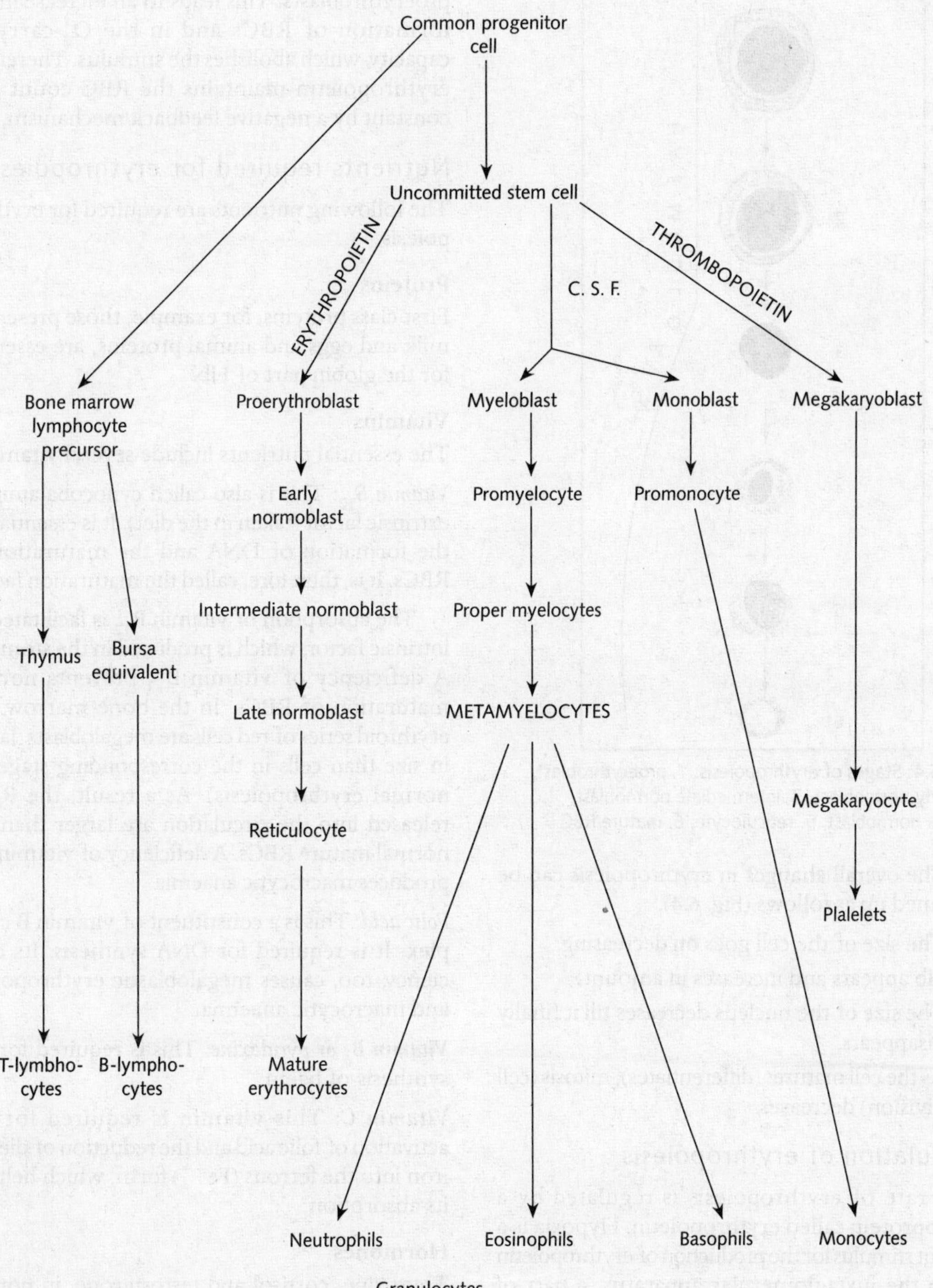


**Fig. 6.3:** Haemopoiesis

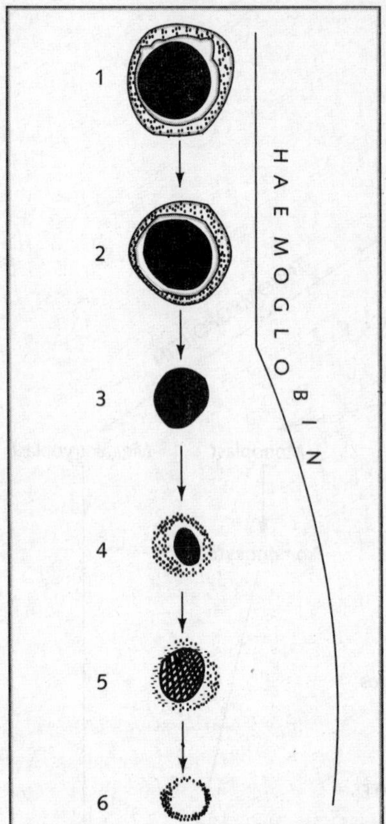


**Fig. 6.4:** Stages of erythropoiesis: 1. proerythroblast, 2. early normoblast, 3. intermediate normoblast, 4. late normoblast, 5. reticulocyte, 6. mature RBC

The overall changes in erythropoiesis can be summed up as follows (Fig. 6.4).

1. The size of the cell goes on decreasing.
2. Hb appears and increases in amount.
3. The size of the nucleus decreases till it finally disappears.
4. As the cell matures (differentiates), mitosis (cell division) decreases.

## Regulation of erythropoiesis

The rate of erythropoiesis is regulated by a glycoprotein called erythropoietin. Hypoxia is a potent stimulus for the production of erythropoietin from the juxtaglomerular apparatus, a part of the kidney. Erythropoietin acts on red bone marrow and causes stem cells to differentiate into proerythroblasts. This leads to an increase in the formation of RBCs and in the $O_2$-carrying capacity, which abolishes the stimulus. Therefore, erythropoietin maintains the RBC count at a constant by a negative feedback mechanism.

## Nutrients required for erythropoiesis

The following nutrients are required for erythropoiesis.

### Proteins

First-class proteins, for example, those present in milk and eggs and animal proteins, are essential for the globin part of Hb.

### Vitamins

The essential nutrients include several vitamins.

*Vitamin $B_{12}$*: This is also called cynocobalamin or extrinsic factor (taken in the diet). It is essential for the formation of DNA and the maturation of RBCs. It is, therefore, called the maturation factor.

The absorption of vitamin $B_{12}$ is facilitated by intrinsic factor, which is produced in the stomach. A deficiency of vitamin $B_{12}$ prevents normal maturation of RBCs. In the bone marrow, the erythroid series of red cells are megaloblasts (larger in size than cells in the corresponding stages of normal erythropoiesis). As a result, the RBCs released into the circulation are larger than the normal mature RBCs. A deficiency of vitamin $B_{12}$ produces macrocytic anaemia.

*Folic acid*: This is a constituent of vitamin B complex. It is required for DNA synthesis. Its deficiency, too, causes megaloblastic erythropoiesis and macrocytic anaemia.

*Vitamin $B_6$ or pyridoxine*: This is required for the synthesis of haem.

*Vitamin C*: This vitamin is required for the activation of folic acid and the reduction of dietary iron into the ferrous ($Fe^{++}$) form, which helps in its absorption.

### Hormones

Thyroxine, cortisol and testosterone, in normal amounts, are essential for a normal concentration of erythropoietin.

### Metals

The following three metals are among the nutrients required for erythropoiesis.

*Iron*: Iron is the raw material required for the synthesis of Hb. About 50 per cent of all the body iron is present in RBCs. Iron is released during the destruction of senile RBCs and is carried by the plasma protein, transferrin, to the red bone marrow for reutilization for the synthesis of Hb.

Normally, about 1 per cent of dietary iron is absorbed in the intestine. The average daily requirement of iron of an adult female is twice that of an adult male since a lot of iron is lost in menstrual blood as well as during pregnancy and lactation. Iron-deficiency anaemia is, therefore, more common among females.

*Copper*: Cerulloplasmin, a copper-containing plasma protein, is essential for the transfer of iron from tissues to plasma transferrin.

*Cobalt*: Cobalt is a part of vitamin $B_{12}$ and is required for erythropoiesis.

## ANAEMIA

Anaemia is a condition in which the RBC count is decreased and the Hb concentration is also lower than normal. This results in a decrease in the $O_2$ supply to various tissues, causing disturbances in their functioning. The patient usually complains of fatigue and breathlessness. The root of anaemia could be an imbalance between the formation and destruction of RBCs.

## Classification

Anaemia can be classified (i) according to the size of the RBC and the Hb content, and (ii) according to the cause of the condition.

### RBC Size and Hb Content

Anaemia classified according to the size of the RBC and the Hb content is of the following three types.

*Microcytic hypochromic anaemia*: In this type, the size of the RBCs is small and the Hb concentration is usually very low. It is mostly due to iron deficiency.

*Macrocytic hypochromic (or normochromic) anaemia*: In this type, the RBC is big, but the Hb content is low, though it is occasionally normal. This is also called megaloblastic macrocytic anaemia. This condition affects the maturation of RBCs. It is due to vitamin $B_{12}$ or folic acid deficiency.

*Normocytic normochromic anaemia*: In this, the size and colour of the RBC is normal, but the total RBC count and Hb content is lower than normal. This condition is seen after haemorrhage.

### Cause of the Condition

Anaemia classified according to the cause of the condition can be of the following three types.

*Dyshaemopoietic (defective formation) anaemia*: Under this category fall sickle-cell anaemia, spherocytic anaemia, thalassaemia, aplastic anaemia and anaemia caused by the deficiency of factors required for RBC formation. As for the latter kind, iron deficiency produces microcytic, hypochromic anaemia and is more common among females. A deficiency of vitamin $B_{12}$ intrinsic factor or folic acid produces macrocytic, megaloblastic anaemia. Anaemia due to vitamin $B_{12}$ deficiency is called pernicious anaemia, in which there is neurological damage. Folic acid deficiency is common during pregnancy. Deficiency of proteins also causes anaemia.

Aplastic anaemia is caused by depression of the bone marrow and the loss of its haemopoietic function. It may be a result of (i) hypersensitivity reaction to drugs such as sulphonamides and chloramphenicol, (ii) overexposure to X-rays (irradiation), (iii) cytotoxic drugs, or (iv) radioactive substances. The last three are used for treating malignancy.

Sickle-cell anaemia is caused by the presence of HbS in RBCs. The RBCs in the venous blood become sickle-shaped and fragile. In spherocytic anaemia, the RBCs are congenitally spherical and, therefore, break early when exposed to hypo-osmolar solutions. Thalassaemia, as mentioned earlier, is due to the presence of HbF in RBCs in post-natal life.

*Haemorrhagic anaemia*: This condition is caused by

chronic blood loss, for example, by vomiting of blood, bleeding piles and excessive menstruation. It results in hypochromic microcytic anaemia.

*Haemolytic anaemia*: This is due to excessive destruction of RBCs, for example, because of mismatched blood transfusion, the presence of certain substances (haemolysins) like toxins, drugs, and snake venom, and congenital defects like the presence of HbF or HbS in RBCs.

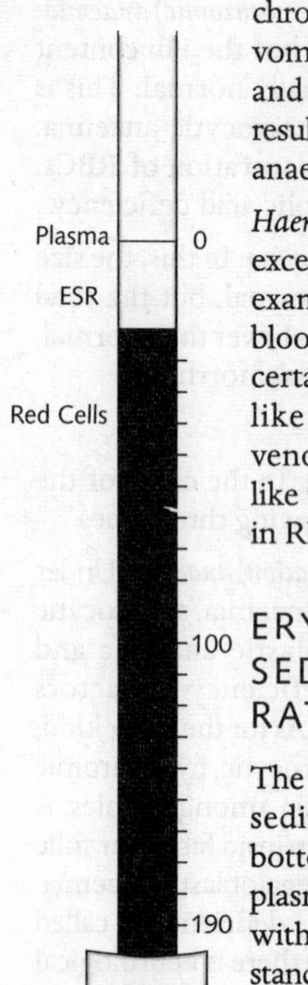

**Fig. 6.5:** Estimation of ESR by Westergren method

## ERYTHROCYTE SEDIMENTATION RATE (ESR)

The ESR is the rate at which RBCs sediment (settle down) to the bottom of the tube, leaving clear plasma on top, when blood mixed with anticoagulant is allowed to stand in a narrow, long tube for one hour (Fig. 6.5).

The normal ESR for males is 0–10 mm, and for females, 0–20 mm.

Physiologically, the ESR is increased during menstruation and pregnancy. Pathologically, it is increased in severe anaemia due to a decreased number of RBCs, rheumatoid arthritis, uberculosis and malignancy.

An increase in the plasma fibrinogen increases rouleaux formation of RBCs (i.e., their piling on top of each other). This increases the mass to surface area ratio of RBCs and favours sedimentation (Fig. 6.6).

An increased ESR has prognostic value in tuberculosis. This is more important than nonspecific diagnostic significance. A progressive decrease in the ESR indicates that the patient is responding to treatment and has a good prognosis.

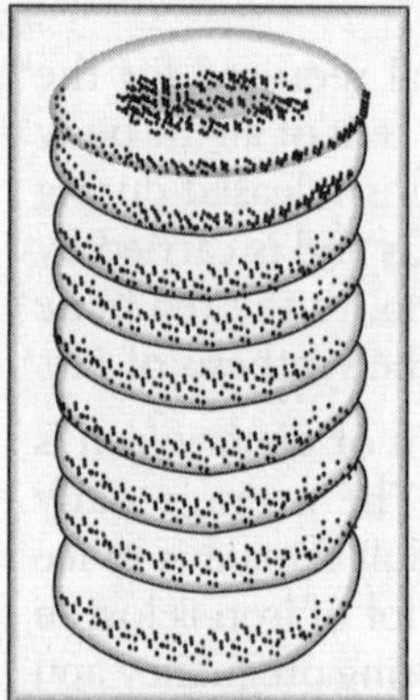
**Fig. 6.6:** Rouleaux formation of RBCs

## FATE OF RBCs

At the end of the normal lifespan of an RBC, which is about 120 days, the activity of cytoplasmic oxidative enzymes in the cell decreases. The membrane of the senile RBC becomes fragile due to the deficiency of energy, and the normal volume and shape of RBCs cannot be maintained. Such deformed cells are disintegrated, mainly in the spleen and liver, by reticuloendothelial cells, also called macrophages.

### Stages of destruction

The following are the stages of destruction of RBCs:

1. Breakdown of the cell.
2. Liberation of Hb.
3. Degradation of Hb, resulting in its separation into haem and globin.
4. Globin is broken down into amino acids, which are reused for the formation of fresh Hb.
5. Haem breaks down into porphyrin and iron.
6. The iron part is removed and stored in the liver as ferritin. Whenever required, it is transported to red bone marrow by transferrin, to be reused for the formation of fresh Hb, myoglobin or iron-containing respiratory enzymes (Fig. 6.7).
7. The remaining part of haem, that is, porphyrin is converted to biliverdin, which is green.
8. Biliverdin is oxidized to bilirubin, which is yellow. Bilirubin is the end-product of Hb destruction.
9. Bilirubin comes out of the reticuloendothelial

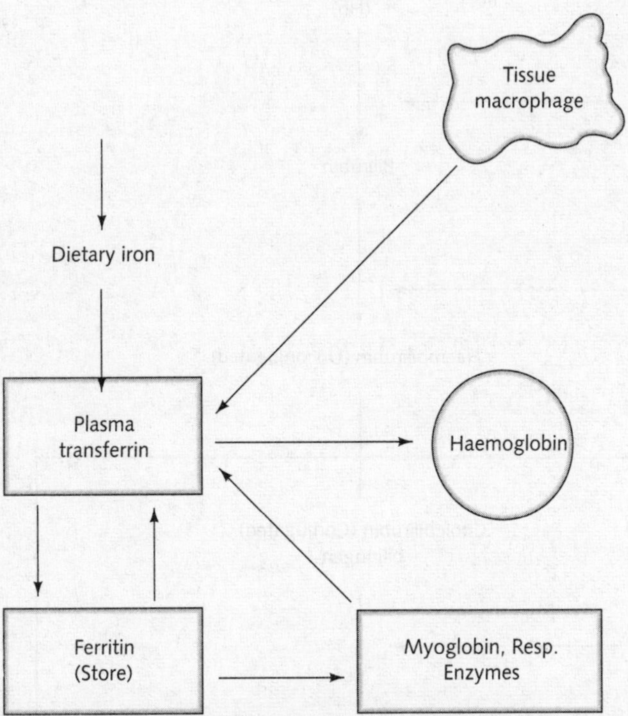


**Fig. 6.7:** Metabolism of iron

cells into blood, and combines with serum albumin to form haembilirubin. This is not water-soluble and, therefore, is not filtered by the glomeruli of the kidney.

10. Haembilirubin is transported to the liver, in which the enzyme glucoronyl transferase frees it from albumin. The bilirubin combines with glucoronic acid to form cholebilirubin, which is water-soluble and can, therefore, be filtered by the glomeruli and appear in urine.
11. Cholebilirubin (conjugated bilirubin) goes into the large intestine and is hydrolysed by the bacteria there into stercobilinogen. This appears in the faeces, giving it a yellow colour. When exposed to air, stercobilinogen gets oxidized and becomes dark in colour due to the formation of stercobilin.
12. Some of the stercobilinogen gets absorbed and goes into the liver. From there, it reaches the kidneys and is excreted in urine as urobilinogen. On exposure to air, it becomes urobilin, which gives the urine a brownish colour (Fig. 6.8).

## APPLIED PHYSIOLOGY

The level of bilirubin in blood is maintained constant as long as the rate of RBC formation equals that of their destruction. If the destruction of RBCs exceeds the excretory capacity of the liver, the level of bilirubin in blood increases, resulting in the discolouration of the skin, conjunctiva and urine to a yellowish hue. This condition is called jaundice. The range of the plasma bilirubin level is 0.5–1 mg%. Jaundice is clinically detectable when the plasma bilirubin level exceeds 2 mg%. Jaundice can occur due to a variety of causes.

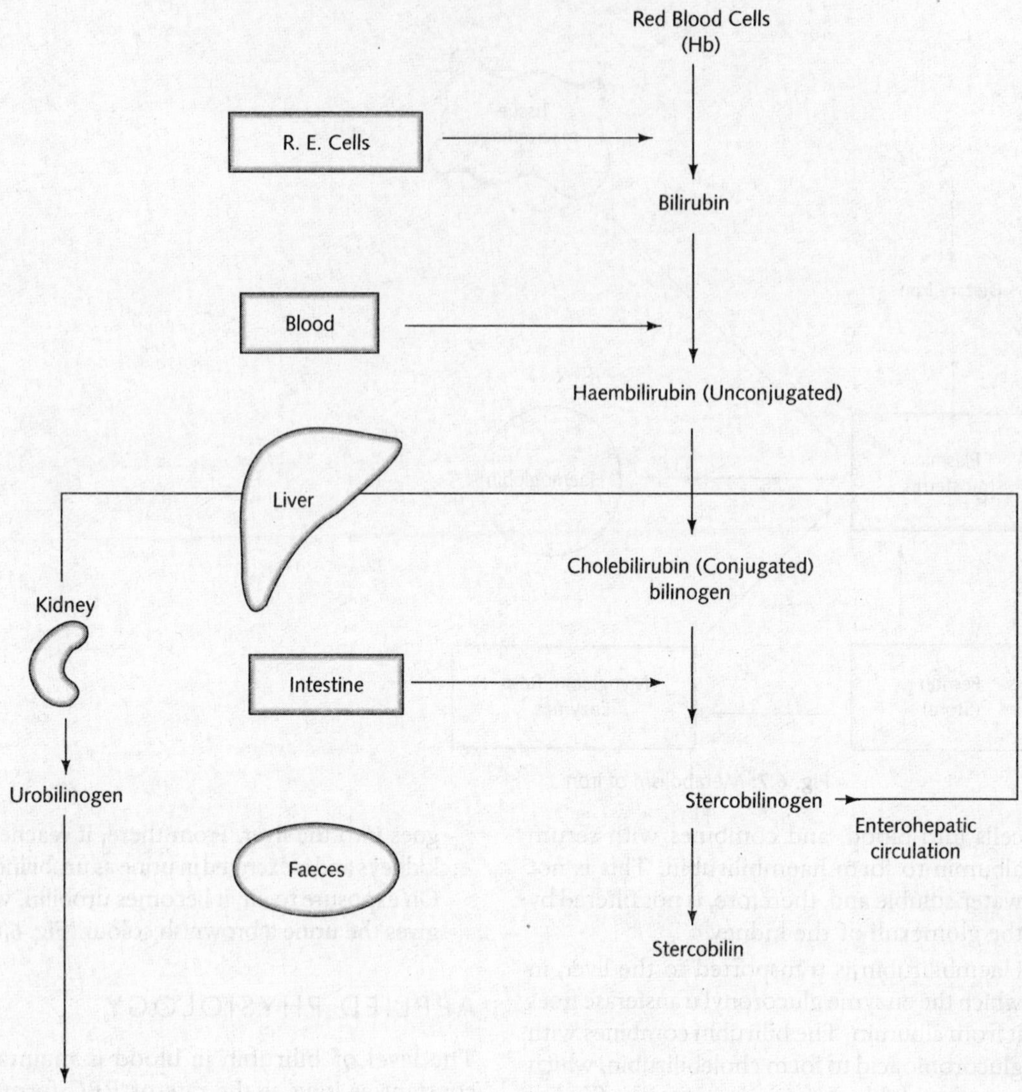

Red Blood Cells
(Hb)
R. E. Cells
Bilirubin
Blood
Haembilirubin (Unconjugated)
Liver
Cholebilirubin (Conjugated)
bilinogen
Kidney
Intestine
Urobilinogen
Stercobilinogen
Enterohepatic
circulation
Faeces
Stercobilin
Urine Urobilin

CHAPTER 7

# White Blood Cells and Immunity

White blood cells (WBCs) are nucleated cells that are irregular in shape and larger than RBCs, their diameter varying from 7–15 microns.

## CLASSIFICATION

WBCs can be classified into two types, according to the presence of granules in the cytoplasm, which can be detected by Leishman's stain. One type is the granulocytes, which have a diameter of 10–14 microns and contain granules. The other is the agranulocytes, which have no granules.

### Granulocytes

Granulocytes can be further classified into three types, according to the staining reaction of the granules:
1. Neutrophils, 2. Eosinophils, and 3. Basophils.

**Neutrophils (polymorphs)**
The cytoplasm of neutrophils contains fine, pale violet granules. The nucleus is multilobed (2–5 lobes), the number of lobes being in proportion to the age of the cell.

**Eosinophils**
The cytoplasm takes an acidic stain, and the granules are coarse and pink. The nucleus is bilobed and spectacle-shaped.

**Basophils**
The cytoplasm of basophils takes a basic stain, and the granules are coarse and deep blue.

### Agranulocytes

Agranulocytes can be divided into two types:

1. Lymphocytes, and
2. Monocytes.

**Lymphocytes**
These can be either small or large. Small lymphocytes have a diameter of 7–8 microns. There is very little cytoplasm in the cell, and the nucleus is large and deep blue.

Large lymphocytes have a diameter of 10–14 microns. They have more cytoplasm, which forms a rim at the periphery, and the nucleus is deep blue.

**Monocytes**
These cells have a diameter of 14–18 microns. They are the largest of the WBCs. The nucleus is kidney-shaped and eccentric in position.

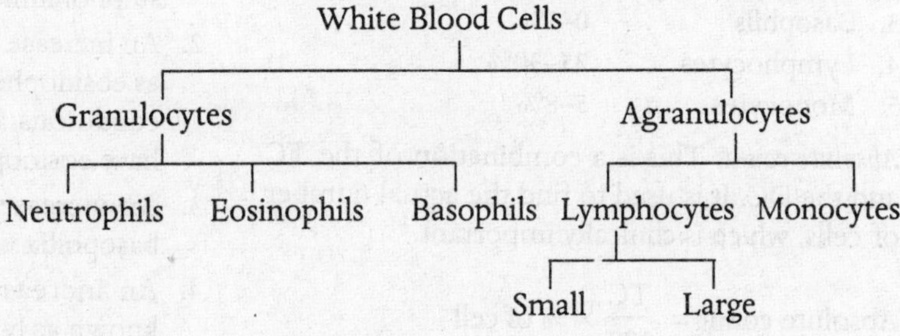

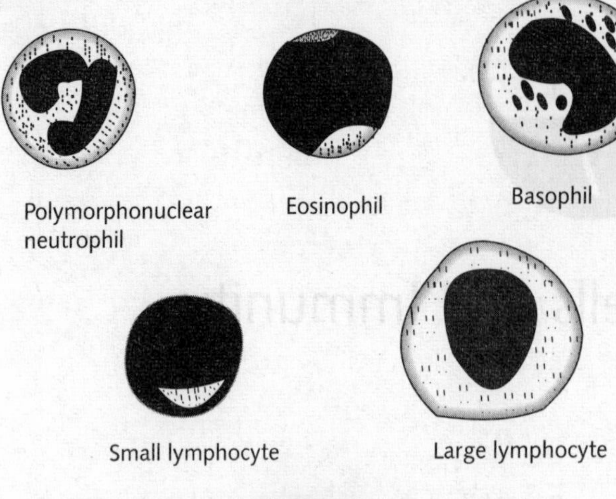


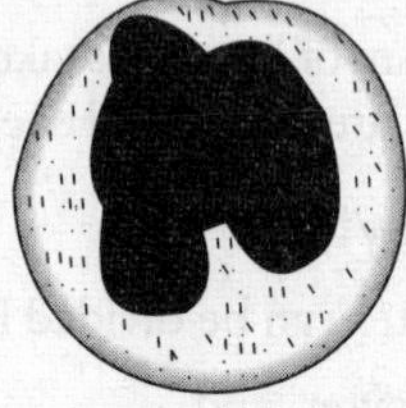


**Fig. 7.1:** Various types of white blood cells

## WBC COUNT

The WBC count is measured in several ways—the total count, differential count and absolute count.

*Total count (TC)*: The normal range is 4000 to 11,000/mm$^3$.

*Differential count (DC)*: This is the percentage of different kinds of WBCs. The normal percentages are listed below.

1. Neutrophils : 50–70%
2. Eosinophils : 2–5%
3. Basophils : 0–1%
4. Lymphocytes : 25–30%
5. Monocytes : 5–8%

***Absolute count***: This is a combination of the TC and the DC. It is used to find the actual number of cells, which is clinically important.

$$\text{Absolute count} = \frac{\text{TC}}{100} \times \text{\% of cell}$$

### Variations in WBC count

Variations in the WBC count can result in abnormal conditions, such as leucocytosis, leucopenia and leukaemia.

Leucocytosis is characterized by an increase of the WBC count to more than 11,000/mm$^3$. In leucopenia, the count decreases to less than 4000/mm$^3$. In leukaemia, the count goes up to more than 50,000/mm$^3$, and immature forms are found in the circulation.

**Causes**

The causes for variations in the WBC count may be physiological or pathological. The important ones are described below.

*Physiological*: In infants, the WBC count is higher and the number of lymphocytes greater. The count decreases with age. It increases with muscular exercise and emotional excitement. It also increases during menstruation, pregnancy and labour. The count increases slightly after a meal, but decreases during starvation.

*Pathological*: The pathological causes for variations in the WBC count are many. These are described below.

1. An absolute increase in the neutrophil count is called neutrophilia, and a decrease is known as neutropenia. The former is seen in acute pyogenic infections, such as pneumonia, tonsilitis and appendicitis. Neutropenia is seen in cases of viral infection, typhoid fever, irradiation (X-ray therapy) for malignancy and often after treatment with drugs like sulphonamides and chloramphenicol.
2. An increase in the eosinophil count is known as eosinophilia. Persons with asthma, allergic conditions and parasitic infections (worms) have eosinophilia.
3. An increase in the basophil count is called basophilia which is seen in leukaemia.
4. An increase in the lymphocyte count is known as lymphocytosis. It is seen in chronic

infections like tuberculosis and leprosy, and in leukaemia.

5. An increase in the monocyte count is called monocytosis. It is seen in chronic infections like tuberculosis and leprosy, and in malaria.

## PROPERTIES

WBCs have the following properties.

### Diapedesis

WBCs can squeeze through small capillaries. A small part of the cell passes through the junction between the endothelial cells. The remaining part gradually follows it and the cell can pass out of the blood vessel into the tissue spaces.

### Amoeboid Movement

WBCs, particularly neutrophils and monocytes, and to some extent lymphocytes and eosinophils, show amoeboid movement when they enter tissues. They form pseudopodia which help them move.

### Chemotaxis

In case of infection, the rate of diapedesis in the affected tissues increases. Different chemical agents cause the movement of WBCs towards them. This is called chemotaxis (chemical attraction). Bacteria, their toxins, products of inflammatory reactions and blood clots are chemotactic agents. WBCs migrate out of the blood vessels towards the site of tissue injury and most of the phagocytic activity occurs extravascularly (Fig. 7.2).

## FUNCTIONS

WBCs perform various vital functions, which are described below.

### Phagocytosis

This process is carried out by neutrophils and monocytes. The cells give out pseudopodia, which engulf the bacteria, ingesting them into the cytoplasm and destroying them. The lysosomes contain proteolytic enzymes which destroy the ingested organisms by hydrolysis.

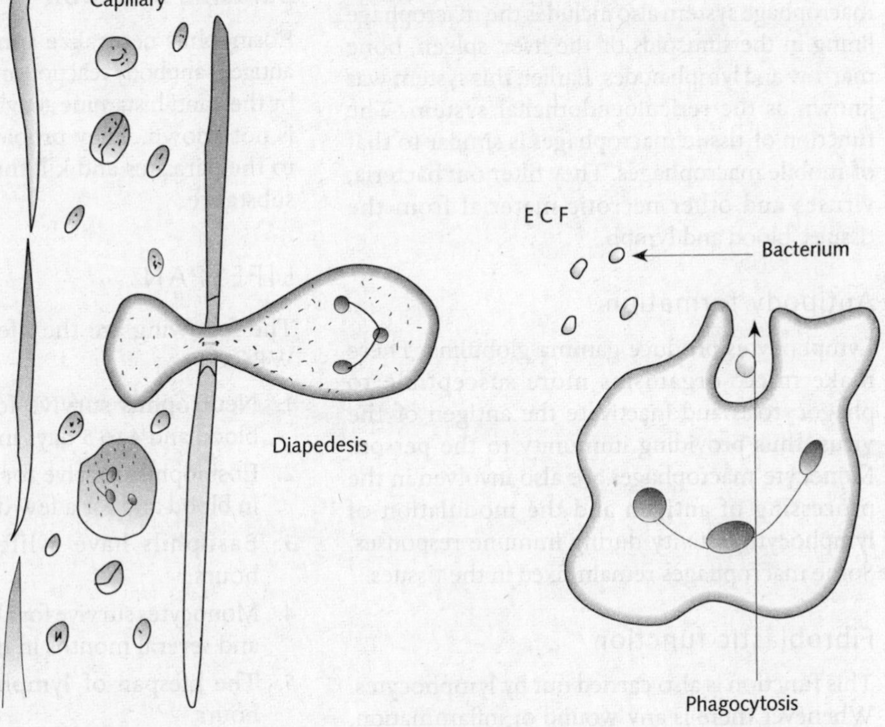


**Fig. 7.2:** Response of neutrophils to infection

Neutrophils form the first line of defence and are effective in acute infection, while monocytes, the second line of defence, are effective in chronic infection. Monocytes also help in the removal of debris from devitalized tissues. This process is called scavenging. Blood monocytes are not capable of phagocytosis as such, and in the tissues, they get converted to tissue macrophages (i.e., they differentiate). They become large and an extremely large number of lysosomes and mitochondria develop in their cytoplasm. A macrophage has greater phagocytic power than a neutrophil. It may engulf as many as 100 bacteria, compared to the neutrophil's ability to engulf just 5–20. Some of them keep wandering in the tissues.

When a neutrophil engulfs a large number of bacteria, the strong proteolytic activity not only destroys the bacteria but also the neutrophil itself. Dead neutrophils are removed by the monocyte macrophages, resulting in the formation of pus, which consists of dead tissue, dead neutrophils and macrophages.

Besides monocyte macrophages, the tissue macrophage system also includes the macrophage lining in the sinusoids of the liver, spleen, bone marrow and lymph nodes. Earlier, this system was known as the reticuloendothelial system. The function of tissue macrophages is similar to that of mobile macrophages. They filter out bacteria, viruses and other necrotic material from the tissues, blood and lymph.

### Antibody formation

Lymphocytes produce gamma globulins. These make micro-organisms more susceptible to phagocytosis and inactivate the antigen of the virus, thus providing immunity to the person. Monocyte macrophages are also involved in the processing of antigen and the modulation of lymphocytic activity during immune responses. Some macrophages remain fixed in the tissues.

### Fibroblastic function

This function is also carried out by lymphocytes. Whenever there is any wound or inflammation, lymphocytes reach the site and form a fibrous tissue, that is, a wall or barrier, which does not allow the infection to spread to other areas. This process not only helps localize the infection, but also helps heal the wound.

### Formation of trephones

With the help of plasma proteins, especially from the albumin part, WBCs form a compound called trephone. Trephones help in the nutrition, growth and repair of tissues and also help build up resistance.

### Formation of heparin

Basophils, also known as mast cells, produce heparin, which is an anticoagulant that prevents intravascular clotting or thrombosis. Basophils also produce serotonin, a vasoconstrictor substance, and bradykinin and histamine, which are vasodilator substances.

### Protection against allergy and parasitic infection

Eosinophils neutralize some of the products of antigen–antibody reaction and reduce inflammation by their anti-histamine activity. Their exact function is not known. They probably attach themselves to the parasites and kill them by releasing some substance.

## LIFESPAN

The following are the lifespans of the various WBCs:

1. Neutrophils survive for about 12 hours in blood and 4 to 5 days in tissue.
2. Eosinophils survive for about 16 to 24 hours in blood and for a few days in tissue.
3. Basophils have a lifespan of just a few hours.
4. Monocytes survive for about 70 hours in blood and several months in tissue.
5. The lifespan of lymphocytes is only a few hours.

## LEUCOPOIESIS

Leucopoiesis is the process of the formation of WBCs. It keeps the WBC count constant in blood.

There are various sites for leucopoiesis. Granulocytes are formed in the red bone marrow, lymphocytes in lymphoid tissue, and monocytes in both the red bone marrow and lymphoid tissue.

The parent cell is the pleuripotent stem cell. It is the same in the case of all blood cells. It differentiates into committed stem cells for different types of WBCs, for example, the granulocyte myeloblast, lymphocyte lymphoblast and monocyte monoblast.

### Regulation of leucopoiesis

The time required for leucopoiesis is about 3 days.

It is not known exactly how leucopoiesis is regulated, but it is probably by leucopoiesis promoting factor, which is liberated by degenerated WBCs in the area of inflammation and transported to the bone marrow through the blood circulation. Leucopoiesis-promoting factor is also called colony-stimulating factor because it causes a single stem cell to proliferate into a colony of a particular type of WBC, for example, neutrophils or monocytes.

The development of WBCs also requires the intake of proteins and vitamins ($B_{12}$ and folic acid) in the diet. A deficiency of these vitamins causes leucopenia, and severe infection can set in, causing death.

## GRANULOPOIESIS

This is the process of the production of granulocytes. The stages of granulopoiesis are described below.

**Myeloblast**

The myeloblast has a large, round nucleus with many nucleoli, mitochondria and an endoplasmic reticulum. The cytoplasm is basophilic and has no granules. Myeloblasts are nonmotile and capable of active division. They form metamyelocytes.

**Myelocyte**

The myelocyte develops in three stages—the promyelocyte, propermyelocyte, and metamyelocyte. In the promyelocyte stage, the nucleus becomes small and the nucleoli disappear. The cytoplasm contains primary azurophilic granules. Motility appears and mitosis is at a maximum.

In the propermyelocyte stage, the nucleus becomes smaller and the chromatin becomes coarse. The cytoplasm contains secondary granules which take a definite stain. According to the stain they take, the cells are called neutrophilic, basophilic or eosinophilic myelocytes. Motility and mitosis are present.

In the metamyelocyte stage, the features of cells can be seen fully. The nucleus has definite lobes, joined together by a fine thread of chromatin. The cytoplasmic granules take definite stains—violet, red or blue—and become further distinguished on the basis of this. Cytoplasmic maturation starts, motility increases and mitosis or multiplication stops.

**Mature granulocytes**

These have well-distinguished granules and according to the colour of the stained granules, they can be classified into neutrophils, eosinophils and basophils. The number of lobes of the nucleus in a neutrophil varies with maturation. Amoeboid movement is present.

## LYMPHOPOIESIS

Lymphoblasts migrate from the bone marrow to the central lymphoid tissues, like the thymus, for preprocessing. They undergo cell division and differentiate to form immunocompetent T-lymphocytes. Most of the processing of T-lymphocytes occurs shortly before and after birth.

Birds have another central lymphoid tissue, the Bursa of Fabricius, where lymphoblasts are preprocessed to immunocompetent B-lymphocytes. In mammals, the equivalent of the bursa is probably located in the foetal liver.

The T- and B-lymphocytes released from the central lymphoid tissues circulate in the blood and within a few hours, they are trapped in the areas of future peripheral lymphoid tissues. These are the lymph nodes, which are present throughout the body, and special lymphoid tissues located in the tonsils, intestine, urinary and respiratory tracts, spleen and bone marrow. The lymph nodes are located at each possible route of entry of invading organisms. The spleen and bone marrow remove organisms which may enter the blood circulation and the lymph nodes remove those which may enter the lymphatics.

In the lymphoid tissues, the T- and B-lymphocytes proliferate and further differentiate when exposed to antigens. The lifespan of T-lymphocytes is 2 to 4 years, while that of B-lymphocytes is only a few weeks. When exposed to antigen, some of the T- and B-lymphocytes do not become effector cells but instead, remain immunological memory cells for months and years. On re-exposure to similar antigen, these memory cells produce a much quicker and larger response.

## MONOPOIESIS

Monoblasts are similar to myeloblasts, but promonocytes are characterized by an indented nucleus and a deep basophilic cytoplasm. Monocytes have a kidney-shaped nucleus and plenty of blue cytoplasm.

## IMMUNITY

Immunity is the ability of the human body to resist most foreign substances that invade it. The body recognizes, destroys or eliminates the materials that do not belong to it.

The purpose of immunity is to protect the body from the harmful effects of bacteria and viruses, the toxins produced by them, and any foreign material that enters the body, for example, a graft, a transplanted organ or malignant cells.

The immune system consists of (i) WBCs, the important cells being the neutrophils and monocytes, which are motile; (ii) macrophages, which are wandering cells and fixed cells in the liver, spleen, bone marrow and lymph nodes; and (iii) the peripheral lymphoid tissues, which produce lymphocytes, the key constituents of the immune system.

There are two types of immune mechanisms. One is phagocytosis, which is carried out by neutrophils, monocytes and tissue macrophages. The other is the formation of antibodies, carried out by the lymphocytes. Immunity is of two types—natural and acquired.

### Natural immunity

This type of immunity is present from birth and is a generalized process, not specific to any particular antigen. It is the first line of defence and previous exposure to a particular antigen is not required.

Part of resistance results from nonspecific processes. Some examples are the resistance of the skin to invasion by organisms, the destruction of ingested bacteria by gastric acid or proteolytic enzymes in the gastrointestinal tract, phagocytosis, and the action of certain other substances naturally present in the body, for example, interferon. However, the natural immune mechanism is not sufficient to give full protection against invading organisms.

### Acquired immunity

This type of immunity is developed after birth. It is a process that is specific to a particular antigen. It is the second line of defence and previous exposure to a particular antigen is required. The mechanisms involved are the formation of specific antibodies for specific antigens, and the sensitization of cells to specific foreign material. The acquired immune mechanism is very powerful and protects the body from particular diseases.

Acquired immunity is of two types—humoral and cellular.

#### Humoral Immunity

Humoral immunity arises from circulating antibodies (immunoglobulins) which are capable of attacking the invading agent. The B-lymphocytes are converted to plasma cells that produce immunoglobulins, which are components of gamma globulin (plasma protein). Immunoglobulins form the major defence system against bacterial infections.

Humoral immunity may be active or passive.

*Active immunity*: This kind of immunity occurs during the course of natural infections due to actual contact with antigen. It can be produced artificially, by injecting small doses of microbes which are incapable of causing a disease but have retained their chemical antigenicity, for example, weakened (attenuated) microbes like smallpox and polio, detoxicated toxins like tetanus, and dead microbes like typhoid. This process, called vaccination, activates the immune process against a particular microbe. Usually, two doses are given with a short interval in between, followed by booster doses to maintain the concentration of the antibodies at a high level.

Active immunity has a long duration and is used for the prevention of a disease.

*Passive immunity*: This is produced by the direct transfer of readymade antibodies formed in an animal or another person, for example, the transfer of antibodies from mother to child across the placenta. Specific antibodies are sometimes used to confer immediate protection against a disease, for example, tetanus. However, such protection lasts for only a short period as the immune mechanism has not been stimulated to produce antibodies actively.

**Cellular (Cell-mediated) Immunity**

Cellular immunity is produced by activated or sensitized T-lymphocytes, which can directly attack intracellular organisms such as viruses, fungi and some bacteria. T-lymphocytes are also involved in the rejection of incompatible tissue grafts and organ transplants, as well as the removal of malignant cells.

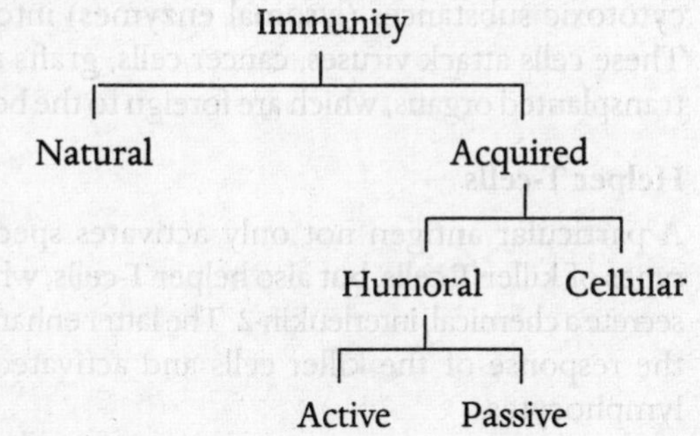


## COMPONENTS OF IMMUNE MECHANISM

### Antigen

An antigen is a chemical compound present in a foreign invader. It is a large molecule and stimulates the formation of a specific antibody, with which it combines on second exposure. The specificity of antigen depends on the position of the prosthetic radicals on the surface of a large molecule. Most invading organisms are first phagocytosed by macrophages, which partially digest them and transfer the antigen to a lymphocyte, with specific receptors for it, on the cell membrane. Macrophages also secrete chemicals, such as lymphokines and interleukin-I, which promote the growth and reproduction of specific activated lymphocytes.

### Antibody

An antibody is a specific substance which combines with a specific antigen that has stimulated its production. Antibodies are gamma globulin in nature. They are produced in the peripheral lymphoid tissue by B-lymphocytes, which differentiate into plasma cells that secrete antibodies for several weeks. These enter the circulation via the lymph. Their specificity depends on the different (specific) amino acids present in the variable portion of the immunoglobulin molecule (Fig. 7.3).

In general, five types of immunoglobulins are recognized: IgA, IgM, IgE, IgD and IgG. These are the most common. Specific antibodies (IgG) and complement proteins adhere to the bacterial membrane, making the bacteria 'attractive' to phagocytosis. This is called 'opsonization' of bacteria. The function of the antibody is to react with a specific antigen, bringing about the antigen–antibody reaction.

### Antigen–antibody reaction

The specificity of an antigen–antibody reaction is due to their complementary structures, which fit into one another like a lock and key.

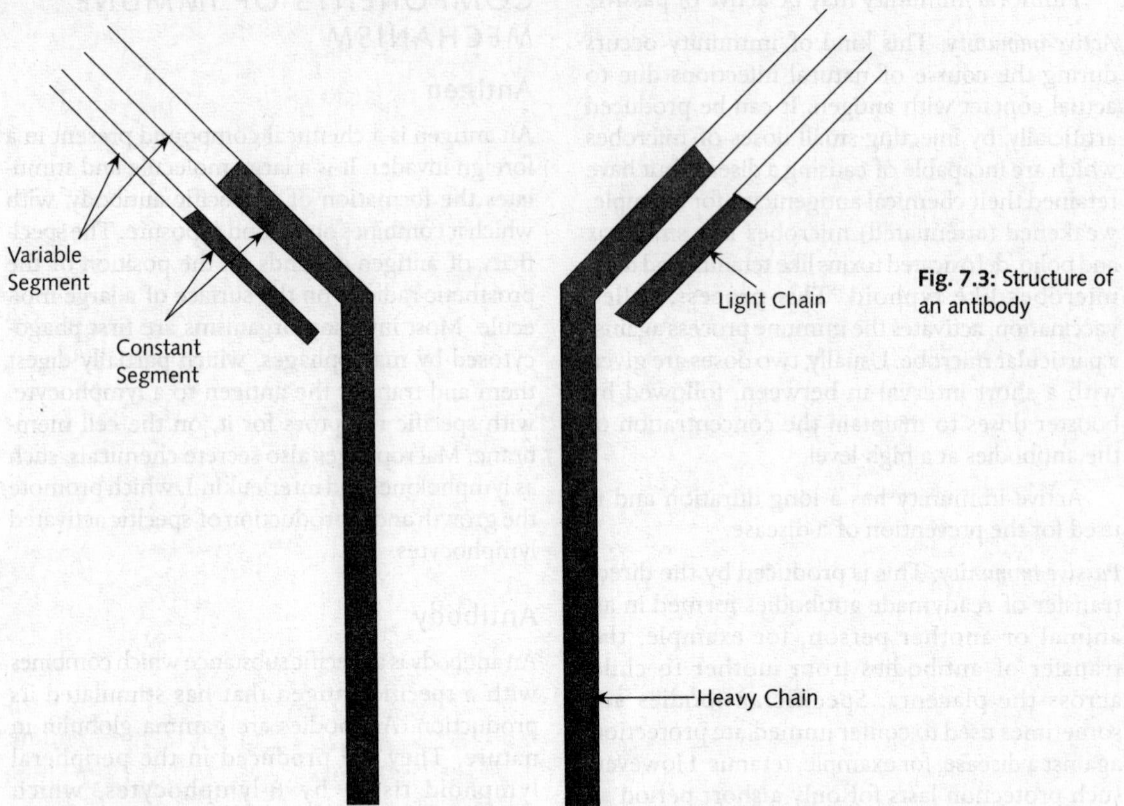


**Fig. 7.3:** Structure of an antibody

The mechanisms by which antigen–antibody reactions destroy the foreign invader depend on the type of antibody produced. The following are the different ways:

1. Lysis: This is the distortion of the cell membrane and rupture of the cell by a cytolysis antibody (e.g., IgA and IgM).
2. Agglutination: In this, the antigens are clumped together and prevented from moving by agglutinin antibody.
3. Precipitation: The soluble antigen is made insoluble and precipitated by precipitin antibody.
4. Neutralization: The antibody covers the toxic sites on the antigen with antitoxic antibody.

Subsequent to the antigen–antibody reaction, antigens are subjected to phagocytosis.

## Sensitization or activation of T-lymphocytes

There are three types of T-cells: cytotoxic or killer cells, helper cells and suppressor cells.

**Cytotoxic or Killer T-cells**

On coming in contact with specific antigen on the surface of an organism or mutant cell, the killer T-cell binds with it, gets enlarged and releases cytotoxic substances (lysomal enzymes) into it. These cells attack viruses, cancer cells, grafts and transplanted organs, which are foreign to the body.

**Helper T-cells**

A particular antigen not only activates specific types of killer T-cells, but also helper T-cells, which secrete a chemical, interleukin-2. The latter enhances the response of the killer cells and activated B-lymphocytes.

**Suppressor T-cells**

These can suppress the activity of killer and helper T-cells. Activated T-cells can function in the blood or any other tissue.

The major function of T-cells is to recognize and destroy cancer cells. They have surface antigen that is different from that of normal cells. The failure of this system leads to the multiplication of mutant cells, resulting in cancer.

## ABNORMALITIES OF IMMUNE MECHANISM

### Immune deficiency

This may be congenital or acquired. Acquired deficiency is due to radiations and chemicals which destroy lymphocytes and viral infection, for example, human immunodeficiency virus (HIV). HIV can be transmitted through transfused blood, syringes, needles and sexual contact with those who have the HIV virus. This disease is known as acquired immune deficiency syndrome (AIDS). The virus causes severe deficiency of helper T-cells, resulting in the failure of cellular and humoral immunity. This leads to severe infection, causing death. The disease is not contagious.

### Allergy or hypersensitive immune response

This condition is characterized by either an increased number of antibodies or abnormal antibodies, which produces harmful effects on the body. Two types of effects are seen—immediate and delayed.

*Immediate*: Immediate hypersensitivity reactions are also known as anaphylaxis. They are caused by an abnormal reaction to a particular antigen. For example, if penicillin is administered to a person sensitive to it, it produces a severe antigen–antibody reaction due to the high concentration of antibodies (IgE). As a result, histamine is released, causing vasodilatation and circulatory shock, often leading to death.

*Delayed*: Various types of skin eruptions are seen after the person has taken certain drugs.

### Autoimmunity

In those suffering from autoimmunity, immunity is produced against the body's own tissue. Usually, this does not happen as the immune system recognizes its own body tissues and does not produce antibodies against them. This is called immunological tolerance. A failure of immunological tolerance leads to autoimmune diseases. The tissues involved may be the joints (rheumatoid arthritis) or muscles (myasthenia gravis), and the condition causes impairment of their function.

CHAPTER 8

# Platelets and Haemostasis

Platelets are non-nucleated, biconvex, circucular circular cells. They are small, their diameters measuring 2 to 4 microns, and occur in clusters.

With Leishman's stain, the cytoplasm of a platelet appears faint blue and contains reddish purple granules. Under the electron microscope, a platelet is seen to contain mitochondria, the Golgi apparatus and endoplasmic reticulum. The cytoplasm also contains microtubules, microvesicles and granules (Fig. 8.1).

Chemically, the granules contain ATP, ADP, histamine, 5-hydroxytryptamine (5-HT), prostaglandins and a phospholipid called platelet factor III.

The normal platelet count is 1–4 lakhs/mm$^3$. A decrease in the platelet count is known as thrombocytopenia. It usually occurs due to depression of the bone marrow. The bleeding time increases and the disease, called purpura, is characterized by capillary haemorrhages in the skin.

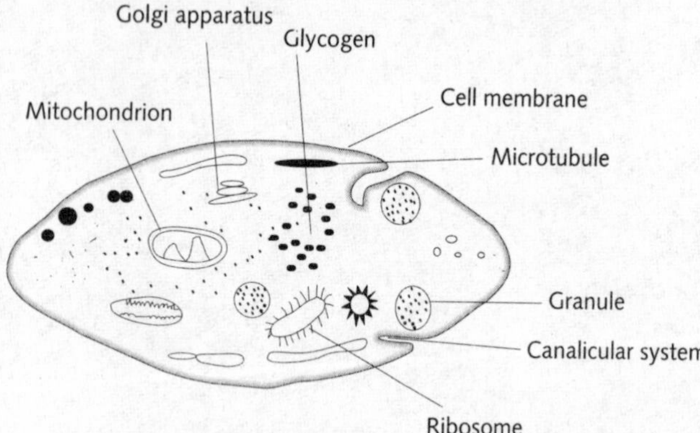


**Fig. 8.1:** Structure of platelet

## FUNCTIONS OF PLATELETS

### Haemostasis

Platelets help arrest bleeding by the following mechanisms.

*Plugging of injured capillaries*: Following a leak in the endothelial lining, platelets tend to form a mass of cells that plugs the opening in the blood vessel. This is due to two important properties of these cells: (i) they are adhesive to the damaged endothelium of blood vessels, and (ii) they can aggregate because they are sticky and thus, stick to each other.

*Vasoconstriction*: Platelets release a chemical called 5-HT, which causes constriction of blood vessels about 20 minutes after an injury.

*Coagulation of blood*: If the vascular injury is severe and the platelet plug does not control the haemorrhage effectively, coagulation of blood occurs. The platelets help initiate this by releasing a phospholipid called platelet factor III.

*Clot retraction*: The clot shrinks so that it can firmly block the opening in the capillary and bring its walls together. The shrinkage occurs because of the thrombosthenin present in it.

**Other Functions**

Viruses and antigen–antibody complex are phagocytosed by platelets. Histamine and 5–HT are stored in platelets. Platelets probably carry blood group (ABO) antigens.

The lifespan of platelets is about 8 to 12 days, after which they are destroyed in the spleen by reticuloendothelial cells.

## THROMBOPOIESIS

This is the process of the formation of platelets and its purpose is to maintain a normal platelet count. Platelets are produced in red bone marrow. The pleuripotent stem cells give rise to committed stem cells, called megakaryoblasts.

Thrombopoiesis occurs in the following three stages.

1. Megakaryoblast: This has a diameter of 15 to 20 microns. The nucleus is oval, while the cytoplasm is deeply basophilic and scanty. The megakaryoblast divides actively and matures into the next stage.
2. Megakaryocycte: The diameter is larger than 20 microns. The nucleus of this large cell is multilobed. The cytoplasm contains reddish purple granules. It gives out pseudopodia or cytoplasmic processes, which get detached and covered by a membrane.
3. Thrombocyte: The thrombocyte circulates in blood.

Thrombopoiesis is regulated by thrombopoietin or megakaryocytic-colony stimulating activity.

## HAEMOSTASIS AND COAGULATION OF BLOOD

Haemostasis is the arrest of haemorrhage by physiological mechanisms. When a blood vessel is injured, a number of mechanisms come into play, ultimately arresting the bleeding. Although these mechanisms are capable of controlling haemorrhages from small vessels, such as arterioles, capillaries and veins, they cannot control haemorrhages from large arteries, which need to be tied surgically.

Haemostasis takes place in the following steps:

1. Constriction of the injured blood vessel
2. Formation of a platelet plug
3. Facilitation of initial vasoconstriction
4. Coagulation of blood

**Constriction of Injured Blood Vessels**

A bleeding vessel immediately constricts at the site of injury due to reflex vascular spasm. This is caused by the direct effect of the injury on the smooth muscle of the vessel wall. The constriction is transient, and is maintained by serotonin released later from the platelets. This mechanism may suffice to stop bleeding from a small vessel.

**Formation of a Platelet Plug**

When the endothelium of a blood vessel is damaged, the collagen underneath it is exposed. When platelets come in contact with collagen, they swell up, become irregular in shape and spread, radiating processes by which they get attached to the exposed collagen. They become sticky and release large amounts of ADP and thromboxane-A, which activate other platelets and make them sticky. Platelets thus tend to aggregate, forming a mass or a plug which seals the opening in the blood vessel.

Platelet plugs deal promptly with the small haemorrhages that occur from capillaries in day-to-day life. However, they cannot prevent bleeding from larger vessels like arterioles, as they are soft. The activated platelets then play an important role in the process of coagulation.

**Facilitation of Initial Vasoconstriction**

On activation, platelets produce vasoconstrictor substances, including histamine, which are powerful and produce secondary vasoconstriction. The latter may last from several minutes to hours. Thus, platelets maintain the initial vasoconstriction.

**Coagulation of Blood**

This is the most important step in the process of haemostasis. However, the first three steps are also

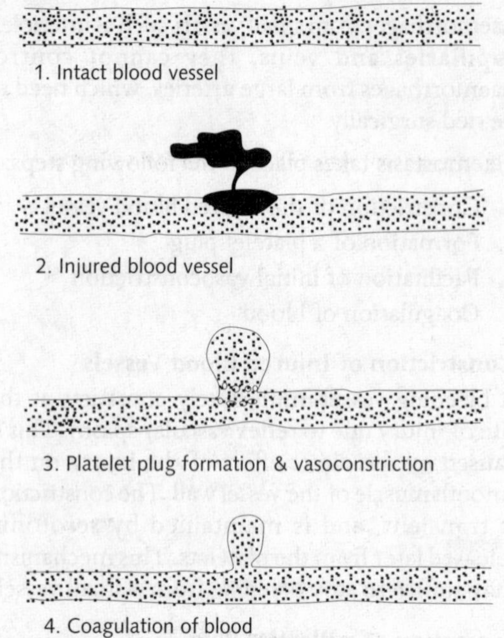


**Fig. 8.2**: Mechanisms of haemostasis

important as they minimize blood loss and facilitate the process of coagulation (Fig. 8.2).

## Coagulation of blood

Coagulation (clotting) is a process by which fluid blood is converted into a semi-solid jelly-like mass, called a clot.

Granules of fibrin appear near the platelets, which form needles and thin long fibres. These stick to one another and also, to the vascular wall, forming a network in the meshes of which are entangled blood cells, RBCs, WBCs and platelets. Therefore, coagulation is a process of plasma and not of RBCs or WBCs (Fig. 8.3).

### Initiation of Clotting

Coagulation is initiated by the formation of a prothrombin activator as a result of vascular injury. An enzyme cascade triggers off the formation of the activator. It is a complex phenomenon, in which one reaction triggers the next, that is, the activation of one clotting factor leads to that of the next clotting factor. The reactions involve coagulation factors which are normally present in blood. They

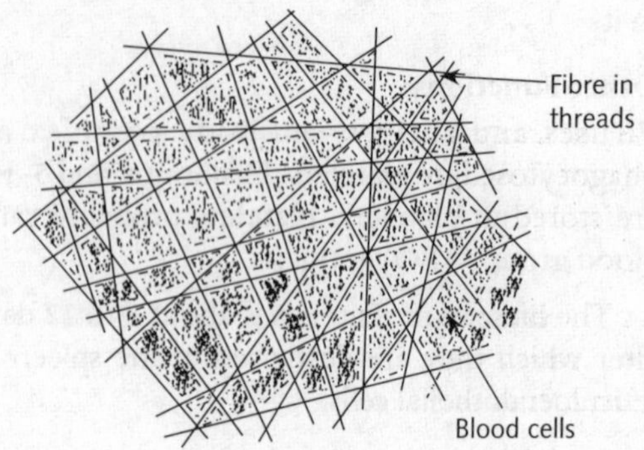


**Fig. 8.3**: Structure of clot

are mostly proteins and are present in an inactive form. They are listed below.

1. Fibrinogen
2. Prothrombin
3. Phospholipid
4. $Ca^{++}$ ions
5. Labile factor
6. Does not exist
7. Stable factor
8. Antihaemophilic factor
9. Christmas factor
10. Stuart power factor
11. Plasma thromboplastin antecedent (PTA)
12. Hagemen or surface factor
13. Fibrin stabilizing factor

The prothrombin activator extrinsic and intrinsic is formed by two mechanisms:

*Extrinsic pathway*: A tissue injury is followed by the release of a tissue factor (glycoprotein) and a phospholipid, called tissue thromboplastin or factor III, from the cell membrane. The tissue factor combines with factor VII and, in the presence of $Ca^{++}$ ions, activates factor X to Xa. The steps subsequent to this are common to the extrinsic and intrinsic pathways.

*Intrinsic pathway*: An injury to the vascular endothelium results in the exposure of the collagen underneath it, which converts the normal smooth surface of the endothelium (non-water-wettable) into a rough one (water-wettable). On contact with blood, it activates factor XII as well as platelets, which release a phospholipid called platelet factor III.

Activated factor XII (XIIa) activates factor XI to XIa, which, in turn, activates factor IX to IXa and then, factor VIII to VIIIa. In the presence of $Ca^{++}$ ions, factor VIIIa converts factor X to Xa.

The activated factor X, factor V and phospholipid liberated by the damaged tissues or platelets in the extrinsic and intrinsic mechanisms, respectively, form prothrombin activator (Fig. 8.4).

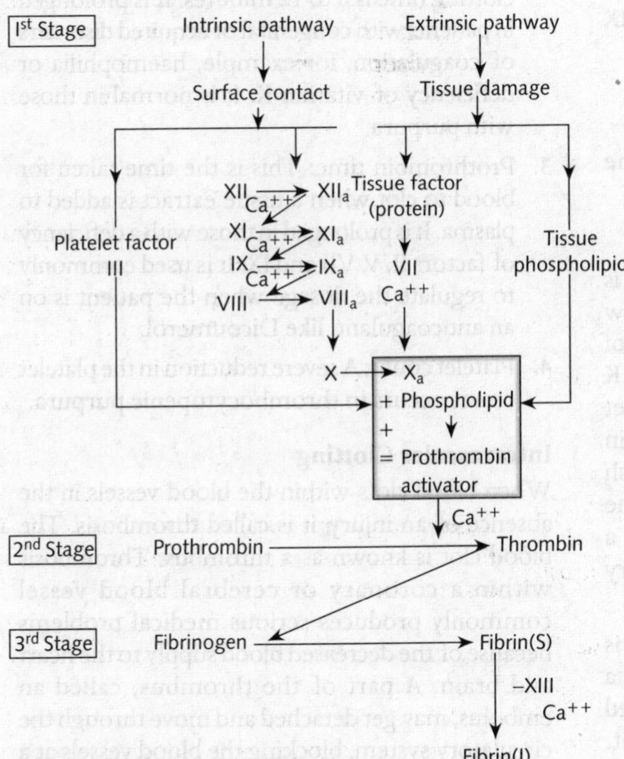


**Fig. 8.4:** Stages of coagulation of blood

## Stages of Coagulation

The mechanism of coagulation involves three essential stages. One is the formation of a prothrombin activator. The intrinsic mechanism acts in such a way that a small amount of factor XIIa produces a large amount of prothrombin activator.

The second stage is the conversion of prothrombin into thrombin by prothrombin activator, in the presence of $Ca^{++}$ ions.

The third stage is the conversion of fibrinogen into fibrin by thrombin. This soluble fibrin is converted into insoluble, sticky fibrin threads by factor XIII, in the presence of $Ca^{++}$ ions. These form a mesh, in which blood cells get entangled to form a clot. The blood clot adheres to the injured vascular walls, plugging it permanently.

## Fate of the Clot

Within a few minutes of its formation, the clot begins to shrink and release serum. Platelets are essential for this process, which is known as clot retraction. They adhere to the fibrin threads and send out pseudopodia which contract, pulling the fibrin threads close to each other. This is due to the thrombosthenin present in them. Retraction of the clot makes it firm and pulls the vessel wall together, so that the haemostatic mechanism becomes the most effective.

Ultimately, lysis of the clot takes place. Fibrous tissue growth into the blood clot permanently seals the opening in the blood vessel. The clot is finally removed by proteolytic enzymes (fibrinolysis). After a few days, the plasminogen present in blood is converted to plasmin, which dissolves the clot, and the blood supply to the tissues is restored.

## Factors Preventing Clotting

The following factors can prevent clotting:

1. Low temperature delays clotting because it involves various chemical reactions.
2. If contact is avoided with water-wettable surfaces, for example, by the use of a siliconized glass container, for collecting blood, clotting can be prevented.
3. Anticoagulants prevent clotting. These include substances that remove $Ca^{++}$ ions from blood.

For example, potassium oxalate and sodium citrate are used for the storage of blood in blood banks, or for the separation of plasma. Substances of biological origin, for example, protamines, peptones and hirudin, are also anti-coagulants, and so are certain drugs, like Dicoumerol (vitamin K antagonist).

**Factors Increasing Clotting**

The following factors increase clotting:

1. Warmth hastens clotting as it increases the rate of chemical (enzymatic) reaction.
2. Contact with water-wettable surfaces, for example, a piece of gauze, helps initiate clotting.
3. Injection of vitamin K (required for the formation of prothrombin and factors VII, IX and X in the liver) helps clotting.

## Disorders of coagulation of blood

There are several disorders relating to the coagulation of blood.

**Bleeding Disorders**

These can be caused by various factors. One is afibrinogenaemia, which is characterized by a low content of fibrinogen. Another is a low level of prothrombin, caused by a deficiency of vitamin K or liver disease. Thrombocytopenia (a platelet count of less than 50,000/mm$^3$) is a condition in which capillary haemorrhages are seen as pinkish blue spots on the skin. As mentioned earlier, the condition is called purpura. It may be due to a deficiency of vitamin C, which increases capillary fragility.

Another bleeding disorder, haemophilia, is caused by a deficiency of factor VIII. It is a congenital bleeding disorder, which is transmitted by the X-chromosome-linked recessive trait. Therefore, it is transmitted by females, but is manifested in males.

The deficiency of any other clotting factor, such as factors VII, IX and X, caused by intestinal malabsorption, causes deficiency of vitamin K.

*Laboratory tests for bleeding disorders*: A number of tests are usually required to pinpoint the exact cause of a bleeding disorder. Some of the tests are described below.

1. The bleeding time: This is the time required for bleeding to stop, when a small subcutaneous vessel is punctured, for example, in the finger-tip. It is normally 2 to 6 minutes. It is prolonged in patients with thrombocytopenic purpura due to delayed vasoconstriction and platelet plug formation. It is normal in clotting disorders like haemophilia or those caused by vitamin K deficiency.
2. The clotting time: This is the time required for blood to clot when removed in a glass tube and kept at a temperature of 37°C. The normal clotting time is 6 to 12 minutes. It is prolonged in patients with congenital or acquired disorders of coagulation, for example, haemophilia or deficiency of vitamin K. It is normal in those with purpura.
3. Prothrombin time: This is the time taken for blood to clot when a tissue extract is added to plasma. It is prolonged in those with a deficiency of factors II, V, VII and IX. It is used commonly to regulate the dosage when the patient is on an anticoagulant, like Dicoumerol.
4. Platelet count: A severe reduction in the platelet count occurs in thrombocytopenic purpura.

**Intravascular Clotting**

When blood clots within the blood vessels in the absence of an injury, it is called thrombosis. The blood clot is known as a thrombus. Thrombosis within a coronary or cerebral blood vessel commonly produces serious medical problems because of the decreased blood supply to the heart and brain. A part of the thrombus, called an embolus, may get detached and move through the circulatory system, blocking the blood vessels at a narrow spot, for example, a capillary. The process is called embolism, for example, pulmonary embolism.

*Factors preventing intravascular clotting*: These are (i) the presence of smooth endothelium, forming a non-water-wettable surface; (ii) the average speed of blood flow, which prevents coagulation factors from concentrating at one spot, and (iii) the presence of natural anticoagulants in the body, for example, heparin and antithrombin (most important). Anti-thrombin inhibits thrombin and its activity is enhanced by heparin.

*Factors favouring intravascular clotting*: These are (i) atherosclerosis, that is, the deposition of lipid and calcium under the lining of blood vessels, which makes the surface rough; and (ii) slow or sluggish circulation, for example, after an operation or after delivery, when person lies in bed. This is why early ambulation is advised. Atherosclerosis occurs due to ageing or an increased level of cholesterol.

CHAPTER 9

# Blood Groups

The various physiological mechanisms which bring about the arrest of a haemorrhage may not be effective under all circumstances.

Excessive haemorrhage results in a decreased volume of blood, oxygen-carrying capacity and coagulation factors. To compensate for this loss, different types of materials can be transfused, depending on the immediate need, for example, saline, plasma and blood.

Fresh human blood is the ideal material for transfusion, although stored blood can be used, as it supplies all the components of blood.

The indications for blood transfusion are the following:

1. Severe haemorrhage. Blood transfusion is a life-saving measure in patients suffering from haemorrhagic shock, following an accident.
2. Severe anaemia.
3. Coagulation defects.
4. During surgery.

It is necessary to take the following precautions for successful blood transfusion. The donor should be healthy and the transfusion apparatus should be sterile, since certain diseases are transmitted through blood transfusion, such as serum hepatitis, malaria and AIDS. The donor's blood must be compatible with that of the recipient. This means that when the blood of both is mixed, there should not be any clumping of RBCs. The clumping of RBCs, which is caused by differences in the antigen and antibody present in the blood and not by any physical forces, is called agglutination. The antigen and antibody responsible for it are known as the agglutinogen and agglutinin, respectively.

## BLOOD GROUP SYSTEMS

The major blood group systems are ABO, Rh and MN.

### ABO system

Depending on the presence or absence of two agglutinogens, A and B, Landsteiner classified blood into four groups in 1900:

1. Group A, containing agglutinogen A,
2. Group B, containing agglutinogen B,
3. Group AB, containing agglutinogens A and B, and
4. Group O, containing neither A nor B.

Agglutinogens are glycolipids present in the membrane of RBCs. They appear in the sixth week of intrauterine life. They may also be present in other tissues, for example, the salivary glands. Agglutinogens can react with agglutinins, resulting in the clumping together of red cells, followed by haemolysis.

Agglutinins are immunoglobins present in the plasma. They appear around 10 days after birth, and reach the maximum concentration by 10 years of age. The agglutinins are alpha (α) and beta (β). A reacts with α, so it is also called anti-A agglutinin and B reacts with β, so it is called anti-B agglutinin.

When a particular agglutinogen is present in blood, the corresponding agglutinin is absent but the opposite agglutinin is always present. This is known as Landsteiner's Law and is applicable to only the ABO system. Group O contains agglutinins α as well as β, and group AB contains neither. Group B is the most common and group AB the least common blood group in the Indian population.

**Table 9.1:** To Summarise

| *Blood group* | *Agglutinogen* | *Agglutinin* |
|---|---|---|
| A | A | β |
| B | B | α |
| AB | AB | — |
| O | — | αβ |

A person's blood group is genetically determined by two genes he/she receives, one from each parent.

## Rh system

This system was discovered by Landsteiner in 1940. It is based on the presence or absence of Rh agglutinogen, which was discovered in the Rhesus monkey.

Those who have Rh agglutinogen are Rh-positive and those who do not are Rh-negative. The percentages of Rh-positive and Rh-negative individuals in the Indian population are 95 and 5, respectively.

The Rh antigens are of three types—C, D and E. Of these, D is the most common. They are important for the transfusion reaction. However, there are no naturally occurring antibodies in the Rh system (unlike the ABO system).

**Table 9.2:** To Summarise

| *Blood group* | *Antigen* | *Antibody* | *Incidence* |
|---|---|---|---|
| Rh-positive | D | – | 95% |
| Rh-negative | – | – | 5% |

Antibodies are produced in a Rh-negative person only after he/she has received Rh antigen. This can occur in the following two ways.

### Rh-negative Mother Bearing a Rh-positive Foetus

The Rh antigen enters the mother's blood when the first child is born, when the placenta separates and the formation of antibodies is stimulated in the mother. These leak back into the foetal blood during the next pregnancy with a Rh-positive foetus, causing an antigen–antibody reaction. Therefore, the effects are seen in further pregnancies with Rh-positive children, and depend on the concentration of antibodies developed in the mother. The concentration increases with each pregnancy with a Rh-positive child, and particularly when pregnancies occur soon.

Usually, the first child escapes from the adverse effects, but the second, third and fourth child may have anaemia or haemolytic jaundice, or may be stillborn. This condition is called erythroblastosis foetalis. The haemolytic jaundice so produced may cause permanent motor or mental disability because bilirubin may be deposited in the brain, particularly in the basal ganglia. This complication is called Kernicterus.

### Rh-negative Person Receiving Rh-positive Blood

Transfusion of Rh-positive blood stimulates formation of anti-Rh antibodies in an Rh-negative person. Therefore the effects of this combination are seen with subsequent transfusions of Rh-positive blood. The anti-Rh antibodies cause severe damage to the transfused RBCs and may be fatal.

## MN system

This system is based on the M and N antigens, which are weak and, therefore, are not concerned with the transfusion reaction. However, they are important medico-legally, in cases of disputed paternity.

## COMPATIBILITY OF BLOOD GROUPS

Before giving blood transfusion, it is necessary to determine whether the blood groups of the donor and recipient are compatible. For this, the reaction between the donor's blood cells and the recipient's plasma is studied, and not that between the donor's plasma and the recipient's blood cells, since the plasma of the former gets diluted in that of the latter, so much so that it has only a negligible effect.

**Table 9.3:** Compatibility between different blood groups

| Donor's cells (agglutinogens) | Recipient's serum (agglutinins) | | | |
|---|---|---|---|---|
| | A (β) | B (α) | AB (–) | O (αβ) |
| A | – | + | – | + |
| B | + | – | – | + |
| AB | + | + | – | + |
| O | – | – | – | – |

The following conclusions can be drawn from the above:

1. Group A can donate blood to groups A and AB.
2. Group B can donate blood to groups B and AB.
3. Group AB can donate blood to group AB.
4. Group O can donate blood to groups A, B, AB and O. Therefore, group O is called the *universal donor*.
5. Group AB can receive blood from groups A, B, AB and O. Therefore, it is called the *universal recipient*.
6. The remaining groups can receive blood ideally from their own group, or from group O in an emergency.

### Effects of mismatched blood transfusion

1. Immediate effects—Fever, rigors, fall of blood pressure, breathlessness and chest pain.
2. Delayed effects—Agglutination of RBCs, plugging of capillaries, haemolysis, anaemia, jaundice, haemoglobinuria, blockage of renal tubules by precipitated haemoglobin, causing acute renal failure and death due to accumulation of toxic products in the body and changes in various cells of the body, including neuronal cells.

## IMPORTANCE OF BLOOD GROUP STUDIES

An Rh-negative person should not receive Rh-positive blood. In an emergency, Group O, Rh-negative blood is given.

Blood group studies are also essential in certain medico-legal cases, for example, for establishing identity or in cases of disputed paternity. Further, certain blood groups can be associated with proneness to certain diseases, for example, group A is prone to pernicious anaemia and group O to duodenal ulcer.

Blood group studies are of great use in the study of human genetics, as well as in racial and anthropological studies.

CHAPTER 10

# Blood Volume

The total amount of blood present in the body is called the blood volume. In normal adults, the value is 70 ml/kg and in children, about 85 ml/kg. The average value in an adult male is about 5 l and in an adult female, about 4.5 l. This amount is constant and varies from person to person.

## DETERMINATION OF BLOOD VOLUME

The blood volume is determined by measuring the volume of the plasma and that of the cells separately, and then adding them to get the total volume.

### Determination of cell volume

For the cell volume, only the RBCs are considered since they form a major fraction of the total cell volume.

The red cell volume can be measured by using radioactive iron ($Fe^{55}$). First, the latter is incorporated into RBCs. Next, they are injected into the blood of the person concerned and their dilution is measured. Radioactive phosphorus ($P^{32}$) or chromium ($Cr^{55}$) can be used.

### Determination of plasma volume

The plasma volume can be measured by various methods.

The dye dilution technique is a satisfactory method. The person concerned is injected with a known amount of dye with a known concentration. After some time, the concentration of the dye in the plasma is measured.

$$\text{Plasma volume} = \frac{\text{Amount of dye injected}}{\text{Concentration of dye in plasma}}$$

The dye used should satisfy the following criteria:

1. It should be non-toxic.
2. It should not leave the plasma and enter the RBCs.
3. It should not be metabolized.
4. It should be easily measured.

Some examples of such dyes are Evan's blue and Congo red. Radioactive iodine ($I^{132}$) can be used to tag albumin. After the person concerned is injected, its dilution is found.

## VARIATIONS IN BLOOD VOLUME

The blood volume is greater in children than in adults. Males have a higher volume than females. Larger people, who have a greater surface area, have a higher volume of blood. During pregnancy, it increases by 20 to 30 per cent. It increases at high altitudes due to the rise in the RBC count. On prolonged standing, the blood volume decreases due to the pooling of blood in the veins of the legs and the transfer of fluid from the blood to the tissue spaces.

Pathologically, the volume increases in cases of congestive cardiac failure, hyperactive thyroid and increased secretion of aldosterone from the adrenal cortex. It decreases following haemorrhage and dehydration due to vomiting and diarrhoea.

## MAINTENANCE OF BLOOD VOLUME

In a person who is in good health, the blood volume is maintained within a narrow range. This is important since an increase in the volume causes a rise in the pressure against which the heart has to pump. This puts an extra load on the heart and may lead to heart failure. On the other hand, if the blood volume decreases, the blood pressure falls and the flow of blood to different organs decreases, causing malfunctioning of the organs.

The mechanisms that are important in maintaining the blood volume are:

1. Absorption of fluid from the gut,
2. Exchange of fluid between the blood and other fluid compartments, and
3. Regulation of urine output.

Whenever the blood volume decreases, more fluid is absorbed from the gut and kidney, and more fluid shifts from the tissue spaces into the blood. If the above mechanisms fail, a permanent variation in the blood volume can occur. Treatment is required in such a situation.

SECTION

# Cardiovascular System

CHAPTER

# Heart and Circulation

## INTRODUCTION

The cardiovascular system consists of the heart, which acts as a pump, and a series of distributing and collecting blood vessels (arteries and veins, respectively), forming a circulatory system.

The function of the cardiovascular system is homeostasis, which is achieved by the maintenance of a continuous flow of blood to the tissues by the heart via the blood vessels. It is a system of transportation, supplying tissues with materials that are necessary for their normal functioning and also, removing waste products produced by cellular metabolism (Fig. 11.1).

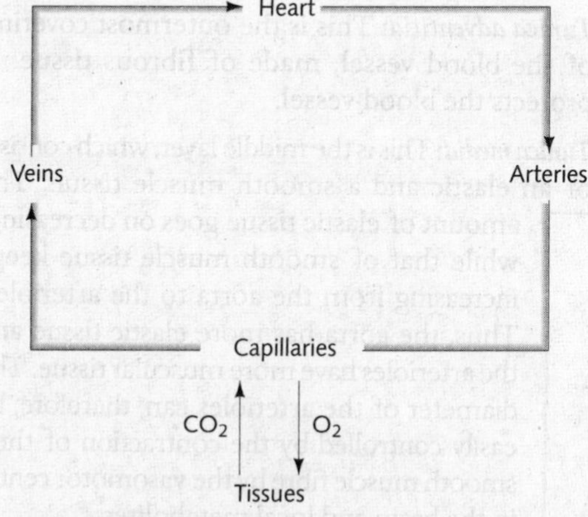


**Fig. 11.1:** Basic plan of circulatory system

## PARTS OF THE CIRCULATORY SYSTEM

The heart and the blood vessels form two circuits in series with each other. One is the systemic circulation and the other is the pulmonary circulation.

The systemic circulation runs through the entire body. It is also known as the greater circulation. It begins from the left ventricle and ends in the right atrium. The systemic circulation carries oxygenated blood to the tissues and deoxygenated blood back from them to the heart. In the tissues, $O_2$ is given out and $CO_2$ is picked up.

The pulmonary circulation runs through the lungs and is also known as the lesser circulation. It begins from the right ventricle and ends in the left atrium. It carries deoxygenated blood to the lungs and oxygenated blood from the lungs to the heart. In the lungs, $CO_2$ is given out and $O_2$ is picked up (Fig. 11.2).

## BLOOD VESSELS

These are of three types—arteries, capillaries and veins.

### Structure

The structures of the different types of blood vessels are described below.

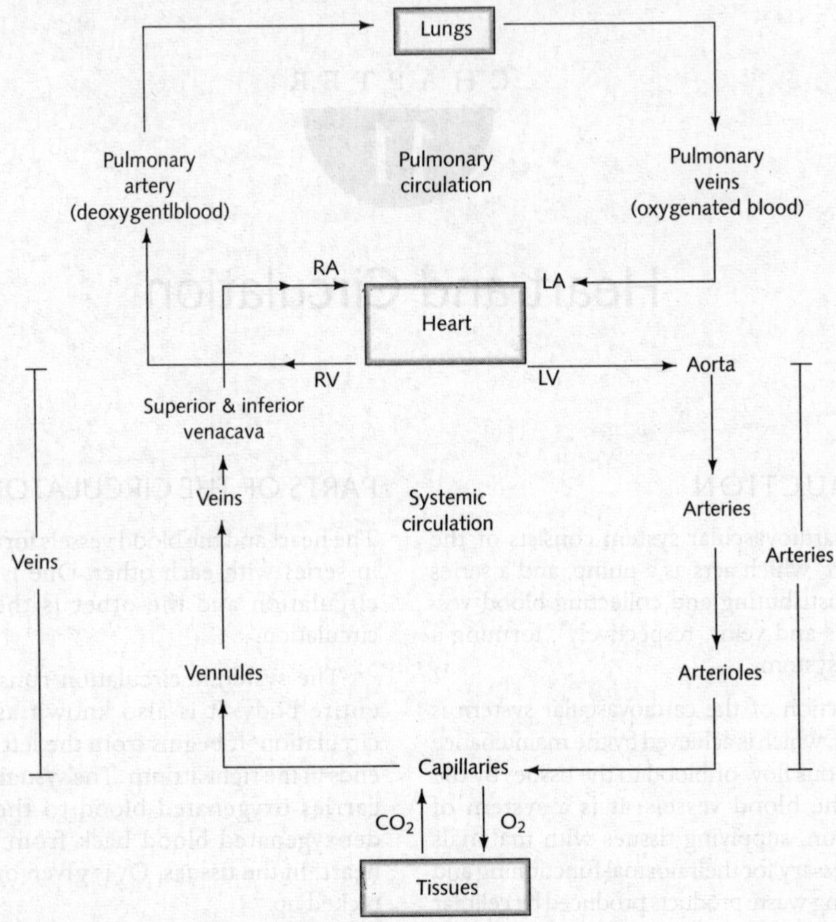


**Fig. 11.2:** Parts of the circulatory system (diagrammatic)

## Arteries and Veins

The walls of arteries and veins are made of three layers—the tunica adventitia, tunica media and tunica intima (Fig. 11.3).

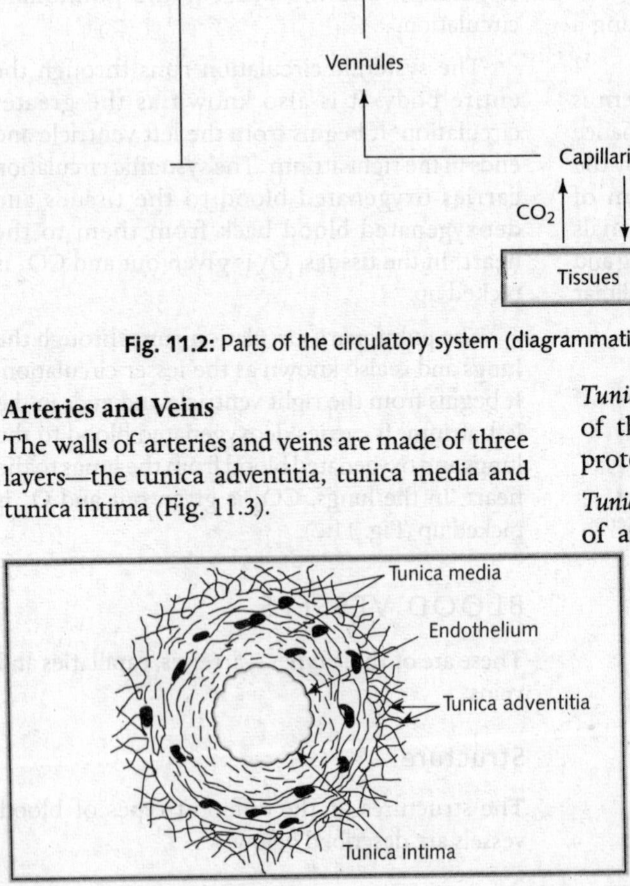

Tunica media
Endothelium
Tunica adventitia
Tunica intima

*Tunica adventitia*: This is the outermost covering of the blood vessel, made of fibrous tissue. It protects the blood vessel.

*Tunica media*: This is the middle layer, which consists of an elastic and a smooth muscle tissue. The amount of elastic tissue goes on decreasing, while that of smooth muscle tissue keeps increasing from the aorta to the arterioles. Thus, the aorta has more elastic tissue and the arterioles have more muscular tissue. The diameter of the arterioles can, therefore, be easily controlled by the contraction of their smooth muscle fibre by the vasomotor centre in the brain and local metabolites.

**Fig. 11.3:** Structure of an artery

*Tunica intima*: This is the innermost layer, which consists of a single sheet of flat epithelial cells, called endothelial cells. It is smooth and prevents clotting of blood within the vessel.

**Differences in Structure of Arteries and Veins**

Arteries are thick-walled, while veins are thin-walled. On sectioning, arteries remain patent, whereas veins collapse. Moreover, arteries do not contain valves, except the pulmonary artery, but veins have valves made of semilunar cusps that allow unidirectional flow of blood (Fig. 11.4).

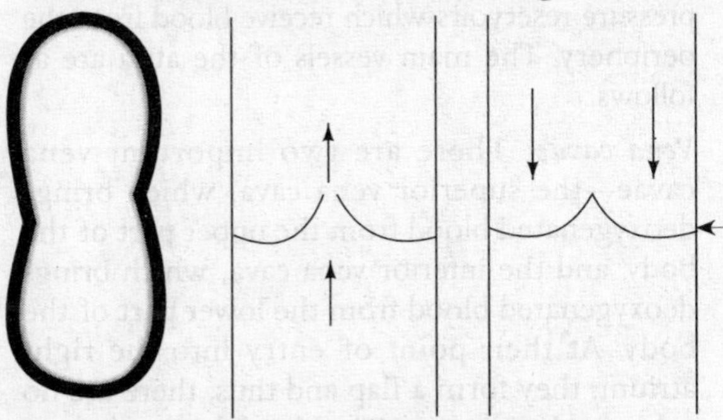


**Fig. 11.4:** Structure of a vein: valves maintaining unidirectional blood flow

**Capillaries**

The walls of capillaries consist of a single layer of endothelial cells, between which there are minute pores or fenestrations (Fig. 11.5).

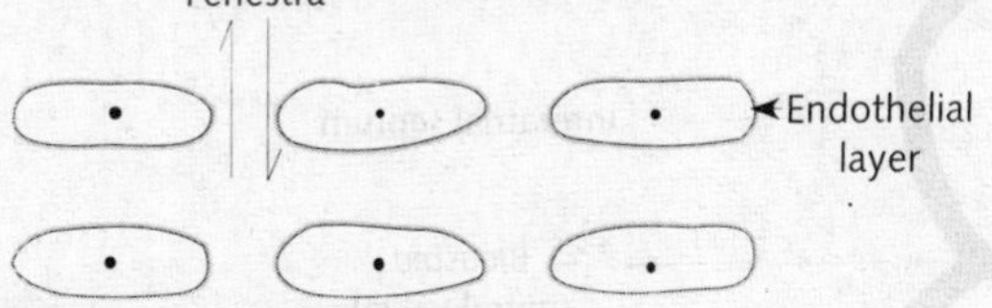


**Fig. 11.5:** Structure of a capillary

## Functions of blood vessels

Different types of blood vessels have different functions. These are described below.

**Arteries**

Arteries conduct blood to the tissues under high pressure. Also, they act as secondary pumps, thereby converting the periodic ejection of blood from heart to a continuous flow in the tissue capillaries.

**Arterioles**

These vessels act as control valves to regulate the amount of blood released into the capillaries. The arterioles are also a major site of peripheral resistance because of the presence of smooth circular muscles in their walls. These muscles offer resistance to the flow of blood. Arterioles are, therefore, called resistance vessels. The peripheral resistance helps maintain blood pressure, which is important for the perfusion of the tissues.

**Capillaries**

These form a fine network in the tissues and have close contact with cells. They are known as exchange vessels because their structure makes them permeable to various substances which can be exchanged between the blood and tissue fluid.

This function is so important that the activity of the cardiovascular system is regulated in such a way as to ensure capillary exchange that is adequate for the metabolic requirement of the tissues.

**Veins**

Veins convey or return blood to the heart. They are known as capacitance vessels because their thin muscular coat and elastic fibres make them highly distensible. They act as reservoirs of blood. Whenever there is blood loss due to injury, their constriction increases venous return to the heart.

# HEART

The heart, situated in the thoracic cavity, is a *mechanical pump,* pumping blood through the arterial system. The blood returns to the heart via the venous system. The heart has a *reserve* which can be drawn upon in emergencies.

## Internal structure

The right side of the heart contains impure or deoxygenated blood, while the left side contains pure or oxygenated blood.

The cavity of the heart is divided into four chambers. The upper two are called atria. These are separated from each other by the interatrial septum. The lower two chambers are called ventricles, which are separated from each other by the interventricular septum.

The atria and ventricles are separated by the atrioventricular (AV) valves. The right AV valve has three cusps and is called the tricuspid valve, while the left consists of two cusps and is called the bicuspid/mitral valve. These valves are important in ensuring a unidirectional flow of blood. They thus prevent regurgitation or backflow of blood in the reverse direction, that is, from the ventricles to the atria.

The lower surface of the AV valves is attached to the papillary muscles through the chordae tendineae so that they do not fall back into the atria during ventricular contraction. The papillary muscles are the projections of the cardiac muscle/myocardium. Therefore, when the ventricles contract, the papillary muscles also contract and hold the AV valves in position to prevent the backflow of blood from the ventricles to the atria (Fig. 11.6).

The *ventricles* are the pumping chambers of the heart. They generate the energy of contraction. The main vessels of the ventricles are described below.

*Pulmonary artery*: This comes out of the right ventricle and carries deoxygenated blood to the lungs through the pulmonary circulation. Semilunar valves at the junction prevent backflow into the right ventricle.

*Aorta*: This is a big vessel that comes out of the left ventricle. It carries oxygenated blood to the tissues through the systemic circulation. The semilunar valves at their junction prevent the backflow of blood from the aorta into the left ventricle.

*Atria*: These are thin-walled, expansile and low-pressure reservoirs which receive blood from the periphery. The main vessels of the atria are as follows.

*Vena cavae*: There are two important vena cavae—the superior vena cava, which brings deoxygenated blood from the upper part of the body, and the inferior vena cava, which brings deoxygenated blood from the lower part of the body. At their point of entry into the right atrium, they form a flap and thus, there are no valves at the junction. The blood does not regurgitate from the right atrium into the vena cavae.

*Pulmonary veins*: These carry oxygenated blood from the lungs to the left atrium. There are four pulmonary veins and there are no valves at their junction (Fig. 11.7).

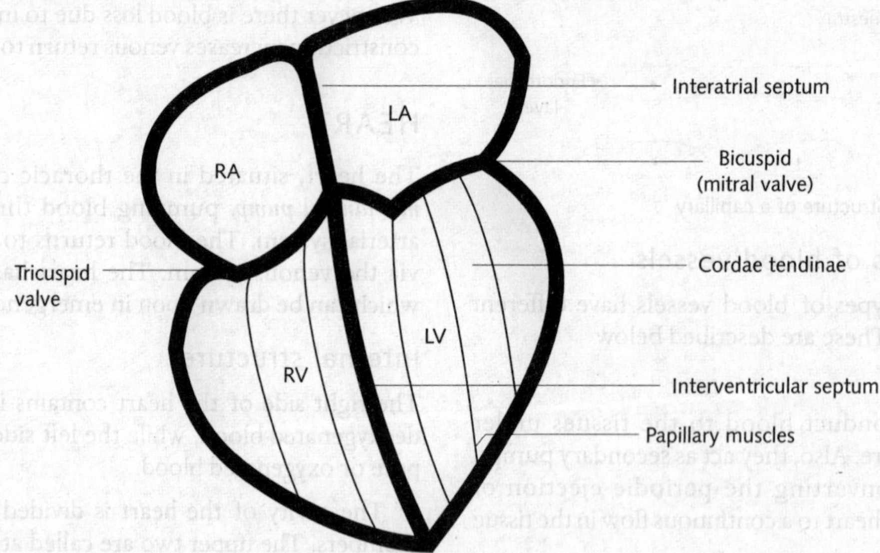


**Fig. 11.6:** Internal structure of heart (diagrammatic)

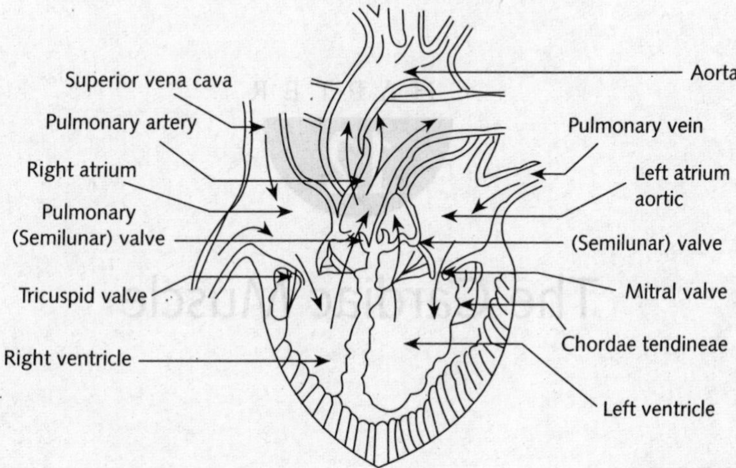


**Fig. 11.7:** The main vessels of the heart

## Wall of the Heart

This consists of three coverings—the pericardium, myocardium and endocardium.

*Pericardium*: This is the outermost covering, made of fibrous tissue. It has two layers, the inner visceral layer and the outer parietal layer, which form a sac, with a thin film of fluid inside. This prevents friction and acts as a lubricant during the pumping action of the heart.

*Myocardium*: This is the middle covering of the cardiac muscle.

*Endocardium*: The endocardium, the innermost covering, is made of a single layer of endothelial cells. It covers the valves and is made of tough fibrous tissue, and is continuous with the endothelium of the blood vessels. It does not allow blood to come in contact with the connective tissue of the heart, thereby preventing intracardiac clotting.

## Nerve Supply

The heart has an autonomic nerve supply, that is, the parasympathetic and sympathetic nerves, which come from the cardio-inhibitory and cardio-accelatory centres, respectively, in brain stem. The parasympathetic supply comes through the vagus nerve. Its stimulation reduces the activity of the heart. On the other hand, stimulation of the sympathetic nerves increases heart activity, that is, the rate and force of contraction. The parasympathetic fibres innervate only the atria, while the sympathetic fibres innervate all parts of the heart.

CHAPTER

12

# The Cardiac Muscle

The cardiac muscle is made of myocardial muscle fibres which form the bulk of the heart. These fibres are known as the working myocardial fibres. They are elongated, branched, nucleated cells, the ends of which are joined together by intercalated discs, forming a network. The intercalated discs or tight junctions act as low-resistance bridges. Therefore, excitation in one area spreads throughout the heart, which contracts as a whole, that is, as if it is made of a single muscle cell or syncytium (Fig. 12.1).

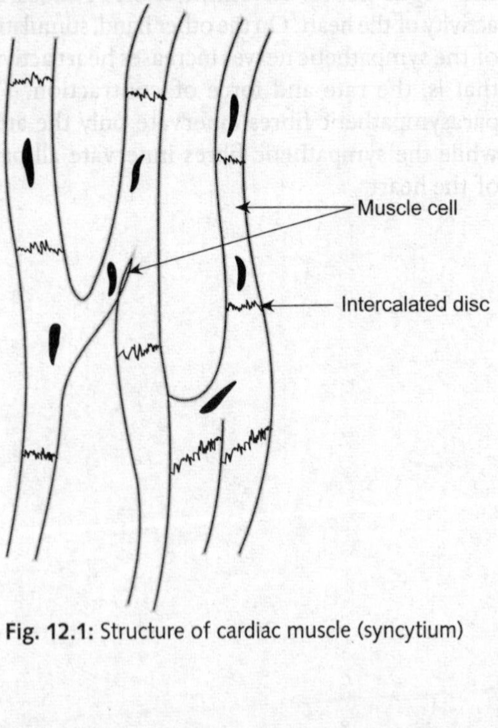

Fig. 12.1: Structure of cardiac muscle (syncytium)

The myocardium is the thickest in the left ventricle and the thinnest in the right atrium. The ventricles are thicker than the atria, and the left side is thicker than the right. The atria are the thinnest because they just have to collect blood and pump it into the ventricles. The right ventricle has to pump blood into the lungs (lower resistance) and, therefore, it is comparatively thinner than the left ventricle, which has to pump blood into the systemic circulation (higher resistance).

## PROPERTIES OF CARDIAC MUSCLE

The properties of the cardiac muscle are described below.

### Excitability

Excitability is the ability to respond to a stimulus. Chronaxie is an index of the excitability of tissues. The cardiac muscle, which is less excitable, has a higher chronaxie than voluntary or skeletal muscles and nervous tissues.

The electrophysiology of cardiac muscle shows it to have the following attributes:

1. Its RMP is about –60 mV, which is less negative than that in the skeletal muscles and nerves. This is because the cardiac cell membrane is more permeable to sodium ions.
2. Its action potential shows a plateau. In the beginning, the opening of fast sodium channels causes depolarization, the opening of slow

calcium sodium channels maintains depolarization, and a delay in the activation of the potassium channels delays repolarization. The action potential results in a mechanical shortening of the muscle.

**Contractility**
This is the ability to contract or shorten isometrically or isotonically. During isometric contraction, the length of the muscle does not shorten, but its tension increases, for example, the increase in the intraventricular pressure during the early phase of systole.

During isotonic contraction, the tension remains the same, the length of the muscle shortens and there is actual work done by the muscle, for example, the ejection of blood during the later phase of ventricular systole.

**'All or None' Law**
If the stimulus is adequate, the cardiac muscle contracts to the best of its ability and if the stimulus is less than adequate, it does not contract at all. Therefore, if the strength of the stimulus is increased, the contraction of the heart does not increase in contrast to skeletal muscle.

**Starling's Law**
Within the limits of normal physiology, the greater the length of the muscle fibres (stretch), the greater the force of contraction.

**Long Refractory Period**
The refractory period is the period that accompanies an action potential, when the membrane is nonexcitable to further stimulation, that is, it does not fire a second action potential within that period.

**Non-tetanizing Property**
The heart remains nonexcitable for a long time due to the plateau, that is, during the entire contraction phase. This ensures that the heart relaxes and does not go into a sustained state of contraction (tetanus), which could lead to the stopping of circulation. Thus, the pumping action of the heart is ensured.

**Conductivity**
This is the ability by which the cardiac muscle conducts an action potential or an impulse over the whole heart. The property of conductivity is present in all myocardial fibres, but the speed of conduction varies. The specialized conducting tissue of the heart has a greater conduction velocity.

**Rhythmicity**
Rhythmicity is the ability to contract at regular intervals. The rhythm of the heart is said to be regular when the distance between the consecutive beats is the same.

## JUNCTIONAL TISSUES OF THE HEART

To maintain rhythmic excitation of the heart, the cardiac muscle has developed a specialized conducting system, made of junctional tissues. These are collections of specialized myocardial fibres. They have a large number of mitochondria, a different histological pattern and greater excitability.

They form only a small bulk of cardiac tissue and do not contribute directly to the pumping action. Their functions are to initiate the cardiac impulse and to conduct it over the myocardium, so that the heart contracts rhythmically.

### Types of junctional tissues

The junctional tissues consist of the sinoatrial (SA) node, atrioventricular (AV) node, AV bundle (bundle of His), the bundle branches and the Purkinje fibres (Fig. 12.2).

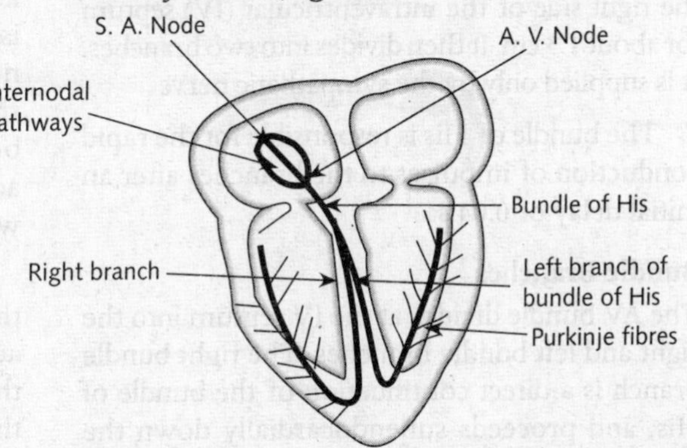


**Fig. 12.2:** Conducting system of the heart (junctional tissues)

**SA Node**

The SA node is situated in the posterior wall of the right atrium, at its junction with the superior vena cava. Its fibres are continuous with the atrial muscle fibre. Its nerve supply comes from the right vagus and the right sympathetic nerves.

The SA node initiates the cardiac impulse or starts the rhythm of the heart. It is the natural pacemaker of the heart. Its role as pacemaker is illustrated by the following facts:

1. It is the first place in the heart to become electronegative.
2. The rate of autorhythmicity is the highest in the SA node.
3. If it is inhibited (excised) or stimulated (increased temperature), the heart rate becomes slower or faster, respectively.

**AV Node**

The AV node is located in the lower part of the interatrial septum, just above the tricuspid valve on the right side. It is supplied by the left vagus and left sympathetic nerves.

It conducts impulses from the atria to the ventricles, via the bundle of His, after a nodal delay of 0.09 seconds(s). The AV node also acts as an auxiliary pacemaker when the SA node is depressed.

**Bundle of His**

This arises from the AV node, passes through the fibrous AV ring, and runs subendocardially down the right side of the intraventricular (IV) septum for about 1.5 cm. It then divides into two branches. It is supplied only by the sympathetic nerve.

The bundle of His is responsible for the rapid conduction of impulses to the branches after an initial delay of 0.04 s.

**Bundle Branches**

The AV bundle divides at the IV septum into the right and left bundle branches. The right bundle branch is a direct continuation of the bundle of His, and proceeds subendocardially down the right side of the IV septum. The left bundle branch perforates the IV septum and runs downwards, subendocardially.

Both branches run down to the apex of the heart, where they turn upwards and travel through the walls of both ventricles.

The bundle branches are responsible for the fast conduction of impulses to the Purkinje fibres in the ventricles.

**Purkinje Fibres**

Both the right bundle branch and left bundle branch ultimately subdivide into a complex network of conducting fibres, called Purkinje fibres. These ramify over the subendocardial surface of both ventricles, and perforate the inner one-third of the ventricles. These are the last arborizations.

These fibres rapidly conduct cardiac impulse in the ventricle, so that all parts of the ventricle contract simultaneously.

## Property of autorhythmicity

All tissues of the conducting system have the property of autorhythmicity, which means that they can initiate their own rhythm in the absence of an external stimulus. However, the working of the heart can be regulated by autonomic nerves and hormones, so cardiac function can be adjusted according to the need of the body during stress.

The area which determines the pace or rhythm of excitability is called the *pacemaker*. The rate of autorhythmicity is maximum in the SA node, that is, 70–80 beats / minute. Therefore, before the AV node or bundle of His can initiate their own rhythm, they are excited by the SA node. Hence, both the atria and the ventricles contract according to the rhythmicity of the SA node, which acts like a natural pacemaker of the heart.

If the SA node fails to produce cardiac impulse, the AV node acts as a pacemaker, but its rate of autorhythmicity is 40–60 beats / minute. That of the bundle of His is 30 beats / minute, and that of the Purkinje fibres is lower still (15 beats / minute), which is incompatible with life. Therefore, if the

SA node does not show normal activity, whichever of these is excited at the highest rate becomes the *ectopic pacemaker*.

## CARDIAC IMPULSE

The cardiac impulse is the action potential generated or the electrical charge across the myocardial cell membrane, produced spontaneously and propagated all along the myocardial fibres.

The electrical impulse that drives the heart originates in a group of pacemaker cells lying in the SA node. These cells display a spontaneous diastolic depolarization, known as the pacemaker potential. After this reaches a firing level, the next action potential follows. No plateau is seen, unlike the action potential of the atrial or ventricular muscle (Fig. 12.3).

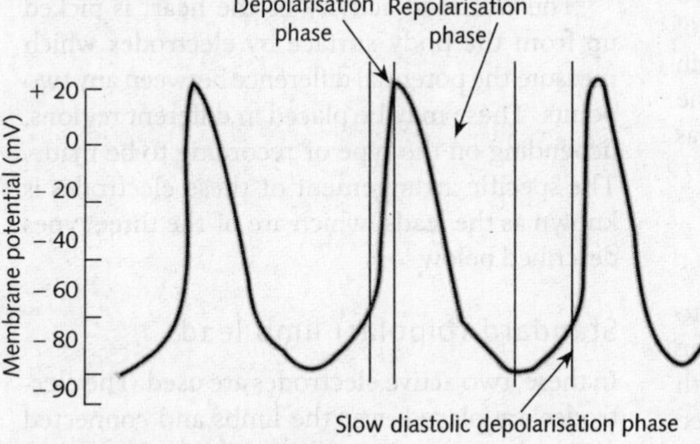


**Fig. 12.3:** Pacemaker potential

The continuous, slow leakage of Na ions into the myocardium is responsible for depolarization and once the firing level is reached, the action potential is generated.

### Propagation of cardiac impulse

The action potential from the SA node lowers the membrane potential of the adjacent cells, which, in turn, depolarizes and triggers off an action potential in these cells.

The action potential from the SA node spreads rapidly in both atria, either through the atrial muscle fibres or through three special tracts in the atria, called internodal pathways. It then enters the conducting system at the AV junction (i.e., AV node), which gathers all the impulses. Once it reaches the AV node, the conduction rate drops and there is a delay in conduction, known as the AV delay. The delay is of 0.13 s (0.09 s in the AV node + 0.04 s in the initial part of the bundle of His).

The cardiac impulse then enters the rapidly conducting fibres of the conduction system, that is, the bundle branches and Purkinje fibres. These carry the depolarizing wave to the right and left ventricles, and this results in their contraction. The entire ventricle contracts as a single chamber. The total conduction time is 0.22 s.

The AV delay serves the important function of preventing simultaneous contraction of the atria and ventricles, and allows ventricular contraction to follow atrial contraction.

***Abnormality in conduction of cardiac impulse***: When the transmission of the cardiac impulse is blocked, it is known as heart block. An electrical pacemaker can be used, if necessary, depending on the type of blockage.

CHAPTER

13

# Electrocardiography

Prior to each contraction of the heart, an electrical impulse is generated in the SA node. The impulse is conducted over the atria, the ventricles and finally, to the surrounding tissues, since the fluid in the body acts as a conductor of electricity. The electrical changes taking place in the heart can, therefore, be recorded from the surface of the body. This procedure is known as the electrocardiogram (ECG).

## BASIS

As the wave of myocardial excitation begins to spread in the heart, the surface of the cells in the depolarized region becomes electronegative with respect to the surrounding region. Thus, the excited and nonexcited parts of the heart act as two terminals of the battery, or a negative and a positive pole, respectively. This generates an electrical field throughout the body fluids.

The wave of excitation spreads in a particular direction only and depending on the position of the recording electrodes, a positive or negative deflection is produced in the sensitive galvanometer, called the electrocardiograph.

## METHOD

The currents generated in the different chambers of the heart are not transmitted equally in all directions. Therefore, the record varies according to the parts of the body from where the action current is picked up. Hence, several records are taken from different parts of the body.

The electrical activity of the heart is picked up from the body surface by electrodes which measure the potential difference between any two points. These may be placed in different regions, depending on the type of recording to be made. The specific arrangement of these electrodes is known as the leads, which are of the three types described below.

### Standard (bipolar) limb leads

In these, two active electrodes are used. The electrodes are placed over the limbs and connected to the electrograph as follows:

| *Leads* | *Negative terminal* | *Positive terminal* |
|---|---|---|
| I | Right arm (RA) | Left arm (LA) |
| II | Right arm (RA) | Left leg (LL) |
| III | Left arm (LA) | Left leg (LL) |

Three electrodes are used, one each on the left arm, right arm and left leg. The electrode placed on the right leg is connected to an electrical ground to minimize electrical interference (Fig. 13.1).

In these leads, the potential difference between the two limbs is recorded. Lead II has the maximum

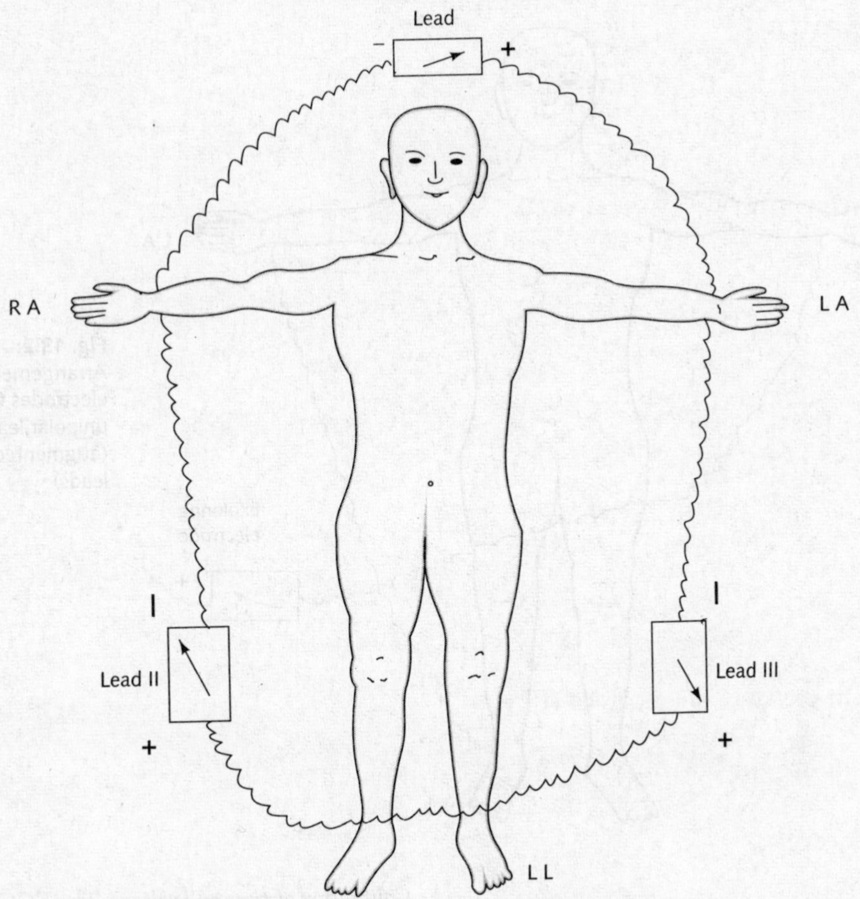


**Fig. 13.1:** Arrangement of electrodes in standard (bipolar) limb leads

voltage and the record is very clear. Therefore, it is taken as a standard record. This lead is more important in finding the rate and conduction in the heart.

## Augmented or unipolar limb leads

In these, one active (exploring) electrode is placed over a limb and connected to the positive terminal of the electrocardiograph. An indifferent electrode is kept at zero potential by connecting the electrodes placed over the other two limbs through a resistance and connected to the negative terminal (Fig. 13.2).

In these leads, the potential change at the site of the exploring electrode is recorded. The position of the exploring electrode is as follows:

| *Unipolar limb leads* | *Positioning of exploring electrode* |
|---|---|
| aVR | RA |
| aVL | LA |
| aVF | LL |

## Unipolar chest leads

In these, a single exploring electrode, connected to a positive pole, is placed over different regions of the heart. An indifferent electrode, connected to a negative pole, is placed on any part of the body. The unipolar leads are designated by the letter 'V'. The different positions over the heart are $V_1$, $V_2$, $V_3$, $V_4$, $V_5$ and $V_6$ (Fig. 13.3).

This lead is more important in diagnosing ischaemia and myocardial damage.

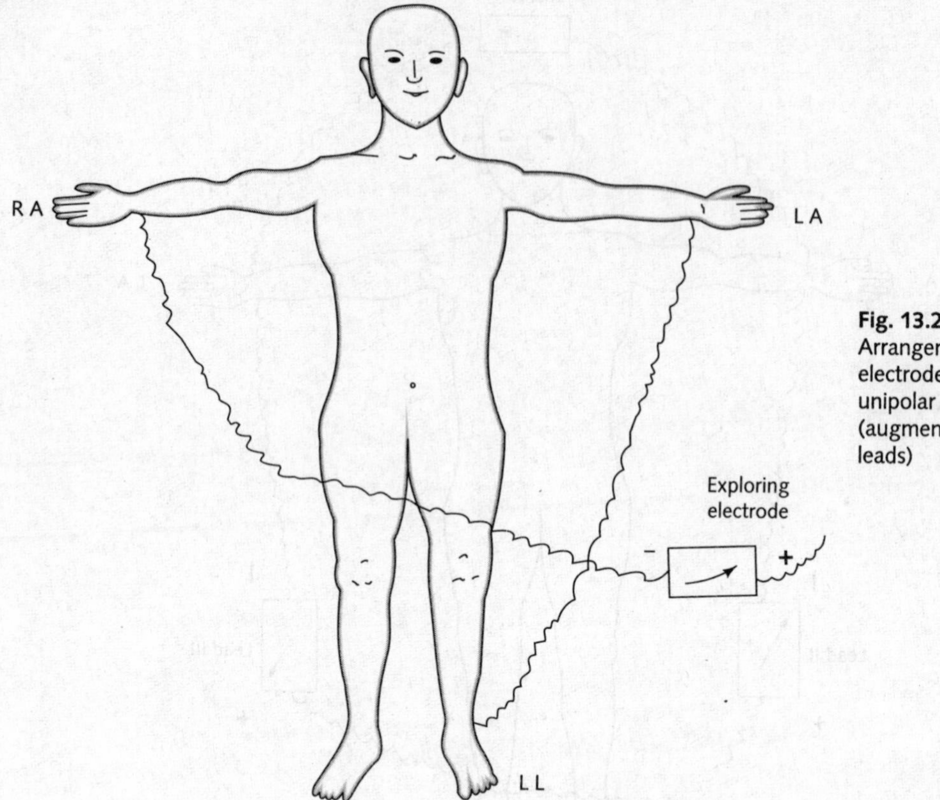


Fig. 13.2: Arrangement of electrodes for unipolar leads (augmented limb leads)

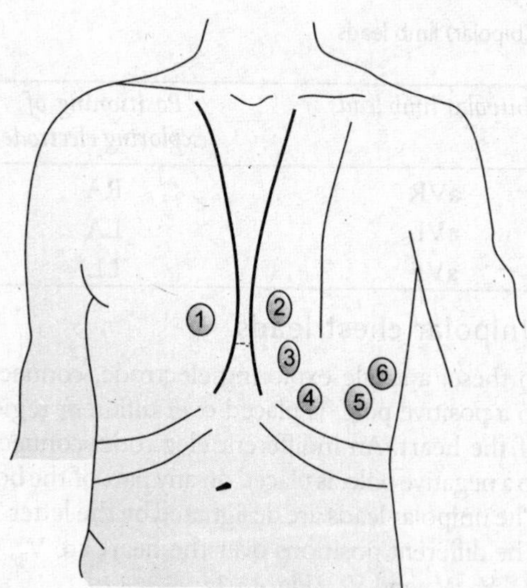


**Fig. 13.3:** Positions of exploring electrode in unipolar chest leads

*Calibration of time and voltage*: The ECG is recorded on a special heat-sensitive graph paper having 1 mm and 5 mm squares. Since the paper moves at a constant speed of 25 mm/s, on the X-axis, each millimetre represents 0.04 s ($\frac{1}{25}$ s). On the Y-axis, each millimetre represents 0.1 mV potential (Fig. 13.4).

## NORMAL ECG RECORD

The ECGs recorded by the three bipolar leads are similar, but the voltages are different. When recorded by lead II, the ECG shows the following pattern. It consists of a series of waves known as P, Q, R, S and T, which go alternately up and down (Fig. 13.5). The P, R and T waves are positive, while Q and S are negative waves. PQ and ST are the isoelectric periods. P is an atrial complex and QRST a ventricular complex.

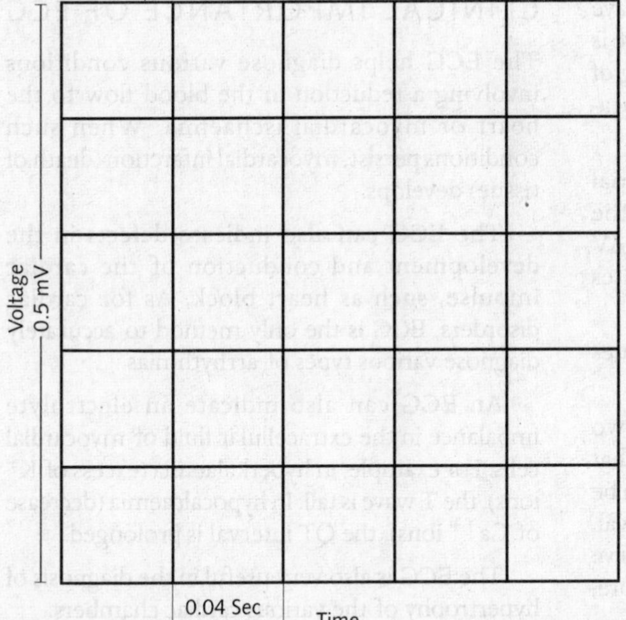


Fig. 13.4: Calibration of ECG paper (speed of movement of paper = 25 mm/s)

## P Wave

The P wave is caused by atrial depolarization. Its duration is 0.1 s and the voltage, 0.25 mV.

A normal P wave indicates that the impulse is originating in the SA node and that its spread through the atria is at a normal rate. An abnormal P wave indicates a defect in the SA node, a defect in the conduction system, or a defect in the atrial musculature itself.

## QRST Complex

This is analysed according to the following categories.

*QRS wave*: This wave is caused by ventricular depolarization and its duration is 0.08 s. A normal QRS complex indicates that the electrical impulse has reached the ventricles in a specified time and is conducted through the ventricles at a normal speed. If the QRS complex is of increased duration, that is, more than 0.1 s, it indicates a conduction defect in the ventricles.

*T wave*: The cause of the T wave is ventricular repolarization, and its shape is round. Flattening, and sometimes inversion, of this wave indicates a damaged ventricular myocardium.

*PQ interval*: This is from the beginning 7P wave

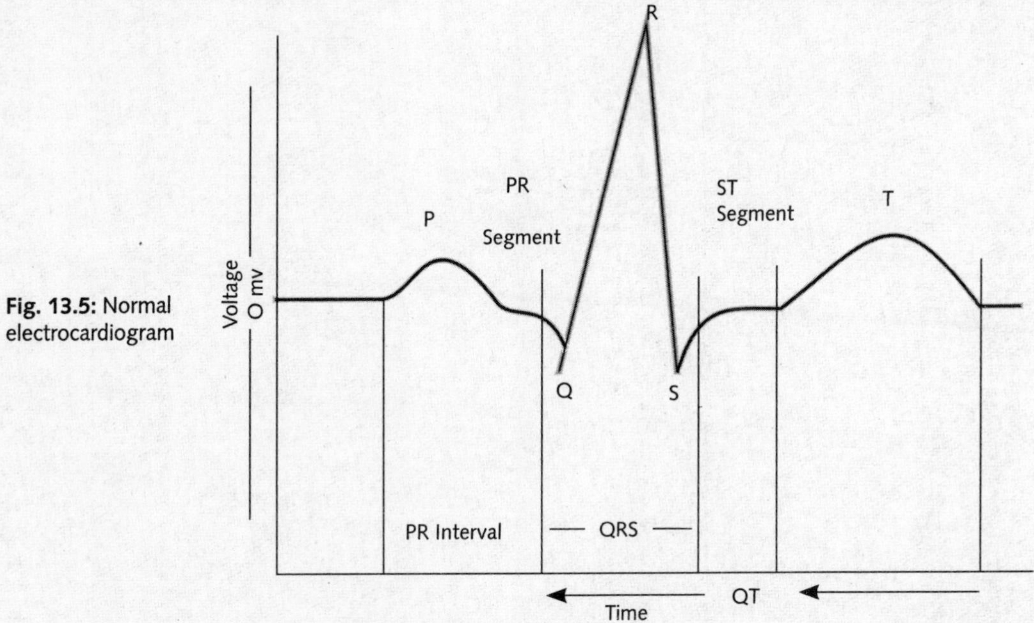


Fig. 13.5: Normal electrocardiogram

to beginning of Q wave. But sometimes Q wave is not seen. Therefore, the beginning of R wave is considered. PR interval is from the beginning of P wave to the beginning of R wave and its duration & 0.16 sec.

The PR interval is related to the entire atrial activity, and also indicates the time taken for the impulse to travel from the SA node to the AV node. If the interval exceeds 0.2 s, it indicates delayed A-V conduction.

*ST segment*: An elevation of this segment indicates myocardial damage.

*RR interval*: The RR interval, between the two consecutive R waves, has a duration of 0.8 s, that is, one cardiac cycle (60–75). The heart rate can be found by dividing 60s (1 min.) by the RR interval. The rhythm can be found by noting the successive RR intervals. Normally, it is same and, therefore, the rhythm is regular.

## CLINICAL IMPORTANCE OF ECG

The ECG helps diagnose various conditions involving a reduction in the blood flow to the heart or myocardial ischaemia. When such conditions persist, myocardial infarction (death of tissue) develops.

The ECG can also indicate defects in the development and conduction of the cardiac impulse, such as heart block. As for cardiac disorders, ECG is the only method to accurately diagnose various types of arrhythmias.

An ECG can also indicate an electrolyte imbalance in the extracellular fluid of myocardial cells. For example, in hyperkalaemia (excess of $K^+$ ions), the T wave is tall. In hypocalcaemia (decrease of $Ca^{++}$ ions), the QT interval is prolonged.

The ECG is also very useful in the diagnosis of hypertrophy of the various cardiac chambers.

CHAPTER

14

# The Heart as a Pump

## CARDIAC CYCLE

Because of the rhythmic excitability of the heart, first the atria contract (due to excitation of the SA node and atrial depolarization), then they relax. After about 0.1 s, the ventricles contract due to excitation of the AV node and ventricular depolarization, then they relax.

These changes, which occur in the heart during one beat, are repeated in the same order in the next beat. The recurring or cyclical series of events in the heart chambers during each beat is called the cardiac cycle. These events are responsible for the pumping of blood from the heart into the systemic circulation at a regular rate, rhythm and volume.

As the normal heart rate is 75 beats per minute, the duration of each cardiac cycle is 60 s/75, that is, 0.8 s.

Thus, the duration of the cardiac cycle is inversely proportional to the heart rate.

Mainly four events take place in the cardiac cycle, two atrial and two ventricular. The atrial events are atrial contraction (systole), followed by atrial relaxation (diastole). These form the atrial cycle. During the cardiac cycle, the atria function mainly as receiving chambers.

The ventricular events are ventricular contraction (systole), followed by ventricular relaxation (diastole). These form the ventricular cycle. The ventricles function as pumping chambers and both ventricles eject the same volume of blood into the circulation during the cardiac cycle.

The atrial and ventricular systoles never overlap at any time due to nodal delay. Hence, there is no interference with the pumping function. The diastoles overlap, but that does not interfere with the pumping action of the heart. The total diastole of the heart is 0.4 s (rest period).

### Atrial events

**Atrial Systole**

The duration of the atrial systole is 0.1 s. The cardiac cycle begins with the atrial events because the pacemaker SA node is situated in the right atrium.

During the atrial systole, blood from the atria enters the ventricles. Initially, the atria compress the volume of blood within the cavity with force, producing an increase in the intraatrial pressure, which causes ventricular filling. This is known as the dynamic phase of the atrial systole, and it lasts for 0.05 s.

Later on, the force of contraction is reduced. This is known as the adynamic phase, which lasts for another 0.05 s. The atrial systole corresponds to the last rapid-filling phase of the ventricle, during which 20 per cent of the ventricular filling occurs.

**Atrial Diastole**

The atrial diastole lasts for 0.7 s. It follows the atrial systole. During this phase, the atria are relaxed. The decrease in their contents causes a fall in atrial pressure. Therefore, the vena cavae on the right side and the pulmonary veins on the left side empty their contents, that is, deoxygenated and oxygenated blood, respectively, into the atria. Thus, the atria gradually distend. This is followed by the atrial systole.

## Ventricular events

**Ventricular Systole**

This lasts for 0.3 s. It starts at the end of the atrial systole. At the onset, the atria and ventricles are relaxed, the AV valves are open and the SL valves (semilunar) closed. Ventricular filling is complete. The ventricular systole consists of the following phases:

1. Isometric contraction phase: The duration of this phase is 0.05 s. In the beginning, blood tries to go back to the atria. This is prevented by the closure of the AV valve since the ventricular pressure exceeds the atrial pressure. Thus, the first heart sound is produced.

   The ventricles contract as a closed chamber since both the AV and SL valves are closed. There is no shortening of the muscle fibre, but the tension increases. Therefore, there is a steep rise in intraventricular pressure. When the pressure exceeds that in the aorta (80 mm of Hg) and pulmonary artery, the SL valves open.
2. Maximum (rapid) ejection phase: This phase lasts 0.11 s. The opening of the SL valve marks its onset. The phase is characterized by a sharp rise in ventricular pressure, as well as the pressures in the aorta (120 mm of Hg) and pulmonary artery. This is because the ventricles contract forcefully and blood gushes into these vessels—oxygenated blood into the aorta and deoxygenated blood into the pulmonary artery—and the ventricular blood volume decreases.
3. Reduced (slow) ejection phase: This phase has a duration of 0.14 s. The ventricular pressure decreases, so that the force of the outflow of blood from the ventricles into the aorta and pulmonary artery is reduced.

The total ejection period, thus, is 0.25 s.

**Ventricular Diastole**

The ventricular diastole, which has a duration of 0.5 s, consists of the following phases:

1. Protodiastolic phase: This lasts 0.04 s. In the beginning, the SL valves remain open for a very short while because ventricular pressure remains greater than that in the aorta and pulmonary artery. The ventricles then relax and the ventricular pressure decreases. As a result, blood from the aorta and pulmonary artery tends to regurgitate back into the ventricles. This is prevented by the closure of the SL valves because the aortic and pulmonary pressure becomes greater than ventricular pressure. This causes the second heart sound.
2. Isometric relaxation phase: This phase lasts 0.08 s. There is a fall in the ventricular pressure, without a change in ventricular volume, because the length of the cardiac muscle does not change. Both the SL and AV valves are closed and the ventricles relax as closed chambers. The pressure in the ventricles continues to drop very rapidly.
3. First rapid-filling phase: In this phase, which lasts for 0.113 s, the ventricles fill rapidly due to high atrial pressure. The pressure in the ventricles is less than that in the atria. Thus, the AV valves open and inflow begins, not due to atrial contraction but passively along the pressure gradient. The sudden rush of blood sets up vibrations which produce the third heart sound.
4. Period of slow-filling phase or diastasis: Only a little ventricular filling occurs in this phase, which lasts 0.167 s. The duration is long but the filling is slow. The fall in the pressure gradient causes the inflow of blood from the atria to the ventricles to slow down. At the end of this phase, about 80 per cent of the ventricular filling is complete and the atria start contracting.
5. Last rapid-filling phase: This phase, lasting 0.1 s, coincides with the atrial systole and accounts

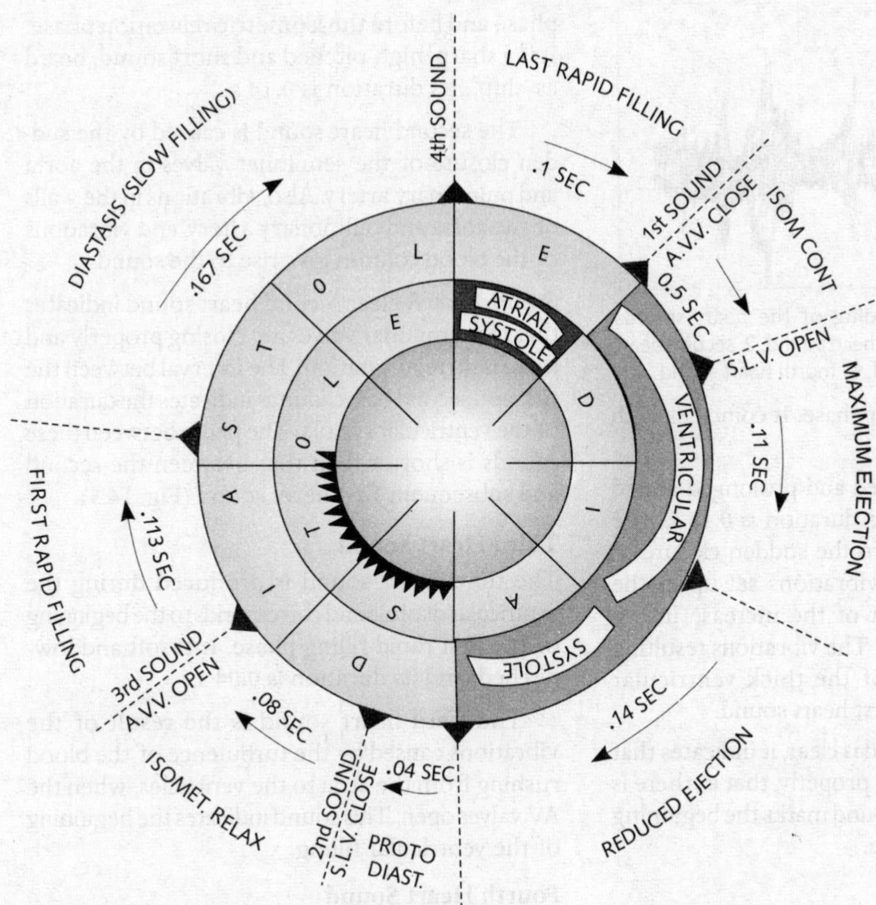


**Fig. 14.1:** The sequence of events during the cardiac cycle. Inner ring represents atrial events, outer ring ventricular events. The events are to be followed in a clockwise manner.

for 20 per cent of the additional ventricular filling since the atria act like a booster pump. The last bit of the blood now gushes into the ventricles. This rapid flow sets up vibrations, producing the fourth heart sound.

Therefore, the last phase of the ventricular diastole overlaps with the atrial systole of the next cycle. This function is important when the heart rate increases at the cost of the ventricular diastole, causing decreased diastolic filling. The ventricular diastole is followed by the ventricular systole (Fig. 14.1).

The end diastolic volume of the ventricles is 120 ml, while the end systolic volume of the ventricles is 50 ml. Therefore, the stroke output is 70 ml, that is, each ventricle ejects 70 ml of blood during each systole.

Minute cardiac output = stroke volume (output) × heart rate

= 70 × 70 = 5000 ml/ min. or 5 l/ min.

## HEART SOUNDS

During each cardiac cycle, four heart sounds are produced. The first and second ones can be heard in all individuals with the help of a stethoscope. The third heart sound can be heard only in 50 per cent of the population. The fourth one cannot be heard, but the third and fourth heart sounds can be recorded with the help of a phonocardiogram, with suitable amplification (Fig. 14.2).

### First Heart Sound

The first heart sound occurs at the onset of the ventricular systole of the cardiac cycle, just before

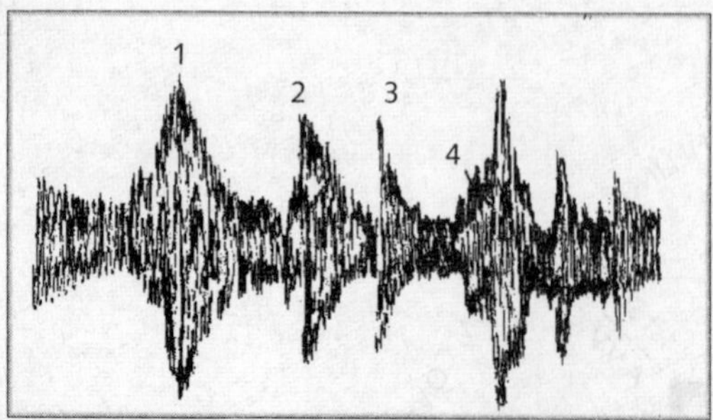


**Fig. 14.2:** Graphic recording of the heart sounds (phonocardiogram): 1. first heart sound, 2. second heart sound, 3. third heart sound, 4. fourth heart sound

the isometric contraction phase. It coincides with the carotid pulse.

It is a dull, low-pitched and prolonged sound and is heard as 'lubb'. Its duration is 0.17 s. The sound is produced due to the sudden closure of the AV valves and the vibrations set up in the valve leaflets as a result of the increase in the intraventricular pressure. The vibrations resulting from the contraction of the thick ventricular muscles also cause the first heart sound.

If the first heart sound is clear, it indicates that the AV valves are closing properly, that is, there is no incompetence. This sound marks the beginning of the ventricular systole.

## Second Heart Sound

The second heart sound occurs at the onset of the ventricular diastole, just after the protodiastolic phase and before the isometric relaxation phase. It is a sharp, high-pitched and short sound, heard as 'dup'. Its duration is 0.14 s.

The second heart sound is caused by the sudden closure of the semilunar valves in the aorta and pulmonary artery. Also, vibrations in the walls of the aorta and pulmonary artery, and vibrations of the blood column give rise to the sound.

*Significance*: A clear second heart sound indicates that the semilunar valves are closing properly and there is no regurgitation. The interval between the first and second heart sounds indicates the duration of the ventricular systole. The pause between these sounds is shorter than that between the second and subsequent first heart sound (Fig. 14.3).

## Third Heart Sound

The third heart sound is produced during the ventricular diastole and corresponds to the beginning of the first rapid-filling phase. It is soft and low-pitched, and its duration is 0.04 s.

The third heart sound is the result of the vibrations caused by the turbulence of the blood rushing from the atria to the ventricles, when the AV valves open. This sound indicates the beginning of the ventricular filling.

## Fourth Heart Sound

This is produced during the ventricular diastole and corresponds to the beginning of the second

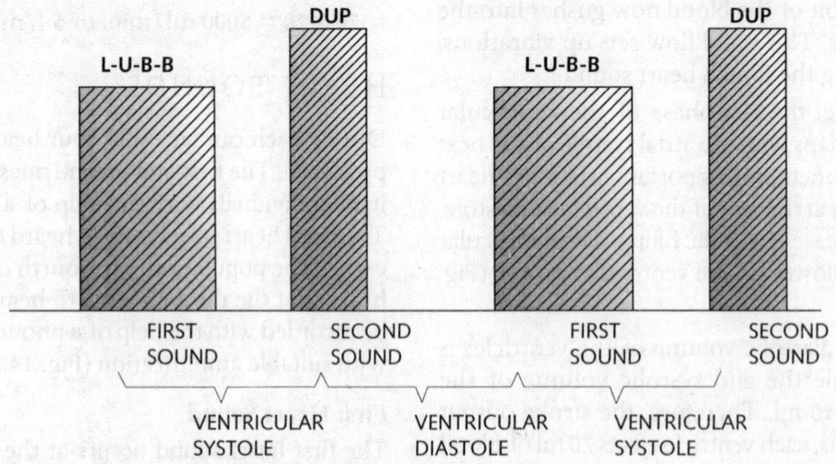


**Fig. 14.3:** Diagrammatic representation of heart sounds

or last rapid-filling phase, which also coincides with the atrial systole.

The fourth heart sound is caused by the contraction of the atria and the consequent rush of blood from the atria to the ventricles, resulting in vibrations of blood and muscle. It indicates the beginning of the atrial diastole.

### Applied physiology

The heart sounds are clinically important. Some of the things they can indicate are listed below.

1. A booming first heart sound indicates ventricular hypertrophy.
2. A booming second heart sound indicates hypertension—on the right (aortic area), aortic hypertension, and on the left (pulmonary area), pulmonary hypertension.
3. The interval between the first and second heart sounds indicates the duration of the ventricular systole.
4. Many valvular defects of the heart can be diagnosed by abnormal sounds (murmur) between the heart sounds. A murmur is the result of the turbulence produced in the blood by a forward flow through a stenosed (narrowed valve), or backflow (regurgitation) through a deformed or incompetent valve.

## ARTERIAL PULSE

The arterial pulse is a pressure wave which originates at the root of the aorta due to the entry of blood from the left ventricle into it, causing it to stretch. It propagates along the arterial wall. The graphical record of the arterial pulse in the radial artery shows a particular pattern (Fig. 14.4).

There is a steep vertical upstroke, which is smooth, and a downstroke that shows irregular fluctuations. The most important of these is the dicrotic notch, followed by the dicrotic wave.

The main or primary wave of the pulse (up stroke) corresponds to the ventricular systole. The down stroke corresponds to the ventricular diastole.

At the beginning of the protodiastolic period, blood from the aorta tries to come back into the left ventricle, which is relaxing and, therefore, has a low pressure. This produces a dicrotic notch, but later, when the blood rebounds on the closed semilunar valve, a dicrotic wave is produced. The other fluctuations which give rise to tiny waves are caused by oscillations of the blood column and aortic wall.

Aortic valvular defects produce characteristic changes in the radial pulse.

An examination of the radial pulse is one of the essential features of the clinical examination of a patient. It is an easy way of finding out the heart rate. In addition, the strength of the arterial pulse reflects the stroke volume of the heart. The radial pulse becomes fast and strong after exercise, indicating an increase in the rate and stroke volume of the heart.

The arterial pulse can be palpated not only from the radial artery, but also from many of the superficial arteries, for example, the common carotid, femoral and dorsalis pedis.

## HEART RATE

The heart rate is determined by the pacemaker activity of heart. Normally, it is equal to the pulse rate. The normal heart rate is 70 to 80 beats per minute, the average being 75 beats per minute.

The following factors regulate the heart rate.

*Autonomic nervous system (ANS)*: Stimulation of the sympathetic system increases the heart rate,

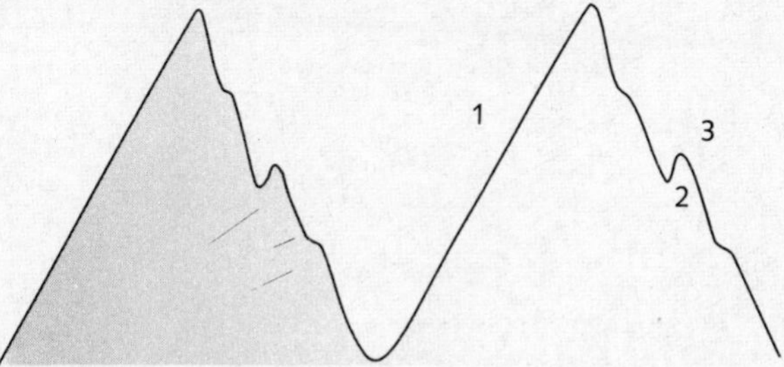


**Fig. 14.4:** Tracing of radial pulse: 1. primary wave, 2. dicrotic notch, 3. dicrotic wave

while stimulation of the parasympathetic system (vagus nerve) decreases it.

*Bainbridge reflex*: The accumulation of blood in the right atrium and great veins stimulates the cardioaccelerator centre, which results in an increased heart rate. Therefore, an increase in venous return causes an increase in the heart rate.

*Marey's Law*: The heart rate varies inversely with the blood pressure. A decrease in the blood pressure causes an increase in the heart rate.

**Variations in Heart Rate**

The heart rate increases under certain conditions, including (i) emotional excitement, (ii) muscular exercise, and (iii) increased secretion of epinephrine and thyroid hormone. It decreases with mental shock, grief and sleep.

CHAPTER

15

# Coronary Circulation

The coronary circulation is responsible for supplying adequate blood to the myocardium.

## PHYSIOLOGICAL ANATOMY

The heart is supplied with blood via two coronary arteries, the left one and the right one, which arise directly from the root of the aorta.

The amount of blood supplied to the myocardium from these two arteries varies in human beings. In 30 per cent of individuals, both arteries supply an equal amount of blood. In 50 per cent, the blood supply is predominantly from the right coronary artery and in 20 per cent, the left coronary artery.

The coronary arteries branch and form a network on the pericardial surface, from which arise perpendicular branches to the subendocardium. Thus, they get compressed during the ventricular systole.

The myocardium is densely populated with capillaries. Each muscle fibre receives one capillary, and the distance between the capillary and the muscle cell is very small. Therefore, the cell receives a good supply of oxygen. The capillary network also provides a large surface area for gaseous exchange.

The venous system is made of two parts. One is the epicardial network, which drains most of the venous blood into the right atrium. This is done via the coronary sinus, which drains the left side of the heart, and the anterior cardiac vein, which drains the right side. Besides the epicardial network, there is the deep system of veins, which arises within the myocardial substance and drains about 10 per cent of the venous blood directly into the heart cavity.

## CORONARY BLOOD FLOW

At rest, the coronary blood flow is about 250 ml/min. During muscular exercise, it increases three to four times in order to meet the body's high demand for oxygen.

### Phasic changes in coronary blood flow

The coronary blood flow changes during various phases of the cardiac cycle. One of the causes is alteration in the aortic pressure,that is, an increase in aortic pressure increases the coronary blood flow. The degree of compression of the coronary vessels is the other determinant. When the compression exerted by the myocardium increases, the coronary blood flow decreases.

During the ventricular systole, the coronary vessels, unlike other vessels, get compressed and the blood flow decreases. During the ventricular diastole, the compression is released and the blood flow increases. Therefore, extramural pressure on the coronary vessels is a somewhat more important factor.

**Isometric Contraction Phase**

In this phase, the ventricular fibres develop quite a degree of tension, producing marked extracellular compression, particularly in the left ventricle. At this time, aortic pressure is the minimum, so there is a steep fall in the coronary blood flow.

**Ejection Phase**

In this phase, there is a sudden rise in the aortic pressure and the coronary blood flow. This is because, although extravascular compression is increased, there is a significant increase in the aortic pressure, which increases the coronary blood flow.

**Isometric Relaxation Phase**

During this phase, there is a sudden fall in tension in the ventricular fibres, so vascular compression decreases and the coronary vessels open up. Also, the aortic pressure is still fairly high, so there is a steep rise in the coronary blood flow.

**Rest of the Ventricular Diastole**

During this period, the coronary vessels are open. The coronary blood flow varies with the aortic pressure and gradually decreases with a decrease in the latter, till the next ventricular systole.

Thus, the coronary blood flow is phasic and most of the coronary filling occurs during the ventricular diastole. Any factor that decreases the duration of the ventricular diastole decreases the coronary blood flow, for example, tachycardia (Fig. 15.1).

## Regulation of coronary blood flow

The factors responsible for the regulation of the coronary blood flow are described below.

**Aortic Pressure**

The systemic arterial pressure is the driving force of coronary perfusion. Though the coronary blood flow varies with changes in the blood pressure, it remains fairly constant over a wide range of arterial blood pressure. It is seriously compromised when the blood pressure falls below 70 mmHg.

**Autonomic Control**

Sympathetic noradrenergic fibres supply the coronary vessels. Their stimulation produces coronary vasodilation and increases the coronary blood flow. This is due to the increased myocardial activity and the formation of local metabolites. The coronary blood flow is directly proportional to the work done by the heart.

**Local Metabolites**

There is a linear correlation between the myocardial oxygen consumption and coronary blood flow. Hypoxia (a decrease in the oxygen tension) is the

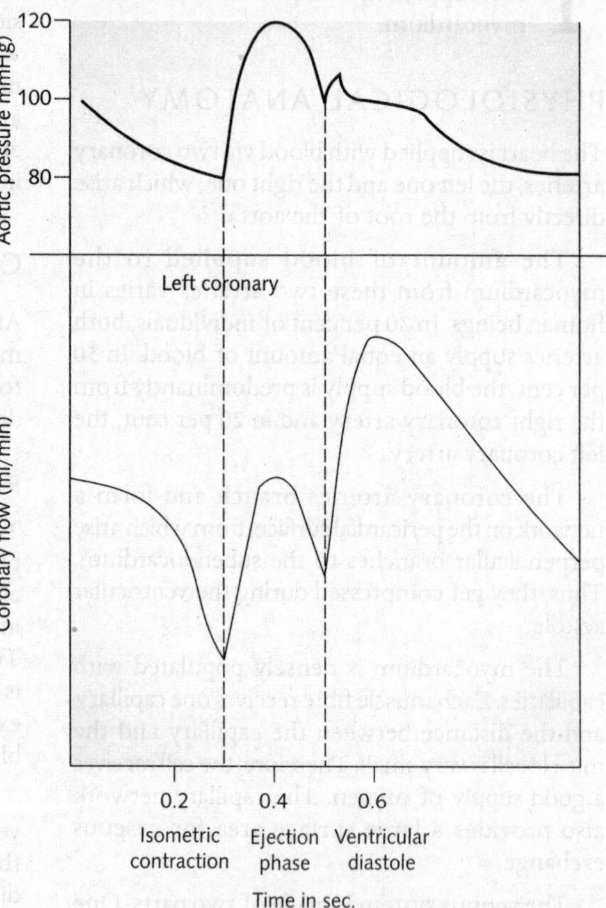


**Fig. 15.1:** Coronary flow in different phases of cardiac cycle

most powerful coronary dilator. Either it relaxes the smooth muscle of the wall of the coronaries directly, or does so indirectly through an increase in the concentration of adenosine, a powerful vasodilator formed by the degradation of ADP.

## Variation in coronary blood flow

The coronary blood flow increases during emotional excitement due to the increased consumption of oxygen. It increases with muscular exercise as well, due to the increased demand for oxygen and an increase in the concentration of $H^+$, temperature and metabolites. The coronary blood flow decreases in shock because of the fall in blood pressure.

## CLINICAL IMPORTANCE—CORONARY ARTERY DISEASE

A decreased coronary blood flow causes myocardial ischaemia (decreased blood supply) and when it is totally blocked, death of the myocardial cells results. This is called myocardial infarction, which is a common cause of death due to failure of the heart pump.

Atherosclerotic changes in the coronary artery reduce its lumen to such an extent that the blood flow to the myocardium fails to increase in times of increased demand for oxygen, such as during exercise. The accumulation of metabolites due to hypoxia stimulates the pain nerve endings in the myocardium, resulting in a condition called angina pectoris. The pain subsides on taking rest and vasodilator drugs like nitroglycerin.

CHAPTER

16

# Blood Pressure

Blood pressure is the lateral pressure (force) exerted by the column of blood on a unit area of the vessel wall.

The arterial blood pressure varies with the phases of the cardiac cycle. Accordingly, it is expressed as the systolic blood pressure, diastolic blood pressure, pulse pressure and mean arterial pressure.

*Systolic blood pressure*: This is the maximum pressure in the arterial system during the left ventricular systole (about 120 mmHg). It indicates the pumping ability of the heart.

*Diastolic blood pressure*: This is the minimum pressure in the arterial system during the left ventricular diastole (about 80 mmHg). It signifies the peripheral resistance.

*Pulse pressure*: This is the difference between the systolic blood pressure and the diastolic blood pressure (about 40 mmHg). It gives an idea of the stroke volume.

*Mean arterial pressure*: This is equal to the diastolic blood pressure plus one-third of the pulse pressure. It is the average arterial blood pressure throughout the cardiac cycle.

The normal arterial blood pressure in a normal healthy adult is denoted as:

$$\frac{120 \text{ mmHg (Systolic)}}{80 \text{ mmHg (Diastolic)}}$$

The systolic pressure varies between 90 and 130 mmHg, while the diastolic pressure varies between 60 and 90 mm Hg.

## PHYSIOLOGICAL VARIATIONS

The blood pressure varies according to several physiological factors. One such factor is age. The blood pressure of a child is usually lower than that of an adult. It may be 80/60 mmHg. As age advances, the blood pressure starts rising. In a normal healthy adult, it is 120/80 mmHg. The systolic blood pressure varies more than the diastolic blood pressure. A rough formula for determining the systolic pressure is the age in years plus 100. For example, the systolic blood pressure of a 50-year-old should be 150 mmHg.

The blood pressure varies with the sex. Females have a slightly lower blood pressure than males (about 5 mmHg less). After menopause, it becomes the same as that of men. The built also affects the blood pressure. Heavily built people who have a greater height and weight have a higher blood pressure.

After exercise, the blood pressure increases to the extent of 50 mmHg. Another factor that affects the blood pressure is the posture. It is the lowest in a reclining position. It increases by 5 mmHg in the sitting position. It is the maximum in the standing position, when it increases by 10 mmHg so as to overcome the effect of gravity.

The blood pressure falls during sleep. Also, it

is the least in the morning and the maximum in the evening.

Emotions affect the blood pressure as well. Any type of excitement causes an increase, for example, anger. The blood pressure may fall in certain emotional states, for example, sorrow.

## METHODS OF DETERMINING BLOOD PRESSURE

The blood pressure can be determined directly or indirectly. The direct method is used in experimental animals. A cannula is introduced in the blood vessel and connected to a mercury manometer. In human beings, the blood pressure is measured indirectly, with the help of a blood pressure apparatus, called the sphygmomanometer, and a stethoscope.

## DETERMINANTS OF BLOOD PRESSURE

The blood pressure is determined by the cardiac output and peripheral resistance.

### Cardiac output

This is the amount of blood pumped by the left ventricle per minute. It keeps the arteries full of blood and hence, determines the blood pressure, especially the systolic pressure. An increase in the cardiac output increases the blood pressure, while a decrease in the cardiac output decreases it. Therefore, the blood pressure varies directly with the cardiac output. Its normal value is 5 l/min.

The cardiac output increases with muscular exercise. The output of the heart increases in proportion to the severity of exercise, and may increase up to 35 l/min. The cardiac output also increases in the later months of pregnancy, as well as in thyrotoxicosis.

A decrease in the cardiac output occurs when the posture is changed from lying to standing. The cardiac output also decreases in those with cardiac diseases, such as myocardial infarction and valvular defects, as well as with shock.

#### Regulation of Cardiac Output

The pumping ability, that is, the contractility of the heart, can be increased by two basic mechanisms: (i) intrinsic (Frank–Starling mechanism), and (ii) extrinsic (autonomic nervous mechanism).

*Intrinsic regulation*: An increase in venous return leads to greater diastolic filling of the ventricles (end diastolic volume). The consequent increase in the length of ventricular muscle results in more forceful contraction (Starling's law) and increases the stroke volume. This mechanism is very important in severe exercise.

Venous return is the amount of blood that returns to the right atrium per minute. An increased venous return increases the cardiac output. Venous return depends on the following:

1. Forward push from behind, provided by arterial pressure, transmitted through the arterioles and capillaries.
2. Suction force of the right atrium during inspiration, created by a fall in the intrathoracic pressure.
3. Muscular contraction, which squeezes the veins, pumping more blood towards the heart.
4. Adequate blood volume.

*Extrinsic regulation*: Sympathetic stimulation increases the force and frequency of contraction of the heart (positive ionotropic and positive chronotropic effects, respectively). This increases the stroke volume at any given end-diastolic volume. This mechanism is important in mild and moderate exercise.

However, if the increase in the heart rate is more than 140/min., the cardiac output decreases due to the decrease in the diastolic filling of the heart.

Parasympathetic stimulation decreases the force and the rate of contraction (negative ionotropic and chronotropic effects, respectively), thereby decreasing the cardiac output.

The following are the other factors affecting the contractility of the heart:

1. Concentration of electrolytes in plasma, for example, $K^+$ and $Ca^{++}$: Hyperkalaemia

(increased potassium) causes a progressive decrease in cardiac contractility, and hypercalcaemia (increased calcium) causes the heart to go into spastic contraction (calcium rigor).

2. Partial pressures of oxygen and carbon dioxide in plasma: Decreased oxygen and increased carbon dioxide tension decreases cardiac contractility.

## Peripheral resistance

This is the resistance offered to the outflow of blood in the arterial system, exerted maximally at the level of the arterioles because they are thinner compared to the arteries. That is, they have a small lumen, greater blood velocity and have plain muscles in the wall. When these muscles contract and relax, the arteries constrict or dilate. Thus, peripheral resistance depends on this. An increase in the peripheral resistance causes an increase in the blood pressure, while a decrease lowers the blood pressure. The blood pressure thus varies directly with the peripheral resistance.

The peripheral resistance depends on several factors, including the lumen of the blood vessels. The greater the lumen, the lower the peripheral resistance. The elasticity of the vessel wall is another factor—the greater the elasticity, the lower the peripheral resistance. Therefore, in old age, the blood pressure increases due to decreased elasticity. The greater the velocity of the blood flow, the higher the peripheral resistance. The peripheral resistance also depends on the viscosity of blood. The greater the viscosity, the greater the peripheral resistance.

Therefore, the peripheral resistance is directly proportional to the velocity and viscosity of blood, and inversely proportional to the lumen and elasticity of the blood vessels.

# REGULATION OF BLOOD PRESSURE

The blood pressure is maintained at a constant level within a narrow limit to ensure an adequate flow of blood to the tissues, particularly the vital organs like the brain and heart, which get damaged due to ischaemia, and to the kidneys for their excretory function.

Blood pressure = cardiac output × peripheral resistance

Therefore, the mechanisms of regulation alter one of the determinants, or both, in an appropriate direction.

The regulation of blood pressure takes place through the nervous (neural) and hormonal mechanisms. The nervous mechanism is a rapidly acting mechanism, and can counteract both a rise and fall of blood pressure. The hormonal mechanism comes into play after a long delay and is effective only against a fall in blood pressure.

The nervous mechanism is involuntary (not under the control of the will). Therefore, the blood pressure is regulated by a reflex mechanism. It depends on a reflex arc, which consists of the (i) receptor organ, (ii) afferent nerves, (iii) centre, (iv) efferent nerves, and (v) effector organ.

The mechanisms can be classified into three types:

1. Immediately acting mechanisms
2. Intermediately acting mechanisms
3. Long-term acting mechanisms

## Immediately acting mechanisms

These start within seconds, last for hours and are of the nervous type. Depending on the receptor organ, they can be divided into the systemic arterial baroreceptor mechanism, systemic arterial chemoreceptor mechanism and the CNS ischaemic response.

### Baroreceptor Mechanism

The range of functioning of baroreceptors is between 60 mmHg and 200 mmHg blood pressure.

*Receptor organs*: These are the stretch receptors situated in the carotid sinus and aortic arch. The carotid sinus is a small dilation of the internal carotid artery, located at the bifurcation of the carotid artery in the neck into an internal and external branch. The carotid sinus and aortic arch form a sino-aortic mechanism (Fig. 16.1).

*Afferent nerves*: These are the glossopharyngeal

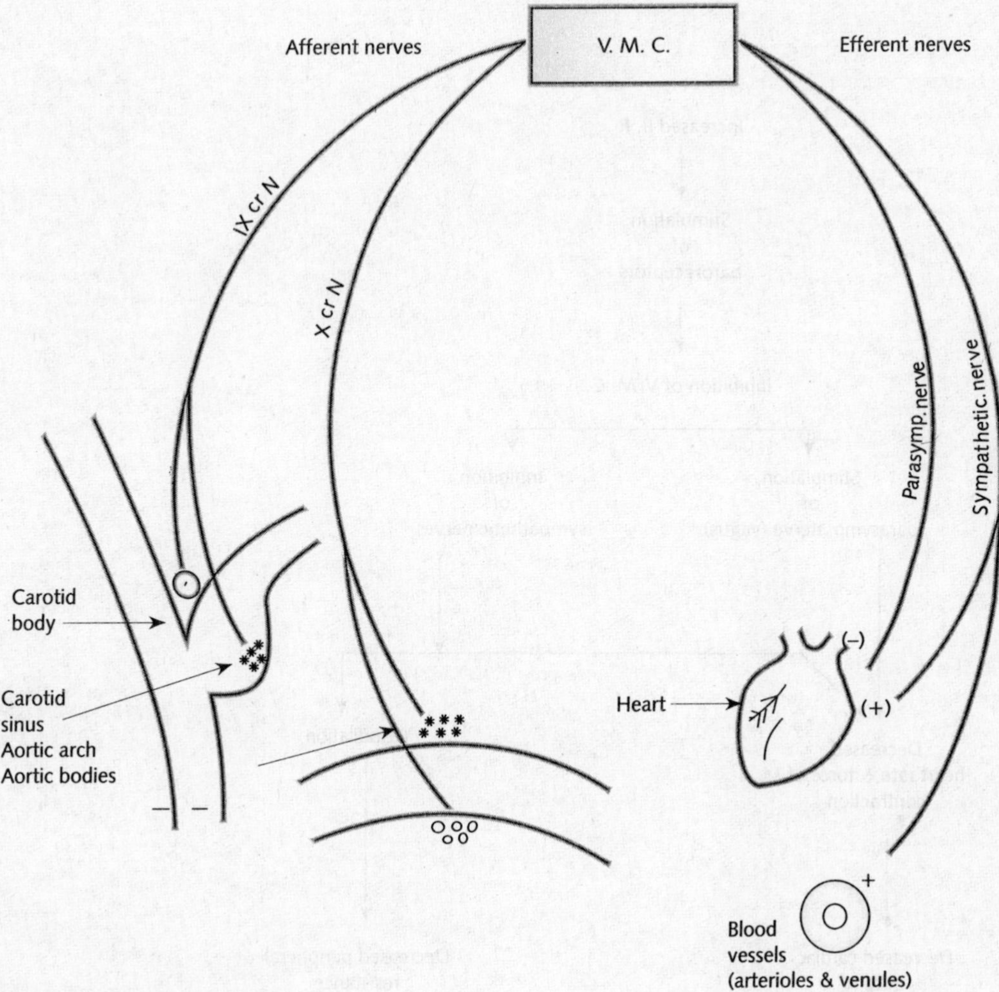


**Fig. 16.1:** Sino-aortic mechanism

(IXth cranial) nerve from the carotid sinus and the vagus (Xth cranial) nerve from the aortic arch. They send information about the sudden changes in blood pressure and, therefore, act as a buffers, that is, they help prevent any rise or fall. This is why they are also called 'buffer nerves'.

*Centre*: The centre is located in the medulla oblangata of the brainstem, called the vasomotor centre (VMC). It controls the pumping efficiency of the heart and the lumen of the blood vessels. There is an inverse relationship between the excitation of the baroreceptors and the VMC.

An increase in the blood pressure causes stimulation of the baroreceptors, which leads to the inhibition of the VMC. This decreases the pumping efficiency of the heart (decrease in cardiac output) and causes vasodilatation (decreased peripheral resistance), which lowers the blood pressure back to normal (Fig. 16.2).

On the other hand, a decrease in the blood pressure results in the inhibition of the baroreceptors, which leads to the stimulation of the VMC. This increases the pumping efficiency of the heart (increase in cardiac output) and vasoconstriction (increased peripheral resistance), which brings the blood pressure up and back to normal (Fig. 16.3).

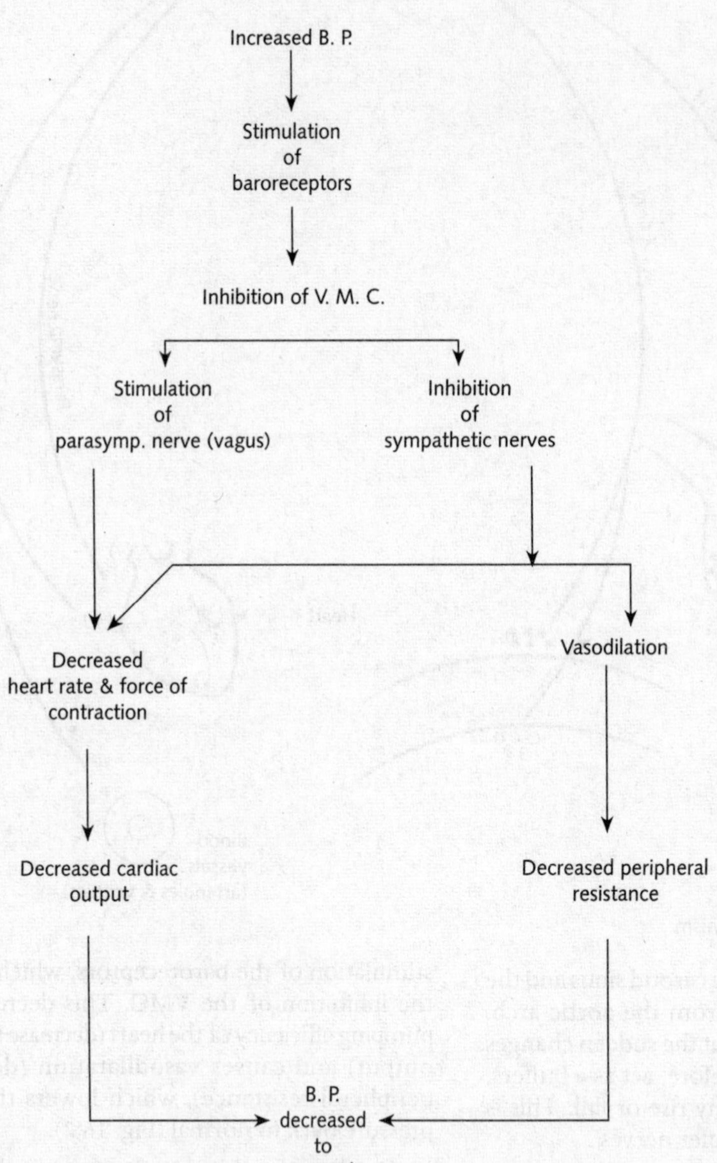


Fig. 16.2: Regulation of blood pressure by baroreceptor mechanism

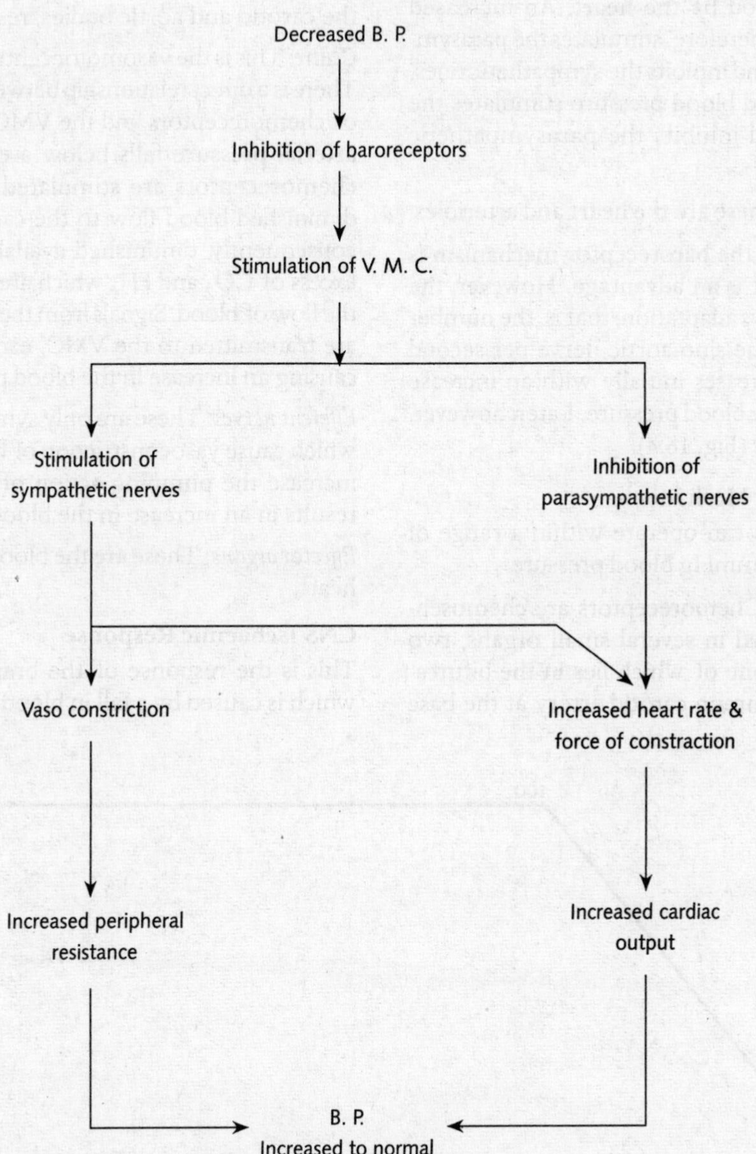


**Fig. 16.3:** Regulation of blood pressure by baroreceptor mechanism

*Efferent nerves*: These can be sympathetic or parasympathetic. The sympathetic nerves bring about vasoconstriction, as well as increased pumping of blood by the heart, while the parasympathetic nerves bring about vasodilatation and decreased pumping of blood by the heart. An increased blood pressure, therefore, stimulates the parasympathetic nerves and inhibits the sympathetic ones, while a decreased blood pressure stimulates the sympathetic and inhibits the parasympathetic nerves.

*Effector organs*: These are the heart and arterioles.

The fact that the baroreceptor mechanism is very quick to act is an advantage. However, the mechanism shows adaptation, that is, the number of impulses in the sino-aortic nerve per second increases or decreases initially with an increase or decrease in the blood pressure. Later, however, it remains steady (Fig. 16.4).

### Chemoreceptor Mechanism

Chemoreceptors can operate within a range of 40 mmHg to 60 mmHg blood pressure.

*Receptor organs*: Chemoreceptors are chemosensitive cells located in several small organs, two carotid bodies, one of which lies in the bifurcation of each common carotid artery at the base of the sinus, and several aortic bodies adjacent to the aorta (Fig. 16.1).

*Afferent nerves*: Chemoreceptors send impulses through the glossopharyngeal (IXth cranial) nerve and the vagus (Xth cranial) nerve, arising from the carotid and aortic bodies, respectively.

*Centre*: This is the vasomotor centre in the medulla. There is a direct relationship between the excitation of chemoreceptors and the VMC. Whenever the arterial pressure falls below a critical level, the chemoreceptors are stimulated because of the diminished blood flow to the carotid bodies and consequently, diminished availability of $O_2$ and excess of $CO_2$ and $H^+$, which are not removed by the flow of blood. Signals from the chemoreceptors are transmitted to the VMC, exciting it and thus causing an increase in the blood pressure.

*Efferent nerves*: These are only sympathetic nerves, which cause vasoconstriction of blood vessels and increase the pumping action of the heart. This results in an increase in the blood pressure.

*Effector organs*: These are the blood vessels and the heart.

### CNS Ischaemic Response

This is the response of the brain to ischaemia, which is caused by a fall in blood pressure. When

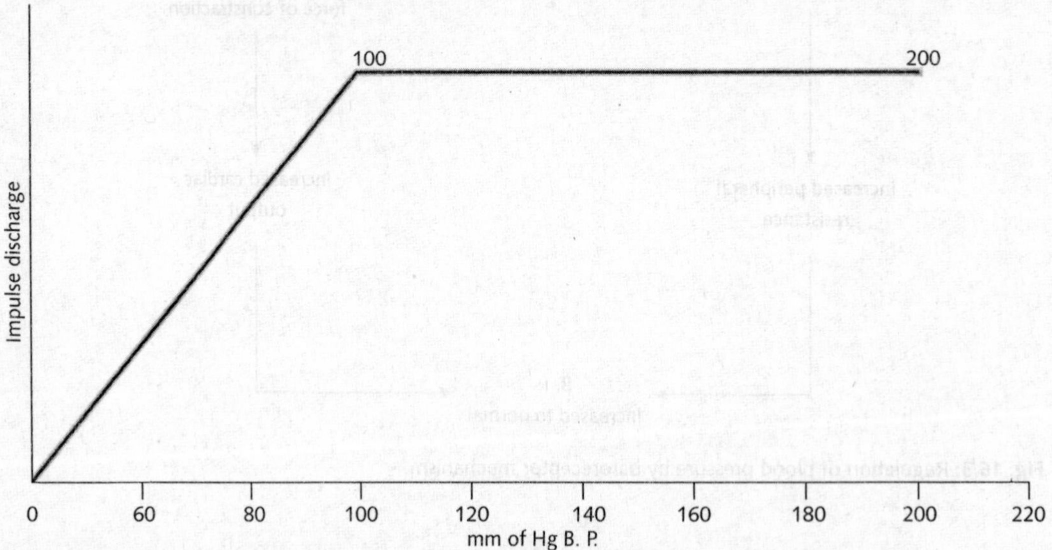


**Fig. 16.4:** Response of baroreceptors at different levels of arterial pressure, showing adaptation

the blood pressure falls below 40 mmHg, the blood supply to the VMC is reduced drastically. Because of this, the supply of $O_2$ and other nutrients also falls, leading to intense stimulation of the VMC, overstimulation of the sympathetic nerves and an increase in the blood pressure. This sequence of events occurs as a last resort.

The degree of sympathetic vasoconstriction caused by internal cerebral ischaemia is so great that often, some vessels become totally or almost totally occluded.

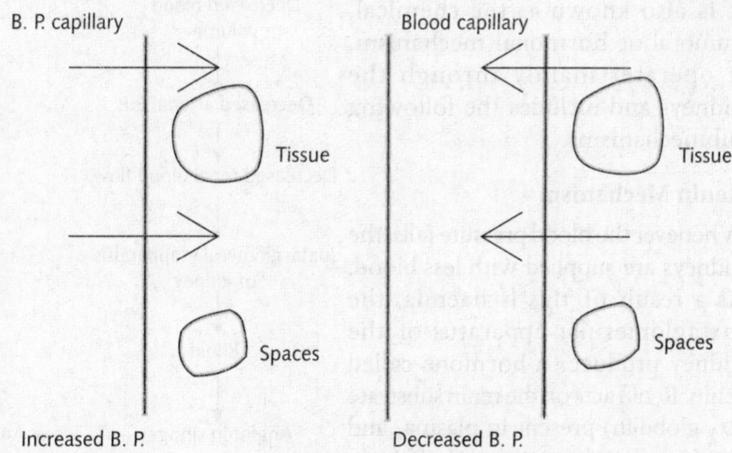


**Fig. 16.5:** Fluid shift mechanism

Thus, the CNS ischaemic response is one of the most powerful of all the activators of the sympathetic vasoconstrictor system. This mechanism works only when the blood pressure is low.

## Intermediately acting mechanism

This mechanism starts acting within half an hour and lasts for a few hours or 3 to 4 days. It consists of two submechanisms, the fluid shift mechanism and the stress relaxation mechanism.

**Fluid Shift Mechanism**

When the blood pressure increases, the hydrostatic pressure increases, so fluid shifts from the intravascular compartment to the extravascular compartment. Fluid formation in the tissues increases, leading to a fall in blood pressure (since the volume of blood has decreased). The reverse mechanism occurs when the blood pressure falls (Fig. 16.5).

**Stress Relaxation Mechanism**

When the blood pressure increases, the vessel wall expands or relaxes and accommodates more blood due to the inherent properties of the wall. Therefore, the blood pressure does not rise. A reverse mechanism occurs when the blood pressure falls, that is, the vessel wall contracts. This is known as reverse stress relaxation (Fig. 16.6).

## Long-term mechanism

This mechanism starts within half an hour and can last for days, months, or even years.

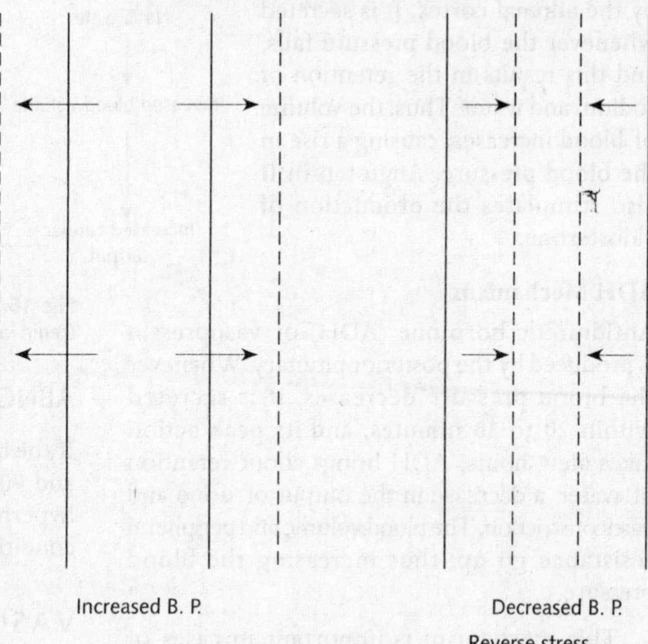


**Fig. 16.6:** Stress relaxation mechanism

It is also known as the chemical, humoral or hormonal mechanism. It operates mainly through the kidneys and includes the following submechanisms.

### Renin Mechanism

Whenever the blood pressure falls, the kidneys are supplied with less blood. As a result of this ischaemia, the juxtaglomerular apparatus of the kidney produces a hormone called renin. Renin acts on the renin substrate ($\alpha_2$ globulin) present in plasma, and converts it to angiotensin I. This, in turn, is converted to angiotensin II by a converting enzyme present in the lungs. Angiotensin II is a very powerful vasoconstrictor, which increases the peripheral resistance and, therefore, the blood pressure.

### Aldosterone Mechanism

Aldosterone is a hormone produced by the adrenal cortex. It is secreted whenever the blood pressure falls, and this results in the retention of sodium and water. Thus, the volume of blood increases, causing a rise in the blood pressure. Angiotensin II also stimulates the production of aldosterone.

### ADH Mechanism

Antidiuretic hormone (ADH) or vasopressin is produced by the posterior pituitary. Whenever the blood pressure decreases, it is secreted within 20 to 30 minutes, and its peak action takes afew hours. ADH brings about retention of water, a decrease in the output of urine and vasoconstriction. The blood volume and peripheral resistance go up, thus increasing the blood pressure.

This mechanism is important in cases of moderate haemorrhage and circulatory shock (Fig. 16.7).

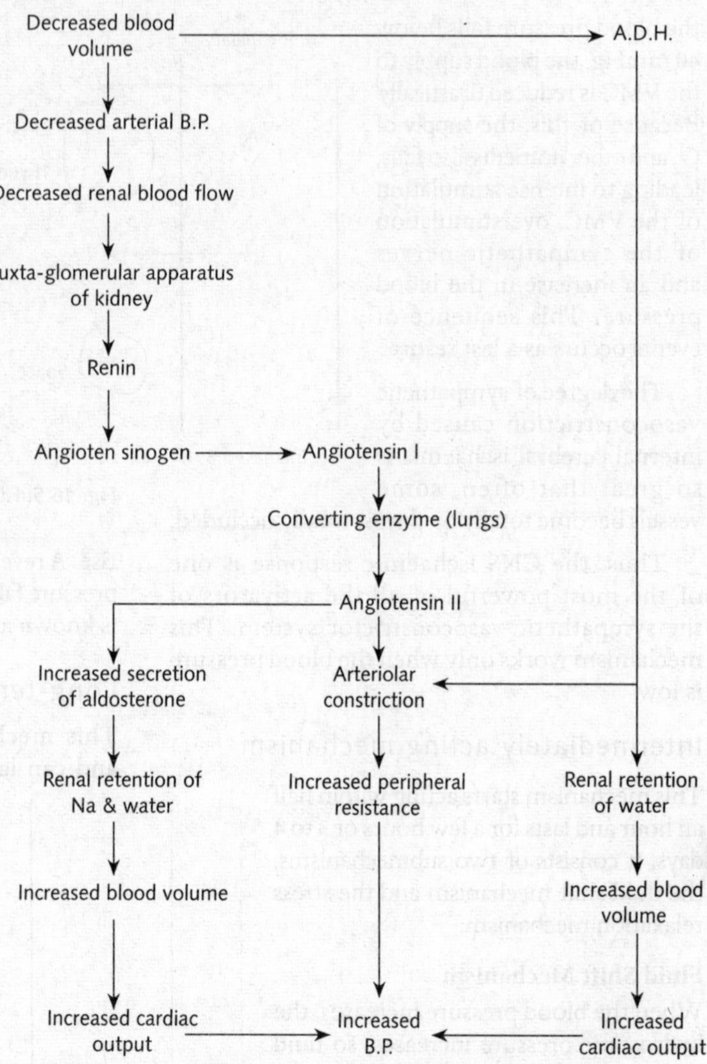


**Fig. 16.7:** Long-term regulation of blood pressure (renin–aldosterone–ADH mechanism)

## ABNORMALITIES OF BLOOD PRESSURE

If the blood pressure is above 140 mmHg systolic and 90 mmHg diastolic, the condition is called hypertension. If it is below the normal range, the condition is called hypotension.

## VASOMOTOR CENTRE

The VMC is located in the medulla oblangata of the brainstem. It is a group of neurons, arranged

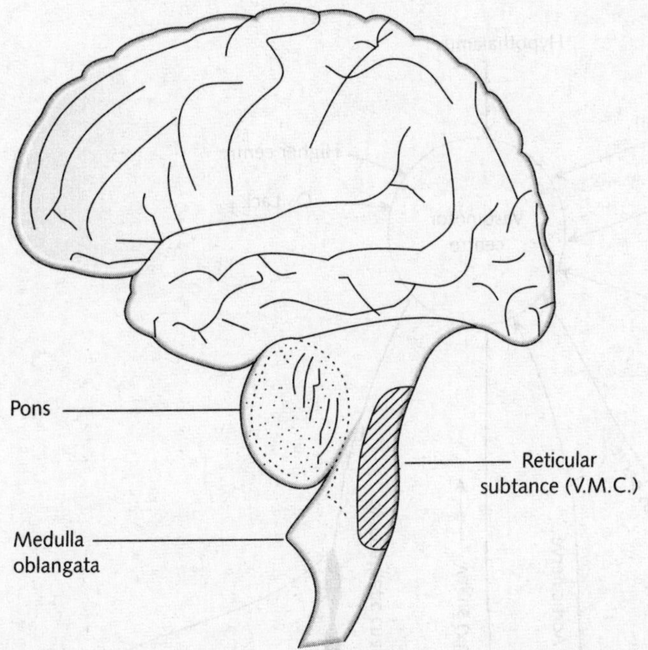


**Fig. 16.8:** Vasomotor centre

bilaterally in the reticular substance of the upper two-thirds of the medulla and lower one-third of the pons (Fig. 16.8). The VMC has a lateral part and a medial part.

*Lateral part*: This part is excitatory in nature and is connected to the sympathetic nerves. It brings about vasoconstriction by the secretion of norepinephrine. It is also called the pressor area.

*Medial part*: This area is inhibitory in nature and is connected to the parasympathetic nerves. It brings about vasodilatation. It is also called the depressor area.

Under resting conditions, the pressor area of the VMC transmits continuous signals to the sympathetic fibres, causing continuous slow firing of these fibres (at a rate of about two impulses per second). Thus, the VMC brings about vasoconstriction and maintains the tone of the arterioles. The depressor area inhibits the pressor area and transmits continuous signals to the parasympathetic vagal fibres, which maintain the heart rate (vagal tone).

Stimulation of the pressor area due to a fallin blood pressure brings about an increase in the vascular tone (peripheral resistance) and also, in the contractility of the heart (cardiac output), thereby raising the blood pressure.

Stimulation of the depressor area due to a rise in blood pressure brings about a decrease in the vascular tone and a decrease in the contractility of the heart, thereby decreasing the blood pressure. Hence, the term 'medullary cardiovascular centre' is more appropriate than VMC.

The neurons of the VMC receive afferent nerve signals, mainly from the vagus (Xth cranial) and glossopharyngeal (IXth cranial) nerves. These signals arise from baroreceptors, whose excitation leads to inhibition of the VMC and chemoreceptors, whose excitation leads to excitation of the VMC. The higher centres of the brain, for example, the limbic system and cerebral cortex, also influence the activity of the VMC. Therefore, different emotions give rise to changes in the blood pressure.

The efferent nerves from the VMC are sympathetic and parasympathetic.

The effector organs are the heart and the blood vessels, mainly the arterioles (Fig. 16.9).

*Applied physiology*: The loss of vasomotor tone produces neurogenic shock, as in deep general anaesthesia, high spinal anaesthesia and brain damage.

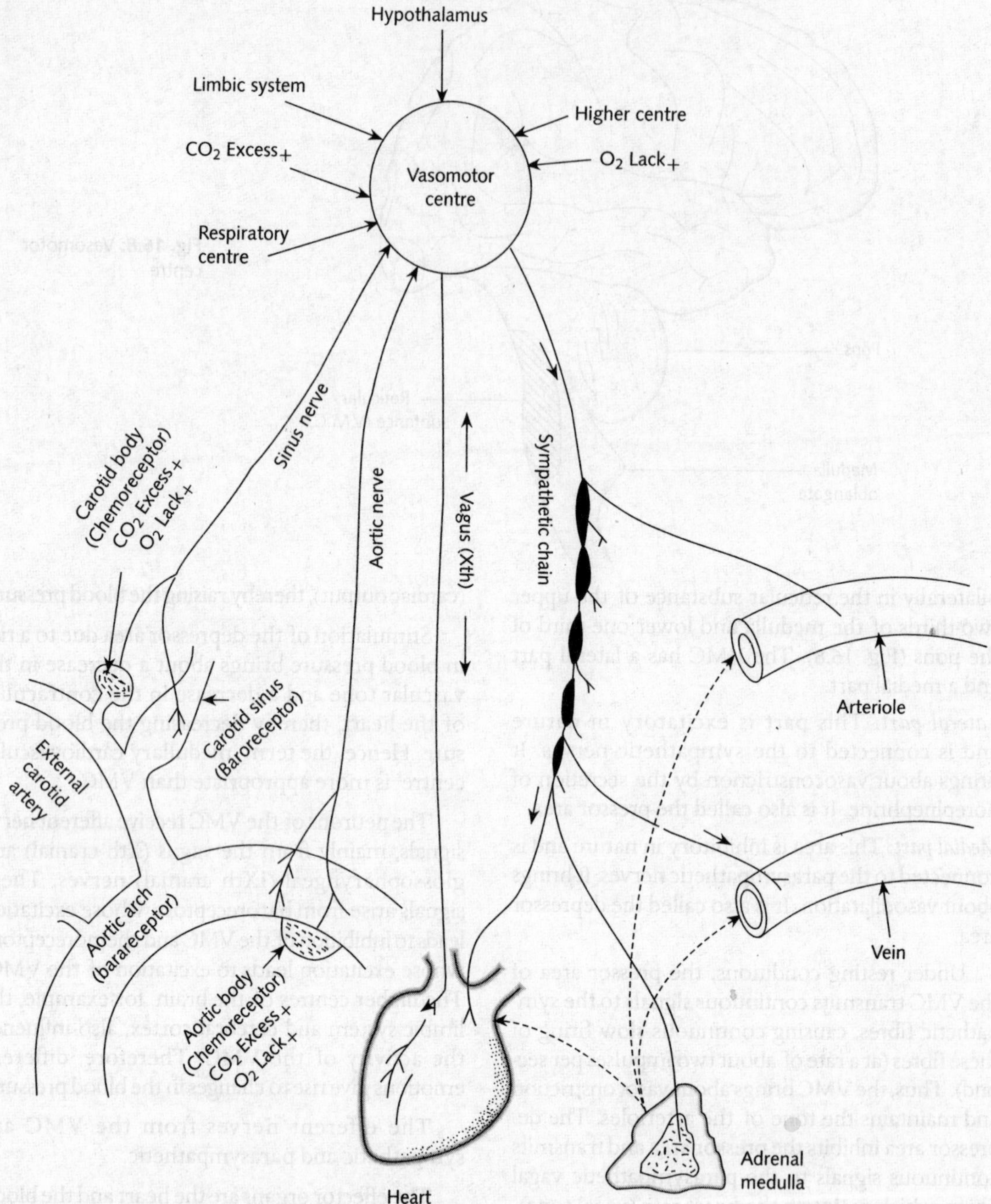


**Fig. 16.9: Diagrammatic representation of different factors that influence the vasomotor centre**

# CHAPTER 17

# Shock

Shock is a clinical condition in which there is inadequate perfusion of the vital organs due to a discrepancy between the cardiac output and the vascular capacity. The discrepancy results in an inadequate supply of nutrients and oxygen to the tissues.

Shock is characterized by an increased heart rate, decreased blood pressure, cold and moist skin, rapid breathing and a lower output of urine. It may be of the following types:

1. Circulatory shock
2. Neurogenic shock
3. Anaphylactic shock
4. Septic shock
5. Traumatic shock

## CIRCULATORY SHOCK

Circulatory shock can be of two types, cardiogenic and hypovolemic. In the former type, the cardiac output is decreased, primarily because of cardiac disorders, for example, myocardial infarction. In hypovolemic shock, the cardiac output decreases due to a reduction in the blood volume, which may be caused by a haemorrhage, burns or dehydration. A haemorrhage, of course, means excessive loss of blood. In severe cases of burn, plasma is lost through the exposed areas, so its volume decreases. In dehydration, excessive sweating, vomiting or diarrhoea reduces the volume of water in the body and, therefore, the blood volume.

### Haemorrhagic shock

This type of shock occurs more commonly than the other types. Acute blood loss, that is, of more than 10 per cent of the total blood volume, leads to a significant decrease in the cardiac output and blood pressure. Haemorrhagic shock may be (i) nonprogressive, reversible or compensatory shock, or (ii) progressive, irreversible or noncompensatory shock.

#### Nonprogressive, Reversible or Compensatory Shock

This occurs when the amount of blood lost is less than 30 to 40 per cent of the total blood volume. In this, tissue perfusion is deficient, but not enough to cause a vicious cycle of cardiovascular deterioration.

Certain compensatory mechanisms enable a person to recover from a moderate degree of shock. These are described below.

*Sympathetic activity*: The baroreceptor and chemoreceptor reflex mechanisms and the CNS ischaemic response elicit powerful stimulation of the sympathetic nerves, so that the cardiac output and blood pressure go back to normal. Generalized vasoconstriction diverts the flow of blood to the vital organs, like the heart and brain, from the peripheral parts of the body.

*Reverse stress mechanism*: This mechanism causes

the blood vessels to contract around the diminished blood volume, so that the blood fills the blood vessels more adequately.

*Recovery of blood volume*: This occurs in the following four ways:

1. Fluid shift mechanism: In this, there is an increased absorption of tissue fluid from the interstitial spaces, that is, from the extravascular to the intravascular compartment.
2. Thirst mechanism: Increased thirst gives rise to a greater intake of water, which results in a replenishment of the blood volume.
3. Aldosterone mechanism: When aldosterone secretion goes up, there is greater conservation of salt and water by the kidneys, which raises the volume of blood.
4. ADH mechanism: An increase in the secretion of ADH causes water retention by the kidneys, which increases the blood volume, and constriction of the peripheral arteries and veins, which increases the peripheral resistance and, therefore, the blood pressure.

## Progressive, Irreversible or Noncompensatory Shock

Such shock occurs when the amount of blood lost is more than 40 per cent of the total blood volume. Shock progresses till the cardiovascular system begins to deteriorate, leading to a vicious cycle which results in death. No treatment whatsoever can save the life of the patient.

Prolonged and sustained peripheral vasoconstriction may give rise to changes in the microcirculation, due to which the cardiac output remains depressed even if the blood volume is restored to normal, and the blood pressure starts to drop.

The vicious cycle of cardiovascular deterioration involves several factors. The decreased cardiac output and fall in blood pressure reduces coronary filling, which lowers the heart's ability to pump and, therefore, gives rise to a further decrease in the cardiac output and blood pressure.

The severe fall in blood pressure reduces the flow of blood to the brain, leading to failure of the VMC, decreased vascular tone and a further fall in the blood pressure. Due to the drop in blood pressure, the blood flow to the tissues becomes sluggish, causing thrombosis of the minute vessels. The decreased blood flow to the tissues increases capillary permeability (due to hypoxia), and toxins are released, particularly from the intestine. These give rise to myocardial depression and a further fall in the cardiac output and blood pressure (Fig. 17.1).

The causes of death are tissue damage, which results in acidosis, the destruction of enzymes and the depletion of ATP (adenosine triphosphate).

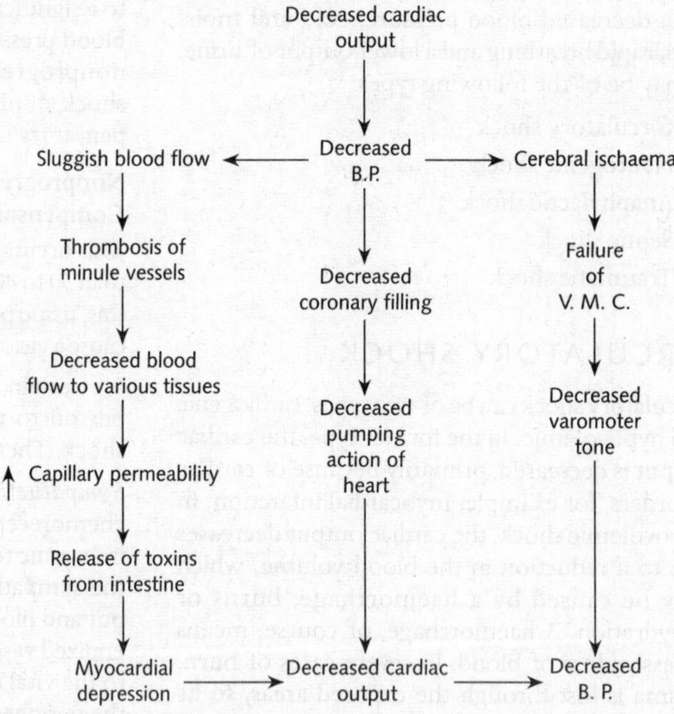


**Fig. 17.1:** Positive feedback mechanisms in irreversible shock

## NEUROGENIC SHOCK

In neurogenic shock, the loss of vasomotor tone throughout the body causes massive vasodilatation of the veins, an increased vascular capacity and shock.

The causes may be either deep general anaesthesia, high spinal anaesthesia, brain damage, or strong emotions.

## ANAPHYLACTIC SHOCK

Anaphylaxis is an allergic condition in which the cardiac output is normal, but the blood pressure falls drastically due to an increased release of histamine. The latter causes severe vasodilatation. It is due to the antigen–antibody reaction, for example, allergy to a local anaesthetic.

## SEPTIC SHOCK AND TRAUMATIC SHOCK

When widespread infection in the body is carried through the blood, it causes extensive tissue damage and severe vasodilatation, resulting in septic shock. An example is peritonitis due to the spread of infection from any organ, like the uterus in septic abortion.

Traumatic shock occurs when the pain caused by severe trauma strongly inhibits the VMC, increases the vascular capacity and decreases venous return.

## PHYSIOLOGICAL PRINCIPLES OF TREATMENT OF SHOCK

A number of physiological measures can be taken to treat shock. One is lowering of the head, which increases venous return, the cardiac output and the blood flow to the brain. Intravenous fluids may be given to the patient as they increase vascular filling, thereby increasing venous return and the cardiac output. The fluids used can be plasma, electrolyte solution (saline) or blood.

Oxygen therapy may be performed to prevent tissue damage. Also, the patient may be given drugs to maintain the blood pressure, relieve pain and combat stress.

## SYNCOPE (FAINTING)

Syncope is a transient loss of consciousness, which is self-limiting and is due to a reduction in the blood supply to the brain. This is caused by reflex depression of the VMC, which can occur due to the reasons enumerated below.

### Strong Emotions ('Vasovagal Syncope')

In this condition, the sympathetic muscle vasodilator system becomes powerfully activated so that the blood flow through the muscles increases several fold. Intense stimulation of the vagus also occurs, slowing down the heart rate markedly.

The arterial pressure falls instantly. This, in turn, reduces the flow of blood to the brain, so that the person loses consciousness.

### Excessive Fatigue

Excessive fatigue causes a marked increase in the flow of blood to the muscles of the body, thereby reducing the flow to the brain. This results in syncope.

### Excessive Hunger

Hypoglycaemia often causes loss of consciousness. As the blood sugar level falls to 50–70 mg%, the person starts sweating and trembling all over. When the blood sugar level goes down to 20–50 mg%, convulsions and loss of consciousness occur.

### Standing Continuously in a Stuffy Room

Syncope may occur if a person stands continuously in a crowded and stuffy room. In this case, all the blood pools into the lower extremities, which means that the blood supply to the brain is reduced.

### Carotid Sinus Syndrome (Tight Collar Syndrome)

In human beings, strong pressure on the neck, over the bifurcation of the carotids, can excite the baroreceptors of the carotid sinuses, making the arterial pressure fall as much as 20 mmHg in a normal person. This reduces the blood supply to the brain and causes fainting. Such a condition is also called carotid sinus syncope.

**Orthostatic Hypotension (Postural)**
A change of posture from lying down to standing can cause excessive vasodilatation, a fall in the blood pressure and syncope.

CHAPTER

18

# The Lymphatic Circulation

The lymphatic system is concerned with the drainage of tissue fluid, which forms the medium of exchange for various substances between the blood capillaries and tissue cells. It begins in the tissue spaces and ends in the venous circulation. Therefore, the lymphatic system is not part of the circulatory system *per se*, but represents a one-way accessory route by which tissue fluid flows from the interstitial spaces into blood.

## ORGANIZATION

The lymphatic system in man consists of an extensive network of thin vessels resembling veins. These carry a fluid called lymph.

The system begins with blind-end lymph capillaries that are present in all tissues of the body, except the brain and cartilage, and are called terminal lymph capillaries. The capillary wall is made of a single layer of endothelial cells and is more permeable than the blood capillary. The edges of the endothelial cells overlap in such a way that they form minute flap-valves. Fluid, and even the large particulate matter in the interstitial space, can push open the valve and flow into the capillary. However, once inside, it cannot flow back as it causes the flap valve to close (Fig. 18.1).

The terminal lymph capillaries join together to form larger lymphatic vessels, which ultimately form two large lymphatic ducts, the thoracic duct on the left side and the right lymphatic duct on the right side. These drain into the left and right subclavian veins, respectively, in the neck.

Along the course of the larger lymphatics are situated the lymph nodes. These produce

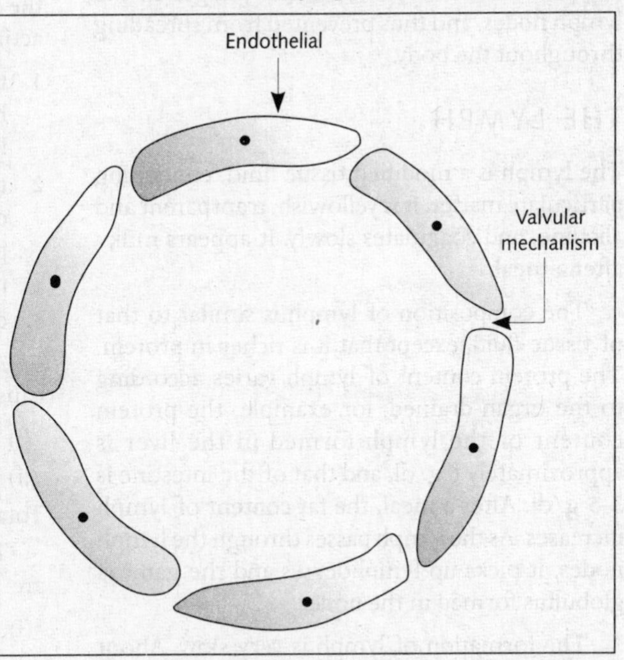

Fig. 18.1: Section of lymph capillary

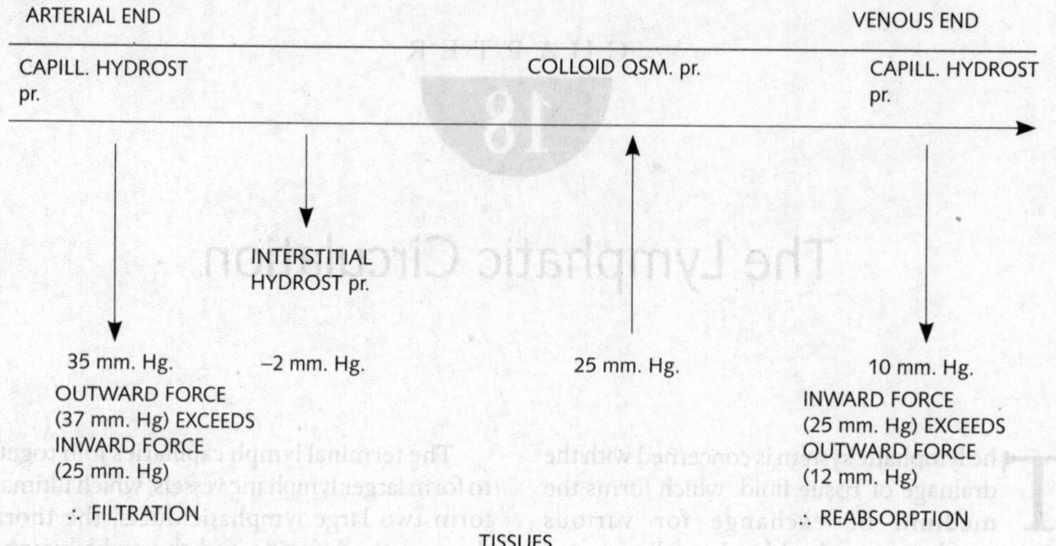


**Fig. 18.2:** Formation of tissue fluid

lymphocytes and act as filters for large molecules. For example, foreign proteins, such as bacteria and tumour cells, which may enter the lymphatics are trapped and destroyed by macrophages in the lymph nodes, and thus prevented from spreading throughout the body.

## THE LYMPH

The lymph is a modified tissue fluid, containing particulate matter. It is yellowish, transparent and alkaline, and coagulates slowly. It appears milky after a meal.

The composition of lymph is similar to that of tissue fluid, except that it is richer in protein. The protein content of lymph varies according to the organ drained, for example, the protein content of the lymph formed in the liver is approximately 6 g/dl, and that of the intestine is 3–5 g/dl. After a meal, the fat content of lymph increases. As the lymph passes through the lymph nodes, it picks up lymphocytes and the gamma globulins formed in the nodes.

The formation of lymph is very slow. About 90 per cent of the fluid filtered out from the blood capillaries is reabsorbed into them at the venous end. The remaining fluid enters the lymphatic vessels to constitute lymph.

The filtration and reabsorption of fluid along the capillary wall depends on the balance of forces acting on it (Fig. 18.2). These include:

1. the hydrostatic pressure gradient, that is, the hydrostatic pressure in the capillary minus that in the interstitial space;
2. the osmotic pressure gradient across the capillary wall, that is, the colloidal osmotic pressure of plasma minus that of the interstitial fluid; and
3. capillary permeability.

At the arteriolar end, the forces that tend to cause the fluid to move outward are:

(i) Capillary hydrostatic pressure = 35 mmHg
(ii) Interstitial hydrostatic pressure = –2 mmHg

Total outward force = 35 – (–2) = 37 mmHg

The forces that tend to move the fluid inward are:

(i) Plasma protein osmotic pressure = 25 mmHg
(ii) Interstitial osmotic pressure = 0 mmHg

∴ Net filtering force = 37 – 25 = 12 mmHg

At the venous end, the outward forces are:

(i) Capillary hydrostatic pressure = 10 mmHg
(ii) Interstitial hydrostatic pressure = –2 mmHg
∴ Total outward force= 10 – (–2)= 12 mmHg

The inward forces are:

(i) Plasma protein osmotic pressure = 25 mmHg
(ii) Interstitial osmotic pressure = 0 mmHg
∴ Total inward force = 25 mmHg
Net inward force = 12 – 25 = –13 mmHg

Therefore, fluid is filtered at the arterial end and reabsorbed at the venous end of the capillary.

### Factors affecting flow of lymph

The valves in the lymphatics allow a unidirectional flow of the lymph, from the periphery to the neck. Contraction of the skeletal muscles increases the rate of flow by its pumping action. The negative intrathoracic pressure during inspiration has a suction action on lymph from the abdomen.

## FUNCTIONS OF LYMPHATIC SYSTEM

The lymphatic system drains interstitial fluid and prevents it from accumulating in the tissues. It also returns proteins to the circulating blood.

The lymphatic system provides a route of absorption to long-chained fatty acids and cholesterol from the intestine, in the form of chylomicrons. In addition, it provides nutrition to the avascular parts of the body.

## APPLIED PHYSIOLOGY

An excessive accumulation of fluid in the tissue spaces is known as oedema. Oedema can occur for the following reasons.

*Increased capillary hydrostatic pressure:* This can occur in venous obstruction and congestive cardiac failure.

*Decreased plasma protein osmotic pressure*: This can occur in malnutrition and renal disease (increased excretion of proteins).

*Increased capillary permeability*: This can occur in local inflammation in which bacterial toxins produce vasodilatation and increase the capillary permeability.

*Chronic lymphatic obstruction*: This can be due to operative removal of the lymph nodes (e.g., in the treatment of cancer). It can also be caused by parasites (e.g., filariasis). There is interference with the drainage of proteins from the tissue spaces, so protein-rich fluid accumulates in there, causing lymphoedema of the nonpitting type (i.e., if pressure is applied on the skin overlying a bone, it does not leave a small depression).

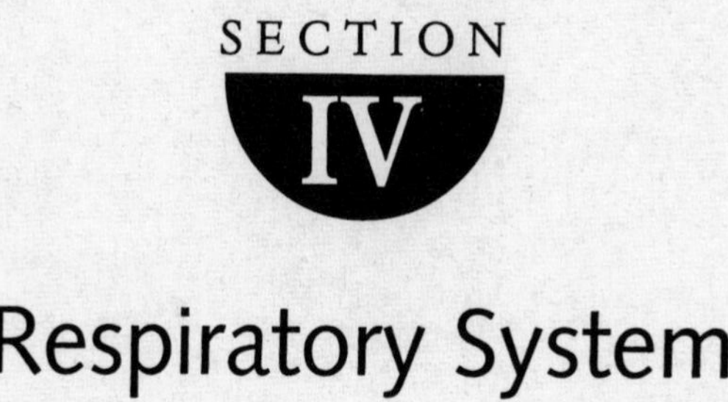


# Respiratory System

CHAPTER

19

# Functional Anatomy

## INTRODUCTION

The most important function of the respiratory system is to supply oxygen to the tissues for the oxidation of food, which is required for the production of energy for work, and to eliminate the $CO_2$ that is formed in the tissues due to metabolism.

The respiratory process involves many steps. The first is the transport of air to the lungs. Atmospheric air passes through the conducting air passages into the lungs. The next step is ventilation, in which air is exchanged between the external atmosphere and the alveoli of the lungs. This is also known as external respiration by convention. Ventilation includes (i) the entry of air ($O_2$) into the lungs and the exit of air ($CO_2$) from the lungs, by inspiration and expiration, respectively; and (ii) the distribution of air from the bronchioles to almost 700 million alveoli in the lungs.

The next step in respiration is diffusion, in which gases are exchanged between the alveoli, which are rich in pulmonary capillaries, and the blood in the capillaries. Oxygen enters the blood and carbon dioxide leaves it. After this, $O_2$ is carried by the blood to the tissue capillaries, and $CO_2$ is carried by the blood from the tissue capillaries to the lungs.

This is followed by the exchange of gases between the blood in the tissue capillaries and the tissues. The tissue cells have less $O_2$ and more $CO_2$ than the blood in the capillaries. Therefore, $O_2$ diffuses into the cells and $CO_2$ diffuses into the capillaries.

The final step consists of metabolism in the tissues. The $O_2$ is utilized or consumed and $CO_2$ is produced (Fig. 19.1).

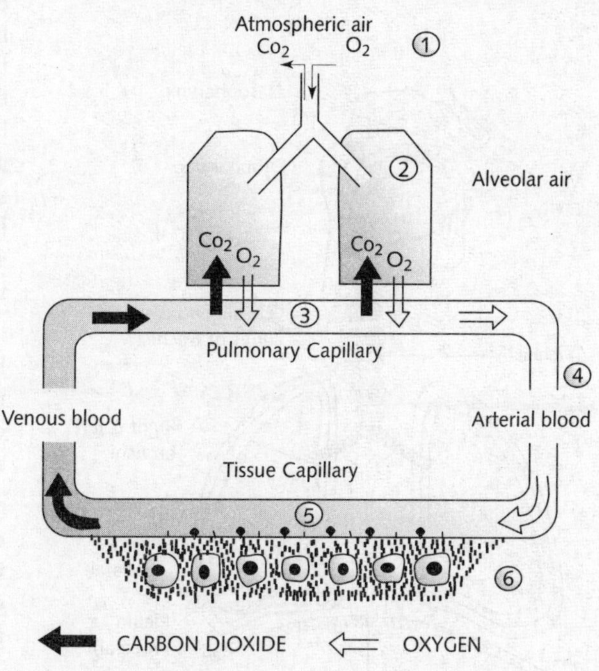


**Fig. 19.1:** Plan of the respiratory system

## Types of respiration

Respiration can be external or internal. The former type takes place at the level of the lungs and includes the first four steps. Oxygen is inspired from the atmosphere and passes from the lungs to the capillaries. Carbon dioxide passes from the capillaries into the alveoli and is expired.

Internal respiration takes place at the level of the tissues and includes the last two steps. Carbon dioxide from the tissues diffuses into the capillaries, and oxygen from the capillaries diffuses into the tissues, via tissue fluid.

# PHYSIOLOGICAL ANATOMY

In order to reach the lungs, air has to pass through a series of air passages (Fig. 19.2). Accordingly, the respiratory system is divided into the upper respiratory tract (URT), lower respiratory tract (LRT) and respiratory unit or lobule.

The URT includes the nose, nasopharynx, oropharynx and the larynx up to the level of the vocal cords. The LRT includes the larynx below the vocal cords, the trachea, bronchi (right and left), bronchioles and ultimately, the terminal bronchioles, which lead to the respiratory bronchioles.

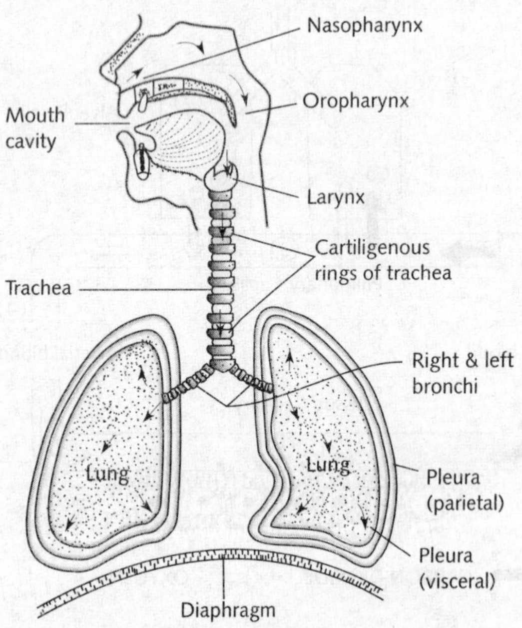


**Fig. 19.2:** Gross anatomy of the respiratory tract

The bronchi and bronchioles divide sixteen times. Their walls have smooth muscle, supplied by parasympathetic nerves. The stimulation of these nerves produces bronchoconstriction and increased airway resistance. Epinephrine produces bronchodilatation.

The respiratory unit or lobule includes the respiratory bronchioles, alveolar ducts and alveoli or air sacs, where the actual exchange of gases takes place (Figs 19.3a and b). The portion up to the terminal bronchiole is called the conducting zone, while the portion from the respiratory bronchiole is the respiratory zone.

# FUNCTIONS OF RESPIRATORY SYSTEM

The respiratory system performs many functions. An important function is protection. The air entering the nose is cleaned in several ways. The hair in the nose filters dust particles and prevents them from entering the respiratory passage. The thick mucus secreted by the respiratory passages helps trap dust particles and bacteria, and ciliary action moves them up to the pharynx. Cigarette smoking paralyses ciliary function, hence the higher incidence of respiratory infection among smokers. Sneezing and the cough reflex help remove irritant particles.

The respiratory system is also responsible for humidification. Air is moistened by the vascular nasal mucosa because dry air is harmful for the ciliary function of the respiratory passages. The system also warms air to body temperature.

One of the crucial functions is the exchange of gases. Oxygen from the atmosphere is taken in and carbon dioxide from the blood is thrown out. In addition, volatile substances such as $CO_2$, acetone, ether and alcohol are excreted.

The respiratory system is responsible for the maintenance of pH, which is maintained at the

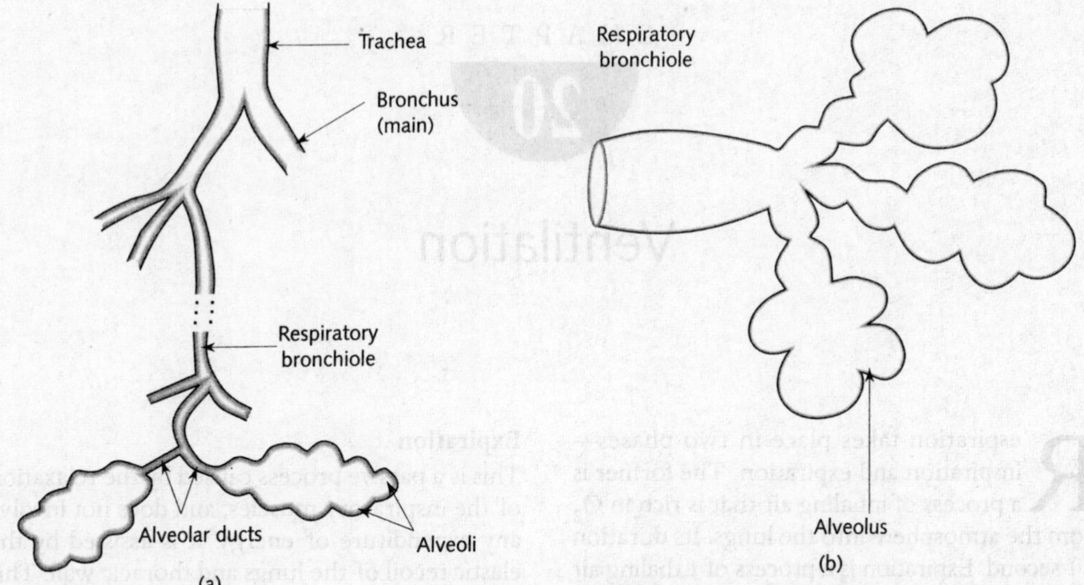


**Fig. 19.3 (a):** Air passages

**Fig. 19.3 (b):** Respiratory unit (lobule)

normal value of 7.4 for the normal functioning of cells. An increased level of $CO_2$ in the body raises the $H^+$ ion concentration and brings down the pH, which increases the respiratory rate, resulting in the elimination of $CO_2$ and the restoration of the normal pH.

Respiration helps regulate the body temperature. This is important in lower animals which have fewer sweat glands. When the external temperature is high, animals pant (i.e., rapid and shallow breathing), and saliva from the tongue evaporates faster, causing increased heat loss and bringing down the body temperature.

Respiration helps maintain the balance of water. About 600–700 ml of water is lost as water vapour during expiration. Respiratory movements help in circulation as well. During inspiration, the pressure in the chest falls, the suction force increases, and blood from the periphery gushes into the heart, increasing venous return and consequently, the cardiac output.

CHAPTER

20

# Ventilation

Respiration takes place in two phases—inspiration and expiration. The former is a process of inhaling air that is rich in $O_2$ from the atmosphere into the lungs. Its duration is 1 second. Expiration is a process of exhaling air rich in $CO_2$ from the lungs into the atmosphere. Its duration is 3 seconds. These phases are repeated in a cyclic fashion, and the entire cycle is called the respiratory cycle. Its duration is 4 seconds. The normal respiratory rate is 60/4, that is, 15/min. The range is 12 to 18 per minute.

## MECHANISM OF RESPIRATION

**Inspiration**

This is an active process, involving contraction of the inspiratory muscles as well as the expenditure of energy. It results in the expansion of the chest.

The muscles involved in inspiration are:

1. Diaphragm
2. External intercostals
3. Scaleni
4. Sternomastoid
5. Serratus anterior
6. Alae nasi

The first three are the main muscles and the remaining three are the accessory muscles, which assist in forced inspiration.

**Expiration**

This is a passive process caused by the relaxation of the inspiratory muscles, and does not involve any expenditure of energy. It is assisted by the elastic recoil of the lungs and thoracic wall. This process brings the chest back to its normal resting size.

The muscles involved in expiration are:

1. Internal intercostals
2. Abdominal muscles
3. Serratus posterior

These contract actively only during forceful expiration.

### Changes in thoracic cavity

Normally, the lungs are enclosed in a thoracic cage and are separated from the walls of the thorax by the pleural membranes. The latter are visceral (covering the lungs) and parietal (lining the thoracic wall), and enclose a potential cavity, called the intrapleural space, between the two layers. The pressure within this cavity is called the intrapleural pressure. The intrapleural pressure is negative throughout respiration (subatmospheric). It is important as (i) it keeps the two layers of the pleura in contact with each other and (ii) it keeps the lungs expanded and prevents them from collapsing (Fig. 20.1). Its normal value during rest is –2 mmHg, and during inspiration, –6 mmHg.

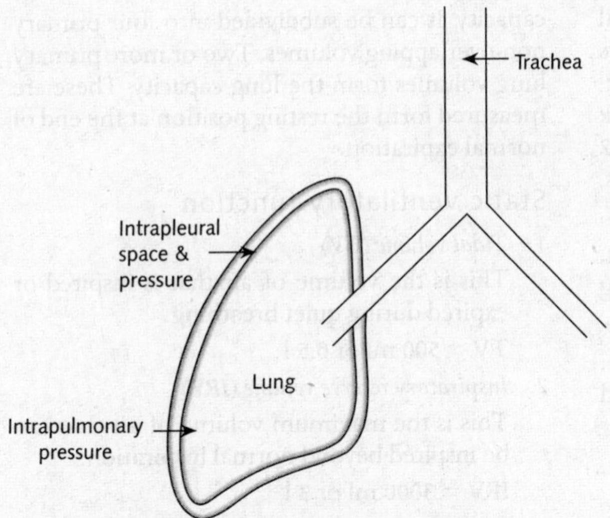


Fig. 20.1: Intrapleural and intrapulmonary pressure

## Changes during inspiration

Inspiration is brought about by the contraction of the inspiratory muscles.

The diaphragm is a dome-shaped muscle which flattens out during contraction. Thus, the vertical diameter of the chest increases by about 1.5 cm and accounts for 75 per cent of the total inspired air.

The external intercostal muscles are located between the ribs, and run forward and downward from the vertebral attachment (Fig. 20.2). Their contraction, therefore, results in the elevation of the ribs. The upward and outward movement of the middle part of the ribs is called the bucket-handle movement, by which the transverse diameter of the chest increases.

The external intercostals also elevate the entire thoracic cage, including the sternum, due to the upward movement of the anterior ends of the ribs. When the sternum is elevated, it thrusts forward and hence, the anteroposterior diameter of the chest also increases.

The accessory muscles of respiration help fix the first rib and the shoulder girdle. Thus, the movement of the second rib onwards helps in respiration. The contraction of the accessory muscles increases in deep or distressed breathing.

As the thoracic cage increases in volume, the intrapleural pressure falls to –6 mmHg, and the volume of the lungs enlarges with the fall in pressure in the alveoli. The pressure within the lungs or alveoli is called intrapulmonary pressure. During the resting condition, it is 0 mmHg and during inspiration, it falls to –1 mmHg. Thus, there occurs a pressure gradient between the atmosphere (760 mmHg) and the alveolar air, causing the air from outside to rush into the alveoli.

## Changes during expiration

During expiration, the muscles involved relax and the thoracic cage becomes smaller, going

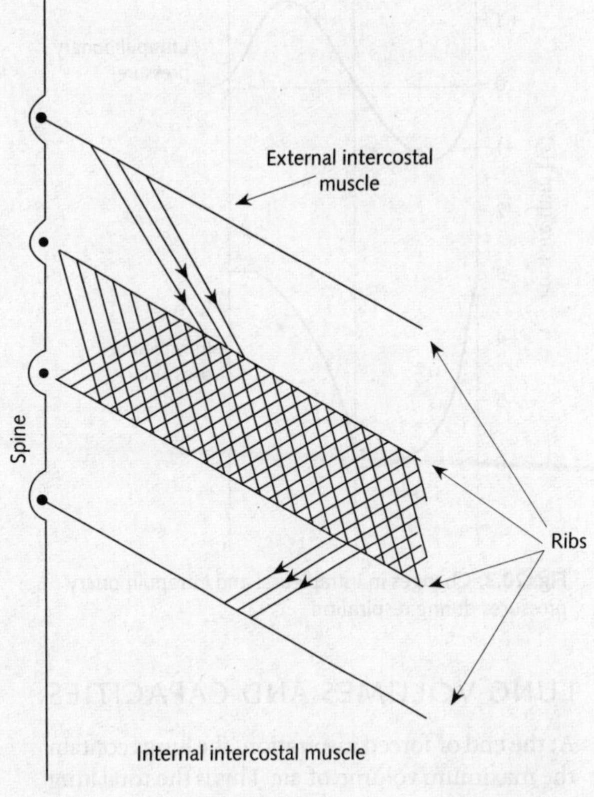


Fig. 20.2: Intercostal muscles

back to the resting condition. The intrapleural pressure rises to –2 mmHg and the lungs recoil, pressing on the alveoli, which also shrink. This brings the intrapulmonary pressure back to '0' and the intrapleural pressure back to –2 mmHg. Thus, a reverse pressure gradient occurs, forcing the air out into the external environment.

In forced expiration or during voluntary effort, the intrapulmonary pressure increases to +2 mmHg (Fig. 20.3).

*Intra-abdominal pressure*: This is always positive. During inspiration, it becomes less positive and during expiration, more positive.

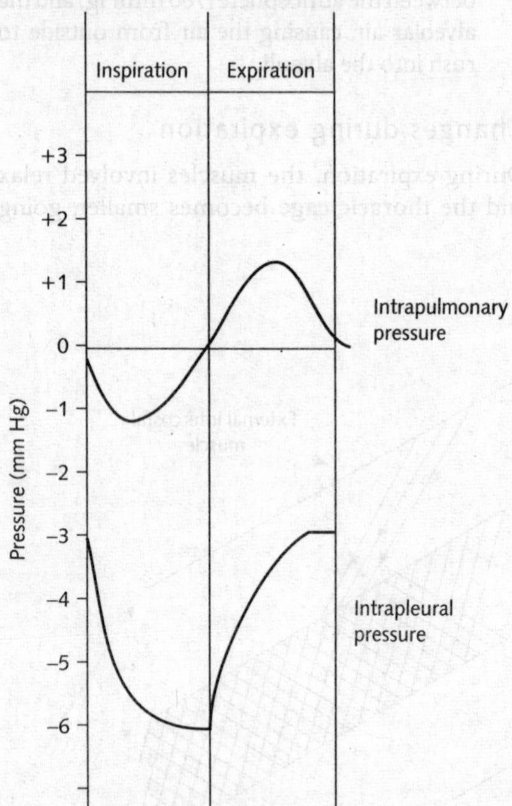


**Fig. 20.3:** Changes in intrapleural and intrapulmonary pressures during respiration

## LUNG VOLUMES AND CAPACITIES

At the end of forced inspiration, the lungs contain the maximum volume of air. This is the total lung capacity. It can be subdivided into four primary non-overlapping volumes. Two or more primary lung volumes form the lung capacity. These are measured form the resting position at the end of normal expiration.

### Static ventilatory function

1. *Tidal volume (TV)*
   This is the volume of air that is inspired or expired during quiet breathing.
   TV = 500 ml or 0.5 l
2. *Inspiratory reserve volume (IRV)*
   This is the maximum volume of air that can be inspired beyond normal inspiration.
   IRV = 3000 ml or 3 l
3. *Expiratory reserve volume (ERV)*
   This is the maximum volume of air that can be breathed out beyond normal expiration.
   ERV = 1100 ml or 1.1 l
4. *Residual volume (RV)*
   This is the volume of air that remains in the lungs after maximum expiration.
   RV = 1200 ml or 1.2 l
5. *Inspiratory capacity (IC)*
   This is the volume of air that can be forcibly inspired at the end of normal expiration.
   IC = TV + IRV = 3500 ml or 3.5 l
6. *Functional residual capacity (FRC)*
   This is the volume of air that remains in the lungs after a quiet respiration.
   FRC = ERV + RV = 2300 ml or 2.3 l
7. *Total lung capacity (TLC)*
   It is the volume of air present in lungs after forced inspiration.
   TLC = VC + RV = 5800 ml or about 6000 ml, that is, 6 l
8. *Vital capacity (VC)*
   It is the volume of air that can be expired forcibly after maximum inspiration.
   VC = TV + IRV + ERV = 4600 ml or 4.6 l (Fig. 20.4).

Various factors affect the vital capacity. It decreases with age and is lower in females. It is

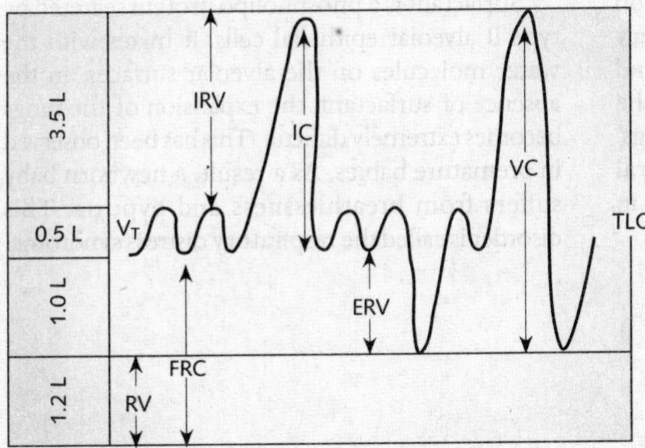


**Fig. 20.4:** Diagrammatic representation of a spirographic tracing (lung volumes and capacities)

higher in taller persons who have a greater surface area. The vital capacity is the highest in the standing position and the lowest while lying down. It is higher in trained athletes and those with muscle strength, such as swimmers.

The vital capacity decreases if the expansion of the lungs is hampered, as in lung fibrosis, neuromuscular disorders such as poliomyelitis, and pulmonary airway obstruction (asthma).

*Measurement*: The TV, ERV and VC can be measured directly by a spirometer, while the RV, FRC and TLC cannot be measured directly. These are measured indirectly by the 'nitrogen wash-out' or 'helium dilution' methods.

## Dynamic ventilatory function

1. *Timed vital capacity*

The fraction of the total vital capacity that can be expired in the first second of the expiratory effort is called the forced expiratory volume (FEV). Its percentage can be measured to diagnose obstructive and restrictive diseases of the respiratory system.

2. *Pulmonary ventilation*

This is a dynamic process.

Pulmonary ventilation = respiratory rate × tidal volume
= 12 × 500 ml
= 6000 ml or 6 l/min.

The maximum rate of pulmonary ventilation that can be sustained for 15 seconds is called the maximum breathing capacity (MBC). During exercise, pulmonary ventilation increases in proportion to the severity of exercise.

## ALVEOLAR VENTILATION

Alveolar air is the air present in the alveoli. This air is available for gaseous exchange. However, all 500 ml of air entering the lungs during inspiration is not available for gaseous exchange.

The dead space air is the air not available for gaseous exchange, that is, it does not participate in the exchange. It is of two types—anatomical and physiological. The former is the amount of air present in the respiratory passages up to the terminal bronchiole (the conducting zone). It amounts to 150 cc. The physiological type is the amount of air in the alveoli that does not finally participate in gaseous exchange. It is either due to the nonexistence of air in the alveoli (not ventilated), or the blockage of the pulmonary capillaries (non perfused alveoli).

Normally, the anatomical dead space is equal to the physiological dead space. In pathological conditions, the anatomical dead space air remains the same, but the physiological one increases to about 300 ml. The respiratory disease then occurs.

Alveolar ventilation = respiratory rate × alveolar air (TV – dead space air)
= 12 × (500 – 150)
= 4200 ml or 4.2 l

## Expansibility of lungs and thorax

Both the lungs and thorax are visco-elastic structures and the major part of the energy expended by the respiratory muscles goes in stretching the elastic structures of the lungs and thorax.

The expansibility of the lungs and thorax is expressed in terms of compliance. The greater the expansibility, the greater the compliance.

Besides the elastic fibres, the surface tension of the fluid lining the alveoli is another very important factor affecting lung compliance and both these factors are also responsible for the normal collapsing tendency (recoil) of the lungs. This is overcome by the negative intrapleural pressure and surfactant, which keep the lungs in the state of expansion.

Surfactant is a phospholipo protein secreted by type II alveolar epithelial cells. It mixes with the water molecules on the alveolar surfaces. In the absence of surfactant, the expansion of the lungs becomes extremely difficult. This has been observed in premature babies. As a result, a newborn baby suffers from breathlessness and hypoxia. This disorder is called the respiratory distress syndrome.

CHAPTER 21

# Pulmonary Gas Exchange

Fresh environmental air is brought into the alveoli by pulmonary ventilation. Pulmonary diffusion consists of the diffusion of $O_2$ from the alveolar air into the pulmonary capillary blood, and diffusion of $CO_2$ from the pulmonary capillary blood into the alveolar air.

The behaviour of gases is governed by physical laws. Some of the important laws are briefly described below.

1. Pressure law: The pressure of a gas is directly proportional to its concentration.
2. Boyle's law: At a constant temperature, the pressure (P) of a gas is inversely proportional to its volume (V).

$$P \propto \frac{1}{V}$$

$$\Rightarrow PV = \text{constant}$$

3. Charle's law: At a constant pressure, the volume (V) of a gas is proportionate to its absolute temperature (T).

$$V \propto T$$

$$\Rightarrow \frac{V}{T} = \text{constant}$$

4. Dalton's law of partial pressures: The pressure of each gas in a mixture of gases is known as its partial pressure (P) or tension. For example, 21 per cent of environmental air contains $O_2$; therefore, its partial pressure ($PO_2$) in the environmental air at sea level (barometric pressure 760 mmHg) is

$$\frac{21}{100} \times 760 = 160 \text{ mmHg}$$

5. Henry's law: According to this,

$$\text{Concentration of dissolved gas} = \text{Partial pressure of the gas} \times \text{Solubility coefficient of the gas}$$

The solubility coefficient of $CO_2$ is twenty times greater than that of $O_2$.

### Rate of diffusion across respiratory membrane

Several factors affect the rate of diffusion of a gas across the respiratory membrane. The most important among these is the pressure gradient of the gas. Gases always diffuse from an area of high pressure to one of low pressure. The rate of diffusion (D) is proportional to the difference in pressure ($\Delta P$) across the membrane ($D \propto \Delta P$).

The cross-sectional area (A) of the membrane ($D \propto A$), as well as the solubility coefficient (S) of the gas ($D \propto S$) also affect the rate of diffusion. The other factors are the distance (d) through which the gas must diffuse ($D \propto \frac{1}{d}$), and the molecular weight (MW) of the gas $\left(D \propto \frac{1}{\sqrt{MW}}\right)$.

All the factors may be expressed by the following formula:

$$D\alpha \frac{\Delta P \times A \times S}{d \times \sqrt{MW}}$$

## EXCHANGE OF GASES IN THE LUNGS

In the pulmonary alveoli, the gases present in the alveolar air in the gaseous form ($O_2$ and $CO_2$) are separated by the respiratory membrane from the dissolved gases present in the blood of the pulmonary capillaries.

The respiratory membrane consists of six layers (Fig. 21.1). The gases have to diffuse through these. The layers are:

(i) a layer of fluid lining the alveolus,
(ii) a layer of epithelial cells,
(iii) the basement membrane of the alveolar epithelial cells,
(iv) the interstitial space between the epithelial and endothelial cells,
(v) the basement membrane of the capillary endothelial cells, and
(vi) a layer of capillary endothelial cells.

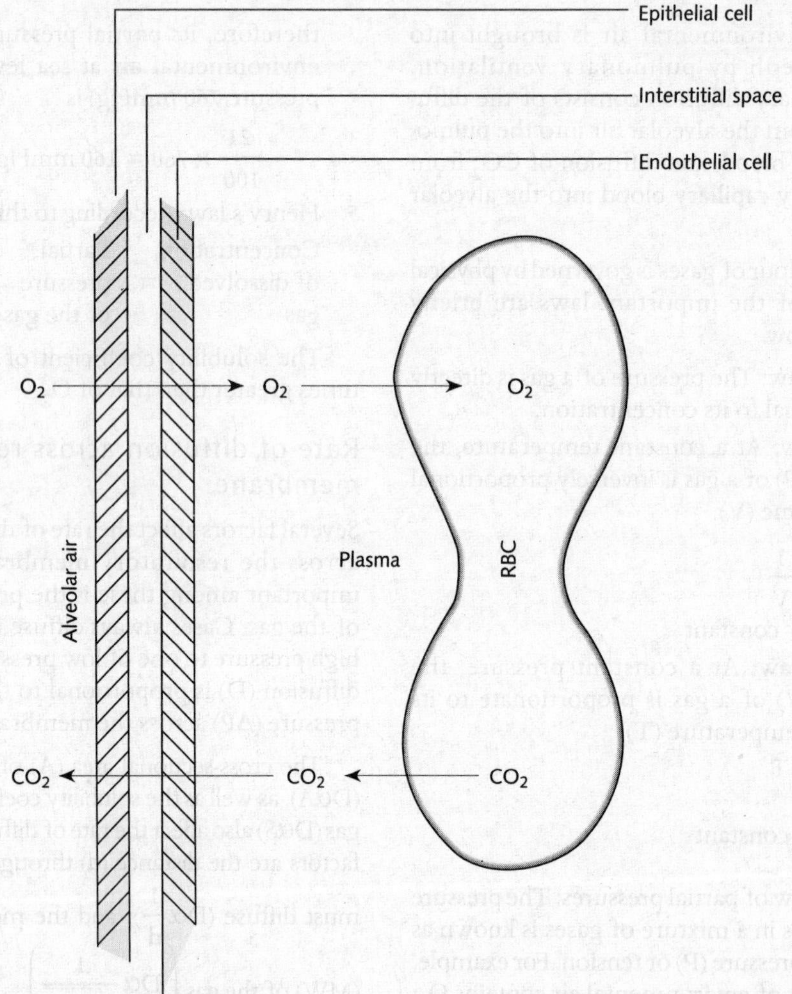


**Fig. 21.1:** The respiratory membrane

Oxygen diffuses from the alveolar air into the capillary blood because the $PO_2$ (pressure of oxygen) in the alveolar air is approximately 100 mmHg, which is far greater than that in the pulmonary capillary blood (40 mmHg). $CO_2$ diffuses from the capillary blood into the alveolar air since the $PCO_2$ in the pulmonary capillary blood is 46 mmHg, which is greater than that in the alveolar air (40 mmHg).

The total surface area of the respiratory membrane is about 70 $m^2$ at rest, and greater still during exercise (since many previously dormant capillaries open up). Pathologically, it may decrease in lung disorders like emphysema, in which many alveoli are destroyed. Surgical resection of a part of the lung has the same result. When the surface area of the respiratory membrane is decreased to about one-third, the diffusion of gases (particularly $O_2$) is affected seriously.

The solubility coefficient and molecular weight of a gas are important factors when diffusion occurs into the liquid medium. $CO_2$ diffuses twenty times more rapidly than $O_2$.

## Diffusion capacity of the respiratory membrane

The diffusion capacity is the volume of a gas that diffuses through the respiratory membrane each minute for a pressure gradient of 1 mmHg.

At rest, 250 ml of $O_2$ diffuses through the respiratory membrane per minute. The diffusion capacity of $O_2$ increases during exercise. The diffusion capacity of $CO_2$ is approximately twice that of $O_2$. Therefore, if the respiratory membrane is damaged, the diffusion of $O_2$ is seriously affected, while that of $CO_2$ is not.

## Effect of ventilation–perfusion ratio on gas exchange

Normally, on the whole, the amount of ventilation of the alveoli perfectly matches the amount of blood flow around it. Thus, optimum conditions are produced for gas exchange. Pathologically, the ventilation–perfusion ratio may decrease or increase above the normal.

### Physiological Shunts

When the ventilation of a part of a lung is not adequate for the amount of blood flowing through it (low ventilation–perfusion ratio), a certain fraction of venous blood does not get oxygenated. It thus appears as if it has been shunted to the arterial side.

In respiratory disorders such as pneumonia and emphysema, physiological shunts lead to a fall in the $O_2$ tension (hypoxia).

### Physiological Dead Space

When the blood flow to a part of a lung is blocked, the ventilation–perfusion ratio increases and the alveoli in that area do not take part in gaseous exchange. This physiological dead space, when large, produces hypoxia.

CHAPTER

# Transport of Respiratory Gases

Oxygen and carbon dioxide are transported to and from the tissues, respectively, by the circulating blood. The exchange of gases across the alveolar and capillary membrane occurs because of the difference in concentration (pressure) of the gases on the two sides of the membrane.

## OXYGEN TRANSPORT IN BLOOD

The transport of $O_2$ is one of the most important functions of blood. Oxygen is transported from the alveolar air into the venous blood due to a pressure gradient, which holds good from the lungs to the tissues. The process is aided by certain other factors, such as haemoglobin, which increases the oxygen-carrying capacity of blood seventy-fold.

The transport of $O_2$ takes place in several stages. The first is the diffusion of $O_2$ from the alveoli into the pulmonary capillary blood. Next, it is transported in the arterial blood. Oxygen then diffuses from the capillaries to the interstitial fluid, and finally, from the interstitial fluid into the cells.

### Diffusion of $O_2$ from alveoli into pulmonary capillary blood

The $PO_2$ in the alveoli is 100 mmHg, while that in the pulmonary capillaries is 40 mmHg. This pressure difference causes $O_2$ to diffuse into the pulmonary capillaries. During exercise, the diffusion capacity of $O_2$ increases.

**Bohr Effect**

This is the effect of $CO_2$ on association and dissociation with $O_2$. As blood passes through the lungs, $CO_2$ diffuses from the blood into the alveoli, causing a decrease in the $PCO_2$ and $H^+$ concentration. This allows a greater quantity of $O_2$ to bind with haemoglobin at any given alveolar pressure, thus allowing for greater transport of $O_2$ to the tissues. In the tissues, the uptake of $CO_2$ by the blood increases the release of $O_2$ into the tissues. The Bohr effect is more important at the level of the tissues.

### Transport of $O_2$ in arterial blood

Oxygen is transported in the blood in physical solution or in chemical combination. In the former, 3 per cent of $O_2$ is carried in the dissolved form in the water of the plasma and cells. As for the latter, about 97 per cent of $O_2$ is carried in combination with Hb in the RBCs.

The haem part of Hb is remarkable in that it can combine loosely and reversibly with $O_2$, forming oxyHb ($Hb + O_2 \rightleftharpoons HbO_2$), when the pressure of $O_2$ is as high as in the pulmonary capillaries. However, when the pressure of $O_2$ is as low as in the tissue capillaries, $O_2$ is released from Hb. The process of oxygenation in the lungs and deoxygenation in the tissues is extremely rapid.

At a $PO_2$ of 100 mmHg, Hb can be fully saturated with $O_2$ and each gram of Hb carries 1.34 ml of $O_2$. Therefore, the oxygen-carrying capacity of arterial blood is 15 (average Hb concentration) × 1.34, or 20 ml of $O_2$ per 100 ml of blood.

## Diffusion of $O_2$ from capillaries to interstitial fluid

The $PO_2$ of arterial blood in the tissues is 100 mmHg, while that of the tissue fluid is 40 mmHg. Due to this pressure gradient, $O_2$ diffuses from the blood into the interstitial fluid. This depends on the rate of blood flow, the Hb concentration of the blood, and the rate of tissue metabolism.

## Diffusion of $O_2$ from interstitial fluid into cells

The $PO_2$ of the interstitial fluid is 40 mmHg, while that of the tissue cells is 23 mmHg. Due to this pressure gradient, $O_2$ diffuses from the interstitial fluid into the cells (Fig. 22.1).

As a result of $O_2$ delivery in the tissues, the $PO_2$ of plasma falls to 40 mmHg, and Hb can have a maximum saturation of 75 per cent. Therefore, every 100 ml of blood can hold only 15 ml of $O_2$, while the remaining 5 ml is released to diffuse into the tissues. Hence, with a normal cardiac output of 5 l/min., 250 ml of $O_2$ is delivered to the tissues per minute. The deoxygenated or venous blood reaches the lungs for oxygenation.

### *Coefficient of $O_2$ utilization*

This is the percentage of blood that gives up its $O_2$ as it passes through the tissue capillaries. Its normal value is 25 per cent.

During heavy exercise, the coefficient of $O_2$ utilization may increase to 80 per cent, and about 400 mL of $O_2$ may be transported to the tissues.

## OXYGEN DISSOCIATION CURVE

The Oxygen dissociation curve is plotted to show the relation between the $PO_2$ and the degree of $O_2$ saturation of Hb. The $PO_2$ values are plotted on the X-axis and the % saturation of Hb on the Y-axis (Fig. 22.2).

The curve is S-shaped and its upper part is flat. At a $PO_2$ of 100 mmHg and above, Hb is 100 per cent saturated. Even when the $PO_2$ falls to 60 mm Hg, Hb is 90 per cent saturated. This ensures a high uptake of $O_2$ when the alveolar pressure is moderately decreased, for example, at high altitudes or with decreased ventilation due to disease.

The upper part of the curve is related to the uptake of $O_2$ by the tissues, and the middle and lower parts are related to the delivery of $O_2$ in the tissues. At a $PO_2$ of 40 mmHg, Hb is 75 per cent saturated with oxygen. Therefore, 100 ml of blood holds 15 ml of $O_2$ instead of 20 ml, and 5 ml is delivered to the tissues. At a $PO_2$ of below 40 mmHg, more oxygen is delivered to the tissues, as in heavy exercise.

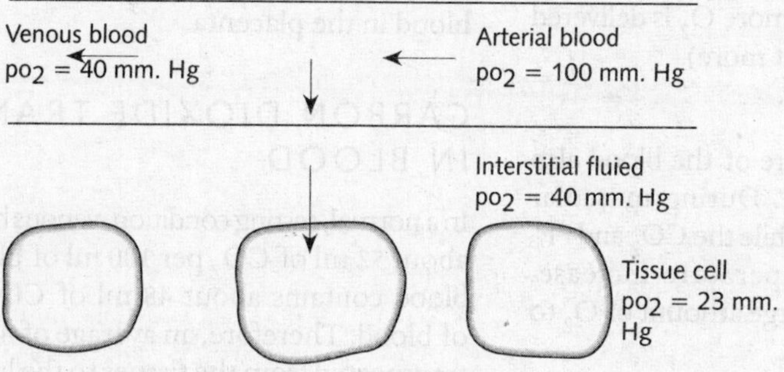


**Fig. 22.1:** Diffusion of $O_2$ from blood capillary to tissue cell via interstitial fluid

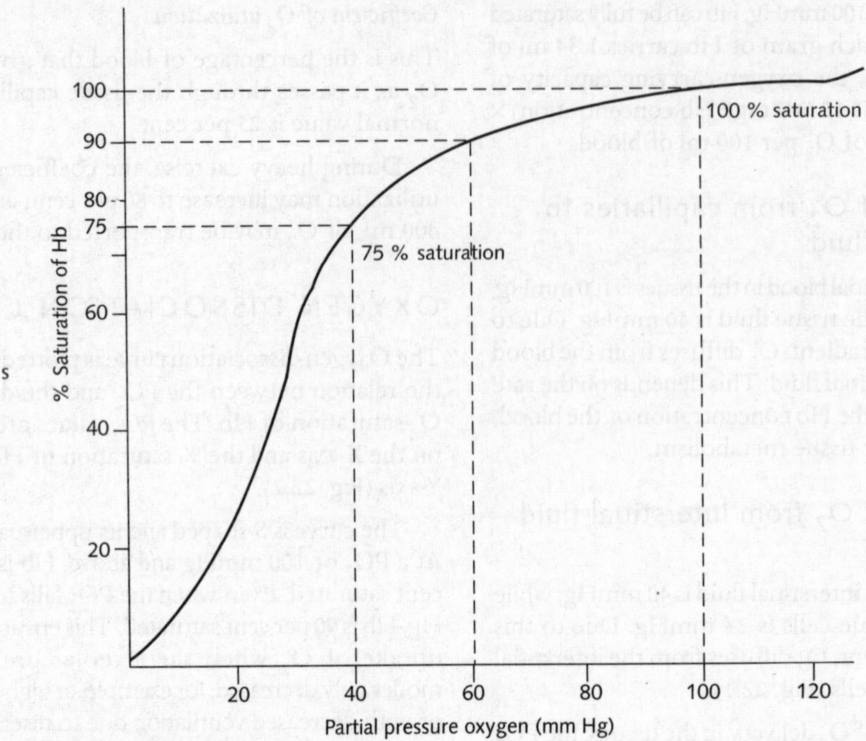


**Fig. 22.2:** Oxygen dissociation curve

## Factors affecting oxygen dissociation curve

The following factors affect the oxygen dissociation curve.

### $PCO_2$ and $H^+$ Ion Concentration

An increase in the $PCO_2$ and $H^+$ ion concentration in arterial blood shifts the curve to the right. This means that at a given value of $PO_2$, the saturation of Hb with $O_2$ decreases and more $O_2$ is delivered to the tissues (about 2 per cent more).

### Temperature

An increase in the temperature of the blood also shifts the curve to the right. During muscular exercise, the $PO_2$ decreases, while the $CO_2$ and $H^+$ ion concentration and temperature increase, facilitating the delivery of a large amount of $O_2$ to the tissues.

### Diphosphoglycerate (DPG)

Red blood cells are rich in 2–3 DPG. An increase in 2–3 DPG, as in chronic hypoxia, decreases the affinity of Hb for $O_2$. This results in a shift of the curve to the right, as well as greater $O_2$ delivery to the tissues.

The $O_2$ dissociation curve is shifted to the left with foetal Hb (HbF). This means an increased affinity of Hb for $O_2$. Hence, the normal volumes of $O_2$ can be taken up by foetal blood, though it is exposed to the low $PO_2$ value of the maternal blood in the placenta.

## CARBON DIOXIDE TRANSPORT IN BLOOD

In a normal, resting condition, venous blood contains about 52 ml of $CO_2$ per 100 ml of blood. Arterial blood contains about 48 ml of $CO_2$ per 100 ml of blood. Therefore, an average of 4 ml of $CO_2$ is transported from the tissues to the lungs by every 100 ml of blood. Some chemical reactions involving $CO_2$, increase the $CO_2$-carrying capacity of blood seventeen-fold.

The transport of $CO_2$ in the blood occurs in the following stages:

1. Diffusion of $CO_2$ from the cells to the tissue capillaries.
2. Transport of $CO_2$ in the blood.
3. Diffusion of $CO_2$ from the pulmonary capillaries into the alveoli.

## Diffusion of $CO_2$ from cells to tissue capillaries

Carbon dioxide is formed in the tissues as a result of metabolism. The $PCO_2$ of the tissues is, therefore, high (46 mmHg), while that of the arterial blood is 40 mmHg. Carbon dioxide, therefore, diffuses from the tissues into the capillary blood.

Carbon dioxide diffuses about twenty times faster than $O_2$. Therefore, the pressure gradient required to cause $CO_2$ diffusion (6 mmHg) is far less than that required to cause $O_2$ diffusion (60 mmHg). At each point of transport, the direction of the diffusion of $CO_2$ is exactly the opposite that of the diffusion of $O_2$ (Fig. 22.3).

## Transport of $CO_2$ in blood

Both plasma and RBCs carry $CO_2$ in physical solution, as well as chemical combination.

**In Physical Solution**

Seven per cent of the $CO_2$ is in the dissolved form, the amount of which is much greater than that of dissolved $O_2$ because $CO_2$ is twenty times more soluble than $O_2$.

In plasma, $CO_2 + H_2O \rightarrow H_2CO_3$

In cells, in the presence of the enzyme carbonic anhydrase,

$$CO_2 + H_2O \rightleftharpoons H_2CO_3$$

$$H_2CO_3 \rightleftharpoons H^+ + HCO^-_3$$

Hb acts as a hydrogen acceptor and consequently, helps in the uptake of $CO_2$.

**In Chemical Combination:**

Ninety-three per cent of $CO_2$ is carried in chemical combination. Of this, 35 per cent is carried as carbamino compound and 65 per cent as bicarbonate ($HCO_3$).

*As carbamino compound:* In plasma, $CO_2$ combines with proteins to form carbamino compound. In the cells, it combines with the amine group of Hb, forming carbamino Hb. The amount of $CO_2$ carried in this form is small, but the speed of association and dissociation is very rapid. Therefore, it is important.

*As bicarbonate:* In plasma, $CO_2$ combines with plasma proteins, for example, Napr (proteinate) + $H_2CO_3$ $\rightarrow$ Hpr + $NaHCO_3$, and with phosphates.

In the cells, diffusion of $CO_2$ from the tissues to the RBCs brings about a very important chemical reaction. An enzyme, carbonic anhydrase, is present

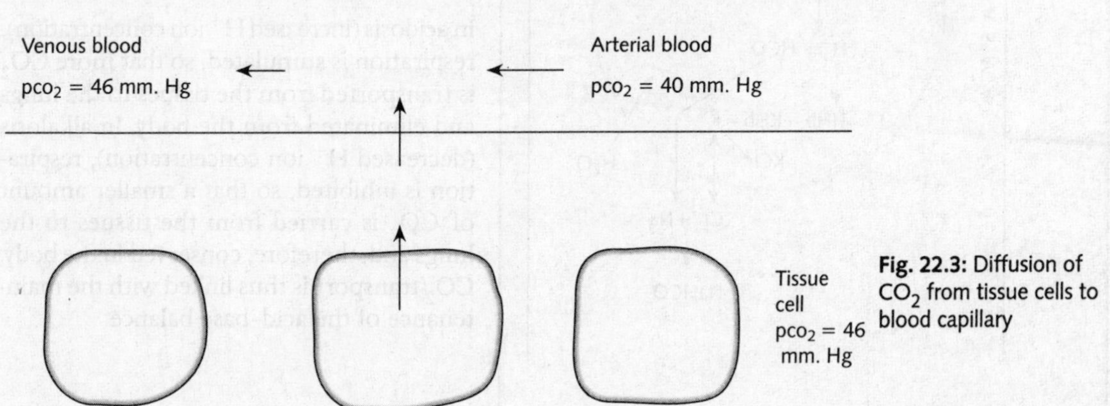


**Fig. 22.3:** Diffusion of $CO_2$ from tissue cells to blood capillary

in the RBCs. This enzyme helps in the rapid production of $H_2CO_3$. The hydration of $CO_2$ to carbonic acid is increased 5000- fold. Most of the $H_2CO_3$ formed in the cells dissociates into $H^+$ and $HCO_3^-$. $H^+$ combines with haemoglobin, as it is a powerful acid–base buffer.

As a result of ionic imbalance due to greater $HCO_3$ formation, $HCO_3^-$ ions move out of the cells into the plasma, along the concentration gradient. Chloride ions, in turn, pass into the cells to maintain electroneutrality. This phenomenon is called Hamburger's chloride shift. The shift of chloride into the cells increases the electrolyte concentration, raising the osmotic pressure of the cells. Therefore, water from plasma enters the cells, increasing their size. This is why the RBCs in venous blood are larger and more fragile than those in the arterial blood (Fig. 22.4).

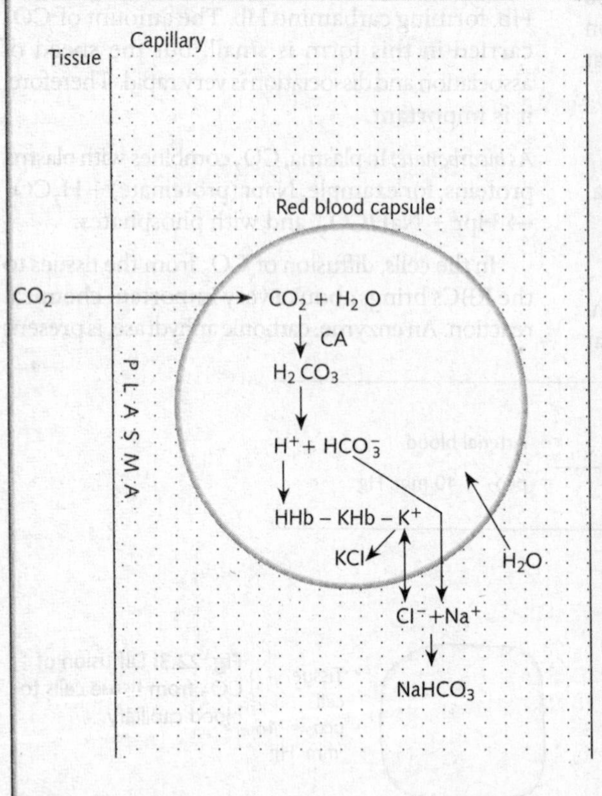


**Fig. 22.4:** The chloride shift

## Diffusion of $CO_2$ from pulmonary capillaries into alveoli

The $PCO_2$ of venous blood is 46 mmHg, and that of the alveoli is 40 mmHg. This pressure difference causes $CO_2$ to diffuse from the blood into the alveoli.

Out of 100 volumes of $CO_2$ evolved into the atmosphere, 72 per cent comes out from bicarbonates, 20 is dissociated from carbamino compound, and 8 from physical solution.

### Haldane's Effect

This is the effect of $O_2$ on $CO_2$ association and dissociation. In the lungs, binding of $O_2$ with haemoglobin tends to displace $CO_2$ from the blood. In the tissues, dissociation of $O_2$ from haemoglobin increases the uptake of $CO_2$ by the blood. This effect is more important at the level of the lungs.

## Rate of total $CO_2$ transport

At rest, about 200 ml of $CO_2$ is transported from the tissues to the lungs per minute. During severe exercise, as many as 4 l of $CO_2$ may be transported per minute. However, this does not bring about any significant changes in the pH of the blood because of the greater solubility and transport of $CO_2$ in different forms.

## Relationship of $CO_2$ carriage to acid–base balance

In acidosis (increased $H^+$ ion concentration), respiration is stimulated, so that more $CO_2$ is transported from the tissues to the lungs and eliminated from the body. In alkalosis (decreased $H^+$ ion concentration), respiration is inhibited, so that a smaller amount of $CO_2$ is carried from the tissues to the lungs and, therefore, conserved in the body. $CO_2$ transport is thus linked with the maintenance of the acid–base balance.

CHAPTER

# Regulation of Respiration

The normal rate of respiration in an adult is 12 to 18 per minute, with a tidal volume of about 500 ml. The rate and depth of respiration is adjusted according to the metabolic needs of the body, for example, the rate and depth of respiration go up with increased metabolic needs, as during exercise, and the arterial $O_2$ and $CO_2$ tensions are maintained in different situations.

Respiration is regulated in two ways, neural and chemical. The neural mechanisms generate rhythmic breathing, while the chemical ones regulate the required ventilatory volume, that is, that which is appropriate for the metabolic need, by changing the pattern of neural discharge to the respiratory muscles.

## NEURAL REGULATION

The activities of the muscles of respiration are regulated by the efferent nerves supplying the muscles. For example, the phrenic nerve supplies the diaphragm and the intercostal nerves supply the intercostal muscles. These nerves originate from the anterior horn cells of the spinal cord. The horn cells, in turn, are regulated by the discharge of impulses from the respiratory centre, which is located in the brainstem.

### Respiratory centre

The respiratory centre consists of a widely scattered group of nerve cells, located bilaterally in the brainstem, that is, pons and medulla. Three main groups of neurons have been identified (Fig. 23.1):

1. The medullary respiratory centre,
2. The apneustic centre, and
3. The pneumotaxic centre.

#### Medullary Respiratory Centre

This consists of two groups of neurons, the dorsal respiratory group (DRG) and the ventral respiratory group (VRG).

*Dorsal respiratory group:* This extends along approximately the entire length of the medulla. The basic rhythm of respiration is generated in the DRG neurons. They are intrinsically rhythmic and emit repetitive bursts of inspiratory action potentials. In normal respiration, they begin very weakly and increase steadily in a 'ramp' fashion for about 2 seconds. Then they abruptly cease for 3 seconds and begin again for the next respiratory cycle. This pattern is repeated.

The advantage of 'ramp' signals is that they cause a steady increase in the volume of the lungs during inspiration (Fig. 23.2).

*Ventral respiratory group:* This extends along approximately the entire length of the medulla, and is located anteriorly and laterally to the DRG. During normal, quiet breathing, VRG neurons remain almost totally inactive. When the respiratory drive for increased pulmonary ventilation becomes

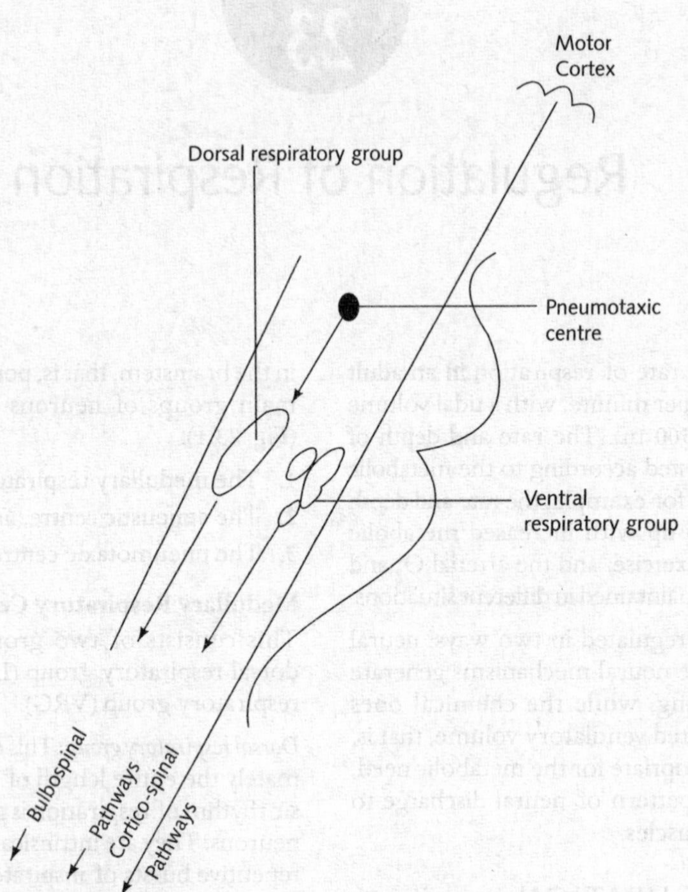


**Fig. 23.1:** The respiratory centre

greater than normal, the respiratory signals spill over from the DRG into the VRG. Some neurons in the VRG stimulate inspiration, while others cause expiration. Both types of neurons fire only during deep breathing. However, these neurons are more important in providing the powerful expiratory forces during expiration than in inspiration.

**Apneustic Centre**

This is situated in the lower part of the pons. Its exact role in the normal physiological state in man is uncertain. This centre sends signals to DRG neurons, which prevent 'switch-off' of the inspiratory ramp signals. Therefore, inspiration continues as long as 10 to 20 seconds, thus greatly overfilling the lungs.

**Pneumotaxic Centre**

This centre is situated bilaterally in the upper part of the pons. It transmits impulses continuously to the inspiratory area (DRG) and controls the 'switch-off' point of the inspiratory ramp, thus controlling the duration of the filling phase of the lung cycle. The main function of this centre is to limit inspiration. Whenever the depth of respiration increases, the respiratory rate slows down.

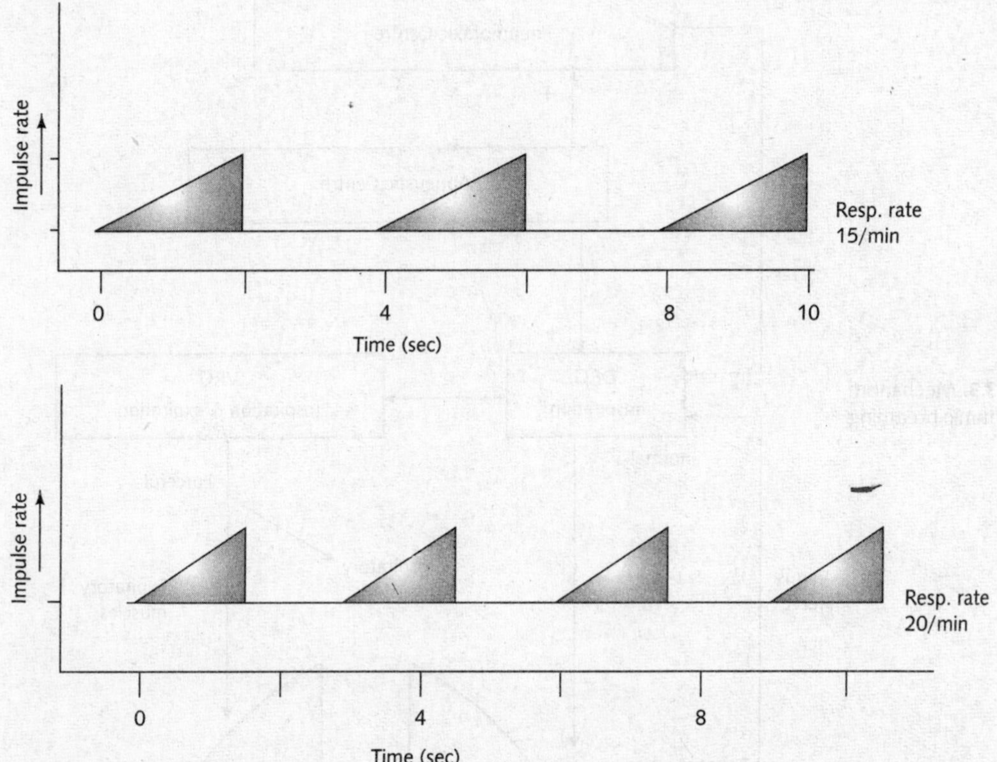


**Fig. 23.2:** The ramp signals in the medullary inspiratory neurons. The impulse discharge rate gradually increases and then comes to an end abruptly

### Mechanism of rhythmic respiration

Hypoxia stimulates the apneustic centre, and inspiration commences with the discharge of impulses from this centre to the inspiratory centre. At the same time, the apneustic centre sends impulses to the pneumotaxic centre which, in turn, sends inhibitory impulses to the inspiratory (DRG) centre. The latter, at the same time, receives inhibitory impulses from the vagus nerve as well, due to stimulation of the stretch receptors in the lungs during inflation. Influenced by a double negative feedback mechanism, the activity of the nerve cells of the inspiratory centre stops and expiration commences passively. The cycle is repeated automatically at the end of expiration since the vagal afferents and pneumotaxic centre are no longer active (Fig. 23.3).

## CHEMICAL REGULATION

### Factors influencing respiratory centre

The respiratory centre is influenced by (i) chemical factors, (ii) peripheral reflexes, and (iii) influences from higher centres.

**Chemical Regulation**

Tissue metabolism involves the utilization of $O_2$ and the release of $CO_2$, which, in turn, increases the hydrogen ion concentration of blood.

The ultimate goal of respiration is to maintain the proper concentration of $O_2$, $CO_2$ and $H^+$ in the tissues in various situations. The $PCO_2$ and $H^+$ concentration are better maintained than the $PO_2$. These agents modify the rate and depth of respiration (i) by directly acting on the respiratory centres, and (ii) by reflexly acting through the chemoreceptors of the carotid and aortic bodies.

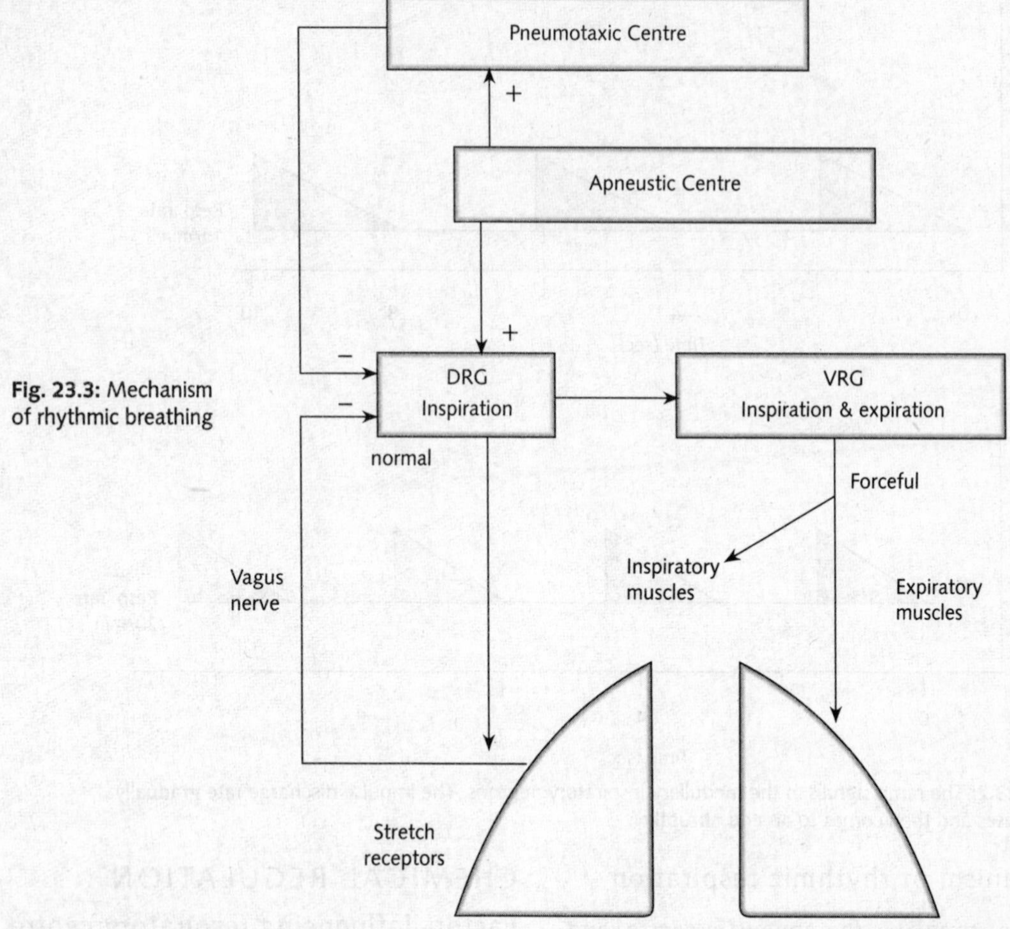


**Fig. 23.3:** Mechanism of rhythmic breathing

This is described as reflex or indirect chemical regulation.

*Direct Chemical Regulation:* An area which is very sensitive to the chemical changes in blood is the central chemosensitive zone. It is present bilaterally below the ventral surface of the medulla (Fig. 23.4). Changes in either the blood $PCO_2$ or $H^+$ concentration stimulate this area, which, in turn, excites the respiratory centre. However, changes in the $PO_2$ have virtually no direct effect on the respiratory centre and thus, do not really alter the respiratory drive.

Effect of $H^+$: An increased $H^+$ concentration strongly stimulates the neurons of the central chemosensitive zone. However, unfortunately, $H^+$ ions do not easily cross either the blood–brain barrier or the blood–CSF barrier. Therefore, changes in the $H^+$ ion concentration of arterial blood hardly have any effect on the chemosensitive neurons, whereas changes in the arterial $PCO_2$ do stimulate these neurons, even though $CO_2$ stimulates them indirectly through $H^+$ ions.

Effect of $CO_2$: An increased $PCO_2$ has a very potent effect on the chemosensitive area. It stimulates it, increasing pulmonary ventilation via $H^+$ ions.

$CO_2$ freely passes through the blood–brain and blood–CSF barriers, unlike $H^+$ ions, and the following reactions occur:

$CO_2 + H_2O = H_2CO_3$ and $H_2CO_3 = H^+ + HCO_3^-$

Therefore, a raised level of $CO_2$ in the blood leads to an increase in the level of $CO_2$ in the medullary interstitial fluid and CSF. This results in an increase in the $H^+$ concentration in the chemosensitive area, an increase that is greater than when the blood $H^+$ concentration increases. Hence, the activity of the respiratory centre is affected more by changes in the blood $PCO_2$ than in the blood $H^+$ concentration.

Pons
Inspiratory centre
Central chemoreceptors
Medulla Oblongata

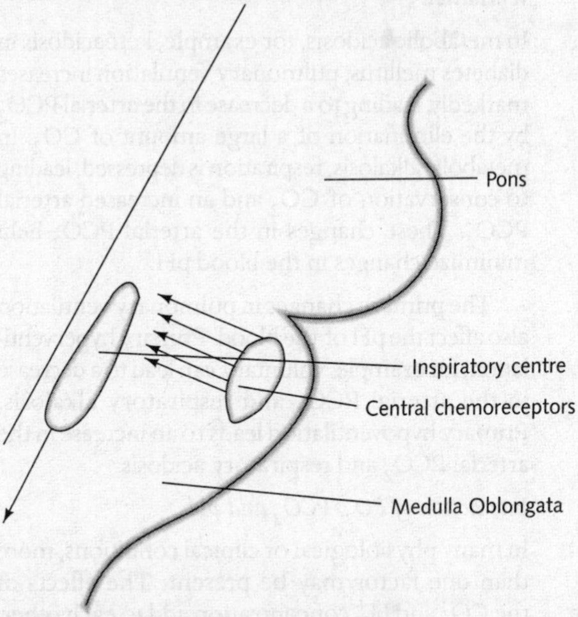

**Fig. 23.4:** The central chemosensitive zone

The direct effects of both $CO_2$ and $H^+$ on the respiratory centre are about seven times more powerful than their indirect effects through peripheral chemoreceptors, though the latter effect is more rapid.

*Reflex or Indirect Chemical Regulation:* This is brought about by changes in the concentrations of $CO_2$, $H^+$ and $O_2$ in the arterial blood, through peripheral chemoreceptors. The latter are special nervous chemoreceptors located in several areas outside the brain, and they detect the changes in these areas. They are mainly carotid and aortic bodies, and they are few in number in relation to the other arteries (Fig. 23.5).

The carotid bodies are located bilaterally in the bifurcation of the common carotid arteries, and their afferent fibres pass through the glossopharyngeal nerves to the DRG neurons. The aortic bodies are located along the arch of the aorta. Their afferent fibres pass through the vagus nerves, again to the DRG neurons.

Both these chemoreceptor bodies receive a large supply of blood and are, therefore, constantly exposed to alterations in the $PO_2$, $PCO_2$ and $H^+$ concentration of arterial blood. Stimulation of these chemoreceptors increases pulmonary ventilation.

Effect of $PO_2$: A decrease in the $PO_2$ is the most potent stimulus for the peripheral chemoreceptors.

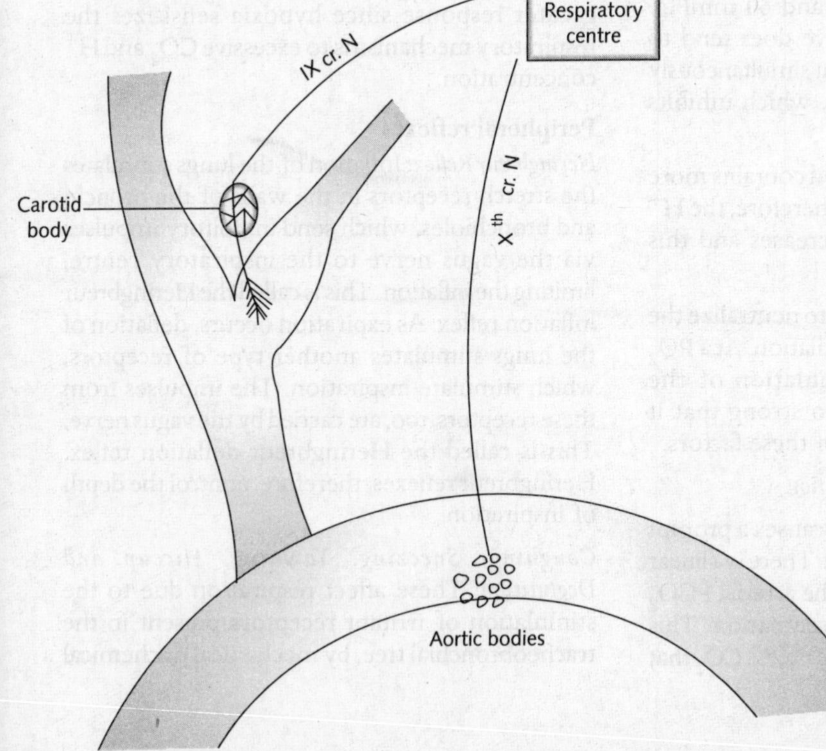


**Fig. 23.5:** Peripheral chemoreceptors

Effect of $PCO_2$: An increase in the $PCO_2$ stimulates the peripheral chemoreceptors, but their sensitivity to $CO_2$ is far less than that of the central chemoreceptors.

Effect of $H^+$: An increase in the $H^+$ ion concentration stimulates the peripheral chemoreceptors.

The effect of an increased $PCO_2$ and $H^+$ concentration on the peripheral chemoreceptors is much faster than their direct effect. An increased $H^+$ concentration, because of factors other than an increased $PCO_2$ (metabolic acidosis), stimulates only the peripheral chemoreceptors as $H^+$ can easily enter carotid and aortic bodies. During exercise, there is a simultaneous increase in the $PCO_2$, increase in the $H^+$ concentration and decrease in $O_2$. The combined effect of this is an extremely strong ventilatory drive.

*Effect of hypoxia on pulmonary ventilation*

Hypoxia stimulates respiration. However, pulmonary ventilation increases only when the arterial $PO_2$ falls below 60 mmHg, although peripheral chemoreceptors begin to discharge when the arterial $PO_2$ is just below 100 mmHg. That is, pulmonary ventilation does not increase between an arterial $PO_2$ of 100 mmHg and 60 mmHg. This is because the hypoxic drive does tend to increase pulmonary ventilation, but simultaneously causes a decrease in the $PCO_2$, which inhibits respiration.

Also, due to hypoxia, the blood contains more deoxygenated Hb than oxyHb. Therefore, the $H^+$ concentration of the blood decreases and this inhibits respiration.

Thus, both these factors tend to neutralize the hypoxic drive on pulmonary ventilation. At a $PO_2$ of below 60 mmHg, the stimulation of the peripheral chemoreceptors is so strong that it overrides the inhibitory effects of these factors.

*Effect of $CO_2$ on pulmonary ventilation*

An increase in the arterial $PCO_2$ causes a prompt increase in pulmonary ventilation. There is a linear relation between an increase in the arterial $PCO_2$ and an increase in pulmonary ventilation. This helps in the prompt removal of the excess $CO_2$ that is produced. $CO_2$ stimulates pulmonary ventilation mainly through the central chemoreceptors.

*Effect of arterial $H^+$ concentration on pulmonary ventilation*

In metabolic acidosis, for example, ketoacidosis in diabetes mellitus, pulmonary ventilation increases markedly, leading to a decrease in the arterial $PCO_2$ by the elimination of a large amount of $CO_2$. In metabolic alkalosis, respiration is depressed, leading to conservation of $CO_2$ and an increased arterial $PCO_2$. These changes in the arterial $PCO_2$ help minimize changes in the blood pH.

The primary changes in pulmonary ventilation also affect the pH of the blood. Primary hyperventilation, for example, voluntary, can lead to a decrease in the arterial $PCO_2$ and respiratory alkalosis. Primary hypoventilation leads to an increase in the arterial $PCO_2$ and respiratory acidosis.

*Interaction of $PO_2$, $PCO_2$ and pH*

In many physiological or clinical conditions, more than one factor may be present. The effects of the $CO_2$ and $H^+$ concentration add to each other, while hypoxia (decreased $PO_2$) and hypercapnoea (increased $PCO_2$) together produce a much greater response since hypoxia sensitizes the respiratory mechanisms to excessive $CO_2$ and $H^+$ concentration.

**Peripheral reflexes**

*Heringbreur Reflex:* Inflation of the lungs stimulates the stretch receptors in the walls of the bronchi and bronchioles, which send inhibitory impulses via the vagus nerve to the inspiratory centre, limiting the inflation. This is called the Heringbreur inflation reflex. As expiration occurs, deflation of the lungs stimulates another type of receptors, which stimulate inspiration. The impulses from these receptors, too, are carried by the vagus nerve. This is called the Heringbreur deflation reflex. Heringbreur reflexes, therefore, control the depth of inspiration.

*Coughing, Sneezing, Yawning, Hiccup and Deglutition:* These affect respiration due to the stimulation of irritant receptors present in the tracheobronchial tree, by mechanical or chemical irritants such as dust particles and irritant gases.

*Chemoreceptor Reflex:* Chemoreceptors are situated peripherally in carotid and aortic bodies. They are stimulated by an increased $PCO_2$ and decreased $PO_2$, and this stimulates them to send impulses to the respiratory centre.

*Baroreceptor Reflex:* Baroreceptors are located in the carotid and aortic sinus. A rise in the blood pressure stimulates the vasomotor centre (VMC). Impulses from the VMC spill over to the respiratory centre, stimulating it.

*Proprioceptors in Joints and Muscles:* These stimulate the respiratory centre, as during exercise, to increase pulmonary ventilation.

**Influences from higher centres**

The cerebral cortex is responsible for voluntary control over respiration. One may hold one's breath or overbreathe for a short period. Voluntary control may be mediated by a pathway which originates in the neocortex and ends directly on the respiratory neurons.

The hypothalamus and limbic system also influence respiration. Pain and emotions influence the rate and depth of breathing because afferents from the limbic system reach the respiratory neurons (Fig. 23.6).

*Breath-holding:* A person can stop breathing voluntarily for about 50 to 70 seconds, after which

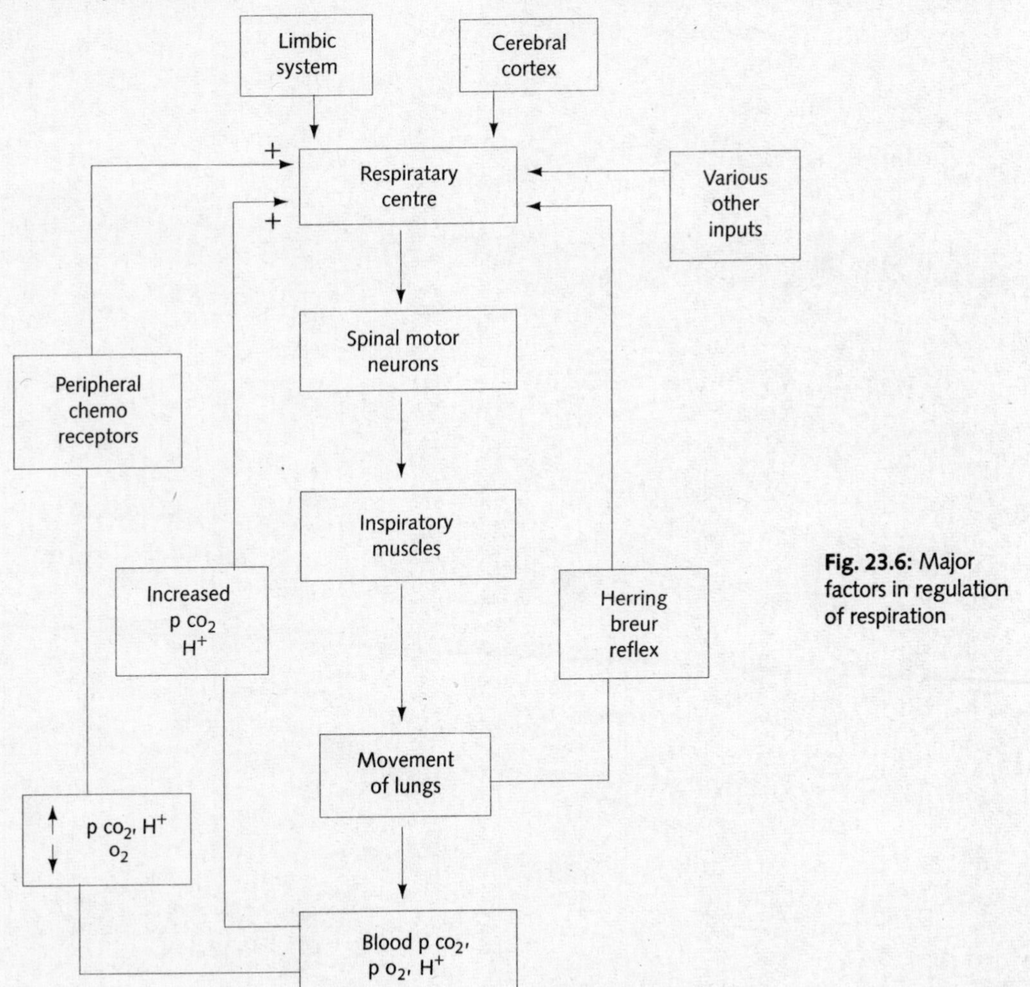


**Fig. 23.6:** Major factors in regulation of respiration

he/she has an uncontrollable desire to breathe. This is known as the breaking point, which is brought about by a decrease in the arterial $PO_2$ and an increase in the arterial $PCO_2$. Therefore, the breath-holding time can be prolonged by 15 to 20 seconds by prior hyperventilation, which lowers the arterial $PCO_2$, or up to 5 minutes by prior inhalation of $O_2$.

*Effects of Hyperventilation:* A two- to five-fold increase inpulmonary ventilationi may be maintained voluntarily in and may also occur in residents of high-altitude areas or clinically hypoxic patients. Since the hyperventilation exceeds the metabolic requirements of the body, a decrease occurs in the alveolar and arterial $PCO_2$.

The effects are as follows:

1. Respiratory alkalosis: A decreased $CO_2$:$HCO_3$ ratio increases the pH of blood to 7.5 or 7.6.
2. Renal changes: A decreased arterial $PCO_2$ decreases $H^+$ secretion in the kidney tubule and consequently, the absorption of $HCO_3^-$ in the proximal tubule, resulting in the excretion of alkaline urine.
3. Neurological changes: Respiratory alkalosis produces features of hypocalcaemic tetany, for example, spasms.

CHAPTER 24

# Respiratory Abnormalities

## HYPOXIA

Hypoxia is the reduction of $O_2$ in the body, resulting in an insufficient supply of $O_2$ to the tissues.

### Types of hypoxia

There are four types of hypoxia: (i) hypoxic hypoxia (formerly called anoxic anoxia), (ii) anaemic hypoxia, (iii) stagnant hypoxia, and (iv) histotoxic hypoxia.

#### Hypoxic Hypoxia

This is the most common type of hypoxia. There is defective oxygenation in the lungs, resulting in inadequate haemoglobin (Hb) saturation. This condition may be caused by any of the following:

1. High altitude (over 10,000 feet): The tension of $O_2$ in the atmosphere is low, compared to areas of lower altitude.
2. Dilution of inspired gas with inert gases, for example, helium during anaesthesia.
3. Lung diseases, for example, pneumonia, lung infection or pulmonary oedema.
4. Right to left cardiac shunt: Impure (deoxygenated) blood is mixed with pure (oxygenated) blood and, therefore, the $PO_2$ of the arterial blood falls significantly.

#### Anaemic Hypoxia

In this type of hypoxia, the amount of Hb available for oxygenation is lower than normal. It may be caused by severe anaemia. Carbon monoxide (CO) poisoning is another cause. CO has a much greater affinity for Hb than does $O_2$. Therefore, all the Hb is used up in combination with CO, to form carboxyHb, and less is available for oxygenation. Nitrite poisoning can also cause anaemic hypoxia. Nitrite combines with Hb, and reduced Hb gets converted to methHb.

#### Stagnant Hypoxia

In this type of hypoxia, the amount of $O_2$ delivered to the tissues is reduced because of slow circulation.

The causes of general hypoxia include congestive cardiac failure (CCF), in which the heart fails and does not pump blood efficiently. Shock can also cause it.

The cause of local hypoxia is the obstruction of an artery to a particular part, for example, coronary or cerebral thrombosis or embolism.

#### Histotoxic Hypoxia

In histotoxic hypoxia, because of the damage to the respiratory enzymes, for example, cytochrome oxidase, the cells cannot utilize the $O_2$ supplied by the blood. This condition may be caused by cyanide poisoning, which damages the cell enzymes, or barbiturate (sleeping pills) or narcotic poisoning.

## Effects of hypoxia

Hypoxia has wide-ranging effects, which are described below. It affects various systems. The effects can be seen once the $O_2$ level drops below 13 per cent. If the drop is rapid, the symptoms appear immediately.

**On the Nervous System**

Hypoxia causes mild to severe headaches, depending on individual reactions. It may also cause depression, as well as lethargy and drowsiness. It affects the reflexes and loss of self-control is the result. Change in mood is another consequence, and the person experiences euphoria, that is, a false sense of well-being. Hypoxia also causes weakness and fatigue.

**On the Digestive System**

Hypoxia gives rise to anorexia, that is, loss of appetite. It also causes nausea and vomiting.

**On the Circulatory System**

The circulatory system is affected by hypoxia in two ways. One is tachycardia, which is an increase in the heart rate. The other is fluctuations in the blood pressure. The peripheral mechanism causes an increase in the blood pressure, while the direct mechanism causes a fall in the blood pressure.

**On the Respiratory System**

Hypoxia leads to hyperventilation because of the increased respiratory rate. It also gives rise to alkalosis, which is the result of the $CO_2$ wash-out that occurs in this condition.

**On the Excretory System**

The output of urine decreases in hypoxia. Whatever urine is produced is alkaline (normal urine is acidic), as the blood is alkaline in hypoxia.

Unconsciousness and death may occur with carbon monoxide and cyanide poisoning. Loss of cabin pressure in an aircraft at an altitude of 30,000 feet has the same effect as it causes hypoxia.

*Common terminology*

| | | |
|---|---|---|
| *Apnoea* | : | Temporary stoppage of breathing—voluntary/involuntary. |
| *Apneustis* | : | Deep prolonged inspiration. |
| *Dyspnoea* | : | Difficulty in breathing, e.g., in asthma. |
| *Tachypnoea* | : | Hyperventilation. |
| *Eupnoea* | : | Normal respiratory rate 16–18/min., 500 ml TV, and normal respiratory patterns. |

## CYANOSIS

Cyanosis is a clinical condition in which the skin and mucous membranes assume a bluish colour. It may be local or general. When general, it is best seen on the lips, tip of the nose, cheeks, ears, hands, feet and fingertips.

Cyanosis is caused by an alteration in the character of the blood circulating in the capillaries. Hence, when blood is pressed out of a particular part, cyanosis disappears temporarily. The dark colour is due to reduced or deoxygenated Hb.

The degree of cyanosis depends on the absolute amount of reduced Hb present in the blood. However, it may also be due to the presence of other Hb derivatives of a darker colour (e.g., methaemoglobin and sulphaemoglobin).

At least 5 g of reduced Hb must be present (normally, the capillary blood contains 2 to 2.5 g of deoxygenated Hb) for cyanosis to occur. Therefore, there should be $5 \times 1.34$ or 6.7 ml less of oxygen per 100 ml of blood before cyanosis can be produced. In an anaemic patient with less than 5 g of Hb (i.e., below 33 per cent Hb), cyanosis is not possible.

The rate of blood flow through the skin also determines the rate of cyanosis, as does the thickness of the skin. The thinner the skin, the easier it is to see the bluish colour of the capillary blood. This is why cyanosis is seen more clearly on the lips and finger nails, for example.

### Factors causing cyanosis

Hypoxia, or inadequate supply of $O_2$ to the tissues, may cause cyanosis. It is seen in hypoxic and stagnant hypoxia. An admixture of venous and arterial blood also causes cyanosis. Such an admixture occurs in certain cardiac diseases, in which there is direct communication between the right and left sides of the heart. Some examples are patent interventricular septum and patent foramen ovale (interatrial septum). Cyanosis is also seen in newborn babies with thin skin, in highly vascular portions of the body, for example, the heels.

Greater reduction of oxyhaemoglobin occurs with local chilling, or venous obstruction, which retards the local circulation and allows more time for greater reduction of Hb. A high metabolic rate and, therefore, a higher utilization of $O_2$ in a particular part can also result in increased reduction of oxyhaemoglobin.

## ASPHYXIA (SUFFOCATION)

Asphyxia occurs with improper aeration or improper ventilation, which lead to a decrease in the $PO_2$ (hypoxia) and an increase in the $PCO_2$ (hypercapnia). If asphyxia continues for a long time, it produces a series of manifestations. It can be tolerated for 3 to 5 minutes and if the cause is not removed, death occurs.

Asphyxia may be the result of drowning or obstruction to the respiratory passage, allergy, choking (i.e., if some article or eatable gets stuck in the throat), or strangulation.

### Stages of asphyxia

**First Stage**

Hyperventilation, the first stage of asphyxia, lasts for 1 minute. The symptoms are an increase in the rate and depth of respiration. Also, inspiration and expiration are initially equal, but later, the expiration phase is prolonged. Dyspnoea is another symptom. These symptoms are caused by an increase in the $PCO_2$ level.

**Second Stage**

This is known as the central excitatory stage (CES). It lasts for 1 to 2 minutes. It is characterized by convulsions, that is, sudden contraction of muscles all over the body. Expiration is prolonged and vasoconstriction occurs, leading to an increase in the blood pressure. Pupillary constriction is seen and the reflexes are exaggerated (hyperreflexia). There is increased salivation. All the sphincters give way, so urination occurs. The $PCO_2$ goes up, while the $PO_2$ falls below 13 per cent. Acidosis (lactic acid accumulation) occurs, causing muscle contractions and hence, convulsions.

**Third Stage**

This is the central inhibitory stage (CIS). It lasts for 1 to 2 minutes. The symptoms are pupillary dilation, slow and deep inspiration, and spasmodic inspiration, that is, gasping, which ultimately leads to death. This happens because the decrease in $O_2$ leads to depression of the respiratory centre.

## ARTIFICIAL RESPIRATION

Artificial respiration is given when the heart continues to beat and respiration fails, so that the respiratory centre is given a chance to revive its normal activity.

There are several indications for artificial respiration. Acute respiratory failure may be due to acute asphyxia, in which artificial respiration is a life-saving measure. Drowning, electrocution, anaesthetic accidents and carbon monoxide poisoning may also cause acute respiratory failure, which can be treated effectively by artificial respiration.

Chronic ventilatory failure, for example, paralysis of the respiratory muscles due to viral infection (as in polio), is another indication for artificial respiration.

### Methods

Several methods can be used, depending on whether respiratory failure is acute or chronic.

**Mouth-to-mouth Breathing**

This is the most simple and effective method used in acute respiratory failure. The victim is placed in the supine position. The neck is extended with one hand and the forehead pressed with the other. The victim's mouth is completely covered by the operator's mouth and the nostrils are pinched. The operator blows into the victim's mouth 12

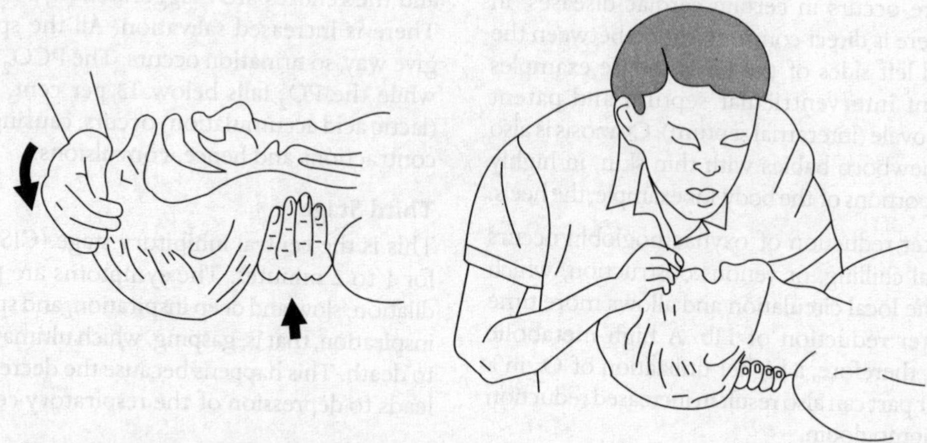

Fig. 24.1: Mouth-to-mouth artificial respiration

to 18 times per minute, with approximately double the tidal volume. Following each inflation, he/she takes his/her mouth away so that the victim can expirate passively (Fig. 24.1).

**Mechanical Respirators**

These are used on patients with chronic ventilatory failure. They are metallic airtight containers which cover the chest. Intermittent negative pressure is applied with the help of a mechanical device. This helps expand the chest. Negative and positive pressure is applied alternately to produce periodic inflation or deflation of the lungs (iron lung).

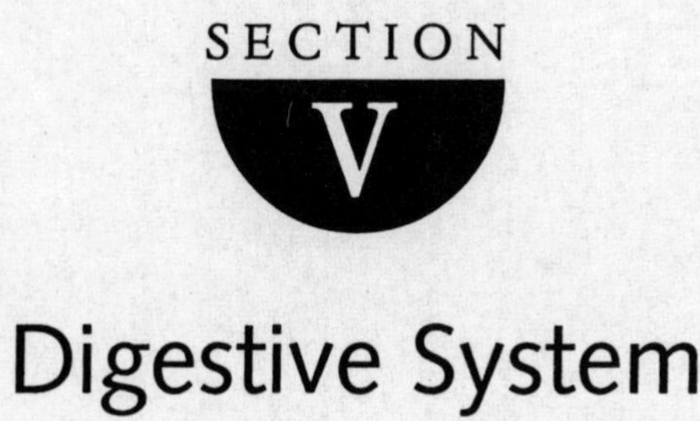


# Digestive System

CHAPTER

25

# Functional Organization

All living organisms require energy to carry out the daily activities. This energy is provided by food, which consists of complex organic substances. The digestive system deals with the reception of food and its preparation, for assimilation by the body.

The adult gastrointestinal tract (GI tract) is a 5-metre-long tube of variable cross section. It extends from the mouth to the anus and is open at both ends. The alimentary canal (Fig. 25.1) consists of the mouth, pharynx, oesophagus, stomach, coils of the small intestine, large intestine, and the rectum and anal canal. The large intestine consists of the caecum, the appendix and the ascending, transverse, descending and sigmoid colon. The mouth contains teeth, which masticate the food, and the tongue, which gives us the sense of taste and helps in swallowing.

The accessory glands of the digestive system are the salivary glands, which secrete saliva; the exocrine part of the pancreas, which secretes pancreatic juice; and the liver, which secretes bile. All these juices are important for digestion and are poured into the GI tract. Some parts of the GI tract contain lymphoid tissue, which provides

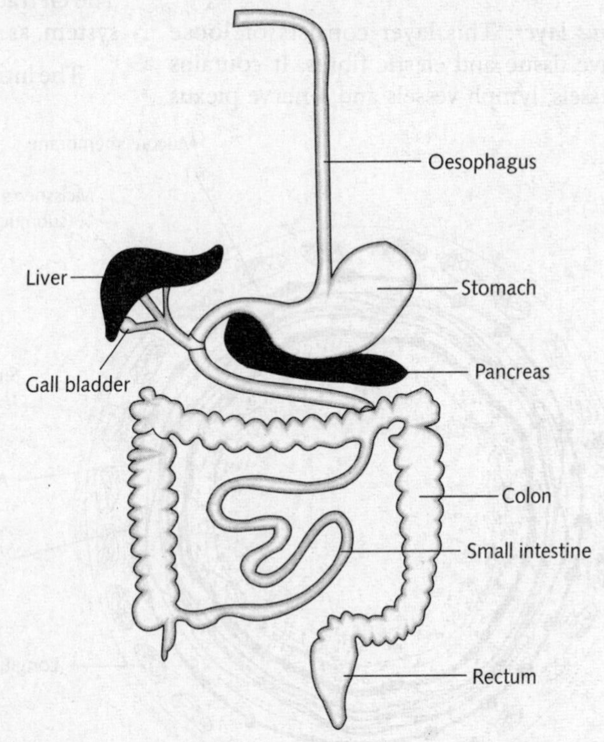


**Fig. 25.1:** Digestive system

immunity against microorganisms trying to enter the body from the GI tract.

## FUNCTIONAL ANATOMY OF GI TRACT

The wall of the gut is formed by four layers of tissue (Fig. 25.2). These are, from the outside inwards:

1. The serous layer,
2. The muscle layer,
3. The submucous layer, and
4. The mucous layer.

*Serous layer*: All organs in the abdomen are covered by a serous membrane, which is made of connective tissue, called the peritoneum.

*Muscle layer*: This consists of two layers of smooth muscle—the outer longitudinal and the inner circular layers. In between these, there are blood vessels, lymph vessels and a plexus of sympathetic and parasympathetic nerves, called the myenteric or Auerbach's plexus.

*Submucous layer*: This layer consists of loose connective tissue and elastic fibres. It contains blood vessels, lymph vessels and a nerve plexus called Meissner's plexus. The latter contains sympathetic and parasympathetic nerves.

*Mucous layer*: This consists of the surface epithelium, lamina propria and muscularis mucosa.

The surface epithelium lines the luminal surface. The lamina propria, or connective tissue layer, contains tubular exocrine glands, small blood vessels, lymphatics and nerve fibres. The muscularis mucosa is a thin layer of smooth muscle, which separates the mucosa from the underlying tissue. The luminal surface is highly convoluted to increase the surface area for absorption.

The functions of the mucosa are protection, secretion and absorption. From the lips to the end of the oesophagus, there is stratified squamous epithelium. From the stomach to the anal canal, it is composed of columnar cells and in the anal canal, it is stratified epithelium.

## INNERVATION OF THE GUT

The GI tract is innervated by an intrinsic nervous system, as well as by the extrinsic nerves.

The intrinsic nervous system consists of (i) the

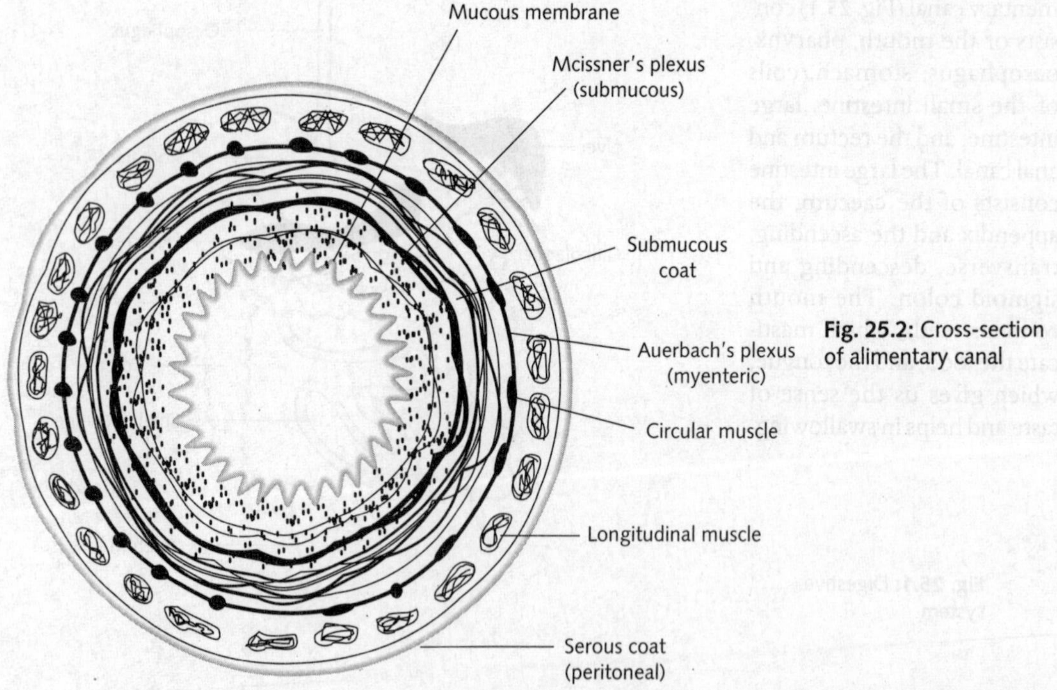


**Fig. 25.2:** Cross-section of alimentary canal

Meissner's plexus in the submucosa and (ii) the Auerbach's plexus in the muscular layer. These consist of neurons that form connections with other neurons within the plexus, and terminate near the smooth muscle fibres or the glands of the gut. The two plexuses are also interconnected with each other and, therefore, produce a widespread response in the GI tract.

The Meissner's plexus mainly controls the secretory activity and the blood flow of the gut. It also serves a sensory function, receiving signals from the mucosal epithelium and the stretch receptors in the wall of the alimentary canal.

The myenteric plexus mainly controls the motility of the gut. Its stimulation increases the tone of the gut wall, as well as the rate and intensity of its rhythmic contractions.

The intrinsic nervous system contains a vast variety of neurons. It has a number of neurotransmitters, for example, acetylcholine, norepinephrine, vasoactive intestinal polypeptide (VIP), substance-P and somatostatin. The extrinsic nerves are the parasympathetic and sympathetic nerves.

The parasympathetic fibres to the gut, extending from the oesophagus to the large intestine, pass via the vagus nerve, which also supplies the pancreas and gall bladder. The distal half of the large intestine receives parasympathetic fibres through the pelvic nerves. Stimulation of the parasympathetic nerves increases the motility and secretory activity of the GI tract.

The sympathetic fibres to the gut are supplied via the splanchnic nerves. Stimulation of the sympathetic nerves causes vasoconstriction and inhibition of the motility in the gut.

### Regulation of GI motility and secretion

The receptors of the GI tract are present in its mucosa. They are stimulated by distension of the gut by the luminal contents, acidity of the chyme, osmolality of the chyme, as well as the products of carbohydrate, protein and fat digestion, for example, peptides and fatty acids.

The stimulation of these receptors produces reflexes whose effector cells are located in the gut itself, for example, the smooth muscle and exocrine glands. The reflex activities maintain conditions that are optimal for digestion and the absorption of foodstuff.

### Neural Regulation

The intrinsic nervous system regulates the motility and secretory activity of the GI tract.

The basic propulsive movement of the GI tract depends on the integrity of the intrinsic nervous system. Peristaltic activity can, therefore, be modified by the mechano-, chemo- and osmoreceptors present in the mucosa. These sensory signals, arising from one part of the gut, can modify secretory activity in another part of the gut.

Extrinsic innervation is involved in the regulation of GI motility and secretion in response to changes in the environment, for example, emotions, taste and smell. It is also involved in the long-loop reflexes of the gut.

## HORMONAL REGULATION

Gastrointestinal secretions and motility are, to some extent, regulated by local hormones. Hormone-secreting cells are scattered in the epithelium of the gut. The epithelium of the mucosa responds to certain chemical substances in food and releases a local hormone which enters the blood circulation. Through the circulation, it reaches the target tissue in the GI tract, where it acts. Gastrointestinal hormones have two characteristics:

1. Each hormone may affect more than one target tissue, and
2. Each target organ may respond to more than one GI hormone.

TABLE: 25.1

Action of various gastrointestinal hormones

| *Hormone* | *Source* | *Amino acid residues* | *Action* | | | | | | |
|---|---|---|---|---|---|---|---|---|---|
| | | | Gastric secretion | Gastric motility | Pancreatic secretion | Bile secretion | Gall bladder contraction | Small intestine secretion | Small intestine motility |
| 1. Gastrin | 'G' cells of gastric antrum | 14, 17, 34 | ↑ Gastric acid, pepsin and intrinsic factor | ↑ | ↑ Secretion of water, electrolytes, insulin | – | – | – | ↑ |
| 2. Cholecystokinin Pancreozymin (CCK- PZ) | 'T' cells of duodenum and jejunum | 8, 12, 33, 39, 58 | – | ↓ | Secretion of enzymes | – | ↑ | – | ↑ |
| 3. Secretin | 'S' cells of upper small intestine | 27 | ↓ | – | ↑ Bicarbonate secretion | ↑ | – | ↑ | – |
| 4. Somatostatin | 'D' cells of stomach and islets of Langerhans | 14 | ↓ | ↓ | ↓ | – | ↓ | – | – |
| 5. Vasoactive intestinal polypeptide (VIP) | | 28 | ↓ | ↓ | ↑ Bicarbonate secretion | – | – | ↑ Water, electrolyte secretion | ↓ |

*(Table contd....)*

(Table 25.1 contd.)

TABLE: 25.1

Action of various gastrointestinal hormones

| *Hormone* | *Source* | *Amino acid residues* | *Action* | | | | | | |
|---|---|---|---|---|---|---|---|---|---|
| | | | Gastric secretion | Gastric motility | Pancreatic secretion | Bile secretion | Gall bladder contraction | Small intestine secretion | Small intestine motility |
| 6. Gastric inhibitory peptide (GIP) | Upper parts of small intest. | 43 | ↓ | ↓ | – | – | – | ↑ | ↓ |
| 7. Motilin | Duodenum | 22 | – | ↑ | – | – | – | – | ↑ |

↑ = increase
↓ = decrease
– = no action

CHAPTER

26

# Movements of GI Tract

Digestion is a process by which complex food material is broken down into simple particles, so that it can be absorbed and assimilated. It is of two types, mechanical and chemical.

In mechanical or physical digestion, food is broken down into small particles. In chemical digestion, various enzymes present in the digestive juices act on the complex food and convert it into the simplest form so that it can be easily absorbed.

The movements of the GI tract constitute mechanical or physical digestion. They are mastication, deglutition, movements of the stomach, small intestine and large intestine, and defaecation.

There are two types of movements, neurogenic and myogenic. The former are brought about by nervous control, while the latter are brought about by smooth muscles which are independent of nervous control. In addition, there are passive movements, which are neither neurogenic nor myogenic in nature.

### Purpose of GI movements

GI movements serve a number of important functions. Food is converted into fine particles because of GI movements such as mastication and segmentation of the small intestine. Peristalsis, a very important process, helps the onward passage of food in the alimentary canal.

Movements like mastication and movements of the stomach and small intestine cause thorough mixing of food with juices, and thus aid in the process of digestion. GI movements also help in the absorption of food, for example, from the stomach, small intestine and large intestine (which absorbs water).

Another important function served by GI movements is the maintenance of the alimentary tract in an active and normal condition. Active circulation of the blood and lymph is ensured by the movements of the stomach and small and large intestines.

GI movements help excrete waste products from the food and the body itself, and the undigested and unabsorbed part of food in the form of faeces.

## MASTICATION

The preliminary stage of motor function is mastication or chewing. This is the first mechanical process to which food is subjected in the GI tract. It is a process by which the food taken into the mouth is crushed under the grinding action of the teeth. The food is moved around in the mouth by the movements of the tongue and the muscles of mastication.

The teeth are designed for chewing. The anterior teeth or incisors cut the food like a sharp knife, while the molars grind it. The difference in their functions arises from the fact that the pressure produced between the two sets of incisors is only about 55 lb, while that between the molars is about 200 lb.

Mastication is mostly a reflex act, but can also be carried out voluntarily. Sensory stimulation of the mouth brings about rhythmic movements of the jaws via a mastication centre in the reticular formation of the medulla. Other areas of the brain, such as the amygdala, hypothalamus and taste and smell areas in the cerebral cortex, also send impulses to the medullary centre.

The chewing reflex is initiated by the pressure of the food in the mouth. This pressure stimulates the mechanical receptors in the oral mucosa. Afferents are carried mainly by the fifth cranial nerve, and also by the seventh and ninth cranial nerves, to the mastication centre. This causes reflex inhibition of the muscles of mastication, which allows the lower jaw to drop, opening the mouth. This is brought about by digastric and mylohyoid muscles, with the help of gravity.

The drop initiates a stretch reflex of the jaw muscles (e.g., the masseters, temporalis and pterygoids, which are supplied by the fifth cranial nerve). This leads to rebound contraction, which automatically raises the jaw, causing the teeth to close and exert their crushing effect.

This compresses the food against the mucous membrane of the mouth, which stimulates the tactile receptors of the mouth, inhibits the jaw muscles once again, and allows the jaw to drop and rebound. This is repeated rhythmically again and again until the food is broken down into small particles.

The rotatory movements of the molars are carried out by the pterygoid muscles, which make the jaws move sideways. The tongue muscles (supplied by the twelfth cranial nerve) move inside the mouth. The muscles of the oropharynx (supplied by the ninth cranial nerve) and the cheek muscles (supplied by the seventh cranial nerve) also move.

Thus, mastication is caused by alternate contraction and relaxation of the muscles involved in the movement of the lower jaw, aided by the muscles of the tongue, lips and cheeks. As a result of this process, coarse food is crushed into fine particles so that it can be swallowed easily.

### Purpose of mastication

Mastication serves a number of important functions, one of which is aiding the process of swallowing. Due to the teeth, the food in the mouth is broken down into small particles. These small bits are moistened with plenty of saliva and converted into a round, semi-solid mass, called the bolus. The first stage of the swallowing of the bolus is further facilitated by the lubricating action of saliva, which is squeezed out from the ducts during the process of chewing.

Mastication helps prevent injury to the mucous membrane. By the grinding action of the teeth, the hard materials in food are broken down into small fragments. The food is also softened. This ensures that the mucous membrane is not damaged.

One of the major purposes served by mastication is facilitation of digestion. Chewing breaks the cellulose covering of raw vegetables, cereals and fruit. The breaking down of food into smaller masses increases its surface area, making for more effective enzyme action, which takes place only on the surface of food. In addition, the movements of the tongue and cheek help in the thorough mixing of food with saliva.

Mastication stimulates the taste buds. During chewing, the secretion of saliva helps dissolve the food material, a process that is required for the stimulation of the sensation of taste. Finally, mastication helps in the secretion of other digestive juices, such as gastric juice.

## DEGLUTITION (SWALLOWING)

Deglutition is the process by which food is passed from the oral cavity into the stomach. It starts after mastication is complete, that is, when the food has been converted into a bolus. Deglutition

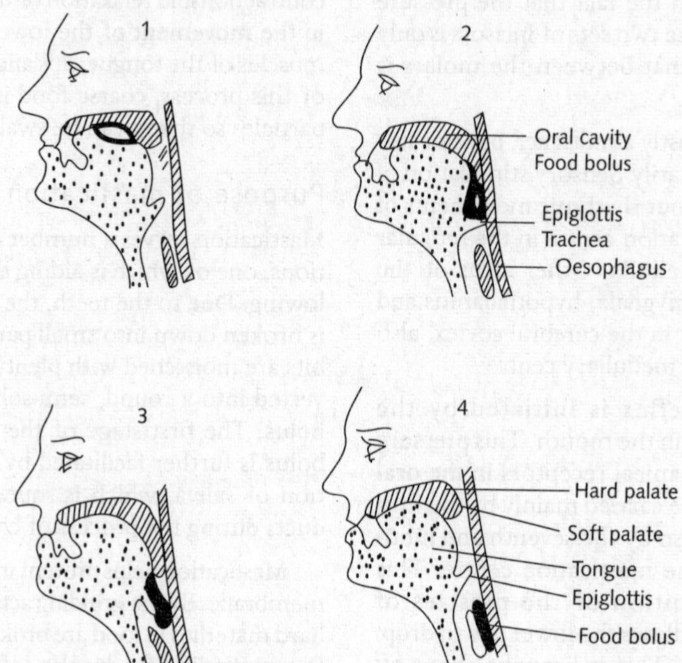


**Fig. 26.1:** Deglutition: Movement of the food bolus in different phases

may be divided into the following three stages (Fig. 26.1):

1. Oral stage: When the food is taken into the mouth, swallowing is initiated. This stage is voluntary.
2. Pharyngeal stage: This involves the passage of food through the pharynx, that is, movement of the food from the entry of the pharynx up to the distal end of the pharynx, till it enters the oesophagus. This stage is involuntary.
3. Oesophageal stage: This involves the movement of the food from the proximal end of the oesophagus to the distal end, till it enters the stomach. This stage is involuntary.

## Mechanism of deglutition

The stages of deglutition are overlapping. They are reflex responses and hence, are initiated basically by the presence of food, which stimulates certain receptors in the mucosa. This results in reflex contraction of the muscles over the mass of food, propelling it to the next segment, which is in a state of receptive relaxation. Food is always propelled from the proximal to the distal end, that is, propulsion occurs in the aboral direction or anal-ward.

The reflex mechanism involves various groups of nerves, mainly the vagus after the oesophageal region, and also the local nerve plexuses, which are situated between the layers of the walls of the GI tract.

## Stages of deglutition

### Oral Stage

In this stage, food which has already been converted into a round mass (bolus) is pressed against the hard palate by the movements of the tongue and cheek. This position (when the lubricated bolus is on the posterodorsal portion of the tongue) is called the preparatory position. Next, the bolus has to pass through the oropharyngeal junction into the pharynx. This movement is also initiated voluntarily. When the bolus is allowed to pass into the pharynx, the nasopharynx is shut off to prevent the regurgitation of food through the nose. At this point, respiration reflexly stops (deglutition apnoea). Mastication also ceases and the lips and jaws are closed. The nasopharynx is shut off by the upward movement of the soft palate and the forward movement of the posterior pharyngeal wall.

**Pharyngeal Stage**

This stage commences with the entry of food from the oropharyngeal junction into the pharynx. Though this is identified as a reflex that is initiated voluntarily, there is also an involuntary response. The mucosa at the oropharyngeal junction has mechano/stretch receptors which are sensitive to the volume/bulk of the food. Thus, the presence of the bolus stimulates the receptors in the oropharyngeal junction. This sends impulses through the afferent nerves to the swallowing centre, resulting in a reflex response.

The response consists of relaxation of the muscles in the oropharyngeal region to permit the passage of the bolus into the pharynx. After the food has entered the pharynx, the oropharyngeal junction undergoes another slight constriction. The bolus now moves from the proximal to the distal end of the pharynx due to peristaltic contractions.

Peristaltic contractions develop in the form of contractions over the bolus, accompanied by simultaneous receptive relaxation in the immediate distal part. The bolus then descends and the contractile wave is now passed on to the next distal segment. This process is seen throughout the GI tract. Known as the propulsive reflex, this process propels the bolus from the oropharyngeal to the pharyngo-oesophageal junction.

Protective reflexes are also present at this stage. These reflexes permit the bolus to move only in the aboral direction in the oesophagus, and prevent it from re-entering the oral cavity, or going through the nasopharynx into the nose, or through the larynx into the respiratory system.

By one such reflex, the soft palate is tightened due to the contraction of the tensor and levator palate, preventing the entry of food into the nasopharynx and nasal cavity.

By another reflex mechanism, the vocal cords of the larynx are strongly approximated, that is, brought near each other, due to contraction of the laryngeal muscles. The hyoid and larynx move upwards, and the epiglottis swings backwards to form something of a cover over the superior orifice of the larynx. As a result, the food is prevented from entering the trachea.

One of the protective reflexes causes the tongue to retract and press against the hard palate. Also, there is a pressure gradient in the downward direction, that is, the pressure in the oral cavity becomes greater than that in the pharyngeal cavity. These factors prevent the re-entry of the bolus into the oral cavity.

*Reflex arc for oral and pharyngeal stage*: The bolus provides mechanical and chemical stimuli to mechano- and chemoreceptors in the oral and pharyngeal mucosa. Afferent impulses are then carried via sensory divisions of the fifth and tenth cranial nerves to the deglutition/swallowing centre. This centre is located in the reticular formation of the medulla and lower part of the pons.

From the deglutition centre, efferent impulses are transmitted via the fifth, ninth, tenth and twelfth cranial nerves to the muscles of the cheeks and tongue, as well as muscles related to jaw movements and pharyngeal muscles.

Reflex response thus gives rise to propulsion of the bolus through the oral and pharyngeal cavities.

*Clinical importance of oropharyngeal stage*: If the reflex arc is nonfunctional at any point, deglutition may be disturbed. Difficulty in deglutition is called dysphagia. The first oral stage may be disturbed due to the following conditions:

1. Inflammation in the oral cavity/tongue/mouth.
2. Neoplasm (tumours) in the oral cavity.
3. Paralysis of the tongue or jaw.
4. Congenital anomaly of the lips and tongue.

The second stage may be disturbed in cases of pharyngitis or tonsilitis, or when the pharyngeal muscles or palate is paralysed. A congenital defect of the palate or carcinoma of the larynx may also disturb the second stage of deglutition.

**Osophageal Stage**

This stage begins with the passage of the bolus from the pharynx to the oesophagus, through pharyngo-oesophageal junction. The bolus is propelled through the lumen of the oesophagus to reach the oesophago-gastric junction. Finally, it is pushed into the gastric cavity by peristaltic contraction.

The upper and lower ends of the oesophagus have sphincter muscles for a distance of about 3 cm. These are called the upper and lower oesophageal sphincters. The latter blends with the cardiac sphincter. Under normal conditions, these regions show tonic contraction of the sphincter muscles. It is only during the passage of the bolus that the sphincter muscles relax, allowing the food to go from the proximal to the distal segment.

When the bolus enters the oesophagus, peristaltic contractions develop to help propel it. Three types of peristaltic waves can be observed in the oesophagus.

*Primary waves*: These are a continuation of the pharyngeal peristaltic wave. Due to the primary wave, the bolus moves from the proximal to the distal end of the oesophagus in about 5 to 8 seconds. It is a reflex response which involves the oesophageal muscles. The reflex consists of the mechanical/chemical stimuli from the bolus, stimulation of the receptors in the oesophageal mucosa, afferent impulses carried to the deglutition centre via the vagus, and efferent impulses transmitted via the vagus to the oesophageal muscles, resulting in the development of peristaltic contraction.

In a normal, healthy adult, the primary peristaltic wave helps propel almost the entire food from the proximal to the distal end of the oesophagus. Gravity has no effect, except in the case of fluid.

*Secondary waves*: When the primary peristaltic wave fails to propel some part of the food, the distended oesophagus initiates a series of secondary peristaltic waves. These are generated through the local nerve plexus present in the submucosa and between the longitudinal and circular muscles in the oesophageal wall.

*Tertiary waves*: These are not seen in normal adults. They are irregular contractions developed by the local nerve plexus, and are observed in elderly persons. They occur in the lower part of the oesophagus.

**Passage of Food from Oesophagus to Gastric Cavity**

When the bolus reaches the lower oesophageal sphincter, the receptive relaxation of the sphincter, as well as that of the early part of the stomach, takes place. The bolus is pushed from the oesophagus into the gastric cavity. Now, the sphincter muscles contract again, preventing the reflux of food back into the oesophagus. The activity of the sphincter is regulated by nervous and hormonal control.

*Clinical importance*: The third stage is affected in the following cases:

1. Paralysis of the oesophageal muscles.
2. Oesophageal spasms/strictures.
3. Oesophageal neoplasms.
4. Hiatus hernia.
5. Achalasia cardia, that is, failure of the cardiac sphincter to open, resulting in regurgitation of food into the oesophagus.

## MOVEMENTS OF STOMACH

The movements of the stomach are studied in human beings in a variety of ways. These are listed below.

1. By inserting a balloon in the stomach and then inflating it. The balloon is connected to a manometer.
2. By a barium meal X-ray.
3. During surgery.

The important stomach movements are hunger pangs, receptive relaxation, peristalsis and gastric emptying.

### Hunger Pangs

These occur when the stomach is empty and the level of glucose in the blood is low. Hunger contractions are caused by unconditioned reflex. Information is carried to the feeding and satiety centre in the hypothalamus. The smell and sight of food tend to intensify hunger contractions.

Appetite, unlike hunger pangs, is the desire for food and is a conditioned reflex. However, hunger is always associated with appetite. The stomach shows tonic rhythmic movements at the rate of 3–4/min.

### Receptive Relaxation

This is the active relaxation of the stomach that occurs when a meal is taken. The solid food is stored in the stomach, but the liquid passes to the antrum.

### Peristalsis

After meals, the body and fundus of the stomach go through rhythmic tonic contractions, while the pyloric region displays peristaltic movements.

The peristaltic action in the stomach consists of a churning movement, which is brought about by the contraction of the three layers of muscle tissue. The churning movement causes further mechanical breakdown of the food (grinding into chyme), the mixing of the food with gastric juice, and its onward movement into the duodenum.

Peristaltic movements are strong at intervals, so that the pyloric sphincter opens and discharges its contents into the duodenum in small jets.

### Gastric Emptying

This is a process by which the stomach empties out its contents into the duodenum. It occurs about 4 hours after an average meal.

*Factors affecting gastric emptying:* The following factors affect gastric emptying:

1. Volume of the meal in the stomach: The larger the volume, the greater the time required for gastric emptying.
2. Osmolarity in the duodenum: Both hypertonic and hypotonic fluids require more time as they are to be made isotonic in the duodenum.
3. Acidity of duodenal contents: If acidity in the small intestine is higher than normal, gastric emptying is inhibited.
4. Products of lipid digestion in the duodenum: These also inhibit gastric emptying and this action (inhibition), is mediated by the hormone enterogastrone.
5. Various hormones liberated by the small intestine: Hormones such as cholecystokinin and secretin decrease the movements of the stomach and thus, gastric emptying.
6. Emotions: Emotions are an important determinant. Excitement increases the rate of emptying, while acute fear may decrease the emptying of the stomach.

## Vomiting

Vomiting is a process by which the contents of the upper gut are expelled to the exterior through the mouth. Normally, the contents of the stomach do not pass upwards because of the cardiac sphincter at the junction of the stomach and oesophagus. In most cases, vomiting rids the body of unwanted and irritant materials. It is also associated with serious diseases, such as appendicitis, gastritis and cholecystitis. Vomiting can also occur due to psychological reasons or motion sickness.

The act of vomiting is integrated at the vomiting centre, which is near the salivary centre. Vomiting usually starts with excess salivation, which causes repeated swallowing and relaxation of the cardiac sphincter. Then a deep breath is drawn, the larynx is closed and a sudden and strong contraction of the abdominal wall muscles, together with antiperistalsis, forces the gastric contents into the oesophagus and out through the mouth.

## MOVEMENTS OF SMALL INTESTINE

The movements of the small intestine are very helpful in the process of digestion and absorption. The different movements can be summarized as follows:

1. Mixing movements
   (i) segmentation
   (ii) pendular movements

2. Propulsive movements:
   (i) peristalsis
3. Antiperistalsis
4. Villous movements

**Segmentation Contractions or Churning**

These consist of alternate localized contraction (constriction) and relaxation of successive segments of the small intestine, with no forward movement of the intestinal contents. This is followed by a constriction in the middle of the relaxed segment, which serves to subdivide the contents. The contents are further subdivided by another batch of contractions in the previously dilated portion. This goes on at the rate of 8–12/min. The rate is the highest in the duodenum. These contractions are myogenic in nature (Fig. 26.2).

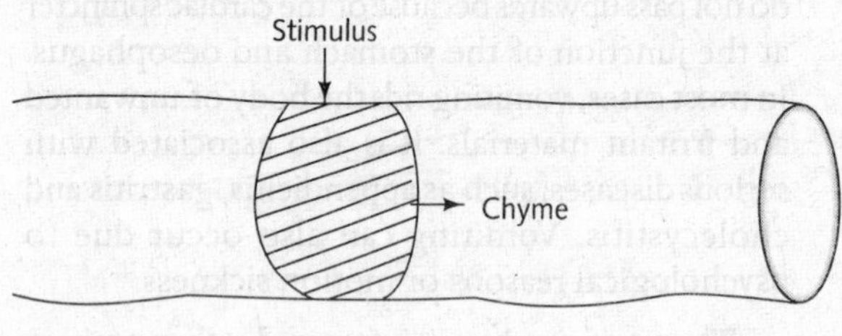


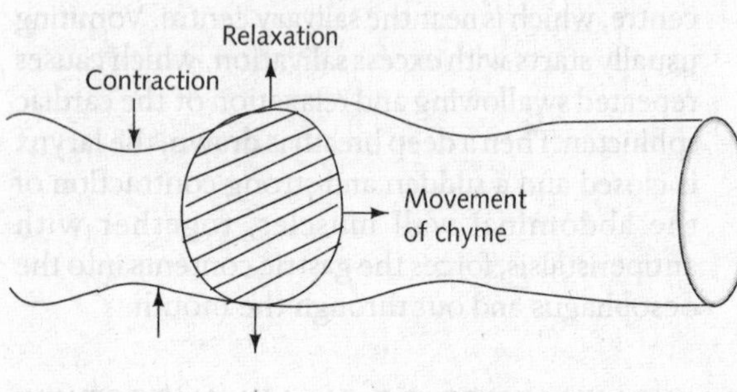


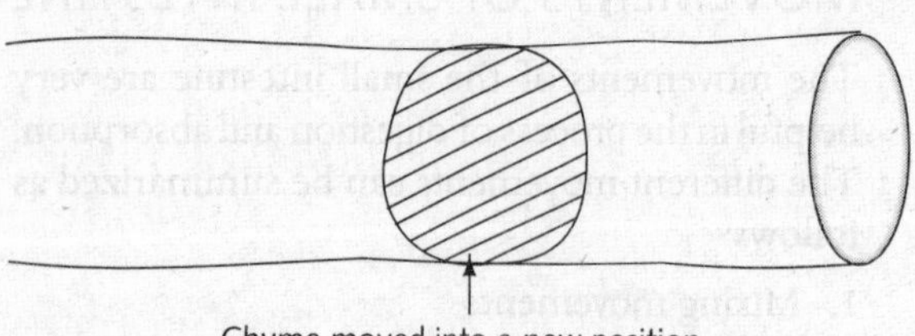


**Fig. 26.3:** Peristalsis

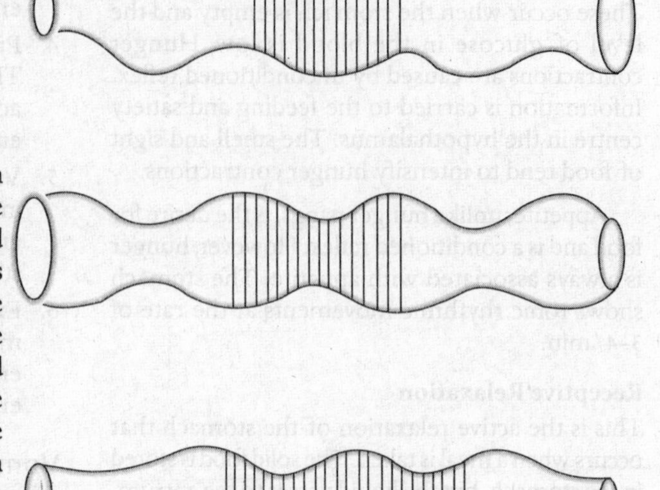


**Fig. 26.2:** Segmentation contraction

*Functions of segmentation*: Segmentation breaks up the intestinal contents and mixes them with digestive juices for proper digestion. It also helps in the process of absorption. In addition, it improves the vascular and lymphatic circulation in the intestine.

**Pendular Movements**

These are side-to-side movements of a long segment of the intestine and are described as pendular because they occur with the regularity of a pendulum. They are entirely passive. They help mix and shake the food contents.

**Peristalsis**

Peristalsis is a propulsive movement which usually succeeds the segmentation movements. It is a wave of constrictions behind the chyme, followed by a wave of relaxation in front, travelling down the gut in the direction of the anus (aboral direction), away from the mouth (Fig. 26.3).

Peristalsis serves many purposes. A series of rapid peristaltic movements, lasting for a second with a break of a few seconds in between, propels the intestinal contents forward. These take about 4 to 5 hours to reach the colon from the duodenum.

Peristalsis prevents bacterial growth in the small intestine by pushing them down the colon. It also augments the lymph and blood flow, and thus helps the process of absorption from the small intestine. Peristalsis also helps expel gases.

Peristaltic movements are reflex in nature, that is, they are neurogenic. The sensory receptors are in the Meissner's plexus, and the motor effectors are in the myenteric plexus.

Peristalsis is stimulated by distension (stretching) of the intestine due to food or juices. The parasympathetic nerves (vagus) enhance the process, while the sympathetic nerves inhibit it. Hormones such as gastrin and CCK-PZ inhibit peristalsis. The intake of food stimulates peristalsis in the regions of the ileum and colon. The former is called the gastroileal reflex. The latter, called the gastrocolic reflex, gives rise to the desire to defaecate.

**Antiperistalsis**

Antiperistalsis consists of peristaltic movements in the direction of the mouth, that is, the direction opposite to peristalsis. Normally, these movements are seen only in the ileum, and abnormally, in vomiting.

**Villous Movements**

There are two types of movements of the intestinal villi. First, there are side-to-side movements (lashing movements), which help mix up the food contents with the digestive juices, and aid in digestion and absorption. Secondly, there are pumping movements, which consist of alternate shortening and elongation of the villi. These help pump out the contents of the lacteals (lymph capillaries in the villi) into the lymphatic vessels, and help the lymph and blood flow in the villi (Fig. 26.4).

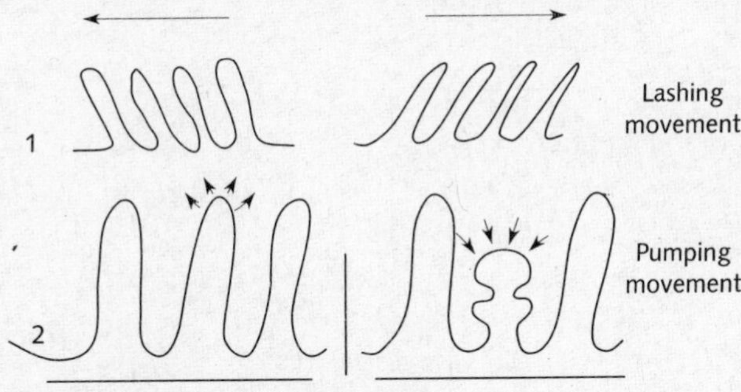


Fig. 26.4: Movement of villi

Besides the nerves, a local hormone called vilicrinin is also involved in the movements of the villi.

## MOVEMENTS OF LARGE INTESTINE

The movements of the large intestine consist of mixing and propulsive movements. Their aim is to prolong the stay of the contents. Therefore, they are slower and antiperistalsis is more prominent. The different movements can be classified as stationary and propulsive.

**Stationary Movements**

These are aimed at agitation of the colonic contents. They consist of segmented contractions, haustral contractions (in which the haustra become prominent), and peristalsis and antiperistalsis. These movements move the colonic contents forward and backward, and are stationary movements.

**Propulsive Movement**

These movements propel the colonic contents forward, that is, towards the rectum. They consist of peristalsis, which is more powerful here than in the small intestine, and mass peristalsis.

*Peristalsis*: When food enters or leaves the stomach, there is reflex discharge of the intestinal contents from the lower ileum into the colon, through the ileocaecal sphincter. This is called the gastrocolic reflex. Also, passive filling of the colon from the ileum takes place about 4 to 5 hours after the ingestion of food.

*Mass peristalsis*: This is peristalsis of a modified and stronger kind. In mass peristalsis, a large segment of the colon contracts at a time and forcefully pushes the contents forward. This is a very important movement. It begins at the hepatic flexture of the colon, so that the contents are moved into the transverse colon, descending colon and sigmoid colon, which stores faecal matter. It may reach the rectum, giving rise to the desire for defaecation. Mass peristalsis occurs after meals, as well as at the time of defaecation. The movements of the colon are influenced by nerves, chemicals, hormones, drugs and emotions.

### Functions of large intestine

The large intestine is responsible for the formation, storage and expulsion of faeces. It also secretes mucus, which acts as a lubricant.

The bacteria in the large intestine supply vitamins K and B complex.

There is no active digestion or absorption in the large intestine, except of water and electrolytes. Sodium and chloride are absorbed, but potassium is secreted. Glucose, saline and drugs (suppositories) can be introduced intrarectally to empty it. This process is known as an enema.

## DEFAECATION

Defaecation is a process by which the faecal matter is expelled from the body. It is effected mainly by the spinal reflex, but is under voluntary control. The rectum is normally empty until just before defaecation.

The filling of the pelvic colon is brought about by the gastrocolic reflex. The contents of the pelvic colon enter the rectum by mass peristalsis. An increase in the intrarectal pressure gives rise to the desire to defaecate and perineal sensation is experienced. The intra-abdominal pressure is increased by the closure of the glottis, as well as the contraction of the diaphragm and abdominal muscles. The anal sphincter relaxes and the act is complete. The act of defaecation is a matter of habit.

The amount of faeces / stool produced per day is 100 to 200 g. It is yellow due to stercobilinogen and it turns brown on exposure to air, due to the formation of stercobilin. Faeces consists of water (70 per cent) and solids (30 per cent), which are organic and inorganic. The organic matter consists of bacteria, protein, fat, carbohydrates and dietary fibres, which help in the normal functioning of the digestive system.

CHAPTER

27

# Salivary Secretion

The process of chemical digestion begins in the mouth, when the food comes in contact with saliva. Saliva is secreted by three pairs of salivary glands—the parotid, submaxillary or submandibular, and sublingual glands. In addition, many buccal glands which secrete mucus are present.

The secretion of the parotid glands is serous (thin and watery) and forms about 25 per cent of the total secretion. The secretion of the submaxillary glands is serous and mucous (mixed) and forms about 70 per cent of the total secretion, while that of the sublingual glands is mucous (thick and viscid) and forms only about 5 per cent of the total secretion.

The salivary gland is an exocrine type of gland, that is, it has ducts. It is of the racemose type, which means that the ducts branch and rebranch. At the ends of the branches are situated a large number of acini. The appearance of a salivary gland is like a cluster of grapes. The primary secretory unit of a gland is called the acinus. There are pyramidal-shaped epithelial cells on the basement membrane of each acinus. These cells are arranged around a central lumen, and are of two types:

1. Serous-secreting cells which store the enzyme ptyalin or salivary amylase in their zymogen granules, and
2. Mucus-secreting cells that store mucus in their mucinogen granules.

Between the cells and the basement membrane are myoepithelial cells, the contraction of which squeezes out the secretion (Fig. 27.1).

The secretion is poured into the lumen, from which it flows through the duct system. Each gland has four generations of ducts (Fig. 27.2).

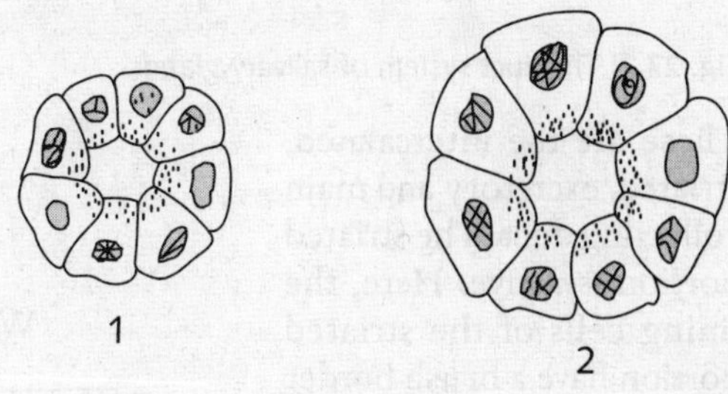


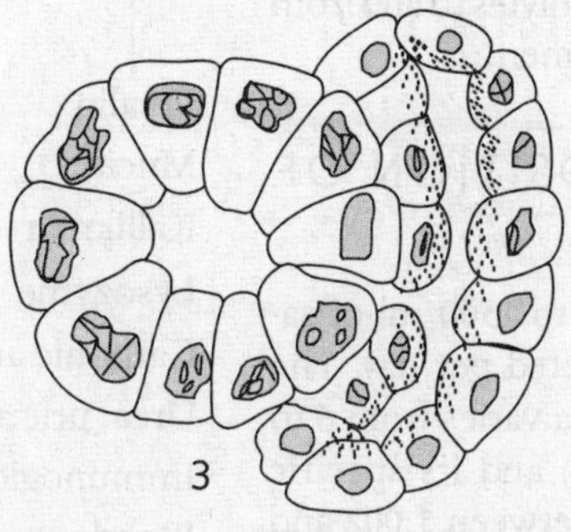


**Fig. 27.1:** Salivary acini: 1. Serous, 2. Mucous, 3. Mixed

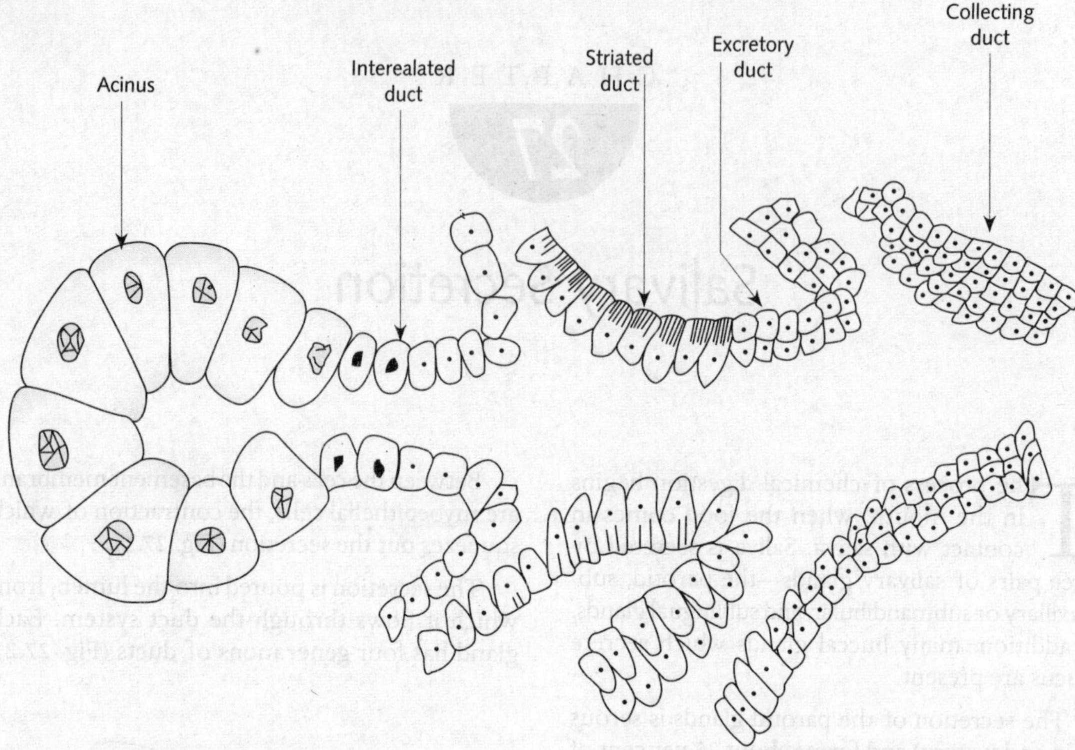


**Fig. 27.2:** The duct system of salivary glands

These are the intercalated, striated, excretory and main collecting duct. The striated portion is active. Here, the lining cells of the striated portion have a brush border on the luminal side, and are involved in the active transfer of electrolytes to and from the duct lumen.

## COMPOSITION OF SALIVA

About 800 to 1500 ml of saliva is secreted per day. The pH of saliva varies from 6 to 7.4 (acidic) and its specific gravity is between 1.002 and 1.012. Its composition is as shown on the right side.

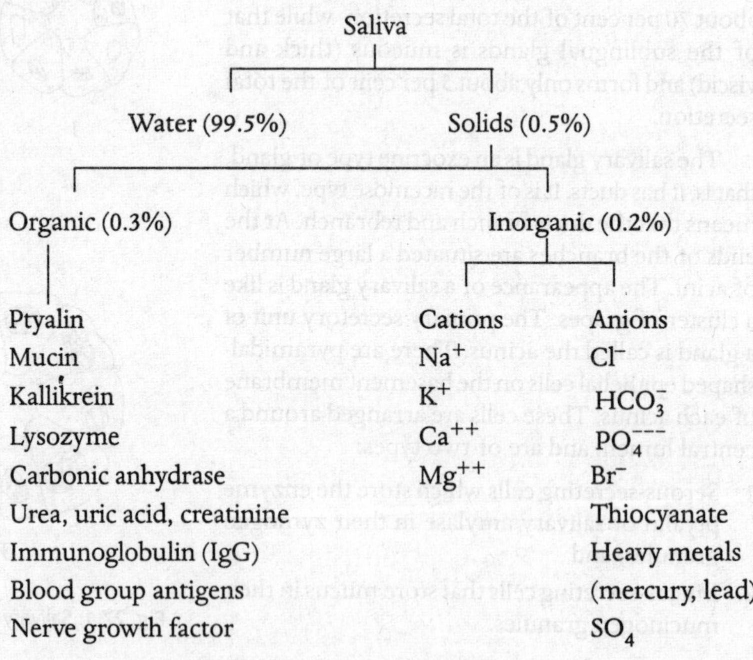

## Important constituents

Ptyalin, an important constituent of saliva, is an amylase or starch-splitting enzyme. It acts best at a pH of 6.8. Mucin, a glycoprotein which is thick and viscid, is another constituent.

Kallikrein is not a true constituent of saliva but is released from nerve endings. It acts on plasma protein (kininogen) to produce bradykinin, a known vasodilator.

Saliva contains lysozyme, which is a proteolytic enzyme that helps kill microorganisms. Bicarbonate is an important buffering agent in saliva. It helps neutralize the gastric acid, to some extent, when no food has been taken. Thiocyanate, which is produced from the detoxification of cyanide, is present particularly in smokers' saliva.

## Factors affecting composition of saliva

The composition of saliva varies according to the water content of the body. Dehydration decreases the water content of saliva.

The kind of saliva produced also depends on the nature of the stimulus. Hot, spicy food stimulates the secretion of profuse and watery saliva, but dry and rough food gives rise to a secretion which has more mucus in it.

The rate of secretion is another determinant. When the rate is slow, the striated portions of the ducts absorb $Na^+$ and $Cl^-$ but secrete $K^+$ and $HCO_3^-$. When the rate is fast, this absorption cannot occur, so there is more $Na^{++}$ and $Cl^-$ in the saliva.

## FUNCTIONS OF SALIVA

Saliva subserves many important functions, both digestive and nondigestive, which are described in this section.

### Mechanical

Saliva helps in the maintenance of oral hygiene, that is, it helps rinse the mouth or wash off food particles in the mouth, and prevents the formation of a coating over the tongue and teeth. It thus prevents bacterial action over food particles and consequently, dental caries. This is the most important function of saliva.

The continuous flow of saliva keeps the mouth and tongue moist and helps in speech/articulation. Speaking becomes difficult when the mouth is dry.

The lubrication of food by mucus, which is thick and viscid, helps in the formation of a bolus. This, in turn, helps in mastication and the deglutition of food. Saliva also helps dilute hot, irritant food and protects the mucous membrane from injury.

### Solvent

As a solvent, saliva helps dissolve food particles, which then stimulate the taste buds to give a sensation of taste. In addition, the lysozyme in saliva is a proteolytic enzyme which dissolves bacteria and thus confers protection from them.

### Digestive

Saliva has some important digestive properties. Salivary amylase/ptyalin acts on polysaccharides and converts boiled starch into maltose. It acts best at a pH of 6.8. The digestion of carbohydrates begins in the oral cavity, but the food remains in the oral cavity for only a short while. Therefore, the action of amylase is short-lived, continuing only until the food enters the stomach and till the pH of the gastric contents becomes too acidic for amylase activity.

### Buffering, Immunity and Excretion

The bicarbonate present in saliva acts as a buffer against gastric acid to some extent. Saliva also provides immunity as the IgG in it acts against bacteria in the mouth.

Saliva plays an excretory role as well. The salivary glands excrete heavy metals, such as lead and mercury, and viruses, such as rabies and poliomyelitis. They also detoxify certain materials.

### Homeostasis

The balance of water is maintained by the sensation of thirst, which occurs when the mouth becomes dry. In lower animals, saliva plays a role in regulating the body temperature. It evaporates in hot conditions, resulting in heat loss.

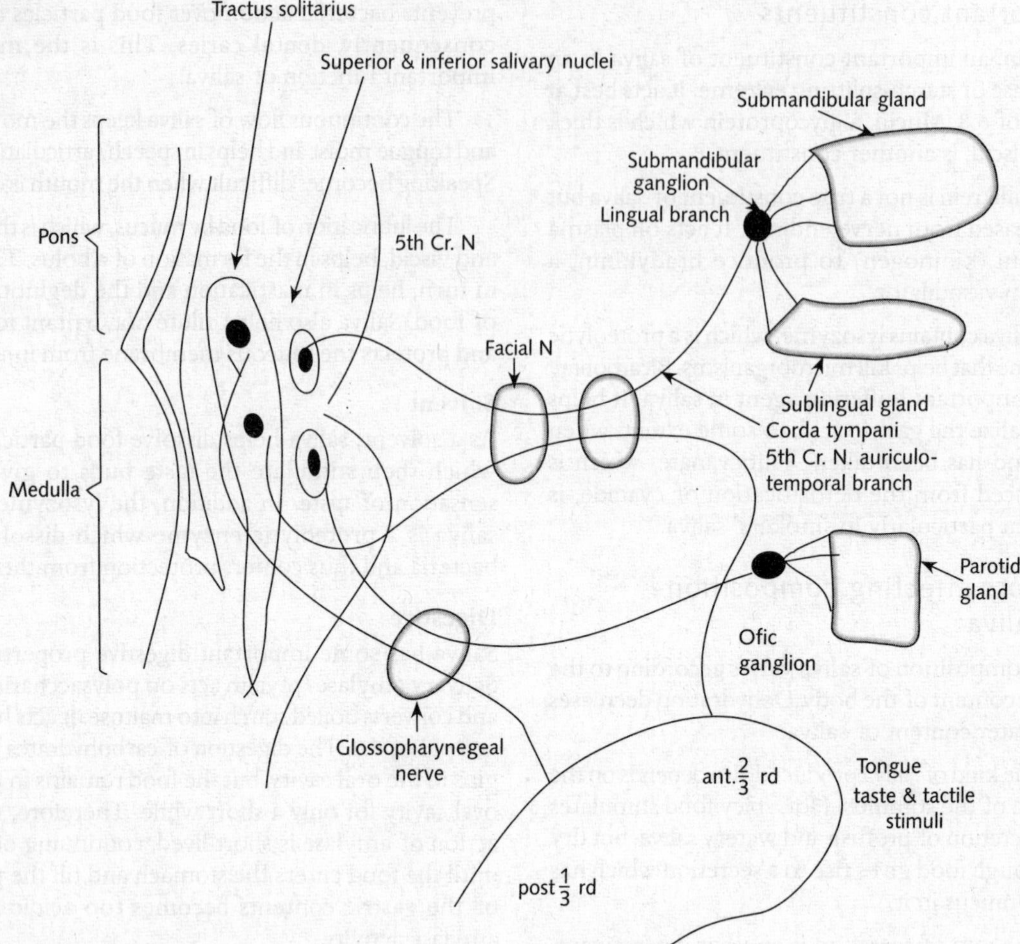


**Fig. 27.3:** Innervation of salivary glands

## REGULATION OF SALIVARY SECRETION

The secretion of saliva is regulated basically by parasympathetic innervation of the salivary glands. This brings about reflex secretion of saliva in response to gustatory or tactile stimuli, or stimuli which arise in the CNS itself. Parasympathetic stimulation causes vasodilatation, while stimulation of glandular tissue gives rise to profuse, watery secretion. Vasodilatation by the parasympathetic nerves is brought about by the formation of bradykinin (Fig. 27.3).

Parasympathetic innervation of the salivary glands arises from the superior and inferior salivary nuclei in the reticular formation of the medulla. These processes take place in the following way:

1. Superior salivary nucleus → VIIth cranial nerve (facial) → chorda tympani branch → Vth cranial nerve (lingual branch) → relay in submandibular ganglion → cells and blood vessels of submandibular and sublingual glands
2. Inferior salivary nucleus → IXth cranial nerve (glossopharyngeal) → relay in otic ganglion → Vth cranial nerve (auriculo-temporal branch) → cells and blood vessels of parotid gland

Sympathetic stimulation increases salivation by direct stimulation of the glandular tissues and contraction of the myoepithelial cells. These help squeeze out the secretion present in the acini. Later on, however, sympathetic stimulation decreases the blood flow to the salivary glands as it also causes vasoconstriction. The resulting secretion is scanty and viscid.

Sympathetic innervation arises from the superior cervical ganglion, along the plexus around the external carotid blood vessels to the salivary glands.

## TYPES OF SECRETION

The secretion of saliva may be basal (spontaneous) or reflex. The former occurs even when no food has been taken. Such secretion takes place at a rate of about 20 ml per hour. It is caused by tonic discharge from the salivary centre. Basal secretion keeps the mouth clean and moist.

Reflex secretion is 8 to 20 times the basal secretion, and is equal to about 5 to 8 ml per minute. Reflex is an involuntary motor response to a sensory stimulus. It depends on the reflex arc, which consists of receptors, afferent nerves, the centre, efferent nerves and the effector organ.

### Receptors

Some of the receptors are located in the mouth. These are the taste buds on the tongue and tactile receptors. The former are stimulated by the acid/ sour taste (chemical stimuli), and the latter by mechanical stimuli, for example, the touch of food or foreign particles (like dentures) present in the mouth.

Tactile receptors are also found in the stomach and upper intestine. Some of the receptors are located in the head. These respond to the sight, smell and thought of food.

### Afferent Nerves

The sensations of taste and touch are carried by chorda tympani branch of facial nerve, from the anterior two-thirds of the tongue and by glossopharyngeal nerve, from the posterior one-third of the tongue.

The sensations of smell and sight from the nose and eyes are carried by the first and second cranial nerves respectively.

### The Centre

The superior and inferior salivary nuclei at the junction of the pons and medulla, present near the tractus solitarious, respiratory and vomiting centre from the centre.

It is connected to other areas, such as the appetite area, the taste and smell areas of the cerebral cortex, and the amygdala.

### Efferent Nerves and Effect Organ

The efferent nerves are parasympathetic fibres via facial (chorda tympani)/glossopharyngeal nerves. The effector organ may be the parotid, submandibular/submaxillary and sublingual glands.

The reflexes may be of the unconditioned or conditioned type. Unconditioned reflexes are present since birth and do not need learning. This is due to the stimulation of the touch and chemical receptors (taste) in the mouth, as well as stimuli arising from the oesophagus and stomach.

Conditioned (acquired) reflexes are based on previous knowledge or learning. Sight, smell and the thought of known food causes the secretion of saliva.

## CLINICAL IMPORTANCE

It is important to maintain oral sepsis in high fever and coma, since the secretion of saliva decreases.

Decreased salivary secretion can cause dental caries, so the mouth has to be rinsed after taking food.

Atropine is administered before general anaesthesia to decrease salivary secretion.

The rabies virus, caused by dog bite, and the virus of poliomyelitis are transmitted through saliva. Sialorrhoea occurs in pregnancy and oesophageal cancer, and also during nausea and vomiting, when irritant substances are present in the stomach. This is a protective mechanism.

CHAPTER

# 28

# Gastric Secretion

Gastric juice is secreted in the stomach, which consists of an upper part called the fundus, the main body, and the lower horizontal part, known as the pyloric antrum. It communicates with the oesophagus through the cardiac orifice, and with the duodenum through the pyloric orifice. Both these openings are guarded by sphincters (Fig. 28.1).

The stomach is a muscular bag, lined by a mucous membrane. The latter contains glands which have three types of cells (Fig. 28.2). These are:

1. Oxyntic or parietal cells, which secrete HCl,

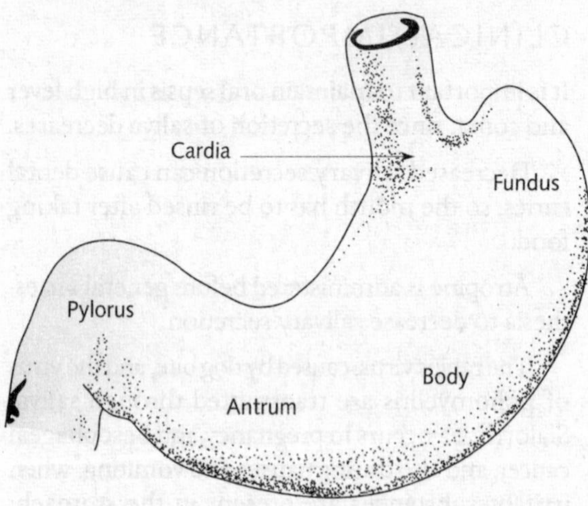


Fig. 28.1: Parts of stomach

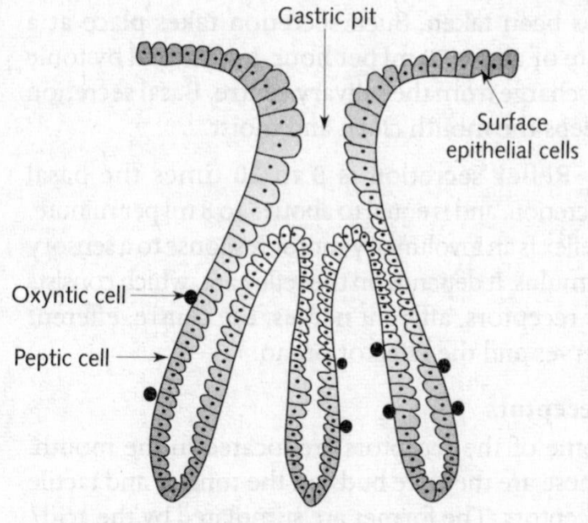


Fig. 28.2: Gastric glands

2. Chief or peptic cells, which secrete enzymes, and
3. Mucous cells, which secrete mucus.

The fundic glands contain all three types of cells, while the pyloric glands contain mucous cells.

## Composition of gastric juice

Gastric juice is clear and colourless. The total amount secreted per day is 1 to 1.5 l. It is strongly acidic in reaction (pH = 0.9 to 1.5). Its contents are as shown on p. 151.

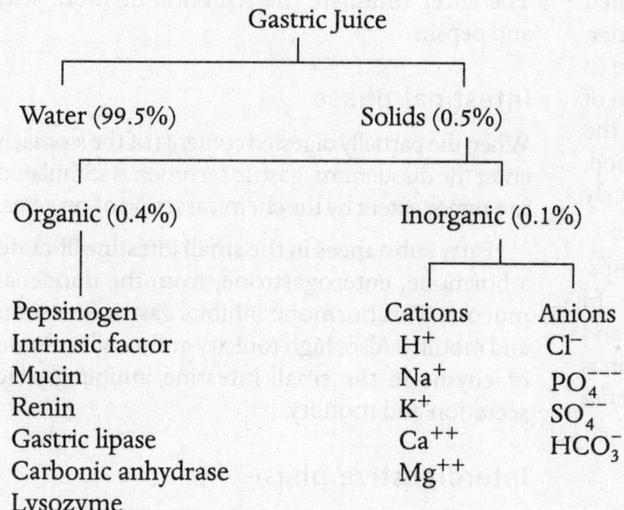


## FUNCTIONS OF IMPORTANT CONSTITUENTS OF GASTRIC JUICE

Gastric juice further liquefies the food that is swallowed.

Hydrochloric acid is present in gastric juice in a large amount and in two forms—free and combined with other materials. It acidifies the food and stops the action of ptyalin, which continues in the stomach. Hydrochloric acid also kills the microorganisms that are harmful, thus working as an antiseptic. In addition, it activates pepsinogen to pepsin and provides an acidic environment for effective digestion by pepsin. The other important functions of hydrochloric acid are the stimulation of the secretion of different hormones from the small intestine, such as secretin, as well as hydrolysis of some food.

Pepsinogen, another constituent of gastric juice, is a proenzyme that is converted into pepsin by HCl at a pH of less than 6. Once formed, it further activates pepsinogen to pepsin by an autocatalytic process. Pepsin is a proteolytic enzyme which converts proteins into peptones. It acts best between a pH of 1.5 and 3.5.

Intrinsic factor is secreted by the oxyntic cells of the gastric mucous membrane. It is necessary for the absorption of vitamin $B_{12}$ (extrinsic factor) and, therefore, for haemopoiesis. A deficiency of intrinsic factor causes pernicious anaemia.

Mucin is an important constituent of gastric juice as it provides protection against the damage which may be caused by an acid. It is of two types—visible or insoluble, and soluble. The former is secreted by the surface mucosal cells and forms a slippery layer over them. It prevents mechanical injury to the stomach by lubricating the contents. Soluble mucin remains dissolved in gastric juice. This provides a buffer against HCl to some extent, thereby preventing the action of HCl on the mucosa and gastric ulcers.

Among the other constituents of gastric juice, gastric lipase helps in lipid digestion. Renin, a milk-curdling enzyme, is not found in the human stomach, as was previously thought.

## CONTROL OF SECRETION

The secretion of gastric juice is controlled by both neural and hormonal mechanisms. The neural control is mainly by the vagus nerve (parasympathetic), through the long and short vagovagal reflexes. Stimulation of the vagus gives rise to a gastric secretion which is rich in acid and pepsin. The secretion takes place via the liberation of acetylcholine and gastrin.

As for hormonal control, the hormones which increase gastric secretion are gastrin and enterooxyntin. These stimulate the secretion of HCl. The hormones which decrease gastric secretion are gastrin inhibitory peptide (GIP), vasoactive inhibitory peptide (VIP), enterogastrone, secretin and CCK-PZ.

The control of gastric secretion can be studied best in four phases, in relation to a meal. The phases are the cephalic phase, gastric phase, intestinal phase and interdigestive phase.

### Cephalic phase

In the cephalic phase, the food is yet to reach the stomach. This phase is caused by a reflex mechanism, which consists of the conditioned reflex and the unconditioned reflex. In the former, the sight, smell and thought of food gives rise to gastric secretion. This is caused by stimulation of the vagus. As for the unconditioned reflex, the presence of food in the mouth, the taste of the food, and the act of chewing and swallowing reflexly secrete gastric juice.

If the vagus nerve is cut, the secretion stops. Hence, this is also called the nervous phase. In this phase, secretion starts within 5 minutes and continues for 30 to 120 minutes. The secretion is rich in acid and pepsin, and is known as the appetite juice. It prepares the stomach for a meal.

### Gastric phase

This phase is initiated about 15 minutes after the food has reached the stomach, and continues for 2 to 3 hours. The stimuli for secretion arise in the stomach.

Both neural and hormonal factors act in this phase. The neural mechanism operates through the long vagovagal reflexes. The presence of food causes distension of the stomach, afferent impulses travel through the vagus to the brain and efferent impulses travel back to the stomach through the vagus. Short local reflexes through the intrinsic nerves are also important. The stimulus for these is the stretch caused by the presence of food in the stomach.

The secretion continues even if the vagi are cut, indicating that there is hormonal control as well. It (secretion) is caused by the hormone gastrin, which is secreted by the 'G' cells of the pyloric mucosa. The gastrin that has been liberated enters the general circulation and after reaching the gastric glands, stimulates them to secrete gastric juice. Gastrin secretion is stimulated by the distension of the stomach and the products of protein digestion. The latter stimulate the secretion of more acid and pepsin.

### Intestinal phase

When the partially digested contents of the stomach enter the duodenum, gastric secretion is stimulated to a minor extent by the chemical action of proteins.

Fatty substances in the small intestine liberate a hormone, enterogastrone, from the duodenal mucosa. This hormone inhibits gastric secretion and motility. Also, high tonicity and a high volume of chyme in the small intestine inhibit gastric secretion and motility.

### Interdigestive phase

This phase is that period when no food is present either in the stomach or the small intestine. It is also known as the phase of basal secretion.

## METHODS OF STUDYING GASTRIC SECRETION

In animals, gastric secretion is studied by sham feeding, as well as Pavlov's pouch. In sham feeding or pretending, an oesophageal fistula is created so that the food comes out of the oesophagus. Gastric juice is collected by intubating the stomach. The amount of gastric juice increases even if the food is not entering the stomach. This is evidence of the cephalic phase of secretion.

In the Pavlov's pouch method, a pouch is created from the gastric mucosa and is brought on to the surface of the body, but its lining mucosa is in contact with the gastric mucosa. It is used to study different factors influencing secretion, including different types of food.

In human beings, gastric secretion is studied by the fractional test meal.

CHAPTER

29

# Pancreatic Secretion

When the contents of the pyloric end of the stomach have reached the required degree of acidity and liquefaction, they are known as chyme. When the acidic chyme enters the duodenum, it is mixed with pancreatic juice and bile, and then with the intestinal juice.

The pancreas act both as an exocrine and endocrine gland. The exocrine part, which is structurally similar to the salivary gland, produces pancreatic juice. This enters the duodenum through the pancreatic duct and the bile duct. The endocrine part, composed of islets of Langerhans, produces insulin, which directly enters the bloodstream.

## Composition of pancreatic juice

Pancreatic juice is an alkaline fluid with a pH of 8 to 8.3. It has the highest digestive power. About 1 to 1.5 l of pancreatic juice is secreted per day. Its composition is as shown on the right side.

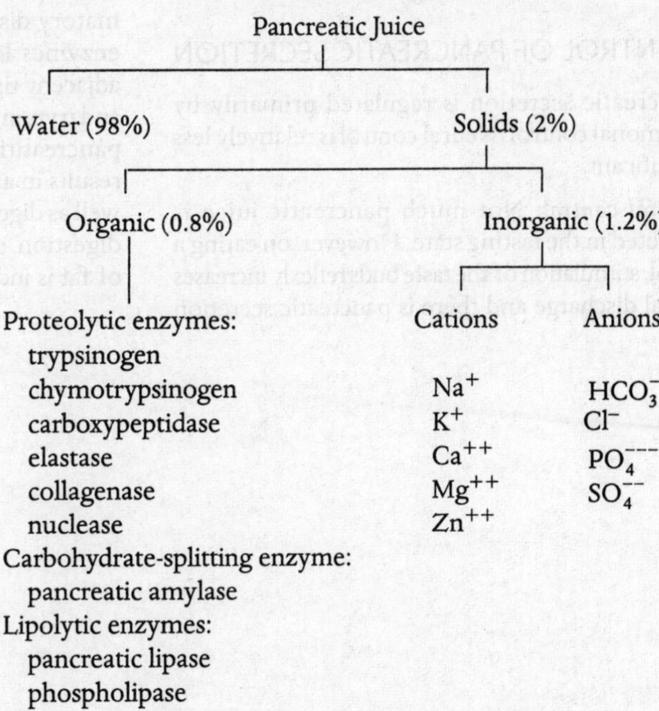


## FUNCTIONS OF PANCREATIC JUICE

Pancreatic juice serves many important functions. Proteolytic enzymes are secreted as inactive proenzymes. These are converted to active enzymes in the small intestine by trypsin, which is initially formed by the enterokinase secreted from the small intestine, and then by the autocatalytic process.

Of trypsin and chymotrypsin, both of which act in an alkaline medium, trypsin is more important. Both hydrolyse protein into peptones and proteoses. The trypsin inhibitor present in pancreatic juice prevents the inactivation of enzymes inside only the pancreas, which is thus protected from autodigestion.

Carboxypeptidases hydrolyse proteins into amino acids. The elastase, collagenase and nucleases act on elastin, collagen and nucleoproteins, respectively.

Pancreatic amylase has strong starch-splitting activity. It is activated in the presence of $Cl^-$ and acts best at a pH of 6.8. It acts both on boiled and unboiled starch, in contrast to salivary amylase, which acts only on boiled starch.

Pancreatic lipase is the most important lipolytic enzyme and also, the most important enzyme from the pancreas. It digests fat into fatty acid and glycerol.

The bicarbonate present in pancreatic juice neutralizes the acidic chyme coming from the stomach and maintains an alkaline pH in the small intestine. This is essential for the proper functioning of the digestive enzymes in the small intestine.

## CONTROL OF PANCREATIC SECRETION

Pancreatic secretion is regulated primarily by hormonal control. Neural control is relatively less significant.

*Neural control*: Not much pancreatic juice is secreted in the fasting state. However, on eating a meal, stimulation of the taste buds reflexly increases vagal discharge and there is pancreatic secretion of a small amount of an enzyme-rich pancreatic juice.

*Hormonal control*: The presence of acid-rich chyme in the duodenum leads to the secretion of two local hormones, secretin and cholecystokinin pancreozymin (CCK-PZ), into the blood circulation. These hormones act on the ducts and the acini of the pancreas, respectively, producing a large volume of pancreatic juice rich in $HCO_3^-$ and enzymes.

If the pH falls below 4.5, there is a prompt increase in the secretion of secretin, which produces a large volume of pancreatic juice rich in $HCO_3^-$. This neutralizes the gastric acid reaching the duodenum and maintains the pH of the upper intestine at a level that is optimum for the action of digestive enzymes.

Fats and the products of partial protein digestion are potent stimuli for the release of CCK-PZ, which causes the secretion of pancreatic juice rich in enzymes.

### Clinical Importance

Acute pancreatitis is a serious and fatal inflammatory disease of the pancreas. The proteolytic enzymes leak out of the acini and destroy the adjacent tissues. High levels of plasma amylase and trypsin are diagnostic of this disorder. Chronic pancreatitis or chronic inflammatory disorder results in a deficiency of pancreatic secretions as well as digestive disturbance (mainly affecting the digestion of fats). An increased faecal content of fat is indicative of the condition.

# CHAPTER 30

# Liver and Bile Secretion

The liver, the largest chemical factory of the body, secretes bile, which is extremely important for the digestion and absorption of lipids.

The functional unit of the liver is a lobule, in which the hepatic cells radiate centrifugally from the central vein. Branches of the portal vein, hepatic artery and bile duct (portal triad) can be seen in the triangular islands of the loose connective tissue in the periphery of each lobule. There is a central vein in the centre of each lobule (Fig. 30.1).

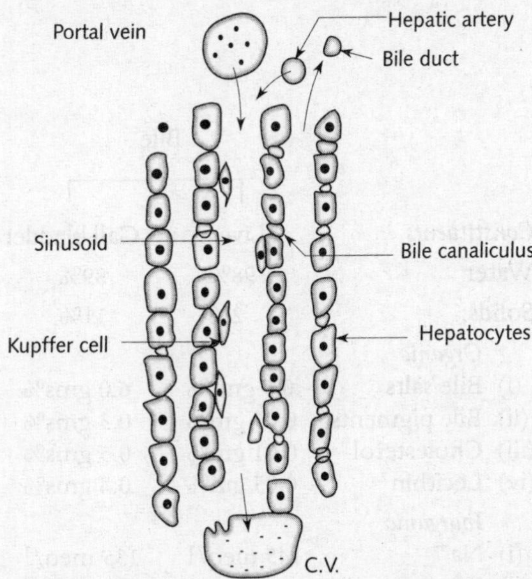


**Fig. 30.1:** Histological structure of a part of hepatic lobule

Large blood sinusoids separate the plates of hepatocytes. Blood from the branches of the portal vein and hepatic artery enters the sinusoids, to be drained by the central vein into the hepatic vein. The portal vein carries blood from the digestive system. This blood contains nutrients. The hepatic artery carries blood rich in oxygen. Therefore, the cells near the central vein are more susceptible to hypoxia. The sinusoids are lined by endothelial cells, among which there are hepatic macrophages (Kupffer cells).

A small bile canaliculus is present between the adjacent hepatic cells, which secrete bile into the canaliculus. The bile is drained into the branches of the bile duct, located in the portal triad. Two hepatic ducts, one from each lobe of the liver, drain the bile secreted by the hepatocytes and join to form a common hepatic duct.

The common hepatic duct joins the cystic duct of the gall bladder to form the common bile duct. The latter joins the pancreatic duct to form the ampulla of Vater. The ampulla opens into the duodenum. The opening is surrounded by the sphincter of oddi (Fig. 30.2).

## COMPOSITION OF BILE

Bile is a greenish yellow, viscid fluid, which is slightly alkaline (pH 7–8). It is continuously synthesized in the liver and transferred to the

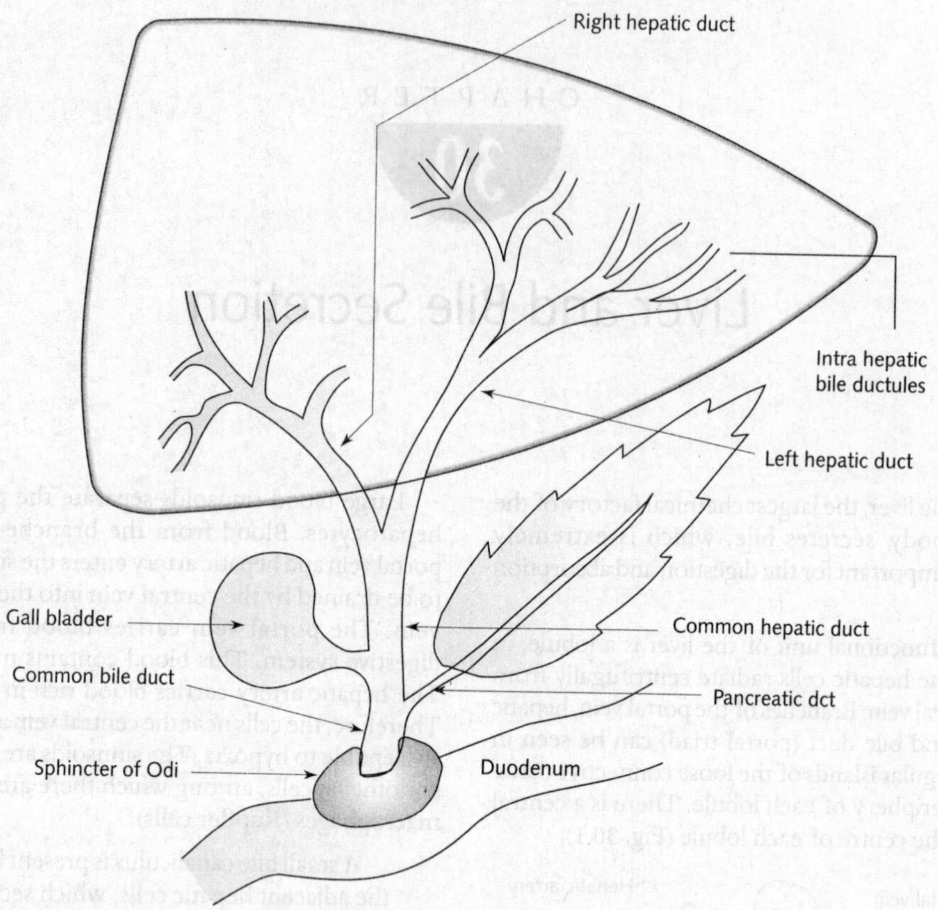


**Fig. 30.2:** Biliary system

gall bladder through the cystic duct. This is because during the interdigestive period, the sphincter of oddi remains closed and the bile cannot enter the duodenum. About 700 to 1200 ml of bile is secreted by the liver per day. Bile is stored and concentrated in the gall bladder. After a meal, the gall bladder transfers about 60 ml of concentrated bile into the duodenum.

The composition of bile is as shown on the right side.

The composition and character of bile change in the gall bladder. Water, NaCl and other inorganic constituents are reabsorbed, so that all the organic components become 5 to 6 times more concentrated. The absorption of $HCO_3^-$ makes the gall bladder bile less alkaline.

| | Bile | |
|---|---|---|
| *Constituents* | Liver | Gall bladder |
| Water | 98% | 89% |
| Solids: | 2% | 11% |
| *Organic* | | |
| (i) Bile salts | 0.5 gms% | 6.0 gms% |
| (ii) Bile pigments | 0.05 gm% | 0.3 gms% |
| (iii) Cholesterol | 0.01 gm% | 0.5 gms% |
| (iv) Lecithin | 0.05 gm% | 0.4 gms% |
| *Inorganic* | | |
| (i) $Na^+$ | 145 meq/l | 135 meq/l |
| (ii) $K^+$ | 4 meq/l | 12 meq/l |
| (iii) $HCO_3^-$ | 30 meq/l | 10 meq/l |

## IMPORTANT CONSTITUENTS OF BILE

### Bile salts

Bile salts are the most important constituents of bile. They are sodium and potassium salts of bile acids, conjugated to the amino acids, glycine and taurine. The important bile acids formed in the liver are cholic acid and chenodeoxycholic acid (primary bile acids), which are formed from cholesterol. These are converted to deoxycholic acid and lithocholic acid, respectively, in the intestine (secondary bile acids), as a result of bacterial action on the primary bile acids. The secondary bile acids are absorbed from the intestine and re-excreted in the bile (enterohepatic circulation).

*Formation of bile acids, their relative amounts in bile and formation of bile salts*

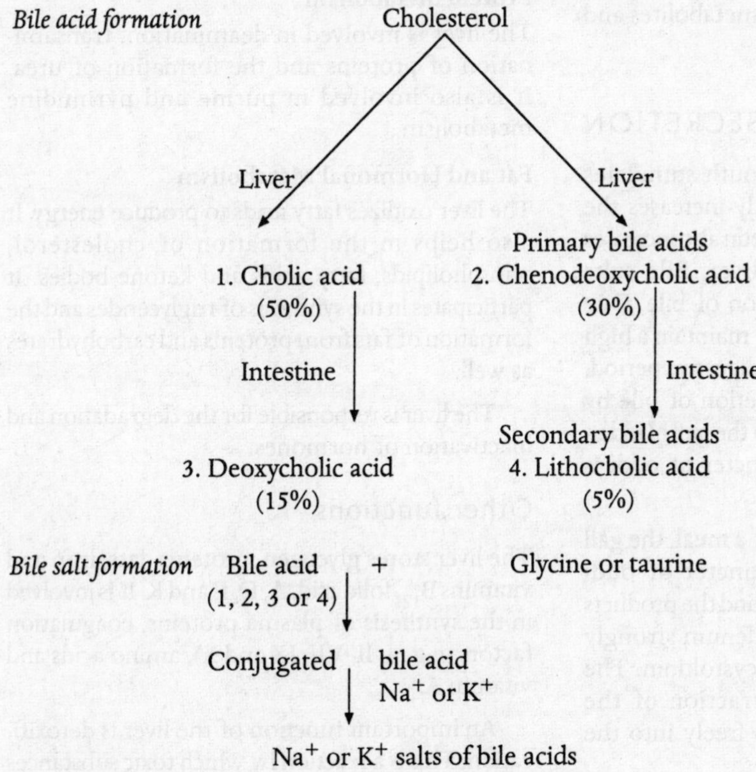


Bile salts help in digestion as well as absorption of fats.

### Bile pigments

Bile pigments, the other important constituents of bile, have no digestive function. They are the degradation products of haemoglobin. The bile pigments are mono- and di-glucoronides of bilirubin and biliverdin. Hepatic cells extract bilirubin (yellow) and biliverdin (green) from the blood, conjugate them with glucoronic acid and transfer them into the bile canaliculi by an active transport mechanism.

Bile pigments are merely excretory products and their only function is to colour the bile and stool.

### Bile lipids

The bile lipids are cholesterol and phospholipid lecithin. Cholesterol has no digestive function and is an excretory product. Lecithin helps in the formation of micelles (loose aggregates of many different molecules). This helps keep the lipids in solution in the bile and intestine.

## FUNCTIONS OF BILE

Bile salts are both water-soluble and lipid-soluble. This property makes them good emulsifiers. Since pancreatic lipase is a water-soluble enzyme, only the surface of a lipid droplet is accessible to its action. Bile salts break up large lipid droplets into smaller droplets by a process known as emulsification, thereby facilitating the digestive action of water-soluble lipase. Thus, bile salts help in the digestion of fats by increasing the surface area of lipid droplets.

Bile salts also combine with the products of the hydrolysis of triglycerides, to form small, water-soluble particles (micelles) and transport them to the brush border of the epithelial cells. They, thus, help in the absorption of digested fats.

Bile salts are responsible for the absorption of fat-soluble vitamins, such as vitamins A, D, E and K. They are also good choleretics, that is, they increase bile secretion from the liver. In addition, they help activate pancreatic lipase, and act as a mild laxative (promote defaecation) as well.

Bile pigments have no function other than to colour the faeces. The waste products of haemoglobin breakdown are excreted as bile pigments in the bile.

The bicarbonate in bile neutralizes the acidity of the gastric juice that enters the duodenum. Bile also helps in the absorption of some metals and the excretion of hormones, metabolites and drugs.

## REGULATION OF BILE SECRETION

The presence of food in the mouth stimulates the taste receptors, which reflexly increases the secretion of bile via the vagus. Secretin also increases the formation of bile in the liver. Bile salts themselves stimulate the secretion of bile. Due to enterohepatic circulation, they maintain a high level of bile secretion during the digestive period. Between meals, the rate of secretion of bile by the liver is slow and it is diverted to the gall bladder, since the resistance of the sphincter of oddi is high.

Shortly after the beginning of a meal, the gall bladder contracts and the sphincter of oddi relaxes reflexly via the vagus. Fats and the products of protein digestion in the duodenum strongly stimulate the secretion of cholecystokinin. The latter produces powerful contraction of the gall bladder and the bile passes freely into the duodenum.

## FUNCTIONS OF LIVER

The liver plays an important role in metabolism, including carbohydrate, protein, fat and hormonal metabolism.

### Metabolic functions

#### Carbohydrate Metabolism

The liver functions as a glucostat, that is, it maintains the blood sugar at a normal level (80 to 120 mg%). Liver cells are highly sensitive to the level of glucose in the blood and, at the same time, highly permeable to glucose. When the blood sugar level decreases, the glycogen in the liver is converted to glucose. This process is called glycogenolysis. On the other hand, when the blood sugar level increases, glucose is converted to glycogen (glycogenesis).

The liver helps in neoglucogenesis, that is, the formation of glucose from noncarbohydrate sources. It also converts fructose and galactose into glucose.

#### Protein Metabolism

The liver is involved in deamination, transamination of proteins and the formation of urea. It is also involved in purine and pyrimidine metabolism.

#### Fat and Hormonal Metabolism

The liver oxidizes fatty acids to produce energy. It also helps in the formation of cholesterol, phospholipids, fatty acids and ketone bodies. It participates in the synthesis of triglycerides and the formation of fats from proteins and carbohydrates as well.

The liver is responsible for the degradation and inactivation of hormones.

### Other functions

The liver stores glycogen, proteins, fats, iron and vitamins $B_{12}$, folic acid, A, D, E and K. It is involved in the synthesis of plasma proteins, coagulation factors (e.g., I, II, VII, IX and X), amino acids and vitamin A.

An important function of the liver is detoxification. This is a reaction by which toxic substances are degraded to relatively nontoxic substances, which can be easily excreted by the kidney. This is achieved by the conjugation of substances with either sulphates, glycine or glucoronic acid. For example:

Benzoic acid + glycine → Hippuric acid
(harmful) (harmless)

The secretion of bile is, of course, a major activity of the liver and has already been discussed.

The liver is responsible for the hydroxylation of vitamin $D_3$ to 25–OH vitamin $D_3$. It is also involved in the formation of RBCs in foetal life. The destruction of old RBCs and the formation of bile pigments from the breakdown of haemoglobin are other functions of the liver.

The liver can produce heat in a large amount. It is also responsible for the excretion of heavy metals like Cu and bismuth through the bile, as well as various toxins produced by bacteria.

## CLINICAL IMPORTANCE—JAUNDICE

Malfunctioning and infection of the liver can lead to jaundice, which can be of three types—infective, obstructive and haemolytic.

### Infective Hepatitis

Also known as hepatic jaundice, this is the most common type of jaundice. It is caused by acute viral infection and is preventable. Hepatocellular failure may occur in patients suffering from hepatic jaundice.

### Obstructive Jaundice

Also known as post-hepatic jaundice, obstructive jaundice is caused by an obstruction to the flow of bile from the gall bladder to the small intestine. The most common cause is gall bladder stone, which is formed because of the excessive secretion of cholesterol or chronic inflammation of the gall bladder, resulting in its precipitation. Another cause may be carcinoma of the head of the pancreas.

The patient passes clay-coloured and bulky stools because bile is obstructed from entering the intestine, preventing the digestion of fat. Fat is thus passed out in the stool.

### Haemolytic Jaundice

This is also known as pre-hepatic jaundice and is caused by excessive breakdown of haemoglobin. This gives rise to excessive formation of bilirubin, an abnormally high level of serum bilirubin and the excretion of a large amount of bile pigment in the urine.

The differential diagnosis of jaundice is done by liver function tests.

CHAPTER 31

# Intestinal Secretion

Succus entericus is the secretion produced by the glands in the small intestine, which are called the crypts of Lieberkühn. These are present as depressions between the intestinal villi. Each villus is lined by a layer of columnar cells and contains connective tissue, blood vessels, smooth muscle fibres and a lymphatic channel, called a lacteal. The luminal surface of the epithelium has microvilli (or a brush border). The villi and microvilli increase the surface area of the mucous membrane, thus helping in absorption (Fig. 31.1).

There are a large number of mucus-secreting goblet cells and argentaffin cells, which secrete 5-hydroxytryptamine (5-HT, serotonin), among the epithelial cells of the crypts. The mucous membrane also contains endocrine cells, which secrete gastrointestinal hormones, such as secretin, CCK-PZ, gastrin, motilin and somatostatin.

## COMPOSITION OF SMALL INTESTINAL SECRETION

The secretion of the small intestine is an alkaline fluid with a pH of 8. The total amount of secretion per day is about 2 l. The composition of the fluid is as shown on the right side.

Succus entericus is almost like extracellular fluid. The only enzyme it contains is enterokinase. Some enzymes are present in the brush border. When these epithelial cells are extruded, they mix with the succus entericus. These enzymes are peptidases, disaccharidases and lipases.

## FUNCTIONS OF SMALL INTESTINAL SECRETIONS

The main function of the secretions is to maintain a suitable environment for digestion and absorption in the small intestine. The bicarbonate present in succus entericus neutralizes the acidic chyme coming from the stomach and helps maintain a

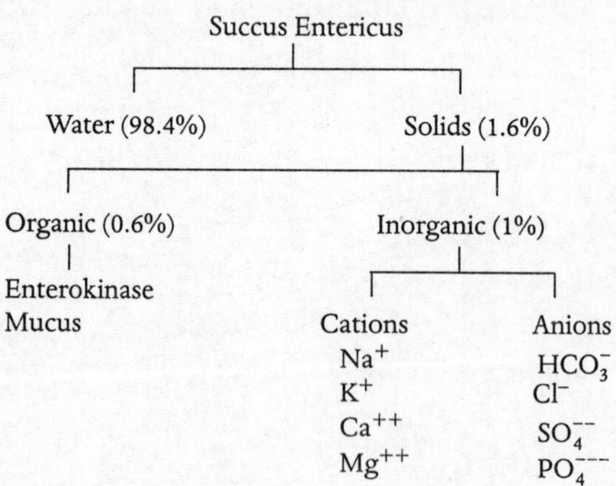

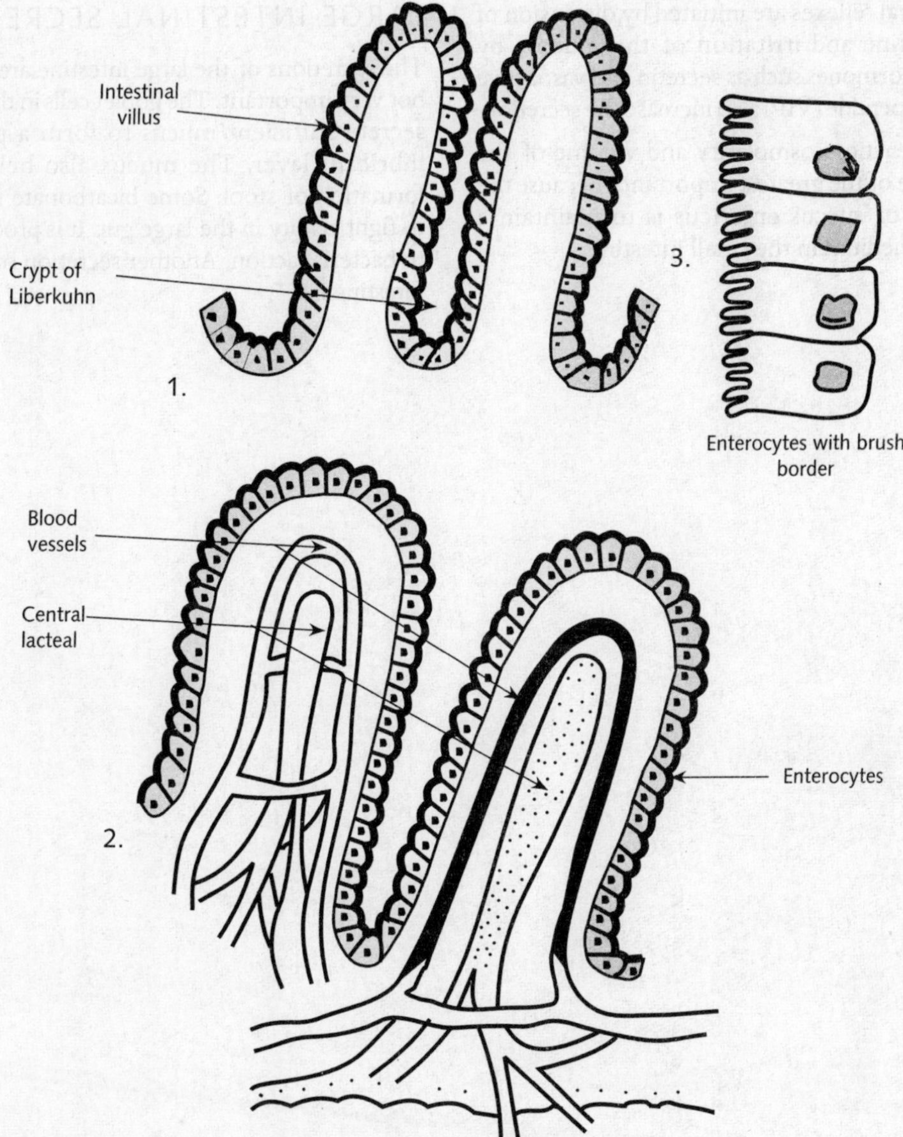


**Fig. 31.1:** Mucous membrane of small intestine

favourable pH for enzyme action in the small intestine.

Mucus is another important component. It forms a layer over the epithelium and protects the mucous membrane from injury.

The enterokinase in succus entericus activates trypsin. The disaccharidases, for example, sucrase, maltase and lactase, split the respective disaccharides into monosaccharides. The peptidases split polypeptides into amino acids. A small amount of intestinal lipase splits triglycerides.

## REGULATION OF SMALL INTESTINAL SECRETION

The secretion of succus entericus is regulated by local neural reflexes and hormonal means. The local neural reflexes are initiated by distension of the intestine and irritation of the mucosa by chyme. Hormones such as secretin and vasoactive intestinal peptide (VIP) also increase the secretion.

The reaction, osmolarity and volume of the chyme are of the greatest importance because the function of succus entericus is to maintain a suitable medium in the small intestine.

## LARGE INTESTINAL SECRETIONS

The secretions of the large intestine are normally not very important. The goblet cells in the mucosa secrete sufficient mucus to form a protective lubricant layer. The mucus also helps in the formation of stool. Some bicarbonate is secreted to fight acidity in the large gut. It is produced due to bacterial action. Another secretion of the large intestine is $K^+$.

CHAPTER 32

# Digestion and Absorption

The human diet consists of carbohydrates, fats and proteins in the form of complex macromolecules. These cannot be absorbed in the alimentary tract as such. Hence, they are broken down to smaller and simpler units by the process of digestion. Digestion is aided initially by the physical forces of mastication and the movements of the gut, particularly the churning movements of the stomach. This is followed by the chemical action of the digestive enzymes on the foodstuff, starting from saliva and ending in the brush border epithelium of the small intestine.

These small, simple units, as well as vitamins, minerals and water, cross the mucosal epithelium and enter the blood circulation or lymph by the process of absorption.

The processes of digestion and absorption take place mainly in the small intestine.

## CARBOHYDRATES

The carbohydrates present in the usual diet are starch (polysaccharide), sucrose, lactose (disaccharides), and glucose and fructose (monosaccharides).

### Digestion

The digestion of carbohydrates begins in the mouth with salivary amylase, but the process actually occurs in the stomach as the food remains in the mouth for only a short while. The action of salivary amylase is optimum at a pH of 6.7 and continues for 20 to 30 minutes, till the highly acidic gastric juice mixes with the food. The enzyme terminates its action at a pH of 4 or less. Although there is no carbohydrate-digesting enzyme in the gastric juice, some hydrolysis of cane sugar occurs in the stomach by HCl.

The pancreatic amylase in the small intestine has an action similar to that of salivary amylase, but its concentration in the pancreatic juice is much greater. Also, it can act on both boiled and unboiled starch. Both salivary and pancreatic amylases are $\alpha$-amylases and hydrolyse 1 to 4 linkages between the glucose molecules of starch. Hence, 1 to 6 linkages remain to form $\alpha$-limit dextrin.

The stages of digestion are as shown below.

Boiled starch
↓
Soluble starch
↓
Erythrodextrin + maltose
↓
Achrodextrin + maltose
↓
Isomaltose + maltose + $\alpha$-limit dextrin

The pancreatic amylase in the small intestine is highly efficient in the digestion of carbohydrates and very rapidly breaks down the carbohydrates delivered from the stomach into the small intestine, where the final digestion of carbohydrates occurs (in the brush border epithelial cells). The enzymes in the brush border act as follows:

$\alpha$-limit dextrin $\xrightarrow[\text{dextrinase}]{\alpha\text{-limit}}$ glucose

Maltose $\xrightarrow{\text{maltase}}$ glucose

Sucrose $\xrightarrow{\text{sucrase}}$ glucose + fructose

Lactose $\xrightarrow{\text{lactase}}$ glucose + galactose

As shown above, the final products of the digestion of carbohydrates are monosaccharides. Given the usual Indian diet, the final product is mostly glucose.

*Clinical importance*: Congenital deficiency of lactase causes intolerance to milk. It results in the formation of gas and diarrhoea.

## Absorption

The absorption of glucose, galactose and fructose occurs in the small intestine.

Glucose and galactose are absorbed by the secondary active transport mechanism. Glucose or galactose and sodium share a common carrier protein. The intracellular sodium concentration of the epithelial cells is kept low by the $Na^+$–$K^+$ ATPase pump, which acts at the basolateral border of the epithelial cells. The forceful flow of sodium down the electrochemical gradient carries glucose/galactose molecules, attached to the carrier, into the cell. The molecules leave the epithelial cell at the basal border by diffusion (Fig. 32.1).

The presence of $Na^+$ ions in the intestinal lumen thus favours the absorption of glucose/galactose. Fructose is rapidly absorbed into the intestinal epithelium independently.

### Dietary Fibre

This includes the components of the plant cell-wall, which are non-starchy polysaccharides, such as cellulose and pectin. These contain $\beta$-glycosidic linkages and hence, cannot be digested by the $\alpha$-amylase present in saliva and pancreatic juice. They are not a source of energy.

These substances slow down gastric emptying and a rise in the blood sugar level after a meal. Further, they retain water, making the faeces bulkier and prevent constipation. They also lower the level of cholesterol by decreasing its absorption.

## PROTEINS

Dietary proteins are long chains of amino acids connected by peptide linkages. They may be simple proteins, such as albumin and globulin, or complex molecules, such as glycoproteins, nucleoproteins and collagen. In addition, some proteins are added in the gut from the shedded cells and enzymes of different digestive juices.

The digestion of proteins entails hydrolysis of the peptide linkages, but most proteins need to be altered by cooking or by the action of acid and alkali in the stomach and small intestine, respectively, before enzymatic digestion can take place.

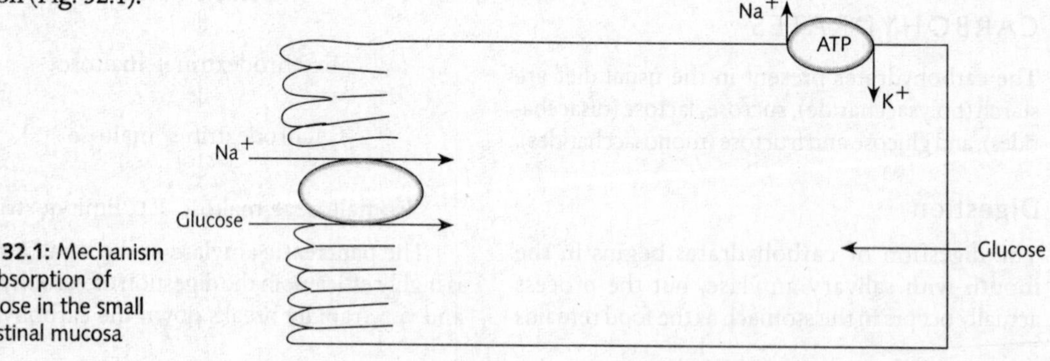


**Fig. 32.1:** Mechanism of absorption of glucose in the small intestinal mucosa

## Digestion

Saliva contains no proteolytic enzyme for the digestion of dietary proteins. In the stomach, pepsin hydrolyses about 15 per cent of dietary protein, with the help of HCl, at a low pH. The stages of protein digestion in the stomach are:

Protein → acid metaprotein → proteoses → peptones

The acid-peptic activity in the stomach digests the collagen.

The pancreatic juice contains a very high concentration of proteolytic enzymes, such as trypsin, chymotrypsin, carboxypeptidase and elastase. These are released as inactive proenzymes, which are converted to active enzymes. The stages of pancreatic digestion are:

Protein → alkali metaprotein → proteoses → peptones → small polypeptides

The pancreatic juice digests elastin.

Further digestion occurs at the brush border and inside the intestinal epithelial cells. The brush border contains peptidases.

These enzymes hydrolyse smaller polypeptides into peptides and amino acids, which then enter the intestinal epithelial cells. Some small peptides that are absorbed intact are converted to amino acids by the peptidases present in the intestinal epithelium.

## Absorption

Amino acids are absorbed from the intestinal epithelium by the secondary active transport mechanism. For this, different types of carrier protein, which bind simultaneously with $Na^+$, are present. A single transport carrier system is responsible for small peptides absorbed across the brush border. At the basal border of the epithelial cells, amino acids are absorbed by passive diffusion.

*Clinical importance*: Some intact protein molecules may be absorbed, particularly in newborns, by endocytosis. An example is the immunoglobulins present in colostrum, which impart passive immunity to the neonate.

# LIPIDS

The most important form of dietary lipids is triglycerides (neutral fat). A small amount of lipids are present as phospholipids, cholesterol and cholesterol esters. The digestion and absorption of dietary fat is a far more complicated process than that of carbohydrates or proteins, since lipids are water-insoluble.

## Digestion

The digestion of lipids in the true sense occurs in the small intestine. The pancreatic juice contains a high concentration of three lipolytic enzymes:

1. Pancreatic lipase, which hydrolyses triglycerides to free fatty acids and glycerol,
2. Cholesterol esterase, which converts cholesterol esters to produce cholesterol and a fatty acid, and
3. Phospholipase, which hydrolyses phospholipids.

Pancreatic lipase is the main enzyme. It is water-soluble and, therefore, acts only on the oil–water interface of the fat droplet. This is why emulsification of fat occurs before digestion, increasing the surface area of the lipids tremendously.

## Emulsification of fats

Lipids are present in the diet in the form of droplets. After emulsification, these droplets are broken down into innumerable tiny particles. This gives enzymes a wide area to act on.

Emulsification is partly achieved by the churning movements of the stomach and intestine. However, it is mostly bile salts that are responsible for emulsification, due to their detergent action. Phospholipid lecithin aids the process.

Lecithin and bile salts have hydrophobic (lipophilic) and hydrophilic ends. The water-soluble hydrophilic ends remain outside, while the fat-soluble lipophilic ends pierce the fat droplet (Fig. 32.2).

This lowers the surface tension of the lipid droplets, which then break up into smaller particles owing to agitation produced by the gut movements.

The products of the digestion of lipids

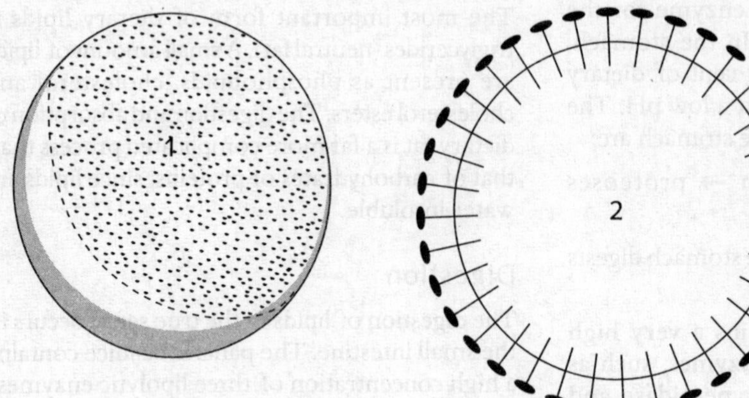


Fig. 32.2: Emulsification of lipid droplets by bile

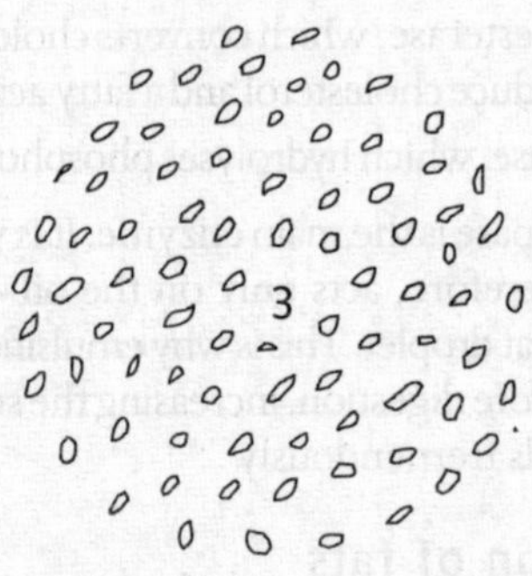


1. Lipid droplet
2. Lipid droplet acted by bile salts and lecithin
3. Emulsified fat

immediately go into micellar solution. Micelles are loose aggregates of bile salts, lecithin and cholesterol, arranged in such a way that the hydrophobic ends are inside and the hydrophilic ends outside the aggregate. These keep cholesterol in a water-soluble state. In the intestinal lumen, they form mixed micelles by including products of lipid digestion in the centre. These help in the absorption of lipids (Fig. 32.3).

## Absorption

The final products of digestion, that is, free fatty acids, monoglycerides, cholesterol and so on, are taken inside the bile salt micelles at the site of their production. They move towards the brush border epithelium through the aqueous medium of the intestinal lumen. Once in contact with the cell membrane, the fatty acids and monoglycerides diffuse freely into the cell, where their concentration is relatively low. The bile salts, now free after unloading the lipids at the brush border, go back to the lumen to form mixed micelles again. This way, the bile salts move to and fro to 'ferry' the lipids to the brush border and are ultimately absorbed from the terminal part of the ileum.

Cholesterol esters and phospholipids are also digested and transported into the cell as triglycerides.

After entry into the mucosal cell, the small-chain fatty acids pass to the blood as they are water-soluble. The larger fatty acids are resynthesized into triglycerides. Cholesterol is converted to cholesterol esters.

The triglycerides, cholesterol and phospholipids are converted into particles coated with protein. These particles, known as chylomicrons, are released into the basolateral space. They enter the central lacteal (lymph) since they are large and

F. A.
M. G.

Mixed micelle

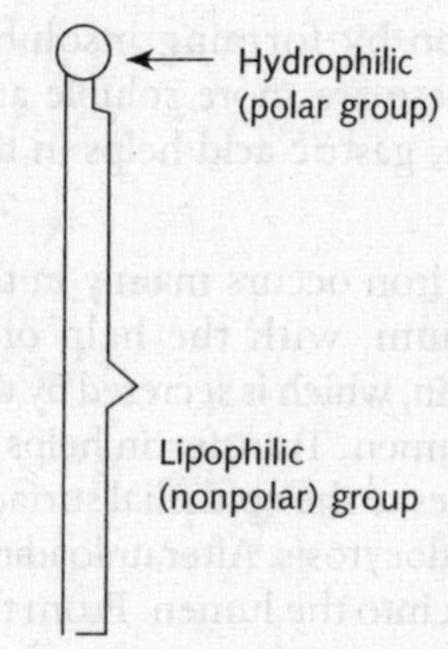

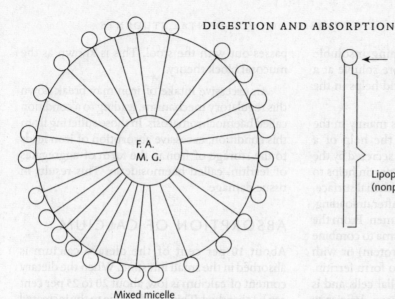

**Fig. 32.3:** A mixed micelle consists of the products of fat digestion, that is, fatty acids (FA) and monoglycerides (MG) enclosed in a globule of bile salt aggregate

cannot enter the blood capillaries. Due to the formation of chylomicrons, the lymph appears milky after a fatty meal. The chylomicrons are formed in such a way that the hydrophilic ends of its phospholipids and proteins remain externally, and the chylomicrons can remain in aqueous solution in the blood and lymph.

## ABSORPTION OF WATER AND ELECTROLYTES

A huge amount of water is absorbed from the gut. About 2 l of water is ingested with food every day and 7 l enters the alimentary canal as gastrointestinal secretions.

The absorption of water starts from the stomach and occurs mainly in the small and large intestines. Water is reabsorbed by passive diffusion, following the reabsorption of NaCl, sugars and amino acids.

Along with the absorption of the products of digestion, the absorption of electrolytes is also a very important determinant of water absorption. $Na^+$ is absorbed from the gut, along with glucose and amino acids. The main driving force for the absorption of $Na^+$ is a very low concentration of $Na^+$ inside the cells, maintained by the $Na^+$ pump. $Cl^-$ is absorbed passively, after $Na^+$. Aldosterone from the adrenal cortex causes the absorption of $Na^+$ and the secretion of $K^+$. The absorption of fluid and electrolytes in the small intestine is actually a net transfer between secretion and absorption. The absorption of fluid and electrolytes in the large gut is the major factor contributing to the formation of the semi-solid stool.

## ABSORPTION OF VITAMINS

Vitamins A, D, E and K are absorbed in the small intestine, together with dietary fats. Their absorption requires the presence of bile salts.

The water-soluble vitamins are absorbed in the small intestine by diffusion or facilitated diffusion. Vitamins C and $B_{12}$ are absorbed by active transport. The absorption of vitamin $B_{12}$ requires the presence of intrinsic factor from the stomach.

## ABSORPTION OF IRON

The average daily diet contains about 10 mg of iron. About 1 mg is absorbed per day, but in states of iron deficiency, such as in growing children and pregnant women, a large percentage of dietary iron can be absorbed.

The iron present in the diet is in the ferric ($Fe^{+++}$) form. This has to be reduced to the ferrous ($Fe^{++}$) form before it can be absorbed in the GI tract. The vitamin C in the diet acts as a reducing agent and helps in the absorption of iron. Dietary phytate, phosphates and fibre decrease the absorption of iron by forming insoluble complexes with it. These are more soluble at a low pH and, therefore, gastric acid helps in the absorption of iron.

The absorption of iron occurs mainly in the duodenum and jejunum, with the help of a protein called transferrin, which is secreted by the epithelial cells in the lumen. Transferrin helps to 'ferry' ferrous molecules to the epithelial surface, where they enter by endocytosis. After unloading, transferrin moves back into the lumen. From the cytoplasm, iron may enter the plasma to combine with transferrin (the transport protein) or with the storage protein, apoferritin, to form ferritin. The latter is stored in the epithelial cells and is lost in the desquamated cells. In iron-deficiency states, a larger percentage of dietary iron enters the circulation. On the other hand, when the iron stores are saturated, most of the absorbed iron is stored in the cells as ferritin.

The regulation of iron absorption probably occurs at the level of the intestinal epithelium. If iron is not required by the body, the epithelium, with its store of iron, is desquamated and the iron passes out with the stool. This is known as the mucosal block theory.

An excessive intake of iron may break down this regulatory mechanism, leading to a condition called haemochromatosis. In those suffering from this condition, excessive absorption of iron leads to the storage of iron in the form of aggregates of ferritin, called haemosiderin. This results in tissue damage.

## ABSORPTION OF CALCIUM

About 10 per cent of the dietary calcium is absorbed in the small intestine. When the dietary content of calcium is low, about 20 to 25 per cent can be absorbed. This could be due to the increased secretion of parathormone and 1, 25-dihydroxy vitamin $D_3$. The latter increases the synthesis of intestinal calcium-binding protein, which increases the absorptive capacity of the intestine.

Dietary proteins promote intestinal absorption of calcium, while dietary phosphates and oxalates, present in vegetables and cereals, interfere with the absorption of calcium by forming insoluble salts.

SECTION

# Metabolism and Nutrition

CHAPTER 33

# Carbohydrate Metabolism

Biochemistry is the branch of science that deals with the chemical aspects of physiology. Biochemical processes have important implications in physiology. Abnormalities in the biochemical phenomena of the body lead to derangements in the physiological processes and hence, different diseases.

The regulation of biochemical processes by the neural and hormonal mechanisms is the most important means of achieving homeostasis.

Our body utilizes carbohydrates, fats and proteins as a source of energy. Energy is used for normal functioning, growth, reproduction and repair. The sum total of all the biochemical processes by which energy is made available and utilized is called metabolism. The term 'catabolism' is used to indicate processes by which energy is liberated. 'Anabolism' indicates processes which take up energy and lead to the synthesis of proteins, fats and complex carbohydrates for storage in the body. The body receives these substrates from the food that we eat, digested and absorbed from GI tract. Vitamins, minerals and water also play an important role in the metabolic processes.

## ENERGY-RICH COMPOUNDS

The energy liberated by catabolism of foodstuff is stored in the form of ATP (adenosine triphosphate) and phosphocreatine. These are known as energy-rich compounds. They contain high-energy phosphate bonds.

### ATP

ATP is a labile chemical substance present in the cytoplasm and nucleoplasm of all cells. It is the immediate source of energy required for all physiological processes.

$$ATP \longrightarrow ADP + P$$

$$ADP \longrightarrow AMP + P$$

The removal of each high-energy phosphate bond releases 12,000 calories. After the loss of one phosphate bond, ATP is converted to ADP (adenosine diphosphate), and with the loss of another high-energy phosphate bond, it is converted to AMP (adenosine monophosphate).

ATP is regenerated by the utilization of energy derived from the oxidation of foodstuff.

### Phosphocreatine

Phosphocreatine contains one high-energy phosphate bond, the removal of which releases 13,000 calories. Although it cannot transfer energy from foodstuff to the cellular mechanism, phosphocreatine can transfer energy to ADP, thereby helping in the resynthesis of ATP.

$$ADP + \text{phosphocreatine} \longrightarrow ATP + \text{creatine}$$

This is important because most cells have a limited store of ATP and extra energy is stored as phosphocreatine, for example, in the skeletal muscle.

The oxidation of foodstuff, leading to the generation of ATP, occurs in the mitochondria. The cytoplasm of the cell contains a series of enzymes that break down carbohydrates, proteins and fat to acetyl coenzyme A (acetyl co-A), which is finally oxidized to $CO_2$ and $H_2O$ in the mitochondria.

The enzymes of the citric acid cycle produce $H^+$ or electrons, the oxidation of which yields ATP.

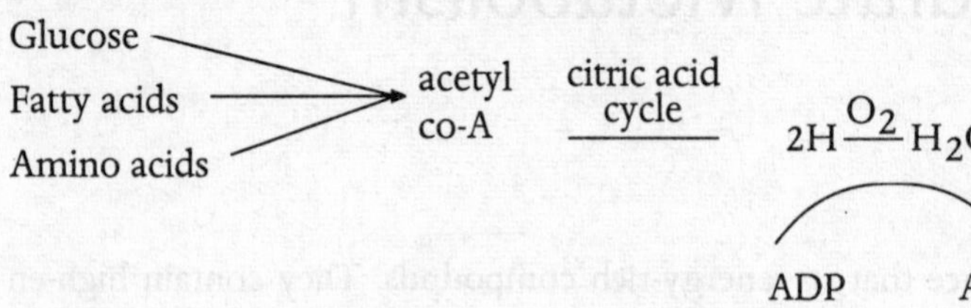


The combination of $H_2$ and $O_2$ (i.e., biological oxidation) requires a series of enzymes called the respiratory chain. These include nicotinic acid, flavoproteins and cytochromes (Fig. 33.1).

The substrate A may be oxidized through the nicotinamide adenine dinucleotide (NAD)–flavoprotein–cytochrome chain, in which case three molecules of ATP are generated, or through the flavoprotein–cytochrome chain only, in which case two molecules of ATP are generated.

## GLUCOSE

Carbohydrates are digested and absorbed from the gut as monosaccharides, of which glucose is the most abundant. These are carried by the portal blood to the liver for further metabolism.

### Transport of glucose into cells

In insulin-dependent tissues, such as skeletal muscle and adipose tissue, glucose is transported across the cell membrane by the process of insulin-dependent facilitated diffusion. That is to say that the permeability of the cell membrane is directly influenced by insulin.

In the non-insulin-dependent tissues, such as neurons and RBCs, glucose is transported by carrier-mediated facilitated diffusion.

In the epithelial cells of the intestinal mucosa and renal tubules, glucose is transported by the active transport mechanism. Different types of carrier proteins are involved in the transport of glucose in different tissues.

In the liver cells, glucose is freely transported in and out, independent of insulin, but once it enters the cells, it is converted to glucose-6-$PO_4$ by the enzyme glucokinase. The activity of glucokinase is accelerated by insulin. Therefore, insulin indirectly enhances the transport of glucose into the cells.

### Metabolism

After glucose enters a cell, it is immediately converted to glucose-6-$PO_4$ by a nonspecific enzyme, hexokinase, which is present in all cells. The phosphorylation of glucose is not a reversible reaction, except in the liver, where the enzyme

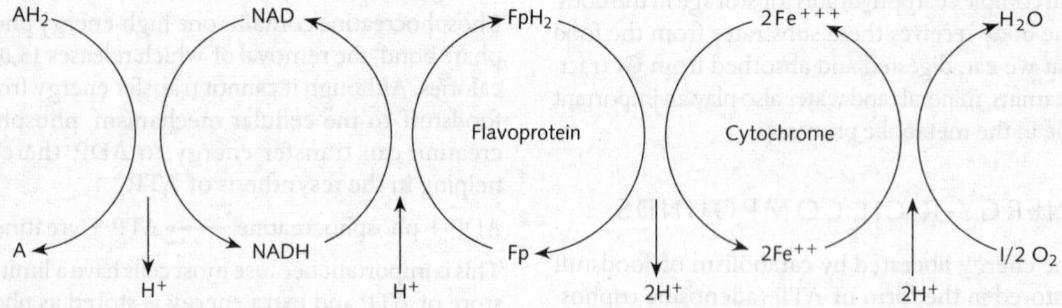


**Fig. 33.1:** Biological oxidation

glucose-6-phosphatase is present. This converts glucose-6-$PO_4$ to glucose, which can come out of the cell.

The cell membranes of other tissues are not permeable to glucose-6-$PO_4$ and, therefore, once formed, it has to be metabolized along one of the four pathways listed below.

1. Synthesized to glycogen, for example, in the liver and skeletal muscle.
2. Catabolized through the glycolytic pathways to produce energy, particularly in the skeletal muscle.
3. Metabolized through the glycolytic pathways for the synthesis of fats, for example, in the liver and adipose tissue.
4. Metabolized through hexose-monophosphate (HMP) shunt.

## Glycogenesis

Whenever the amount of glucose entering the cells is much greater than that required for energy, the excess of glucose is converted to glycogen, a large polymer of glucose. Although all cells contain some glycogen, the liver and skeletal muscle can store large amounts of glycogen. Insulin promotes glycogenesis in the liver and skeletal muscle by activating the enzyme glycogen synthetase. The chemical reactions involved are shown in Fig. 33.2.

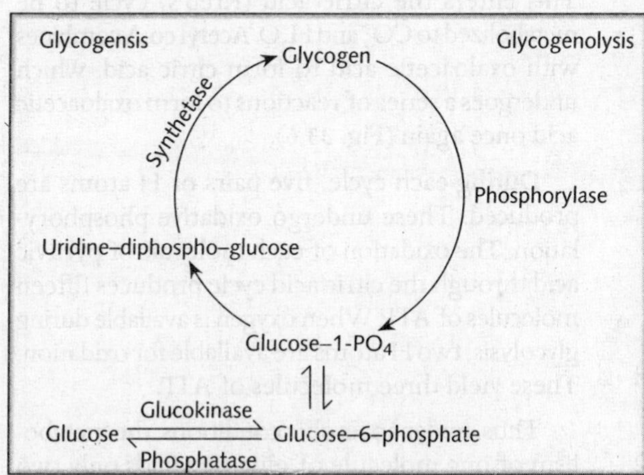


**Fig. 33.2:** Steps of glycogenesis and glycogenolysis

## Glycogenolysis

The degradation of glycogen to glucose-6-$PO_4$ occurs through phosphorylase. This enzyme is activated by glucagon and catecholamines, but inhibited by insulin.

In the liver, glucose-6-$PO_4$ is converted to glucose by the enzyme glucose-6-phosphatase (Fig. 33.2). Hence, in the liver, the result of glycogenolysis is glucose, which enters the blood circulation to maintain the blood glucose level.

In the skeletal muscle, the result of glycogenolysis is glucose-6-$PO_4$ since the phosphatase enzyme is absent. As the muscle cell membrane is not permeable to glucose-6-$PO_4$, it can be catabolized only by glycolytic pathways. Therefore, glycogenolysis in the skeletal muscle results more in the utilization of glucose than an increase in the blood sugar level. Thus, the liver glycogen can be a source of blood glucose but the skeletal muscle glycogen cannot.

## Glycolysis

The breakdown of glucose to pyruvic or lactic acid is called glycolysis, which can occur via the Embeden-Meyerhof pathway or via a direct oxidative pathway.

*Embeden–Meyerhof (EM) pathway:* The various steps of glycolysis via the Embeden–Meyerhof pathway are shown in Fig. 33.3.

Glycolysis is an anaerobic process. Although the breakdown of each molecule of glucose to pyruvic acid produces only two molecules of ATP, this process is very important because (i) the formation of pyruvic acid is essential for subsequent oxidative metabolism, which produces a larger amount of energy; (ii) it is a central point in the intermediary metabolism and pyruvic acid can be converted to a number of compounds, for example, fatty acids; and (iii) it can also be reduced to lactic acid. Hence, glucose continues to be metabolized and generate energy, even if small in amount. Without this step, the process of glycolysis would stop in the middle, due to lack of NAD.

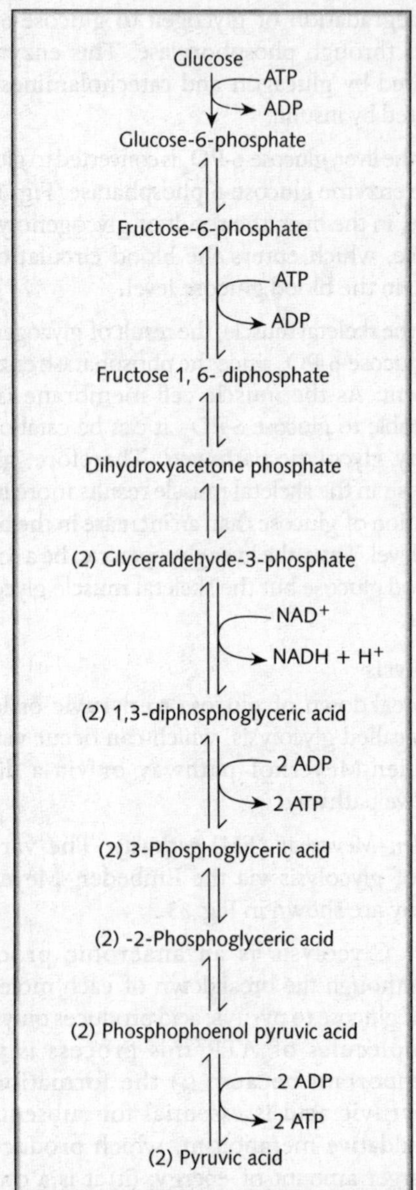


**Fig. 33.3:** Steps of glycolysis (Embeden–Meyerhof's pathway)

Pyruvic acid $\xrightarrow{\text{NADH} \rightarrow \text{NAD}}$ Lactic acid

NADH is reduced NAD.

Lactic acid diffuses readily out of the cells into the blood circulation. Subsequently, when oxygen is available, it is converted back to pyruvic acid, mainly in the liver, and is either oxidized or converted to glycogen (Cori's cycle) (Fig. 33.4).

*Hexose-monophosphate (*HMP*) shunt:* The steps of the HMP shunt are shown in Fig. 33.5. The HMP shunt or oxidative pentose pathway includes reactions in which glucose-6-$PO_4$ is oxidized to pentose phosphate.

This pathway is important as it generates pentose ribose-5-$PO_4$ and NADPH. The former is used in the synthesis of nucleotides and nucleic acid, while the latter compound is useful in various reducing reactions.

In all cells of the body, glucose is metabolized mainly through the EM pathway and, to a minor extent, through the HMP shunt. However, in some tissues such as adipose tissue, the mammary glands and adrenal cortex where NADPH (reduced NAD phosphate) is required for the synthesis of fat and steroids and also in RBCs, where NADPH is required to keep Hb in reduced state, glucose is metabolized through rhw HMP shunt to a large extent.

Both the EM pathway and HMP shunt occur in the cytoplasm of the cell.

## CITRIC ACID CYCLE

Under aerobic conditions, pyruvic acid enters the mitochondria and gets converted to acetyl co-A. This enters the citric acid (Kreb's) cycle to be metabolized to $CO_2$ and $H_2O$. Acetyl co-A combines with oxaloacetic acid to form citric acid, which undergoes a series of reactions to form oxaloacetic acid once again (Fig. 33.6).

During each cycle, five pairs of H atoms are produced. These undergo oxidative phosphorylation. The oxidation of each molecule of pyruvic acid through the citric acid cycle produces fifteen molecules of ATP. When oxygen is available during glycolysis, two H atoms are available for oxidation. These yield three molecules of ATP.

Thus, under anaerobic conditions, the metabolism of one molecule of glucose yields only two molecules of ATP, but under aerobic conditions, an additional thirty-six molecules of ATP [(15 + 3)

(Blood)
Glucose

(Liver)
Glycogen
Glucose
Pyruvic acid
Lactic acid

(Muscle)
Glycogen
Glucose
Lactic acid

(Blood)
Lactic acid

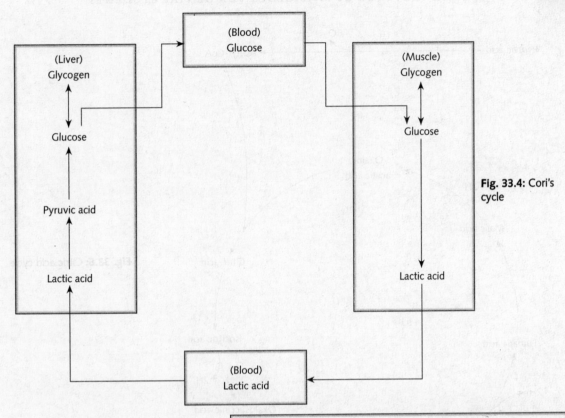

**Fig. 33.4:** Cori's cycle

× 2)] are produced for each molecule of glucose oxidized. The release of energy by the anaerobic glycolytic reaction may be a life-saving measure for a few minutes, till an adequate supply of oxygen is made available.

**Importance of Citric Acid Cycle**

Besides carbohydrates, fatty acids and some amino acids can also be metabolized to acetyl co-A and degraded in the citric acid cycle for the production of energy. Therefore, the citric acid cycle plays a central role in the degradation of all metabolites.

## Gluconeogenesis

Glucose is the only source of energy of the brain. It is also necessary for the production of many vital intermediates.

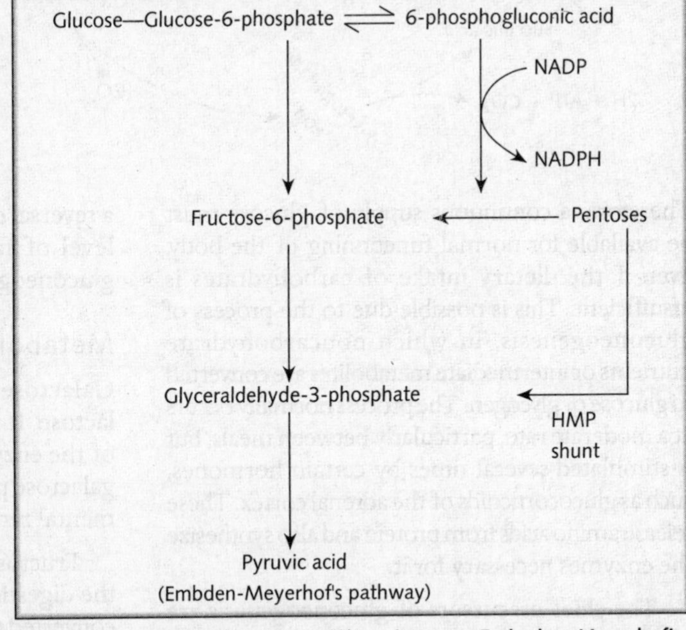


**Fig. 33.5:** Steps of HMP shunt and its relation to Embeden–Meyerhof's pathway

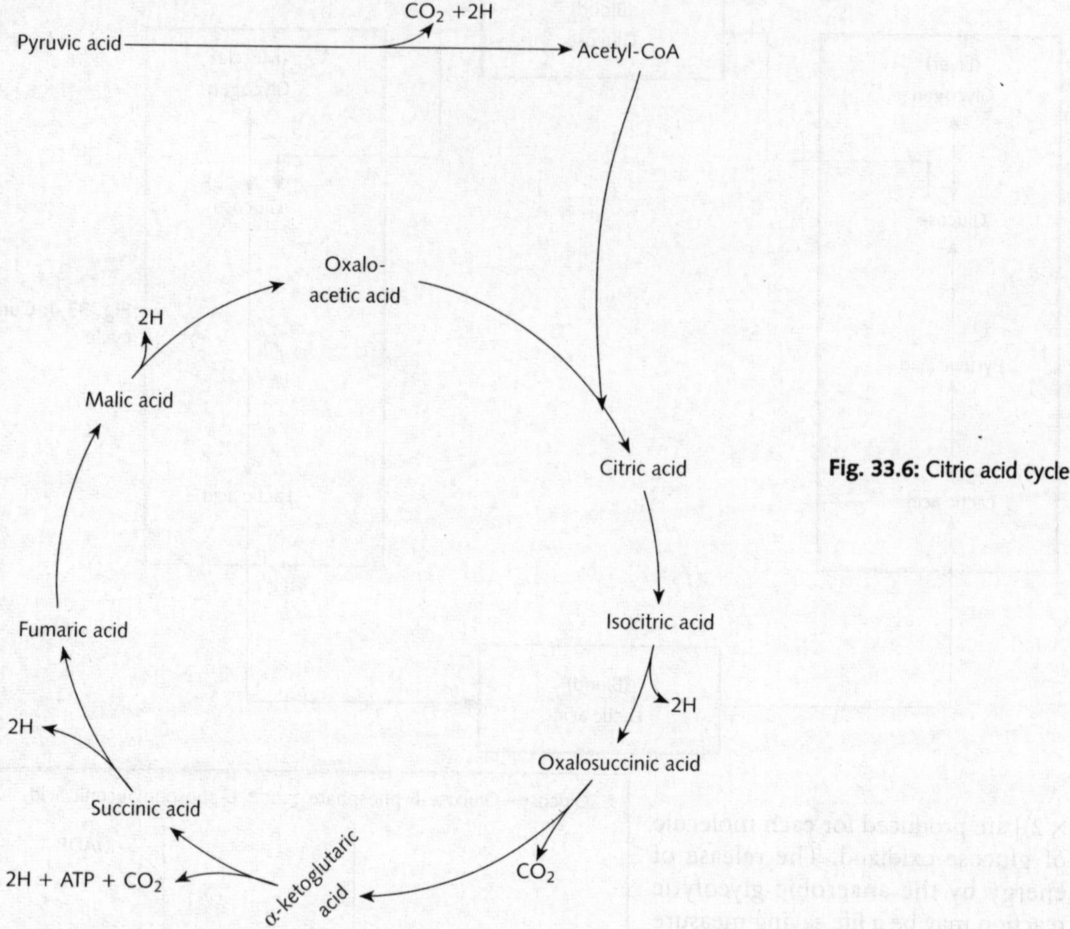


**Fig. 33.6:** Citric acid cycle

Therefore, a continuous supply of glucose must be available for normal functioning of the body, even if the dietary intake of carbohydrates is insufficient. This is possible due to the process of gluconeogenesis, in which noncarbohydrate nutrients or intermediate metabolites are converted to glucose or glycogen. The process normally occurs at a moderate rate, particularly between meals, but is stimulated several times by certain hormones, such as glucocorticoids of the adrenal cortex. These release amino acids from protein and also synthesize the enzymes necessary for it.

The chief precursors of gluconeogenesis are amino acids, pyruvate, lactate and glycerol. The process occurs mainly in the liver and is essentially a reversal of the glycolytic pathway. An increased level of fatty acids and acetyl co-A increases gluconeogenesis.

## Metabolism of galactose and fructose

Galactose is released during the digestion of lactose. It is converted to glycogen with the help of the enzyme uridyl transferase. A deficiency of galactose produces galactosaemia, which leads to mental retardation.

Fructose is ingested as such or liberated during the digestion of sucrose. It enters the liver and is converted to fructose-1-$PO_4$, which is metabolized by the EM pathway.

CHAPTER

34

# Protein Metabolism

Proteins are nitrogen-containing compounds present in all cells of the body. They are essential structural and functional components of the body. All enzymes, and many hormones and neurotransmitters are proteins. Proteins transport many substances, form contractile components of the muscle and mediate gene expression.

## AMINO ACIDS

Proteins are the polymers of amino acids, which are linked to each other by peptide bonds, as shown below.

R – CH – [CO – NH] – CH – R

The primary structure of protein molecules depends on the number and sequence of the amino acids it contains. If a molecule contains a chain of 2 to 10 amino acids, it is called a peptide; if 11 to 100 amino acids, a polypeptide; and if more than 100, a protein.

The secondary structure of protein molecules depends on the pattern in which the amino acid chains are folded. The tertiary structure depends on the relation between these folds. The quaternary structure depends upon the arrangement of the subunits, e.g., haemoglobin. The complex nature of the protein molecule is responsible for many of its functional properties.

The proteins in the diet are digested and absorbed from the gut as amino acids. These are used to synthesize the different proteins found in the body. Twenty amino acids are found in human body proteins. Of these, 8 are called essential amino acids as they are not produced in the body and must be supplied through the diet. The rest are called nonessential amino acids, which can be synthesized in the body whenever required. The essential amino acids are methionine, threonine, tryptophan, valine, isoleucine, leucine, phenylalanine and lysin. A deficiency of these leads to abnormal protein synthesis and a negative balance of nitrogen.

## AMINO ACID POOL

The total amount of amino acids in the body at any moment constitutes the amino acid pool. The normal concentration of amino acids in plasma is 35 to 65 mg% and is maintained fairly constant by the addition and removal of amino acids from the pool.

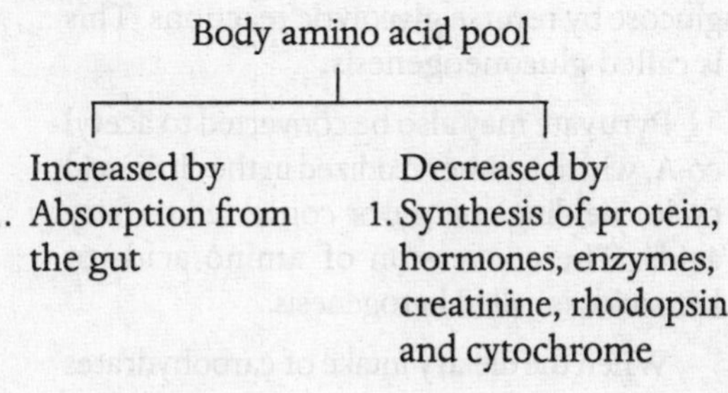

| | |
|---|---|
| 2. Catabolism of body proteins | 2. Deamination, transamination and then oxidation or synthesis of carbohydrates and lipids |
| 3. Synthesis of amino acids | 3. Excretion of small amount in urine |

## Transamination and deamination

In the process of transamination, which is reversible, the amino acid to be catabolized loses its amino group to become a ketoacid, and a ketoacid receives the amino group to become an amino acid. For example:

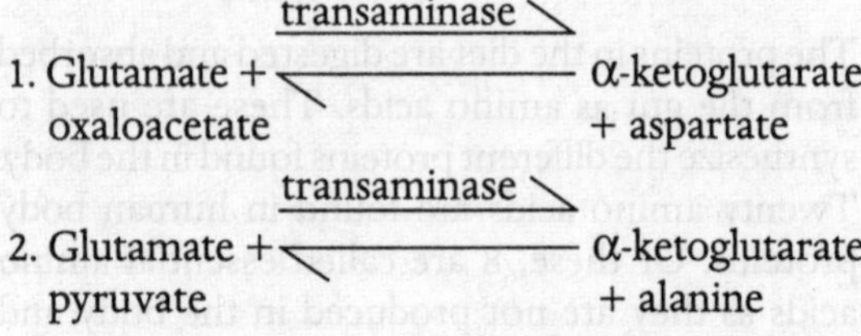


The different ketoacids formed this way are utilized for the production of energy, synthesis of new amino acids, ketoacids, and gluconeogenesis.

The levels of the enzymes catalyzing the two reactions shown above, that is, serum glutamate–oxaloacetate transaminase (SGOT) and serum glutamate pyruvate–transaminase (SGPT) are elevated in patients with myocardial damage and acute liver damage, respectively.

Some amino acids undergo oxidative deamination to produce ammonia. After deamination, amino acids can also enter the common metabolic pool formed by pyruvates and the intermediates of the citric acid cycle. They are ultimately converted to pyruvate, which may be converted to glucose by reverse glycolytic reactions. This is called gluconeogenesis.

Pyruvate may also be converted to acetyl co-A, which is either oxidized in the citric acid cycle, yielding energy, or converted to fatty acids. The conversion of amino acids to ketoacids is called ketogenesis.

When the dietary intake of carbohydrates and fats is normal, only 10 per cent of the energy requirement is derived from proteins. An excessive intake of carbohydrates prevents the breakdown of proteins for the generation of energy. This is known as protein-sparing action. A large amount of protein may be degraded for purposes of energy production in cases of prolonged starvation, when the carbohydrates and fat stores are exhausted. The plasma proteins and tissue proteins are used up for the production of energy.

However, our diet must contain at least 20 to 30 g of protein every day to compensate for the daily degradation of proteins which occurs normally.

## UREA CYCLE

Ammonia is formed as a result of oxidative deamination, mostly in the liver.

$$\text{Amino acid} \longrightarrow \text{Ketoacid} + NH_3$$

The liver converts this highly toxic product ($NH_3$) into a relatively harmless compound urea through a series of cyclic reactions, called the urea cycle (Fig. 34.1).

In man, urea is the chief product of protein-nitrogen metabolism. The amount of urea produced

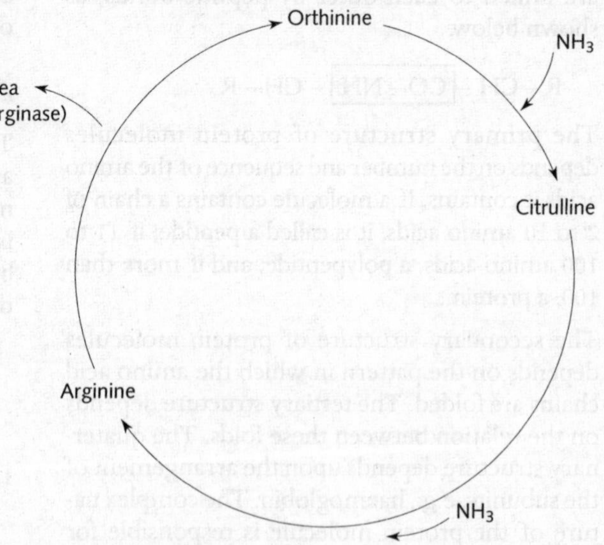


**Fig. 34.1:** Urea cycle

per day varies with the daily intake of proteins. After synthesis, it enters the general blood circulation and is excreted by the kidneys. In acute and chronic liver failure, the liver cells fail to convert the ammonia produced due to the degradation of protein to urea. The accumulation of $NH_3$ in the blood produces toxic effects on the brain, leading to hepatic coma, which may be fatal.

**Uric acid**

Uric acid is formed from nucleic acids in the diet, or by the catabolism of nucleic acids in the body. It is also synthesized in the body and excreted in the urine. A raised level of the uric acid in the blood produces gout, in which uric acid crystals are deposited in the joints.

CHAPTER 35

# Lipid Metabolism

Lipids are energy-rich compounds and are an important constituent of the body. They are stored in the adipose tissue. They are soluble in organic solvents but insoluble in water.

Lipids can be of the following types:

1. Neutral lipids or triglycerides of fatty acids
2. Phospholipids
3. Cholesterol, cholesterol esters
4. Free fatty acids

The fatty acids are long-chain compounds containing 16 to 18 carbon atoms. These may be unsaturated (with double bonds), such as oleic acid, or saturated (without double bonds), such as palmitic and stearic acid. Saturated fatty acids are difficult to metabolize. Some fatty acids (linoleic, linolenic and arachidonic acids) are called essential and must be supplied in the diet. These are related to the reproductive function, general growth and the health of the skin.

The lipids in the diet are digested and absorbed into the blood via the lymph, in the form of free fatty acids and chylomicrons. Free fatty acids are transported in plasma, bound to albumin. The chylomicrons are lipid particles, formed within the intestinal epithelial cells, and are composed of proteins with lipids like phospholipids, cholesterol and triglycerides. These are removed as the blood passes through the capillaries of the liver and adipose tissue, by lipoprotein lipase. This enzyme hydrolyses the triglycerides of chylomicrons into fatty acids and glycerol.

The fatty acids diffuse rapidly into the cells of the adipose tissue, where they are re-esterified. The liver then metabolizes the chylomicron remnants and other lipids to produce another particle called very-low-density lipoprotein (VLDL).

## LIPOPROTEINS

As lipids are insoluble in water, they are transported as lipoproteins. On the basis of their density, they are classified as follows.

### Very-Low-density Lipoproteins (VLDLs)

These lipoproteins consist of nearly 90 per cent lipids, made of high concentrations of triglycerides and a moderate concentration of both phospholipids and cholesterol.

### Low-density Lipoproteins (LDLs)

The VLDLs lose some triglycerides while circulating and take up cholesterol to form LDLs. These lipoproteins, consist of 70 to 80 per cent lipids (triglycerides) and a high concentration of cholesterol. The latter is transported from the liver to the tissues.

### High-density Lipoproteins (HDLs)

After the degradation of LDLs inside the cells, HDLs are formed. These contain equal amounts of proteins and lipids (cholesterol and phospholipids).

The cholesterol in HDL is transported from the tissues to the liver.

These lipoproteins, including the chylomicrons, circulate in plasma along with free fatty acids. The cholesterol of the HDLs does not cause atherosclerosis, like that of the LDLs. An abnormally high level of LDLs and a decreased cholesterol level lead to atherosclerosis, but the reverse situation prevents it. Exercise, as well as a diet rich in unsaturated fatty acids and low in fat, decrease the ratio and thus, the risk of atherosclerosis.

## SYNTHESIS AND STORAGE OF LIPIDS

All lipids, except essential fatty acids, can be synthesized in the body from acetate, that is, glycerol, through the EM pathway. Lipid synthesis occurs in the liver, particularly when the in take of carbohydrates exceeds the amount that can be utilized by the body. Lipids are deposited in fat depots (adipose tissue) when the glycogen stores in the liver and skeletal muscle are saturated. Amino acids can also be converted to acetyl co-A and then, to fats.

Lipids are present as part of the cell membrane in all cells. Adipose tissue constitutes fat depots, where the neutral fats are stored until required for the production of energy. As much as 80 to 90 per cent of the volume of fat cells in adipose tissue may contain triglycerides, which are continuously broken down and resynthesized. That is, they are renewed every 2 to 3 weeks. The importance of the conversion of carbohydrates into fat lies in the fact that just a few hundred grams of glycogen can be stored in the body, while several kilograms of fat can be stored in the adipose tissue.

### Lipid catabolism

Fat stored in the adipose tissue can be mobilized and transported by the blood, to be used in the tissues for the production of energy. Hormone-sensitive lipase (tissue lipase), an enzyme present in the adipose tissue, hydrolyses triglycerides into glycerol and fatty acids. Glycerol enters the EM pathway. Fatty acids are broken down into acetates through β-oxidation and the acetates then enter the citric acid cycle.

### β-oxidation of fatty acids

Free fatty acids can enter the cell membrane freely, but their transport into the mitochondria occurs via a carrier called carnitine. The degradation and oxidation of fatty acids occurs in the mitochondria. At first, fatty acids combine with co-A (coenzyme A). Then, over a series of reactions, acetyl co-A is liberated and the fatty acid chain becomes shorter by two carbon atoms. The process is repeated until the entire fatty acid is split into acetyl co-A.

The acetyl co-A enters the citric acid cycle and is degraded to $CO_2$ and H atoms, which are oxidized by oxidative phosphorylation to yield energy. The energy produced by the oxidation of fatty acids is much greater than that produced by the oxidation of glucose. Fatty acids are, therefore, a major source of energy in most tissues, particularly the myocardium.

## FORMATION AND UTILIZATION OF KETONE BODIES

Although large amounts of fatty acids are degraded to acetyl co-A in the liver cells, only a small part is used for energy. The remaining amount is converted to aceto-acetic acid. A large part of this is converted to β-hydroxybutyric acid and a small part to acetone. Aceto-acetic acid, β-hydroxybutyric acid and acetone are called ketone bodies. The blood transports them to other tissues, where they are converted back to acetyl co-A and oxidized in the citric acid cycle, since the liver cells cannot oxidize them. The skeletal muscle is particularly adapted to using ketone bodies as a fuel. Normally, the utilization of ketone bodies keeps pace with their synthesis and, therefore, they are not excreted in the urine. Under conditions in which fats, and not glucose, is utilized for the production of energy, the formation of ketones exceeds their utilization. This leads to an accumulation of ketone bodies in the blood (ketosis) and their subsequent excretion through urine (ketonuria). Some examples of such a condition are diabetes mellitus, prolonged starvation and a diet rich in fats but low in carbohydrates.

**Hormonal Control of Fatty Acid Utilization**

Hormone-sensitive lipase controls the release of fatty acids from the adipose tissue. The activity of the enzyme is stimulated by hormones, such as glucagon, growth hormone, glucocorticoids and catecholamines (epinephrine, norepinephrine), released due to stress. It is inhibited by the insulin released following a carbohydrate-rich meal.

## CHOLESTEROL METABOLISM

Cholesterol is a component of the cell membrane. It is also a precursor of steroid hormones and bile salts, and is synthesized in the liver. Cholesterol cannot be catabolized as such. When it infiltrates into the subendothelial region of the arteries, the blood vessel becomes rigid and narrow. This condition, known as atherosclerosis, disposes a person to coronary and cerebral thrombosis. Elevated levels of plasma cholesterol and LDLs are responsible for it.

## PROSTAGLANDINS

These are the substances produced from arachidonic acid, a polysaturated fatty acid. They produce a variety of actions in the body. For example, prostaglandins have been used therapeutically to induce abortion in mid-pregnancy.

Prostaglandins are mediators of the inflammatory reaction, which primarily help to protect the body against infection. In certain diseases, the inflammatory response is strong and destructive, and may produce permanent tissue damage. Therefore, nonsteroidal, anti-inflammatory drugs which inhibit the synthesis of prostaglandins are used to suppress inflammatory response.

CHAPTER 36

# Nutrition

All living organisms need energy for the maintenance of the vital functions of the body.

## EXPENDITURE OF ENERGY

The body uses energy to do external work, like carrying an object from one place to another or a simple walk, which involves contractions of the skeletal muscles. Energy is also expended on internal work, such as the beating of the heart, secretion from glands, conduction of nerve impulses, maintenance of the membrane potential, active transport mechanisms involved in various processes of absorption, as well as synthetic reactions involved in growth and development.

The body utilizes energy for the production of heat, which is normally a by-product of the processes of energy utilization but is vital for the maintenance of the body's temperature.

Energy expenditure = External work done + Energy liberated as heat since energy used for internal work is ultimately liberated as heat

All the energy needed by the body for different processes is supplied from outside, that is, by the oxidation of foodstuffs such as carbohydrates, proteins and fat. If the intake of energy exceeds the immediate requirement, it is stored in the body as glycogen or fat.

Energy supplied by food stored = Energy used + Energy stored

## THE BASAL ENERGY REQUIREMENT

*Unit of heat*: The unit of heat is the calorie (cal), which is the amount of heat required to heat 1 g of water through 1°C. A larger unit is the kilocalorie (kcal) which is equal to 1000 cal.

The energy required by the body to do external or physical work varies according to the degree of work performed. However, even at rest (when no external work is being done), the body needs energy for the various metabolic processes occurring within it. This energy is known as the basal metabolic rate (BMR), which is fairly constant. Therefore, the BMR is the rate at which energy is expended by the body, that is, the amount of energy liberated per unit time under basal conditions.

### Determination of BMR

Since all the energy required by the body is derived from the oxidation of foodstuff, the amount of energy expended can be indirectly calculated from the oxygen consumption of the body.

**Method**

For the BMR to be calculated, the person has to fulfil the following conditions:

1. He/she must be in the post-absorptive state (12 to 18 hours after the last meal).
2. He/she must be in a state of complete physical and mental relaxation.
3. He/she should be in thermo-neutral surroundings (25–27°C).

The oxygen consumption of the person concerned is estimated for 6 minutes with the help of Benedict–Roth apparatus. This is basically an oxygen-filled spirometer, with a $CO_2$-absorbing system that contains soda lime, a one-way breathing valve and a pen to write on a kymograph (Fig. 36.1).

The amount of oxygen consumed per hour is found and corrected to standard temperature and pressure. The amount of energy produced or consumed by the body can be determined from the corrected value since the calorific value of $O_2$ is 4.82 kcal/l.

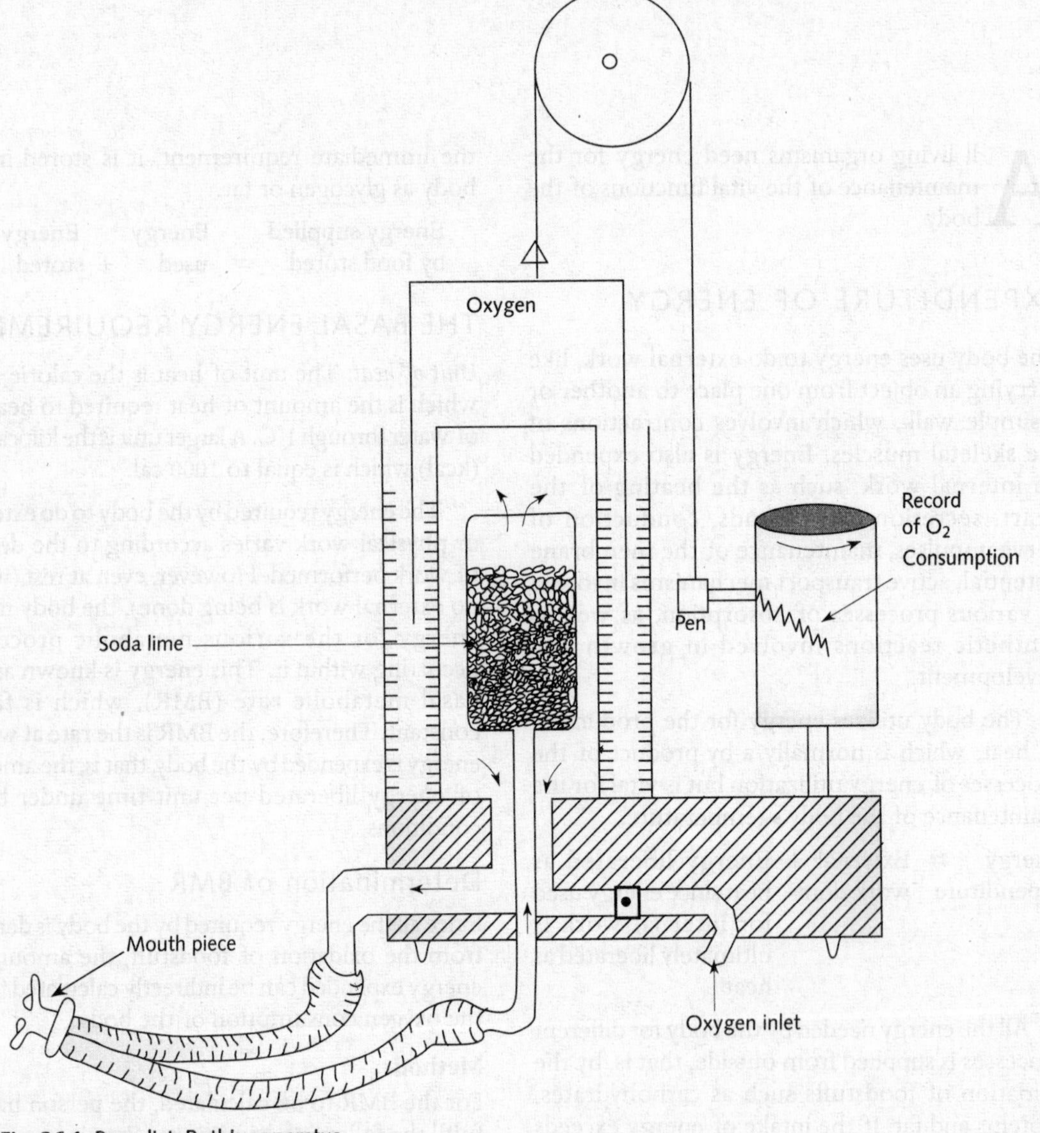


**Fig. 36.1:** Benedict–Roth's apparatus

The BMR is expressed as kilocalories per hour per square metre body surface area.

**Normal Value**

The average BMR value in a normal adult male is 40 kcal/hr/$m^2$ body surface area. For clinical use, the BMR is reported as a percentage of the increase or decrease in the measured value over the value predicted for the subject, in respect of his/her age and sex. Values that are 10 per cent higher or lower than the normal average are considered to be within the normal range.

## Factors affecting BMR

The BMR varies according to the age of a person. The metabolic rate of children is higher than that of adults, and it decreases in old age.

Males have a higher BMR than females with the same surface area, since females have a larger percentage of subcutaneous fat. The BMR is closely related to the body surface area, and has less to do with the height and weight alone.

The BMR increases during pregnancy, and also varies with the external temperature.

Thyroxine is the main hormone that regulates the BMR. In hyperthyroidism, the rate increases, while in hypothyroidism, it decreases. Epinephrine also increases it. The intake of proteins particularly increases the BMR. This is known as the specific dynamic action of proteins.

During sleep, the BMR decreases. A rise in body temperature increases it, as does physical activity (in proportion to the degree of muscular effort). Prolonged starvation causes a fall in the metabolic rate, while anxiety and tension increase it.

**Importance**

It is important to know the BMR for determining the amount of energy required by the body, for example, for planning the diet. A knowledge of the BMR is also useful in the study of different factors affecting it. Further, the diagnosis of diseases which alter the metabolic rate is easier if the BMR is known.

**Total Caloric Requirement**

The total caloric requirement of an individual can be calculated by adding the basal metabolic requirements to the energy required for his/her professional/recreational/household activities. A sedentary worker needs much less energy than a labourer.

An average sedentary male requires 2400 kcal per day, while a sedentary female requires about 2000 kcal.

# BALANCED DIET

Nutrition is a dynamic process which involves the supply of the correct amount of nutrients to the body for repair, growth and maintenance. Different cells of the body are continuously active at different rates, and for this, energy and other necessities must be supplied. The various activities cause wear and tear, which must be repaired. Other than this, growing children, pregnant or lactating women, convalescents and aged people require extra materials. All these needs are met through nutrition.

Nutrients are the substances which provide nutrition to the body. These include carbohydrates, proteins, fats, vitamins, minerals and water. A diet is said to be balanced when the various nutrients are present in the proper proportion and in amounts that are sufficient to meet all the needs of the body.

## Carbohydrates

These are found in abundance in various cereals, roots, tubers and fruit, all of which are of plant origin.

Carbohydrates constitute the cheapest dietary source of energy. It takes a larger amount of carbohydrates than fat to meet the energy demand. They fulfil over 50 per cent of the total caloric requirement, the rest being provided by the oxidation of fats and proteins. Carbohydrates are essential for the smooth functioning of the Tricarboxylic Citric Acid (TCA) cycle, without which ketosis would develop. Although they can be synthesized in the body, a minimum intake of

50 to 100 g is essential to prevent ketosis and the loss of muscle proteins.

Carbohydrates have a protein-sparing effect, that is, they prevent the breakdown of body proteins. They also provide materials for the synthesis of lipids, as well as some amino acids.

## Proteins

Proteins are nitrogenous substances of both plant and animal origin. They are an indispensable constituent of the diet as they supply the essential amino acids. They are also needed for repair, growth of tissues during childhood and pregnancy, and synthesis of enzymes, hormones and other proteins required by the body, for example, plasma proteins and haemoglobin.

The daily requirement of proteins is 1 g/kg body weight, provided the quality of the proteins is such that 65 per cent of the nitrogen can be retained. However, the requirement is greater in the case of growing children and pregnant and lactating women.

### Types of Proteins

First-class proteins are those which contain essential amino acids, such as proteins of animal origin. Those which are deficient in some amino acids are called seconds-class proteins, for example, proteins of plant origin.

A protein whose nitrogen is retained maximally in the body is said to have high biological value. This depends on the amino acid composition of the protein. The amino acid composition of animal proteins such as egg, fish, meat and milk is similar to that of human tissue. These are said to have high biological value. Individual vegetable protein, which is deficient in one or more essential amino acids, is said to have low biological value. However, when a mixture of vegetable proteins is ingested, it provides all the essential amino acids. As the efficiency of the utilization of vegetable proteins is about 65 per cent that of the utilization of animal proteins, the intake of vegetable proteins has to be proportionately higher than that of animal proteins.

Amino acids which are not incorporated in the tissues are deaminated and excreted as urea in the urine.

### Nitrogen Balance

Normally, in an adult individual, the amount of protein catabolized in the body is replaced by exactly the same amount of protein in the diet, that is, a protein balance is maintained. However, since the proteins are quantified by nitrogen, the actual term used is 'nitrogen balance.'

A positive nitrogen balance is seen in growing children, convalescents, pregnant women and so on, while a negative nitrogen balance is seen in those with an excess of thyroxine and glucocorticoid secretion, as well as in cases of protein malnutrition.

## Fats

Lipids include both the solid (fats) and the liquid (oil) variety. They are obtained from animal as well as plant sources. One advantage of the lipids is their high energy content. One gram of fat on oxidation, yields 9 kcal as, compared to 4.5 kcal in the case of carbohydrates and proteins. Lipids have a long staying power, that is, it takes longer for a person to feel hungry after he/she has had a fatty meal. However, fats are costly, and difficult to digest.

Lipids are also essential nutrients as they supply the essential fatty acids required for the synthesis of prostaglandins. They not only enhance the taste of food, but are also essential for the absorption of fat-soluble vitamins. Further, lipids are the main component of the cell wall and also, the myelin sheath of nerves. Steroid hormones and bile salts are formed from lipid. Therefore, it is essential that the diet contain lipids, though lipids other than essential fatty acids can be synthesized within the body.

An excess intake of lipids results in obesity, atherosclerosis and various diseases, such as coronary artery disease. Saturated oils are responsible for these problems. Unsaturated fatty acids, on the other hand, have a protective effect.

## Minerals and vitamins

Normally, minerals come with food and water. The important minerals include iron, iodine, zinc and calcium. The diet must include a proper amount of these elements. The normal dietary intake of calcium is 1 g/ day. This should be increased during pregnancy and lactation.

Vitamins are complex organic molecules without energy value, but are essential for growth and the maintenance of a healthy body. They must be supplied from outside as they are not formed in the body. They may be of the fat-soluble or water-soluble type.

The sources of vitamins, their role in the body and the disorders caused by the deficiency of different vitamins are summarized in Table 36.1.

**Table 36.1:** Vitamins, their sources, action and deficiency disorders

| *Vitamin* | *Sources* | *Action* | *Deficiency disorders* |
|---|---|---|---|
| FAT-SOLUBLE | | | |
| A | Fish liver oil, liver, butter, egg, cheese, carrot, spinach,mango, papaya, tomato, milk and milk products. | Constituent of retinal photo-pigments.<br>Maintenance of the integrity of glandular and epithelial tissues, especially of the skin and eyes.<br>Supports growth. | Night blindness, conjunctival xerosis (dryness), Bitot's spot, corneal xerosis, phrenoderma or toad skin, respiratory infection. |
| D | Cutaneous synthesis; animal food such as liver, egg yolk, butter, cheese and fish liver; fortified vanaspati ghee. | Intestine: Promotes calcium absorption.<br>Bone: Stimulates mineralization.<br>Kidney: Increases calcium reabsorption.<br>Teeth: Formation of enamel. | Rickets in children, osteomalacia in adults. |
| E | Vegetable oils, sunflower seed, egg yolk, butter, wheat germ oil and spinach. | An important antioxidant on cellular and subcellular membrane phospholipids.<br>Maintains reproductive function. | Anaemia in pregnancy, neurological disorders, sterility and muscular dystrophy. |
| K | Green vegetables synthesized by intestinal bacteria. | Synthesis of clotting factors II, VII, IX and X. | Clotting disorders. |

*(Table Contd...)*

*(Table 36.1 contd.)*

| *Vitamin* | *Sources* | *Action* | *Deficiency disorders* |
|---|---|---|---|
| WATER-SOLUBLE | | | |
| *B complex Group of Vitamins* | | | |
| $B_1$, Thiamin | Whole grain cereals, wheat germ, pulses, groundnut, egg, milk, fish. | Coenzyme for oxidative decarboxylation and trans-ketolase reaction HMP shunt. | Beri-beri<br>Dry: neuropathy<br>Wet: cardiovascular degeneration. |
| $B_2$, Riboflavin | Milk, egg, liver, green vegetables, yeast, pulses, germinating seeds. | As cofactor in cellular oxidation in energy metabolism.<br>As coenzymes FMN (Flavin mononucleotide), and FAD (Flavin adenine dinucleotide) to dehydrogenases. | Stomatitis, glossitis, cheilosis. |
| Niacin | Liver, meat, egg, fish, groundnut. | Coenzyme in NAD-linked dehydrogenases. | Pellagra: weight loss, diarrhoea, dermatitis and dementia. |
| $B_6$, Pyridoxine | Milk, egg yolk, meat, cereals and vegetables. | Role in metabolism of carbohydrates, fats and amino acids. | Irritability and convulsions in children. |
| Pantothenic acid | All foods. | Present in cells as coenzyme-A. | Dermatitis and alopecia. |
| Folic acid | Leafy vegetables, meat, egg, milk, cereals. | Role in nucleic acid synthesis. | Megaloblastic anaemia, glossitis, diarrhoea. |
| $B_{12}$, cyano-cobalamin | Liver, meat, fish, egg, milk, cheese; also synthesized by colonic bacteria. | DNA synthesis. | Pernicious anaemia, megaloblastic anaemia and subacute combined degeneration of spinal cord. |
| Biotin | Foods of plant and animal origin. | Deamination of some amino acids and synthesis of fatty acids. | — |
| C | Citrus food, green leafy vegetables, amla, guava. | Role in tissue oxidation, collagen synthesis, absorption of iron, health of vascular endothelium. | Scurvy, bleeding from gums, local haemorrhages, increased capillary fragility, microcytic anaemia, lack of resistance to infection. |

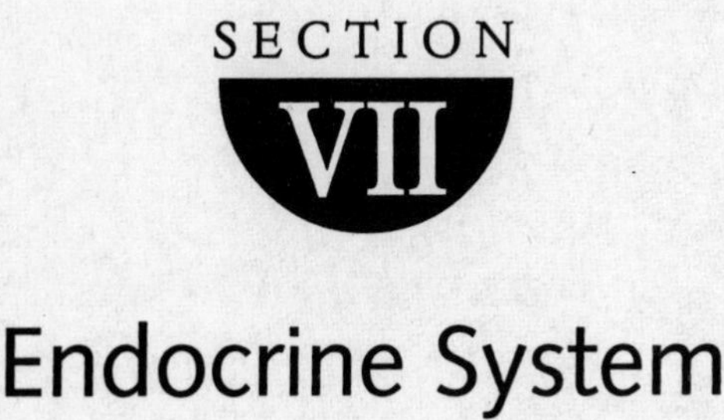


# Endocrine System

CHAPTER

37

# Hormones

The endocrine system, together with the nervous system, controls and coordinates the functions of different parts of the body. This is necessary for homeostasis. In the nervous system, intercellular communication is carried out by nerve impulses, which control the rapid activities of the body, such as muscular contraction. In the endocrine system, on the other hand, intercellular communication is carried out by means of hormones, which control the metabolic activities of the body. However, both systems are closely interlinked.

A hormone, a chemical substance secreted directly into the blood by a group of cells, exerts a physiological control on some distant cells of the body. Some hormones exert their action on tissues nearby and are called local hormones (e.g., secretin). Hormones secreted by endocrine (ductless) glands exert their action on a large number of tissues situated far away from the glands. Such hormones are called general hormones or systemic hormones. Chemically, they are peptides or steroids in nature. Specific hormones act on specific cells or tissues of the body, which are called target cells or tissues.

The various endocrine glands in the body are listed below (Fig 37.1).

1. Pituitary
2. Thyroid
3. Parathyroids
4. Adrenals
5. Pancreas (islets of Langerhans)
6. Gonads (ovaries in females and testes in males)

## MECHANISM OF HORMONE ACTION

Hormones act through their receptors, which are large proteins. The receptors may be located either in the membrane, cytoplasm or nucleus of the cell. The binding of a hormone molecule with a specific receptor leads to the formation of a receptor-hormone complex. The target tissues have specific receptors for the hormone concerned. Once the receptor-hormone complex is formed, the activation of the receptor brings about a conformational change in it, leading to one of the following mechanisms of action.

### Through Cell Membrane

The activated receptors may directly alter the permeability of the cell membrane. For example, insulin increases cell permeability to glucose.

### Through Protein Synthesis

The activated receptors may alter protein synthesis in the target cell, as in the case of the thyroid hormone and steroid hormones of the adrenal cortex and gonads. The receptor for the thyroid hormone is located in the nucleus, while that for steroids is in the cytoplasm and later binds to the nucleus. Some of the proteins synthesized

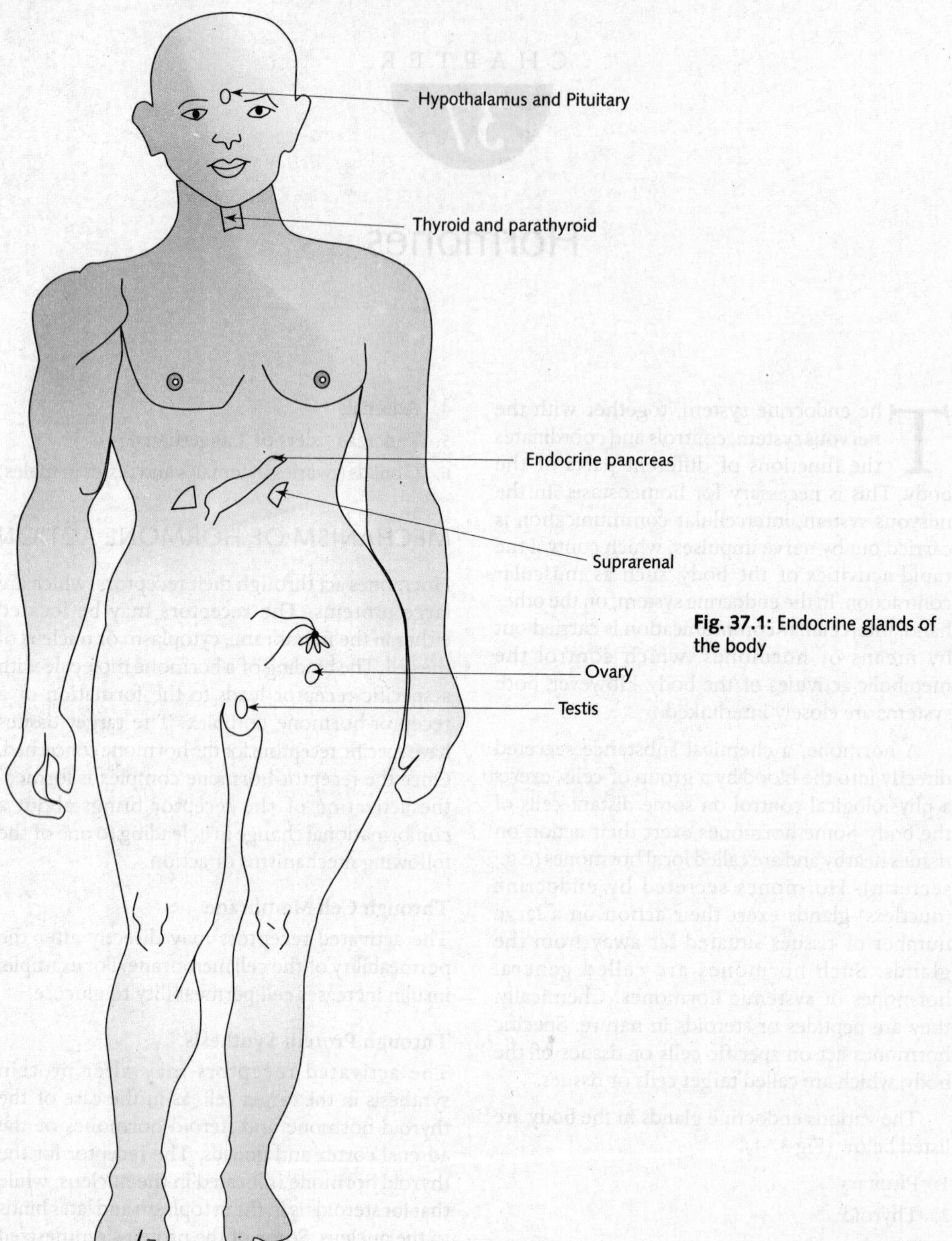


**Fig. 37.1:** Endocrine glands of the body

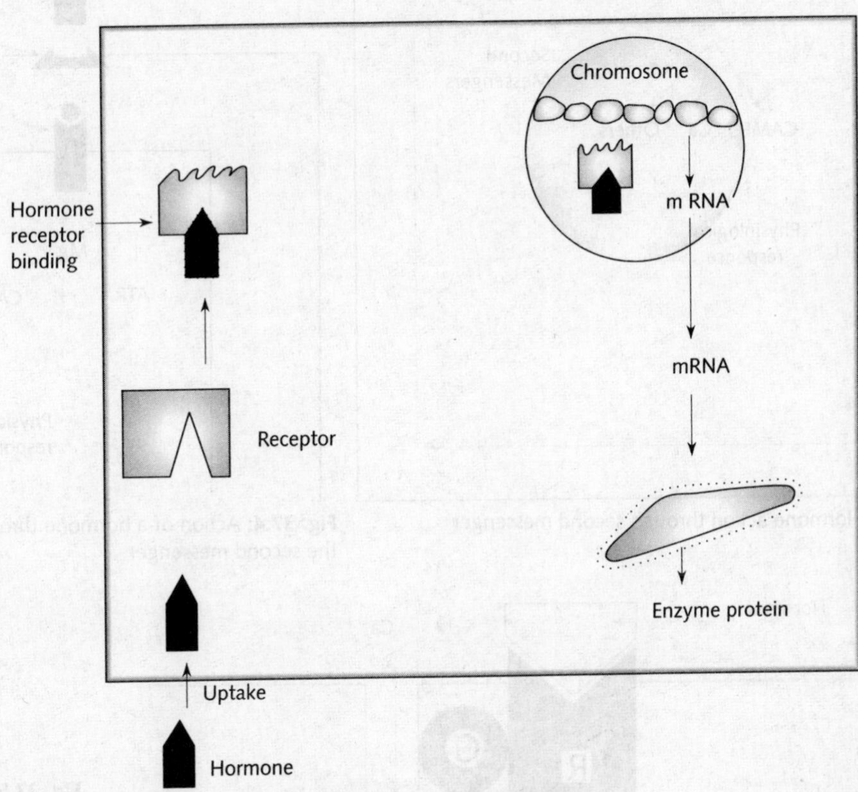


**Fig. 37.2:** Action of hormones through changes in protein synthesis

are enzymes, which may, in turn, alter the function of other cells in the body (Fig. 37.2).

**Through Second Messenger**

In the cell membrane, the activated receptor, called the first messenger, exerts its biological effect by increasing the intracellular concentration of another regulatory molecule called the second messenger, some examples of which are cyclic AMP and $Ca^{++}$. Peptide hormones act this way (Fig. 37.3).

*Cyclic AMP (cAMP)*: When the hormone binds with the receptor in the cell membrane, the hormone-receptor complex activates an enzyme, adenyl cyclase, in the cell membrane. This enzyme converts cytoplasmic ATP into cAMP. The cAMP may cause the following changes in different tissues (Fig. 37.4):

1. Alteration in cell membrane permeability.
2. Initiation of secretion.
3. Synthesis and activation of specific intracellular enzymes.

Hormones such as parathormone and oxytocin may act through this mechanism.

*Calcium ions and calmodulin*: The hormone-receptor complex may increase the concentration of intracellular $Ca^{++}$ by opening the $Ca^{++}$ channels in the cell membrane, or mobilizing it from the endoplasmic reticulum. The $Ca^{++}$ ions then bind with and activate the intracellular $Ca^{++}$-binding protein, called calmodulin, which produces biological responses (Fig. 37.5). Hormones such as oxytocin and angiotensin II act by increasing intracellular $Ca^{++}$.

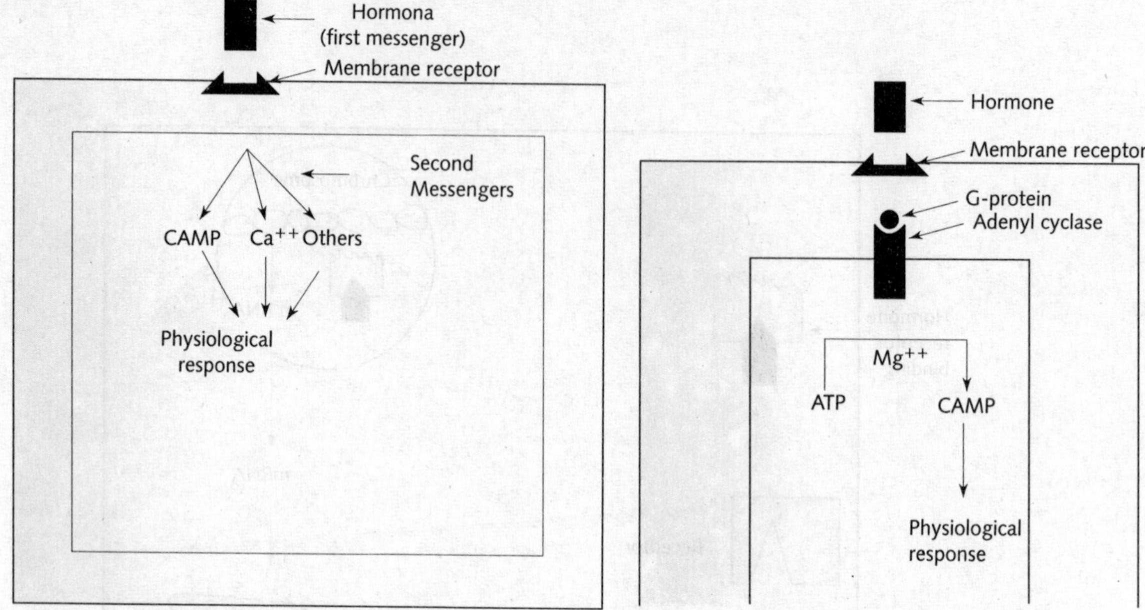


**Fig. 37.3:** Hormone action through second messenger

**Fig. 37.4:** Action of a hormone through cAMP as the second messenger

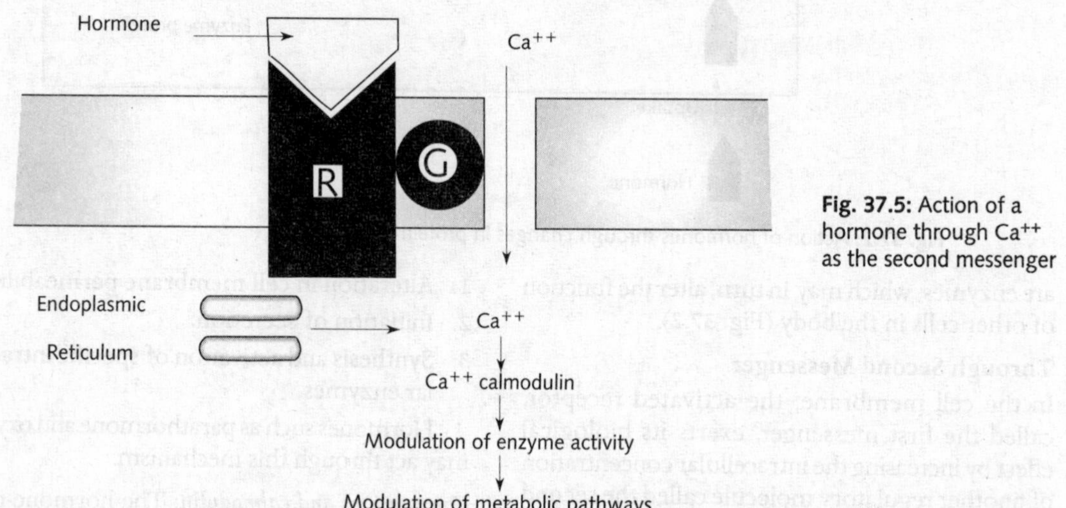


**Fig. 37.5:** Action of a hormone through $Ca^{++}$ as the second messenger

*Degradation of hormones:* The degradation of hormones occurs after they have performed their functions in the target cells. It takes place mainly in the liver and kidney by oxidation, reduction, hydroxylation, sulphation and glucoronidation. Inactivated hormones are excreted through the urine.

*Estimation of hormones*: The estimation of hormones is done from the serum or body fluids in order to know whether or not an endocrine gland is functioning normally. The common methods used are radioimmunoassay (RIA), in which radioactivity and the antigen–antibody reaction are used, and enzyme-linked immunosorbent assay (ELISA), in which the antigen–antibody reaction is used without radioactivity.

### Regulation of Endocrine Secretion

Endocrine secretion is regulated mainly by the feedback mechanism. In this, the plasma level of the hormone determines whether further secretion of the hormone is required. If a high level of a hormone in the plasma inhibits the secretion of that hormone, the mechanism is known as negative feedback. On the other hand, if a high level of a hormone in the plasma increases the secretion of that hormone, the mechanism is known as positive feedback (Fig. 37.6).

Regulation through the feedback mechanism is effected through the releasing hormones of the hypothalamus, or the trophic hormones of the pituitary gland.

In addition to the hormones involved in feedback regulation, other agents act directly on the respective glands, for example, an increased level of $Na^+$ inhibits the secretion of aldosterone, while a high blood sugar level stimulates the secretion of insulin.

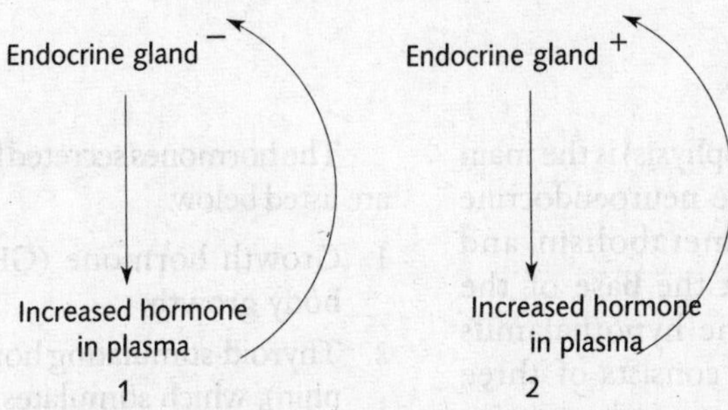


**Fig. 37.6:** Feedback mechanisms: 1. negative, 2. positive

CHAPTER 38

# The Pituitary Gland

The pituitary gland (hypophysis) is the main endocrine gland for the neuroendocrine regulation of both metabolism and reproduction. It is located at the base of the brain and is connected to the hypothalamus above by a pituitary stalk. It consists of three lobes: the anterior, intermediate and posterior lobes.

## ANTERIOR PITUITARY

The anterior lobe of the pituitary gland is of glandular nature and is hence, called the adenohypophysis. It has been described as the 'master of the endocrine orchestra' as it controls most of the endocrine glands in the body. However, according to the current state of knowledge, the real master seems to be the hypothalamus.

The hormones secreted by the anterior pituitary are listed below.

1. Growth hormone (GH), which accelerates body growth.
2. Thyroid-stimulating hormone (TSH, thyrotrophin), which stimulates thyroid secretions.
3. Adrenocorticotrophic hormone (ACTH, corticotrophin), which stimulates adrenocortical secretions.
4. Follicle-stimulating hormone (FSH), which stimulates the growth of the ovarian follicles in females and spermatogenesis in males.
5. Luetinizing hormone (LH), also known as interstitial-cell-stimulating hormone (ICSH) in males; it stimulates ovulation and luetinization of the ovarian follicles in females and the secretion of testosterone in males.
6. Prolactin (PRL, mammotrophin), which stimulates the secretion of milk.

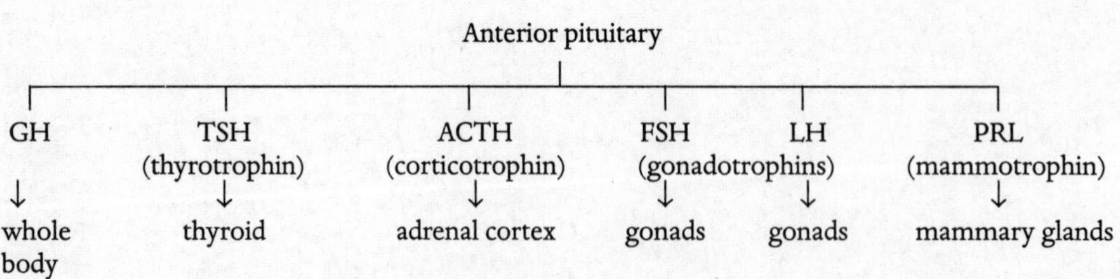

When the secretion of one hormone controls the secretion of another, it is known as a trophic hormone, for example, thyrotrophin.

According to their staining properties, the cells of the anterior pituitary are classified into two types—chromophobes, which do not stain, and chromophils, which take stains. Chromophil cells consist of acidophils, which take the acidic stain, and basophils, which take the basic stain. The chromophobes secrete ACTH, the acidophils secrete GH and PRL, while basophils secrete TSH, FSH and LH.

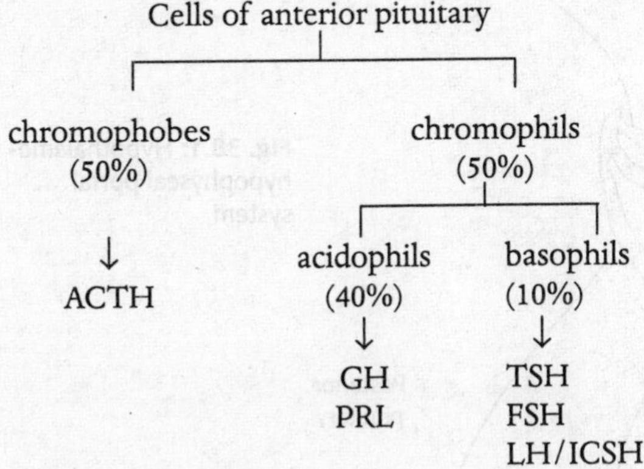


## Regulation of anterior pituitary hormones

### Hypothalamic Control

The nervous system receives information about changes in the internal and external environment. The appropriate neural and endocrinal adjustments are made so as to maintain the internal environment within the physiological range.

The hypothalamus and pituitary act as a single unit due to their structural and functional relationships. The anterior pituitary is connected with the hypothalamus through the hypothalamo-hypophyseal portal circulation. The superior hypophyseal arteries form a capillary plexus in the median eminence of the hypothalamus. The capillaries converge to form long portal vessels, which descend along the pituitary stalk and break up into a second set of capillary sinusoids in the adenohypophysis. The blood is finally drained into the vein (Fig. 38.1).

Several chemical agents or hypothalamic hormones (releasing and inhibiting factors) reach the anterior pituitary via the hypothalamo-hypophyseal portal circulation and regulate the secretion of one or more of the anterior pituitary cells. These hormones are listed below.

1. Growth-hormone releasing hormone (GRH).
2. Growth-hormone inhibiting hormone (GIH), also called somatostatin.
3. Corticotrophin-releasing hormone (CRH).
4. Thyrotrophin-releasing hormone (TRH).
5. Gonadotrophin-releasing hormone (GnRH), which promotes the release of both FSH and LH.
6. Prolactin-releasing hormone (PRH).
7. Prolactin-inhibiting hormone (PIH).

The axons of the hypothalamic neurons, which secrete releasing factors, terminate in the median eminence, near the capillaries. Most of the hypothalamic hormones are polypeptides in nature.

### Feedback Control

The anterior pituitary and its target glands have a negative feedback relationship. The former secretes a trophic hormone which promotes the secretion of its target glands. When the plasma level of the secretion of a target gland exceeds a certain critical level, it inhibits the secretion of its own trophic hormone by the anterior pituitary (Fig. 38.2).

Negative feedback control helps maintain the plasma level of the target gland hormone. However, the negative feedback mechanism may not operate when a person is under stress. This increases the level of the gland hormone.

## Physiology of anterior pituitary hormones

### Growth Hormone (GH)

This is also known as somatotrophic hormone (STH). It is secreted from the acidophil cells of the anterior pituitary gland. GH is a protein with 191 amino acids. It has structural and functional similarities with the placental somatotrophin. It

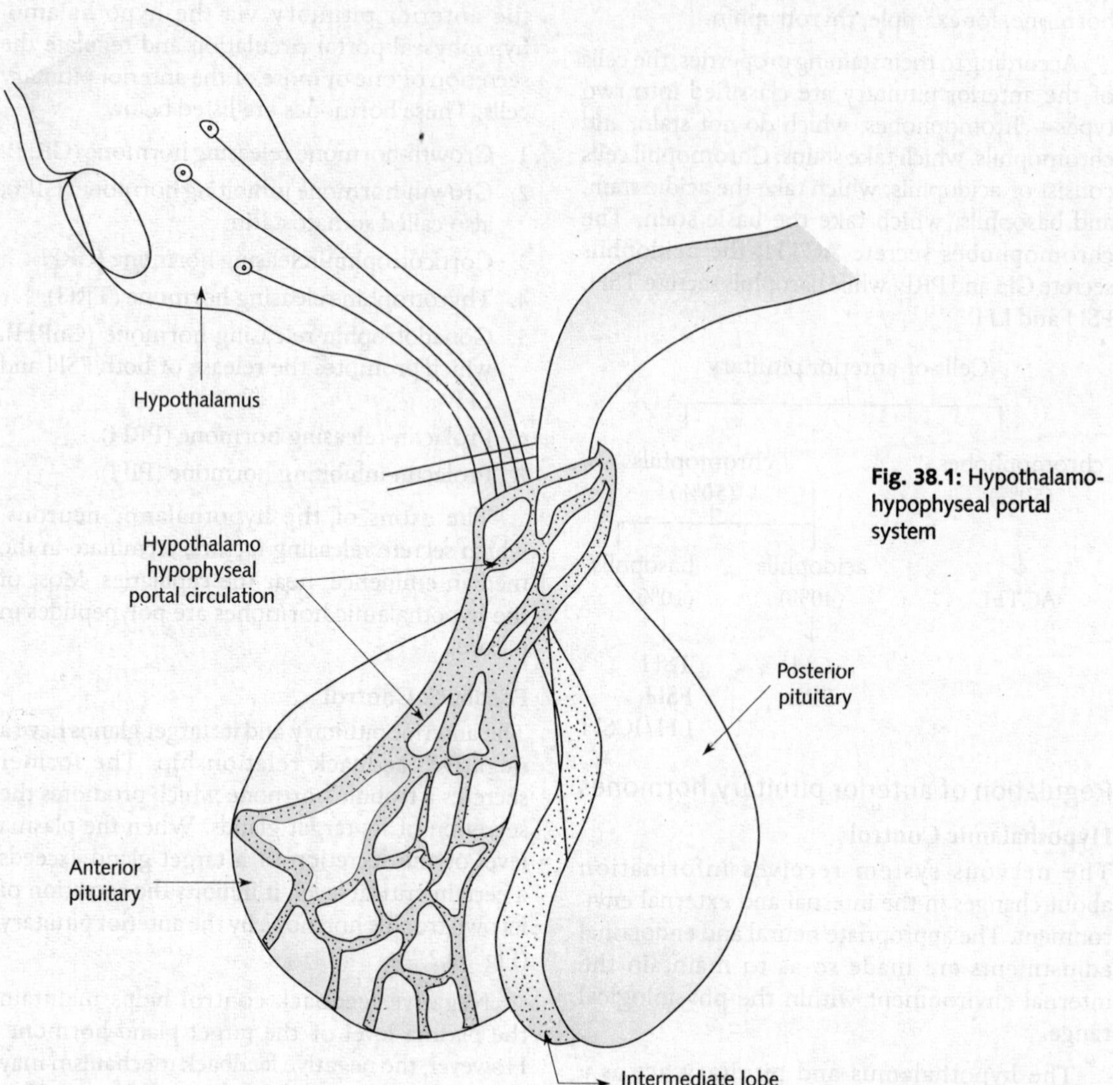


**Fig. 38.1:** Hypothalamo-hypophyseal portal system

causes growth of all the tissues which are capable of growing.

**Action**

At the cellular level, GH increases the number and size of the cells (hyperplasia and hypertrophy, respectively). At the tissue level, it stimulates somatic growth, helping accelerate growth in the skeletal and soft tissues.

On skeletal tissues: GH causes growth of the epiphyseal plate of cartilage. The formation of more matrix and deposition of calcium increases the length of the bones, as well as their thickness.

However, after puberty, the length of the bones does not increase, though their thickness does. This is due to epiphyseal closure of the long bones, which occurs at puberty because of the secretion of sex hormones.

On soft tissues: Most of the soft tissues, for example

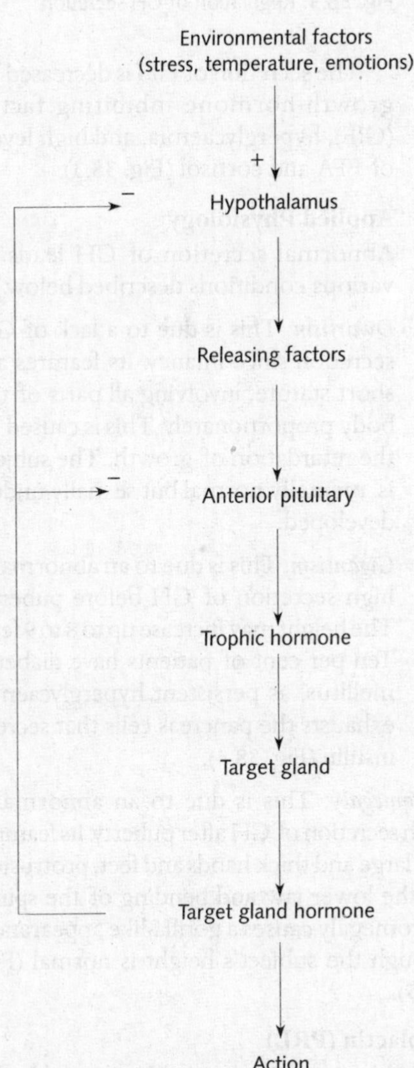

Fig. 38.2: Negative feedback control of anterior

skeletal muscles, the viscera and endocrine glands, increase in size due to the action of GH. The soft tissues continue to grow. However, GH does not have action on nervous tissue.

Metabolism: GH increases the rate of protein synthesis in all cells, that is, it is anabolic in action. This is effected by an increase in the rate of amino acid transport into the cells, which results in increased protein synthesis. Proteins are thus accumulated in the body. GH prevents the breakdown of protein for the production of energy. Therefore, the result is a positive nitrogen balance.

GH plays an important role in fat metabolism. It increases the mobilization of free fatty acids (FFAs) from the adipose tissue depots, increasing the plasma FFA level. Mostly, fatty acids are used for the production of energy. GH also helps convert FFAs to ketone bodies in the liver (i.e., it has ketogenic action).

As for carbohydrate metabolism, GH decreases the uptake and utilization of glucose for the production of energy, thereby increasing the level of glucose in the blood, that is, hyperglycaemia. This is known as anti-insulin action. In addition, GH enhances neoglucogenesis. Since long-standing hyperglycaemia can produce diabetes mellitus, GH is said to have diabetogenic action.

GH enhances the level of all the electrolytes that can be used for growth. It increases the absorption of $Ca^{++}$ from the gut, as well as the reabsorption of different electrolytes in the kidney.

**Mechanism of Action**

GH acts on various tissues of the body via polypeptides, called somatomedins, produced in the liver (mediator of somatic actions).

**Regulation of Secretion**

GH is secreted throughout life. However, there are two spurts of increased production, one during infancy and the other at puberty. The secretion of GH is controlled both by GRF & GIF.

The secretion of GH is increased by the GRH secreted from the hypothalamus. The latter is a polypeptide that acts on acidophils of the anterior pituitary. Its secretion is under feedback control. The factors acting on the hypothalamus are hypoglycaemia, infusion of some amino acids, sleep and exercise.

The factors acting on the pituitary are thyroid hormones, oestrogens and the normal level of cortisol.

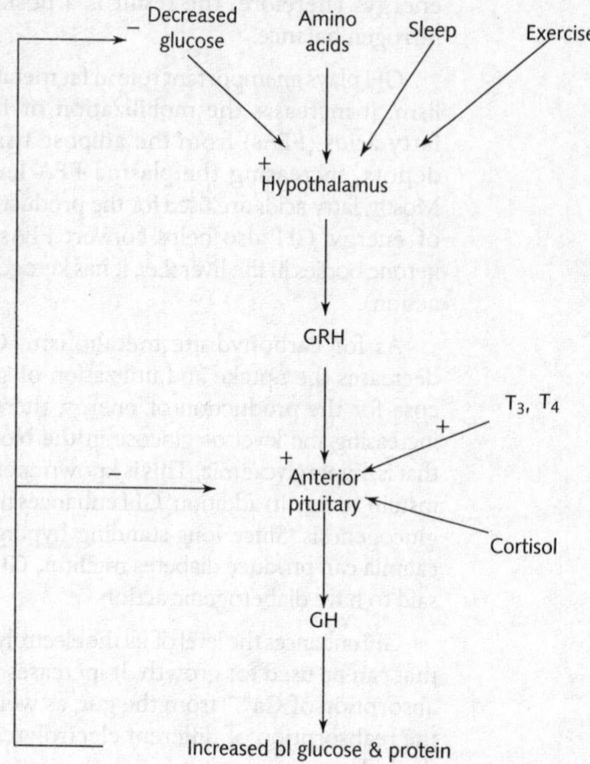


Fig. 38.3: Regulation of GH secretion

The secretion of GH is decreased by growth-hormone inhibiting factor (GIF), hyperglycaemia, and high levels of FFA and cortisol (Fig. 38.3).

## Applied Physiology

Abnormal secretion of GH leads to various conditions described below.

*Dwarfism*: This is due to a lack of GH secretion since infancy. Its features are short stature, involving all parts of the body proportionately. This is caused by the retardation of growth. The subject is mentally normal but sexually under-developed.

*Gigantism*: This is due to an abnormally high secretion of GH before puberty. The height may increase up to 8 to 9 feet. Ten per cent of patients have diabetes mellitus, as persistent hyperglycaemia exhausts the pancreas cells that secrete insulin (Fig. 38.4).

*Acromegaly*: This is due to an abnormally high secretion of GH after puberty. Its features are large and thick hands and feet, protrusion of the lower jaw and bending of the spine. Acromegaly causes a gorilla-like appearance, though the subject's height is normal (Fig. 38.5).

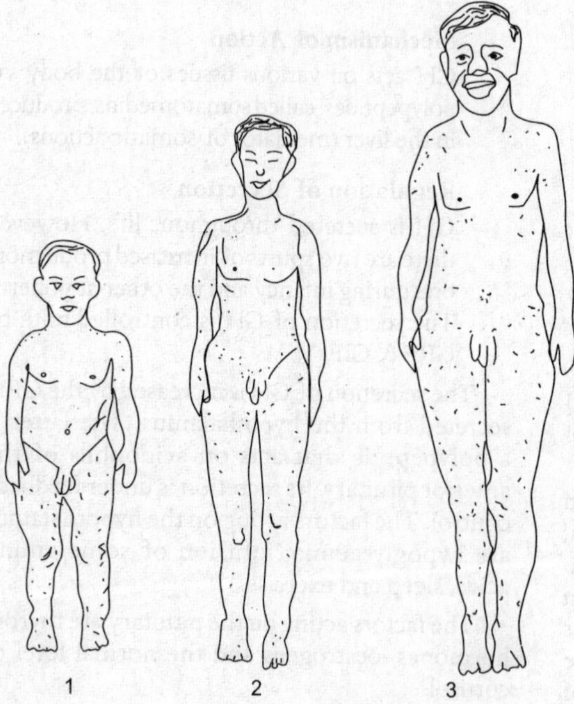


Fig. 38.4: Abnormalities of GH secretion: 1. dwarfism, 2. normal, 3. gigantism

## Prolactin (PRL)

This hormone is secreted by the acidophil cells of the anterior pituitary. It is a polypeptide in nature, containing 199 amino acids.

### Action

During pregnancy, the development of the breast is aided by PRL, along with other hormones, such as insulin, thyroxin and cortisol. It also helps in the synthesis of milk proteins. However, lactation does not occur during pregnancy inspite of the marked increase in

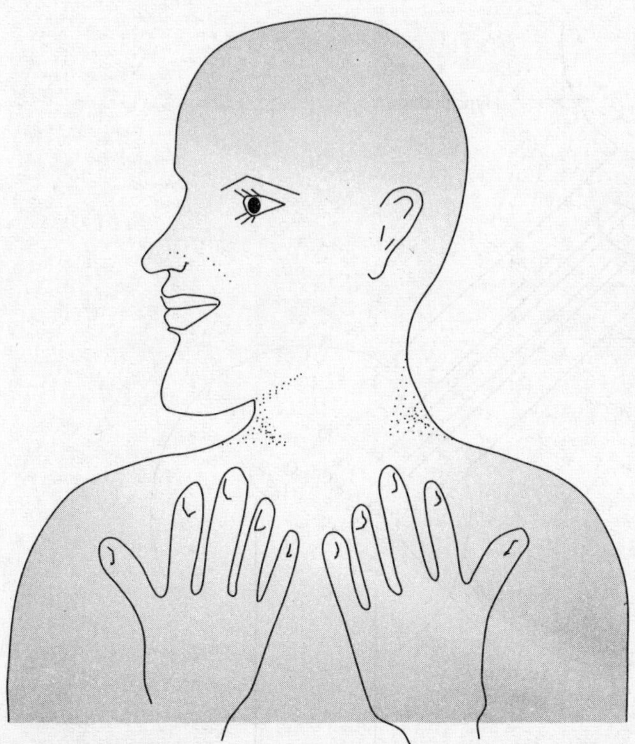

**Fig. 38.5:** Acromegaly

secretion of PRL, because of the inhibitory effects of oestrogen and progesterone. The primary function of PRL is to stimulate lactation after childbirth, which becomes possible due to a fall in the level of oestrogen and progesterone.

PRL inhibits the synthesis of GnRH (FSH, LH) and leads to amenorrhoea (no menstruation) after childbirth, that is, during lactation. It also blocks the action of gonadotrophins on the ovaries, preventing pregnancy during lactation (natural contraception).

PRL has no apparent function in males. Excessive secretion of PRL can lead to impotence as it interferes with the production of testosterone.

**Regulation of Secretion**

Secretion of PRL is stimulated by PRH from the hypothalamus. The PRL level is high during pregnancy, decreases after childbirth and increases again during breast-feeding. The secretion of PRL is inhibited by PIH.

The physiology of TSH, ACTH and gonadotrophins is discussed along with the respective target gland hormones.

## INTERMEDIATE LOBE OF PITUITARY

This lobe is rudimentary in humans and does not secrete melanocyte-stimulating hormone (MSH), as it does in some animals. In lower animals, a large amount of MSH is secreted in response to light and other environmental factors. This hormone acts on the melanocytes of the skin and leads to the synthesis of melanin. The pigmentary changes in skin play an important role in the protection of lower animals.

In human beings, the clinical importance of MSH lies in the fact that the $\alpha$ form of MSH resembles ACTH in structure. Therefore, ACTH has a weak MSH activity and causes pigmentation of the skin whenever there is hypersecretion of ACTH, as in Addison's disease.

## POSTERIOR PITUITARY

The posterior pituitary is also called the neurohypophysis. It is an outgrowth of the hypothalamus and contains the dilated ends of the axons of the hypothalamo-hypophyseal tract, the cell bodies of which are located in the hypothalamus. The hormones are synthesized in the cell bodies and transported in the axons, to be stored in the axon terminals of the posterior pituitary (Fig. 38.6).

In response to an appropriate stimulus, action potentials are generated in the hypothalamic nuclei. These are conducted down the axons to the nerve terminal, where they trigger the release of the appropriate hormone.

The posterior pituitary gland produces two hormones, antidiuretic hormone (ADH) and oxytocin.

### Anti-diuretic hormone (ADH)

This is also known as vasopressin. It is synthesized mainly in the neurons of the supraoptic nucleus

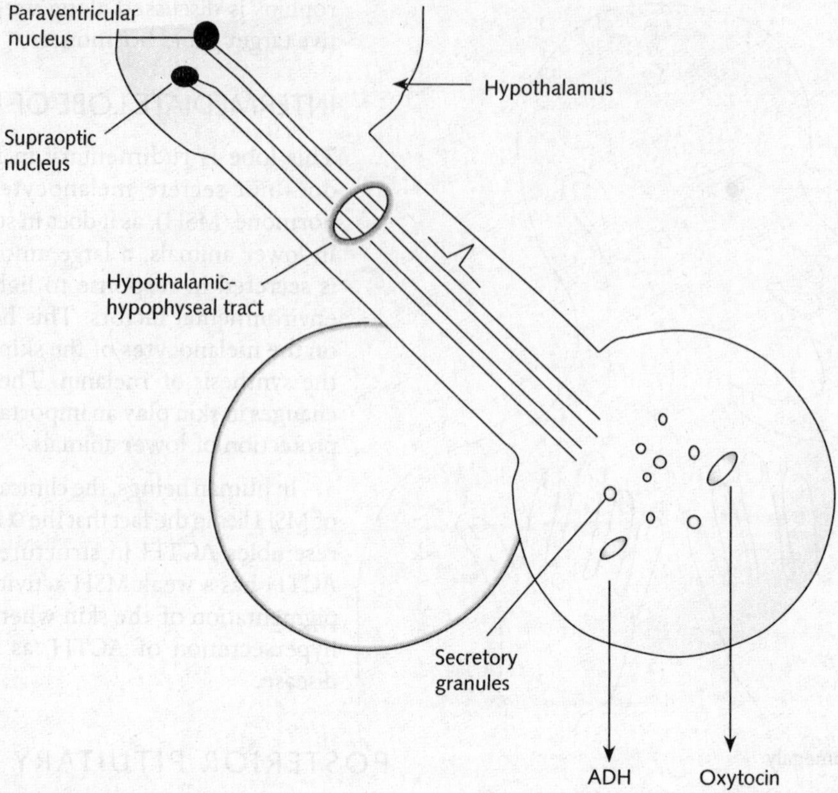


**Fig. 38.6:** The neurohypophysis (posterior pituitary)

and, to some extent, the paraventricular nucleus of the hypothalamus. It is a peptide, containing nine amino acids.

### Action

ADH acts on the kidneys as well as smooth muscles.

*Kidneys*: The kidneys are the chief site of the action of ADH, which decreases the free excretion of water from them. It regulates the amount of water reabsorbed from the collecting ducts by increasing their cAMP-mediated permeability. In the presence of ADH, the collecting ducts become freely permeable to water. Therefore, water is reabsorbed along the osmotic gradient, from the hypotonic luminal fluid to the hypertonic medullary interstitial fluid. Thus, a small amount of highly concentrated urine is excreted. In the absence of ADH, the collecting ducts become impermeable to water and a large volume of dilute urine is excreted (diuresis). ADH thus prevents diuresis, hence the name.

*Smooth muscles*: ADH also causes contraction of the smooth muscle fibres of blood vessels, thereby increasing the blood pressure. This is why ADH is also known as vasopressin. However, the plasma concentration of ADH required to produce vasoconstriction is far higher than that required for maximal water conservation.

### Regulation of Secretion

The secretion of ADH is chiefly regulated by changes in the plasma osmolality. Increased osmolality of the body fluids stimulates ADH secretion via the hypothalamic osmoreceptors. The consequent conservation of water restores the plasma osmolality to normal.

A decreased volume of extracellular fluid

(ECF) is another important stimulus for the secretion of ADH (e.g., severe hypovolaemia). Volume receptors are present in the atria, great veins and pulmonary circulation.

The secretion of ADH decreases with a drop in the plasma osmotic pressure, an increase in the ECF volume or alcohol intake.

**Applied Physiology**

In the absence of ADH, an abnormally high volume of water is excreted through the urine, resulting in polyurea. This condition is called diabetes insipidus.

## Oxytocin

Oxytocin is synthesized mainly by the neurons of the paraventricular nucleus and, to some extent, the supraoptic nucleus of the hypothalamus. It is a polypeptide, containing nine amino acids. It is similar to ADH, but the type and sequence of amino acids differs.

**Action**

Oxytocin acts on the mammary glands and uterus.

*Mammary glands*: Oxytocin causes contraction of the myoepithelial cells around the alveoli, thereby forcing milk into the ducts and sinuses opening through the nipple of the breast. Known as milk ejection, this is reflexly triggered by suckling of the nipple by the baby.

*The pregnant uterus*: Oxytocin causes powerful contraction of the smooth muscles of the pregnant uterus. The sensitivity of the uterus to oxytocin keeps increasing during pregnancy due to a high concentration of oestrogen and uterine distensibility in the later months of pregnancy. Once the labour starts, dilatation of the cervix reflexly produces a rise in the plasma oxytocin level. This causes more forceful contraction of the uterus, resulting in the expulsion of the baby.

*Non-pregnant uterus:* The oxytocin released in response to coitus may produce uterine contractions, which facilitate the ascent of sperm from the vagina to the fallopian tubes, where fertilization normally takes place.

CHAPTER

# The Thyroid Gland

The thyroid gland is a highly vascular endocrine gland situated across the trachea in the lower part of the neck.

The gland consists of a large number of follicles which have parafollicular cells between them. The follicles are lined by cuboidal epithelium and the lumen contains a secretory substance, called colloid, the major constituent of which is thyroglobulin. Thyroglobulin is a glycoprotein synthesized by the follicular cells and secreted into the lumen.

During activity, the follicles become smaller, the epithelium becomes tall and columnar, and the amount of colloid decreases (Fig. 39.1).

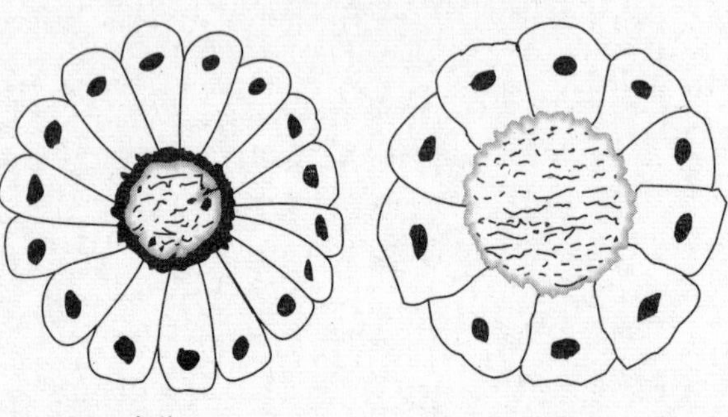


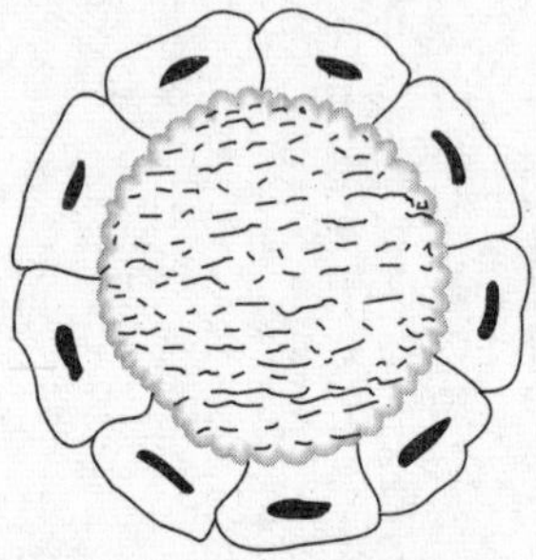


**Fig. 39.1:** Thyroid gland: different stages of follicle

## THYROID HORMONES

The thyroid hormones are thyroxine ($T_4$), which is the most abundant, and triiodothyronine ($T_3$), which is the most potent. Both hormones are protein in nature.

### Synthesis

The site of synthesis is the colloid in the lumen, on the apical side of the follicular cells. The raw material required is iodine, which is taken in the diet. The normal requirement of iodine is 200 micrograms/day. It is absorbed as iodide in the GI tract.

Synthesis takes place in two steps. First, the iodide is trapped by the acinar cells of the thyroid gland, via the active transport mechanism, and it is converted into elemental iodine by the enzyme peroxidase. Next, the tyrosine in thyroglobulin is iodinated to form the thyroid hormones in four stages: monoiodotyrosine (MIT), diiodotyrosine (DIT), triiodothyronine ($T_3$), then thyroxine ($T_4$) (Fig. 39.2).

### Storage and release

The hormones thus synthesized remain attached to the thyroglobulin molecule and are stored as a

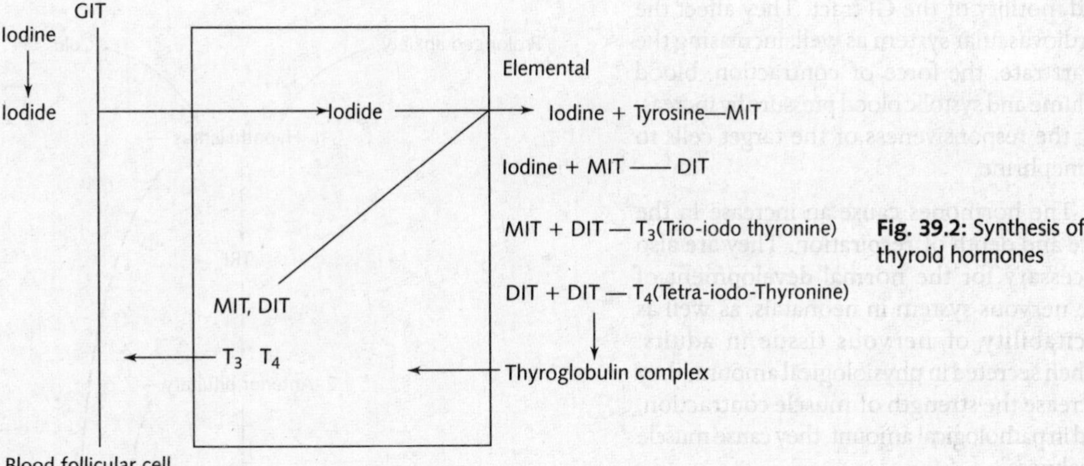


**Fig. 39.2:** Synthesis of thyroid hormones

thyroglobulin complex in the colloid. They are released by pinocytosis of colloid into the acinar cells, and then proteolysis of the thyroglobulin complex by proteases. This releases MIT, DIT, $T_3$ and $T_4$. Only $T_3$ and $T_4$ are released into the circulation, while the iodine from MIT and DIT is re-utilized for the synthesis of the hormones.

The stimulus for the synthesis and release of the hormones is TSH, released from the anterior pituitary. All the steps, starting from the uptake of iodine to the release of the hormone, are stimulated by TSH.

## Transport

Most of the $T_3$ and $T_4$ circulates in the blood, in combination with plasma protein and thyroxine-binding globulin (TBG), which has greater affinity for $T_4$ than $T_3$. Therefore, more free $T_3$ is present in the blood than free $T_4$. As it is the free form of the hormone that is biologically active, $T_3$ is three times more potent than $T_4$.

*Inactivation and excretion*: Both $T_3$ and $T_4$ are disposed from the body after their action is over. They are inactivated in the liver to glucoronides, and are excreted in urine as tetrac and triac, respectively.

# ACTION

The thyroid hormones act by increasing the synthesis of protein in the target cells. Their action is generalized and is of delayed onset and long duration.

## Metabolism

The thyroid hormones cause an increase in the BMR, the consumption of $O_2$ and the production of heat (calorigenic action) in most tissues.

They play a role in carbohydrate metabolism by bringing about an increase in glycogenolysis, neoglucogenesis and the absorption of glucose. Therefore, the blood sugar level increases.

As for protein metabolism, when secreted in the normal physiological amount, the thyroid hormones induce anabolism and, therefore, growth of the body. In pathological amounts, they induce catabolism and, therefore, muscle weakness.

The thyroid hormones bring about an increase in the breakdown of fats in order to provide energy. They also decrease the cholesterol level due to greater degradation. As for vitamin metabolism, they convert carotene into vitamin A. In addition, they are related to $Ca^{++}$ and $PO_4^{---}$ metabolism. Excessive secretion causes osteoporosis.

## Other action

The thyroid hormones bring about an increase in the appetite, as well as in absorption, secretion and motility of the GI tract. They affect the cardiovascular system as well, increasing the heart rate, the force of contraction, blood volume and systolic blood pressure by increasing the responsiveness of the target cells to epinephrine.

The hormones cause an increase in the rate and depth of respiration. They are also necessary for the normal development of the nervous system in neonatals, as well as excitability of nervous tissue in adults. When secreted in physiological amount, they increase the strength of muscle contraction, and in pathological amount, they cause muscle weakness.

The thyroid hormones are essential for maturation of the embryo, as well as the growth and development of the embryo's nervous system. They are also necessary for normal gonadal activity. This is why they are secreted in higher amounts during puberty, menstruation and pregnancy. The thyroid hormones are necessary for the formation of milk (i.e., lactogenesis), as well as RBC formation (i.e., haemopoiesis). Further, they are required for the maintenance of the skin's normal texture.

## REGULATION OF THYROID HORMONES

The secretion of thyroid hormones is controlled by the hypothalamus, the anterior pituitary, as well as the level of free hormone in the blood. Prolonged anxiety, emotional stress or exposure to cold stimulates the hypothalamus to produce TRH.

The anterior pituitary produces TSH, which enhances the uptake of iodine by the gland. It also increases the formation of the thyroid hormones, as well as their release. TSH is a glycoprotein which also increases the number and size of follicular cells. However, iodine must be available for the synthesis of the hormones.

An increase in the level of free hormone in plasma causes inhibition of the hypothalamus and anterior pituitary (Fig. 39.3).

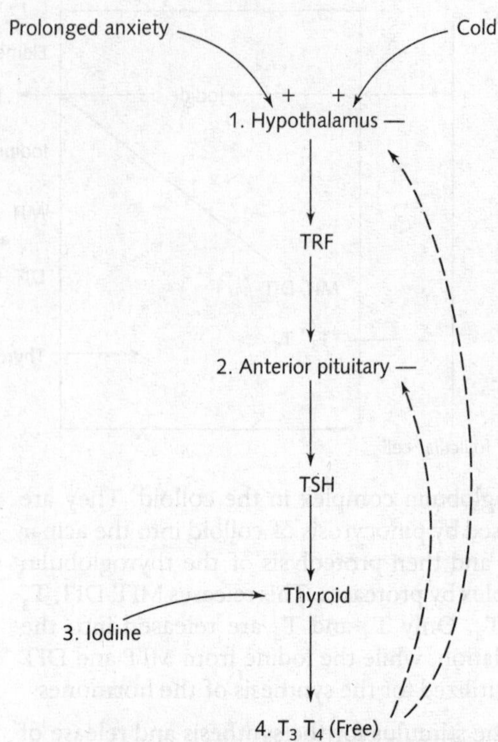


**Fig. 39.3:** Regulation of thyroid hormone secretion

## APPLIED PHYSIOLOGY

The abnormalities in the secretion of the thyroid hormones consist of hyposecretion and hypersecretion, the effects of which are described in this section.

### Hyposecretion

In childhood, hyposecretion produces a condition called cretinism. Such a child is known as a cretin (Fig. 39.4). The condition is characterized by shortness as general growth is stunted, and mental retardation. The tongue protrudes out of the mouth and may fall back, causing choking and death. A cretin has a pot belly because fat from the limbs is mobilized to the abdomen.

In an adult, hyposecretion produces a condition called myxoedema (Fig. 39.5). Its features are a swollen or 'moon face', nonpitting oedema all over the body due to deposition of myxomatous

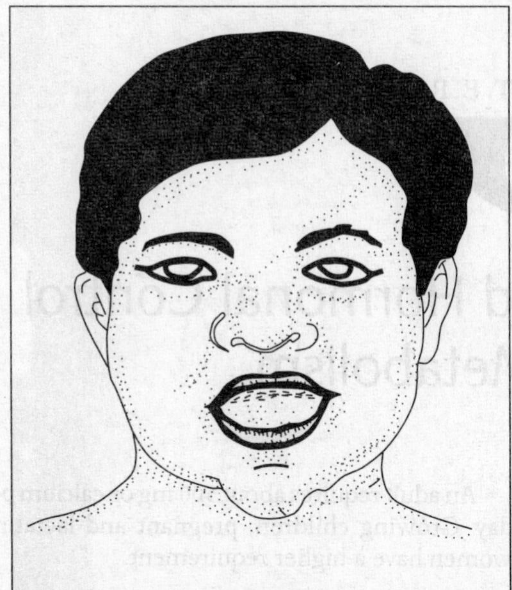

Fig. 39.4: A cretin

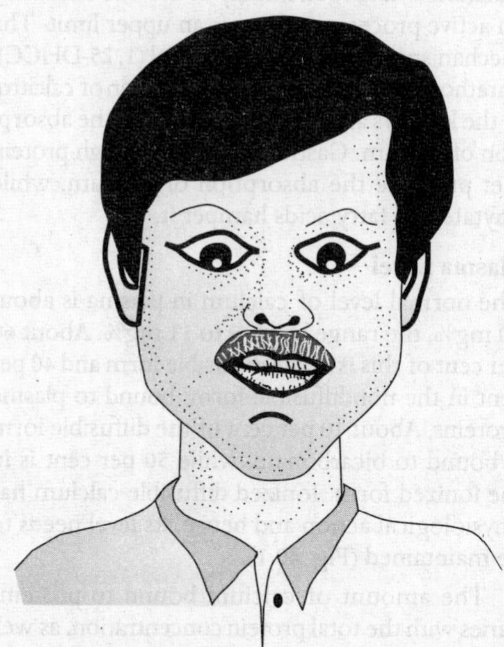

Fig. 39.6: Hyperthyroidism

tissue, and weight gain due to a decreased BMR. The subject feels more sleepy than normal people do and has a greater susceptibility to cold. Further, he/she is slow in thought, speech and action.

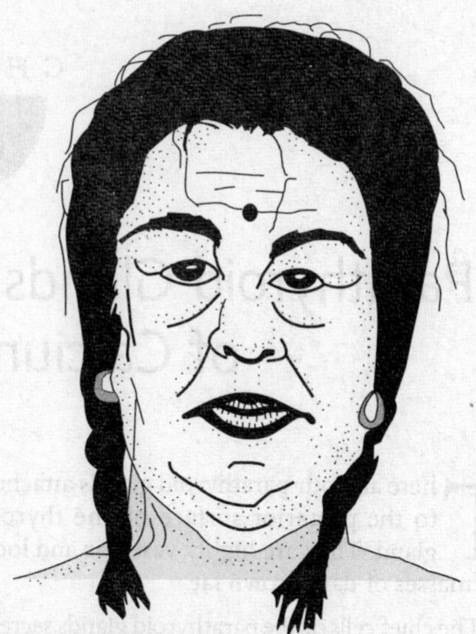

Fig. 39.5: Myxoedema

Hyposecretion also causes a fall in the pulse rate and body temperature, as well as infertility.

*Iodine deficiency goitre*: A deficiency of dietary iodine causes a fall in the secretion of the thyroid hormones, an increased level of TSH and hypertrophy of the thyroid gland (goitre).

## Hypersecretion

Hypersecretion is common in teenage girls and is physiological. In an adult, it produces a condition called thyrotoxicosis (Fig. 39.6), which is characterized by the following:

1. Normal appetite, high BMR and, therefore, decreased weight.
2. Abnormally high body temperature and sweating.
3. Exophthalmos or protrusion of the eyeballs.
4. Occurrence of fine tremors.
5. Loss of sleep due to increased excitability of the central nervous system.
6. Osteoporosis.

CHAPTER

40

# Parathyroid Glands and Hormonal Control of Calcium Metabolism

There are four parathyroid glands attached to the posterior surface of the thyroid gland. They are highly vascular and look like masses of dark brown fat.

The chief cells of the parathyroid glands secrete a hormone called parathormone, which is essential for life. This is because it regulates the extracellular calcium ion concentration. The other hormones directly related to calcium metabolism are calcitrol and thyrocalcitonin. These are closely related to calcium and phosphate metabolism and the formation of teeth and bone. They are responsible for maintaining homeostasis, as well as growth.

It is important to maintain the plasma calcium level within a narrow range because of its marked effect on neuromuscular and cardiac excitability. In addition, it is also important for bone mineralization, many intracellular biochemical reactions, excitation–contraction coupling in muscles and blood coagulation, among other things.

## CALCIUM METABOLISM

Normally, the human body contains about 1 kg of calcium. Of this, about 99 per cent can be found in the skeleton as hydroxy-apatite, and the remaining 1 per cent in the soft tissues and ECF.

Our food (milk, milk products, green vegetables) and water contains plenty of calcium.

An adult requires about 500 mg of calcium per day. Growing children, pregnant and lactating women have a higher requirement.

### Absorption

Calcium is absorbed mainly in the duodenum by an active process, so there is an upper limit. The mechanism is regulated by calcitrol (1, 25-DHCC). Parathormone increases the production of calcitrol in the kidneys and, therefore, helps in the absorption of calcium. Gastric acidity and a high-protein diet promote the absorption of calcium, while phytate and fatty acids hamper it.

### Plasma Level

The normal level of calcium in plasma is about 10 mg%, the range being 9 to 11 mg%. About 60 per cent of this is in the diffusible form and 40 per cent in the nondiffusible form, bound to plasma proteins. About 10 per cent of the diffusible form is bound to bicarbonate, while 50 per cent is in the ionized form. Ionized diffusible calcium has physiological action and hence, its level needs to be maintained (Fig. 40.1).

The amount of calcium bound to proteins varies with the total protein concentration, as well as the pH of the plasma. In alkalosis, although the total plasma calcium level is normal, the symptoms of hypocalcaemic tetany occur. This is because more plasma proteins are ionized with an increase in the pH, so the proteins bind more calcium, thus decreasing the concentration of free ionic calcium.

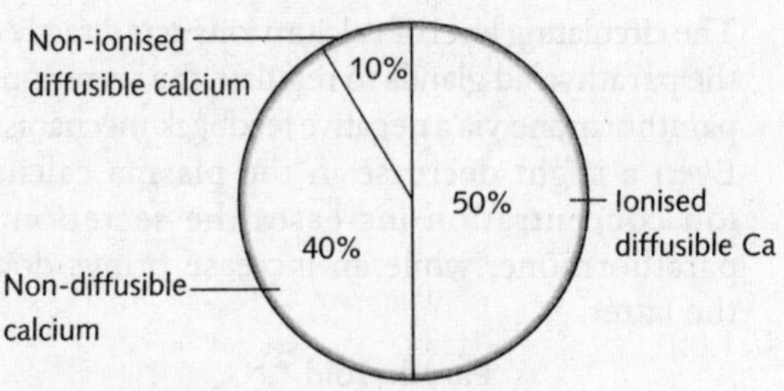


**Fig. 40.1:** Distribution of calcium in plasma

## Calcium balance

If the average intake of calcium is 1000 mg, its net intestinal absorption is only 175 mg/ day. The total ECF space contains about 900 mg of calcium, which is in dynamic equilibrium with the skeleton. About 1 per cent of skeletal calcium is readily exchangeable with the calcium in the ECF and forms a large reservoir. The remaining 99 per cent of bone calcium is only slowly exchangeable. Nearly 500 mg of calcium is deposited into and mobilized from the bone daily in a continuous process of remodelling. The calcium secreted into the intestine through the bile, pancreatic juice and intestinal juice is completely reabsorbed.

About 60 per cent of the plasma calcium is filtered by the kidneys. Of this, 99 per cent is reabsorbed in the renal tubules. About 60 per cent of the reabsorption occurs in the proximal convoluted tubule, and the remaining 40 per cent occurs in the loop of Henle and distal tubule. Distal tubular reabsorption of calcium is regulated by parathormone.

In a normal adult, the calcium balance is always maintained by excretion (in the urine and faeces) of the same amount as is absorbed from the gut (Fig. 40.2). The calcium balance is positive in growing children and becomes negative in persons with osteoporosis.

## PARATHORMONE

Human parathormone is a polypeptide. It causes a decrease in the $PO_4^{---}$ concentration of the ECF. This effect is seen earlier and is of short duration. Its main effect is an increase in the $Ca^{++}$ concentration of the ECF.

## Action

Parathormone has direct action on the bones and kidneys via the cAMP mechanism. It has indirect action on the intestine via calcitrol (vitamin D).

**On Bones**

The bone consists of (i) matrix, which is made of collagen fibres and has calcium phosphate salts deposited in it, and (ii) bone cells. The latter may be osteoblasts, which cause deposition of

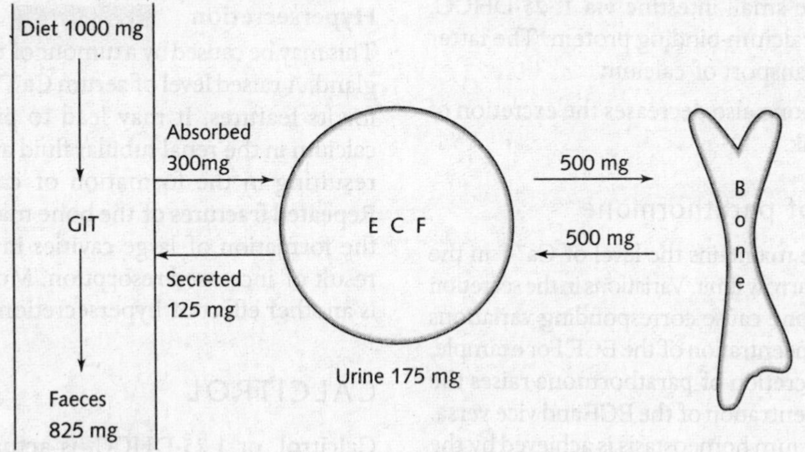


**Fig. 40.2:** Calcium metabolism

bone, or osteoclasts, which cause resorption of bone.

Parathormone promotes the resorption of bones by activating the osteoclasts already present in the bone and also, by the formation of new osteoclasts, followed by their activation. The activation of osteoclasts increases the secretion of proteolytic enzymes and acids, such as citric and lactic acids. The enzymes cause dissolution of the matrix and the acids dissolve the bone minerals. Hence, the calcium and phosphate released by osteoclastic activity are mobilized from the bone into the blood, that is, the ECF. However, the resorption of bone does not affect the structure of the bone since bones contain a large amount of calcium.

**On Kidneys**

Parathormone increases the resorption of calcium from the distal convoluted tubules of the kidneys and decreases calcium excretion in the urine. It also decreases the resorption of phosphates in the kidney tubules and increases their excretion in the urine.

Parathormone helps convert 25-hydroxycholecalciferol (25-HCC) to 1, 25-dihydroxycholecalciferol (1, 25-DHCC) via $\alpha$-hydroxylase, an enzyme which is present in the kidneys.

**Other Action**

Parathormone increases the absorption of calcium from the small intestine via 1, 25-DHCC, which forms calcium-binding protein. The latter helps in the transport of calcium.

Parathormone also decreases the excretion of calcium in milk.

## Functions of parathormone

Parathormone maintains the level of $Ca^{++}$ in the ECF within a narrow limit. Variations in the secretion of parathormone cause corresponding variations in the $Ca^{++}$ concentration of the ECF. For example, a rise in the secretion of parathormone raises the $Ca^{++}$ ion concentration of the ECF and vice versa. Therefore, calcium homeostasis is achieved by the regulation of parathormone secretion.

## Regulation of parathormone secretion

The circulating level of calcium ions acts directly on the parathyroid glands to regulate the secretion of parathormone via a negative feedback mechanism. Even a slight decrease in the plasma calcium ion concentration increases the secretion of parathormone, while an increase brings down the latter.

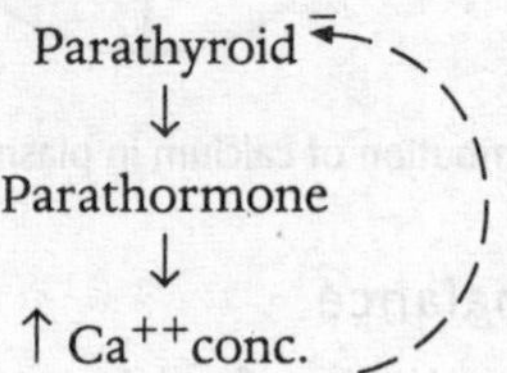


## Applied physiology

Abnormalities in the secretion of parathormone have the following effects.

**Hyposecretion**

This may be produced by accidental removal of the parathyroid glands during total removal of the thyroid gland. Its features are because of a fall in the serum calcium level. When this level falls below 6 mg%, a condition known as tetany is produced. Owing to an increase in the excitability of the nerves and neuromuscular junction, spontaneous discharge occurs, producing muscular twitches (e.g., carpopedal spasm). Spasms of the laryngeal muscles can lead to asphyxia and death.

**Hypersecretion**

This may be caused by a tumour of the parathyroid gland. A raised level of serum $Ca^{++}$ is responsible for its features. It may lead to precipitation of calcium in the renal tubular fluid and soft tissues, resulting in the formation of calcium stones. Repeated fractures of the bone may occur due to the formation of large cavities in the bone as a result of increased resorption. Muscle weakness is another effect of hypersecretion.

## CALCITROL

Calcitrol, or 1,25-DHCC, is actually the active form of vitamin D. It behaves like a true hormone.

Vitamin D-containing food includes fresh liver, eggs, milk and other food of animal origin. Vitamin $D_2$ (ergocalciferol) is found in plant sources. The sources of vitamin D in the body are dietary intake, and more importantly, cutaneous synthesis of vitamin D (cholecalciferol).

## Synthesis

Calcitrol is produced by the action of ultraviolet irradiation on 7-dehydrocholesterol, which is normally present in the skin. Excessive exposure to the sun does not produce vitamin D toxicity, because of a blockade in the synthetic reactions and the conversion of provitamin $D_3$ to inert metabolites, such as lumisterol and tachysterol. (Fig. 40.3)

The synthetic reactions are as follows: The cholecalciferol formed in the skin is absorbed in the blood and is then carried to the liver, with the help of a vitamin D carrier protein. Here, it is converted to 25-OHCC by the enzyme 25-hydroxylase. 25-OHCC is converted to 1, 25-DHCC (active form) in the kidney by the enzyme α-hydroxylase. The calcitrol is then carried by the blood to the target organs.

## Action

1,25-DHCC acts like a steroid hormone, increasing the synthesis of proteins and the concentration of calcium-binding protein in many tissues, particularly the intestine.

The intestine, kidney and the bone are the chief target organs. In the intestine, 1,25-DHCC increases the absorption of dietary calcium, and the rate of calcium absorption is directly proportionate to the amount of calcium-binding protein present in the mucosal cells. It promotes the reabsorption of calcium from the renal tubules.

In the bone, vitamin D is conducive to the

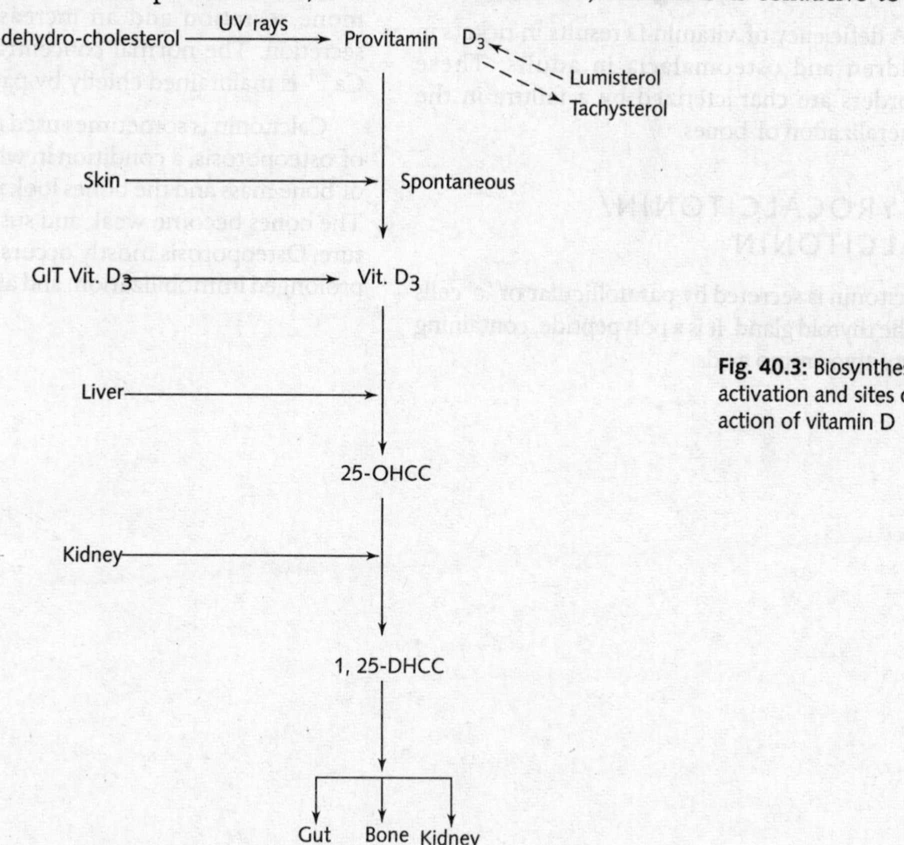


**Fig. 40.3:** Biosynthesis, activation and sites of action of vitamin D

action of parathormone. The active pump which transfers calcium ions out of the osteocytic membrane into the ECF is vitamin D-mediated. Vitamin D also has a direct effect on bone mineralization.

### Feedback control on synthesis

The formation of 1,25-DHCC is tightly regulated even if there is an excess of vitamin D in the diet.

The activity of α-hydroxylase is increased by parathormone, oestrogens and prolactin. The latter two help provide more calcium to pregnant and lactating women. Normally, a decrease in the calcium and phosphate levels in the plasma enhances the secretion of parathormone. This, in turn, boosts the formation of 1, 25-DHCC and restores the calcium level in the plasma to normal. When plasma calcium level is adequate, the activity of α-hydroxylase gets inhibited.

A deficiency of vitamin D results in rickets in children and osteomalacia in adults. These disorders are characterized by a failure in the mineralization of bones.

## THYROCALCITONIN/ CALCITONIN

Calcitonin is secreted by parafollicular or 'c' cells of the thyroid gland. It is a polypeptide, containing thirty-two amino acids.

The bone is the only target organ of calcitonin. It inhibits osteoclastic activity and increases the deposition of calcium in the bones, thereby bringing down the serum calcium level. Calcitonin is not essential for life and even its absence seems to have no effect on the body.

Calcitonin may play a role in bone formation in the foetus and in young life.

### Regulation of secretion

The plasma calcium ion concentration regulates the secretion of calcitonin. When there is a rise in the former, the secretion of calcitonin is stimulated. The secretion of both parathormone and calcitonin is regulated by the plasma calcium level in a reciprocal manner. A fall in the plasma calcium level increases the secretion of parathormone but decreases that of calcitonin, while an increase in the plasma calcium level causes a drop in parathormone secretion and an increase in calcitonin secretion. The normal concentration of plasma $Ca^{++}$ is maintained chiefly by parathormone.

Calcitonin is sometimes used in the treatment of osteoporosis, a condition in which there is loss of bone mass and the bones look porous on X-ray. The bones become weak and susceptible to fracture. Osteoporosis mostly occurs in old age, after prolonged immobilization, and after menopause.

CHAPTER

# The Adrenal Gland

The adrenal gland is present at the superior pole of each kidney and consists of two parts. One is the outer adrenal cortex, which is essential for life and secretes a group of lipid-soluble steroid hormones called corticosteroids. The other part is the inner adrenal medulla. This is connected to the sympathetic nervous system and secretes a number of water-soluble hormones known as catecholamines.

Although the adrenal cortex and medulla are embryologically two different components of the adrenal gland, their physiological roles are closely integrated, especially in the matter of adaptation to stress.

## THE ADRENAL CORTEX

The cells of the adrenal cortex are arranged in three layers (Fig. 41.1). Going inwards, these are:

1. The zona glomerulosa, in which the cells are arranged parallel to the surface,
2. The zona fasciculata, in which the cells are arranged perpendicular to the surface, and
3. The zona reticularis, in which the cells are arranged irregularly.

Corticosteroids may be classified into three groups—glucocorticoids, mineralocorticoids and sex steroids.

Glucocorticoids (e.g., cortisone and corticosterone) are secreted mainly by the zona fasciculata and also from the zona reticularis. They have a widespread effect on glucose (and protein) metabolism.

Mineralocorticoids (e.g., aldosterone and 11-deoxycorticosterone) are secreted by the zona glomerulosa. They regulate the sodium balance and the volume of ECF in the body.

Sex steroids (e.g., dehydroepiandrosterone) are secreted mainly by the zona reticularis. These are the androgenic hormones.

*Biosynthesis of corticosteroids:* All corticosteroids are synthesized from cholesterol. Synthesis may take place in the adrenal cortex from acetate, or they may be derived from blood. In the presence of ACTH from the anterior pituitary, cholesterol is converted to an intermediate compound, pregnanelone, which is converted to various hormones. The different layers of the adrenal cortex produce different groups of hormones due to the difference in the enzyme content of the layers. For example, the zona glomerulosa contains an enzyme 18-oxidase, which is necessary for the synthesis of mineralocorticoids, while the zona fasciculata and zona reticularis contain an enzyme 17-α-hydroxylase, which is necessary for the synthesis of glucocorticoids.

Most of the hormones (90 per cent) are transported in combination with corticosteroid-binding globulin (CBG) in the plasma. The free form of hormones is responsible for their function.

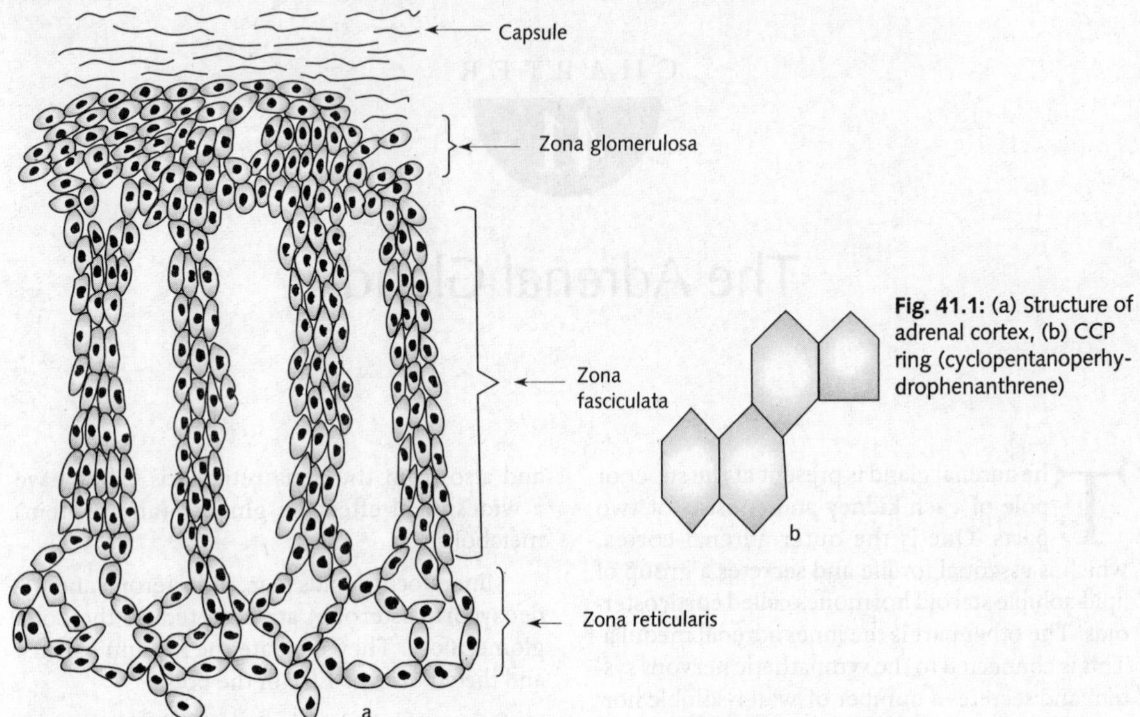


**Fig. 41.1:** (a) Structure of adrenal cortex, (b) CCP ring (cyclopentanoperhydrophenanthrene)

Corticosteroids are mostly metabolized in the liver. The hormone metabolites are conjugated either with sulphate or with glucoronic acid, and then excreted through the urine. Like all steroid hormones, corticosteroids raise the level of protein synthesis in the target cells.

## GLUCOCORTICOIDS

Cortisol is the main glucocorticoid.

### Action

#### Metabolism

Glucocorticoids increase the absorption of glucose from the gut. They promote neoglucogenesis by stimulating the production of the enzymes required. Further, they decrease the peripheral utilization of glucose.

Due to these anti-insulin actions, the net effect of glucocorticoids on carbohydrate metabolism is hyperglycaemia (diabetogenic action). Hence, they are not given to diabetes mellitus patients.

Glucocorticoids promote the breakdown of proteins in the skeletal muscles and mobilize amino acids from the peripheral parts, raising the level of amino acids in the plasma. They also increase entry of amino acids into the liver, thus providing a substrate for neoglucogenesis.

Glucocorticoids help in the mobilization of fats from adipose tissue, thereby boosting the level of free fatty acids in the plasma. They increase the body store of $Na^+$ and deplete the level of $K^+$ (weak mineralocorticoid activity). They also mobilize $Ca^{++}$ from the bones.

#### Anti-inflammatory Action

Glucocorticoids are extremely effective in preventing inflammation when given in large doses. They prevent the migration of white blood cells and macrophages to the site of inflammation, the release of proteolytic enzymes, as well as the growth of fibroblasts in the area of inflammation.

Due to these actions, they are used extensively in the treatment of diseases such as rheumatoid arthritis and acute glomerulonephritis. As glucocorticoids suppress inflammation, infection may occur insidiously and rapidly. Hence, they are used judiciously.

**Other Action**

Glucocorticoids increase the secretion of HCl in the stomach and bring down mucosal resistance to it. Hence, they are not given to those with peptic ulcer. They bring about a fall in the eosinophil and lymphocyte count, but increase the count of other cells.

Glucocorticoids act effectively against stress. A wide variety of nonspecific stimuli, such as injury, surgery, infection and exposure to excessive heat or cold, increases the secretion of cortisol from the adrenal cortex. These stimuli act on the hypothalamus to make it secrete more ACTH.

Glucocorticoids suppress the immune mechanism and are hence used to prevent the rejection of organ transplants. They prevent the release of histamine, which is provoked by the antigen-antibody reaction. Hence, they are used in allergic conditions such as eczema, bronchial asthma and life-threatening anaphylactic shock.

The presence of glucocorticoids is conducive to the action (such as lipolysis, glycogenolysis, vasoconstriction and bronchodilatation) of other hormones activated by epinephrine. Further, they improve the performance of skeletal muscles and help in bone formation. In excess, however, they cause muscle weakness and osteoporosis.

## Regulation of secretion of glucocorticoids

The secretion of glucocorticoids is regulated by the hypothalamus, anterior pituitary and the level of free hormone in the blood.

**Hypothalamus**

Various types of physical or mental stimuli (stress) act on the hypothalamus and increase the secretion of corticotrophin-releasing hormone (CRH). CRH then reaches the anterior pituitary through the hypothalamo-hypophyseal portal system. Within minutes, it increases the secretion of ACTH from the anterior pituitary, followed by a twenty-fold increase in the secretion of cortisol.

The secretion of ACTH and consequently, that of cortisol, is also controlled by the biological clock located in the hypothalamus. This clock is responsible for the diurnal (circadian) rhythm. ACTH secretion is the lowest during the night and the highest early in the morning.

**Anterior Pituitary**

Corticotrophin (ACTH), produced by the anterior pituitary, is a single polypeptide chain containing thirty-nine amino acids. The secretion of glucocorticoids increases minutes after an injection of ACTH. The secretion of aldosterone and adrenal androgens also goes up, though to a minor extent. In addition to regulating the secretion of glucocorticoids, ACTH also maintains the normal morphology of the adrenal cortex.

**Level of Free Hormone in Blood**

High plasma levels of free glucocorticoids inhibit the secretion of ACTH by the negative feedback mechanism, which acts both at the anterior pituitary and hypothalamic levels (Fig. 41.2). This stabilizes the level of cortisol in the plasma. However, during stress, the feedback mechanism and the circadian rhythm is disrupted, so there is always an increase in the secretion of both ACTH and glucocorticoids.

A knowledge of the negative feedback control of ACTH secretion is clinically important. Prolonged administration of large doses of glucocorticoids completely suppresses ACTH secretion and causes atrophy of the adrenal cortex. If glucocorticoid therapy is withdrawn suddenly, the adrenal cortex fails to respond to stressful stimuli, such as surgical trauma or infection, which may prove fatal. This can be prevented by slow withdrawal over a few weeks.

# MINERALOCORTICOIDS

These are essential for life, as they maintain the blood volume and blood pressure. They are responsible for mineral metabolism, and also act similarly to glucocorticoids in some ways. Aldosterone is the main mineralocorticoid.

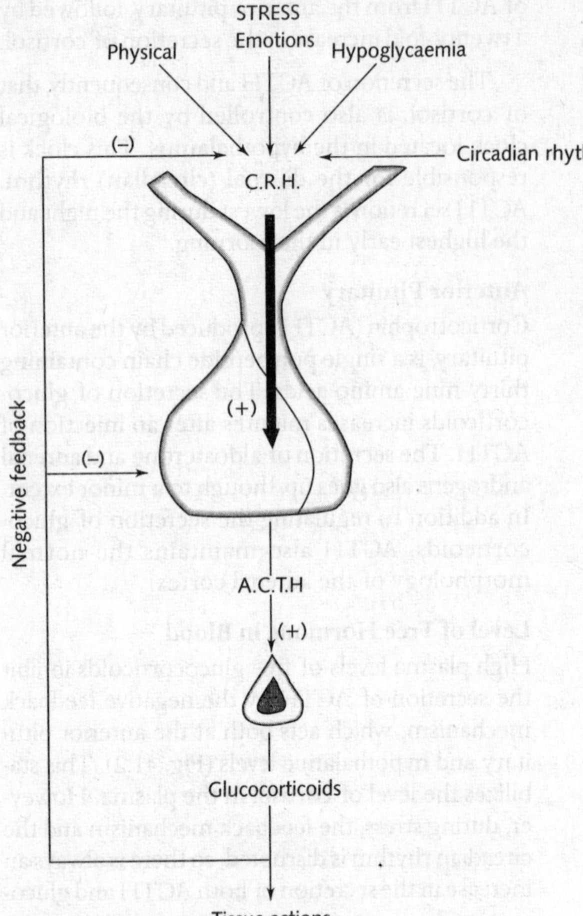


Fig. 41.2: Regulation of secretion of glucocorticoids

## Action

Aldosterone increases the activity of ATPase enzyme which increases the activity of $Na^+$–$K^+$ pump at the basal border of renal tubular epithelium cells.

Aldosterone acts on the distal convoluted tubules and collecting ducts of the kidneys (Fig. 41.3). It increases sodium reabsorption, that is, promotes the active transport of $Na^+$ from the tubular fluid to the renal interstitial fluid, and thereby, into the ECF. It also increases the excretion of potassium in the urine.

Aldosterone acts on the sweat glands, salivary glands, and gastric and intestinal glands. It decreases the excretion of $Na^+$. Its effect on the sweat glands is important in the matter of adaptation to heat. Normally, sweat is hypotonic due to aldosterone-dependent reabsorption of $Na^+$ in the ducts of the sweat glands. The effect becomes more prominent during adaptation to heat. Aldosterone prevents excessive loss of salt in sweat.

### Secondary Effects of Action

Aldosterone raises the sodium concentration of the ECF, thereby increasing the blood volume and blood pressure. It brings down the concentration of potassium in the ECF.

The loss of $H^+$ into the tubular fluid in exchange for $Na^+$ may cause alterations in

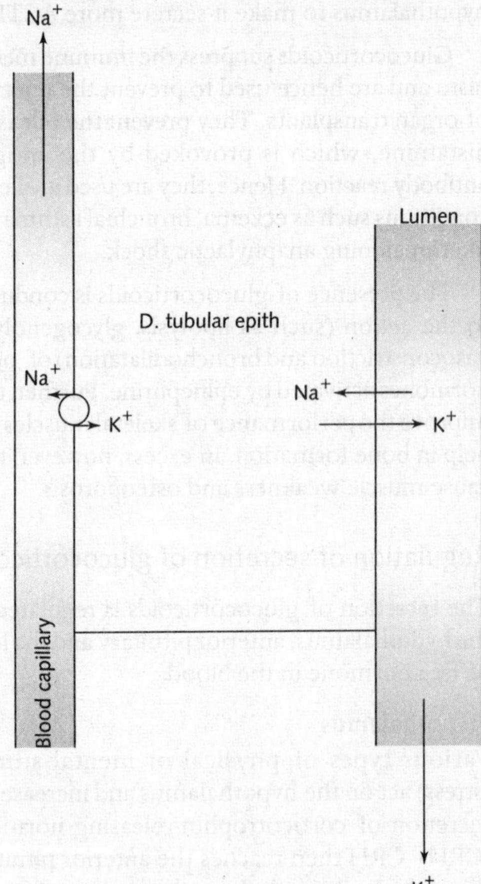


Fig. 41.3: Action of mineralocorticoid on renal tubule

the blood pH. Aldosterone helps increase the acidity of urine and, at the same time, may produce alkalosis.

As $Na^+$ is the main osmotically active substance in the ECF, changes in its concentration bring about changes in the volume of water in the body. Aldosterone helps maintain the volume of the ECF.

## Regulation of secretion

The secretion of aldosterone is brought about by angiotensin II, an increase in the $K^+$ concentration of the ECF, a lower level of $Na^+$ in the ECF, and ACTH.

### Angiotensin II

This is the strongest stimulus for the secretion of aldosterone.

The juxtaglomerular cells of the kidney secrete a proteolytic enzyme, renin, in response to a variety of stimuli, such as a decreased renal blood flow (perfusion pressure), sympathetic stimulation and the composition of fluid in the distal convoluted renal tubule. Renin acts on angiotensinogen, a glycoprotein synthesized in the liver. The latter, which circulates as $\alpha_2$ globulin, is split by renin to form angiotensin I, a decapeptide. A converting enzyme found in the lungs further splits angiotensin I to angiotensin II, an octapeptide which is a powerful vasoconstrictor. This binds with the cells of the zona glomerulosa and boosts the secretion of aldosterone. The resultant retention of $Na^+$ and $H_2O$ in the kidney helps restore the volume of the ECF to normal (Fig. 41.4).

### Increased $K^+$ in ECF

The concentration of potassium in the plasma is an important regulator of aldosterone secretion, as the cells of the zona glomerulosa are very sensitive to it. Even a small increase in the $K^+$ concentration increases the secretion of aldosterone. Changes in the plasma $K^+$ concentration affect the level of $K^+$ excreted in the urine, which helps maintain the plasma $K^+$ concentration at a normal level.

A high $K^+$ level in the ECF (hyperkalaemia) is a stronger stimulus for aldosterone secretion than a low $Na^+$ level (hyponatraemia).

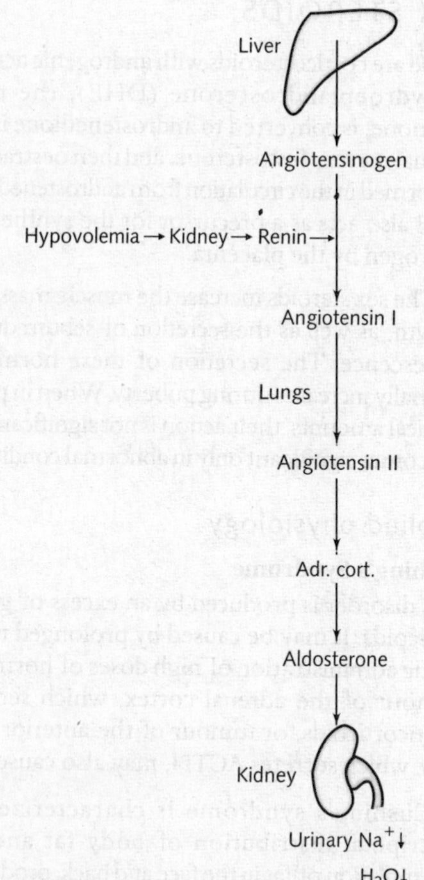


**Fig. 41.4:** The renin–angiotensin II mechanism of aldosterone secretion

### Decreased $Na^+$ in ECF; ACTH

A decreased level of $Na^+$ in the ECF directly acts on the cells of the zona glomerulosa to increase the secretion of aldosterone. Changes in the plasma $Na^+$ concentration affect the urinary excretion of $NA^+$, which helps maintain the plasma $Na^+$ concentration at a normal level.

ACTH is the weakest stimulus for the secretion of aldosterone. Basically, the zona glomerulosa of the adrenal cortex is independent of anterior pituitary control. A high concentration of ACTH in the plasma brings about a transient and very mild increase in aldosterone secretion during stress.

## SEX STEROIDS

These are corticosteroids with androgenic activity. Dehydroepiandrosterone (DHE), the main hormone, is converted to androstenedione in the adrenal cortex. Testosterone, and then oestradiols, are formed in the circulation from androstenedione. DHE also acts as a precursor for the synthesis of oestrogen by the placenta.

The sex steroids increase the muscle mass, hair growth, as well as the secretion of sebum during adolescence. The secretion of these hormones normally increases during puberty. When in physiological amounts, their action is not significant and it becomes significant only in abnormal conditions.

### Applied physiology

**Cushing's Syndrome**

This disorder is produced by an excess of glucocorticoids. It may be caused by prolonged therapeutic administration of high doses of hormone. Tumour of the adrenal cortex, which secretes glucocorticoids, or tumour of the anterior pituitary, which secretes ACTH, may also cause it.

Cushing's syndrome is characterized by centripetal distribution of body fat and the accumulation of fat in the face and back, producing the appearance of a 'moon face' and 'buffalo neck'. Excessive protein catabolism causes thinning of the skin and subcutaneous tissue, producing purple striae on the abdomen and thighs (Fig. 41.5).

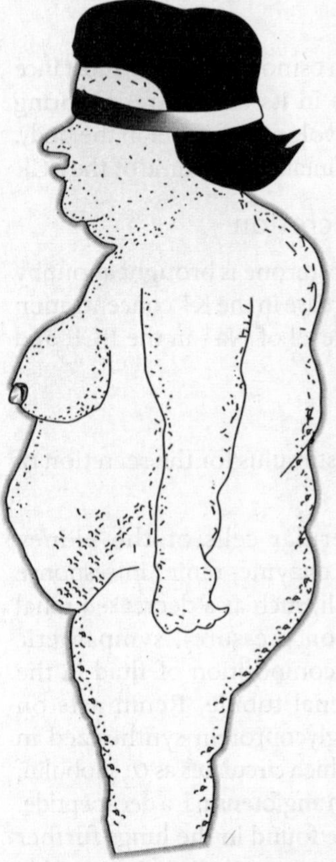

**Fig. 41.5:** Cushing's syndrome

The blood sugar and FFA levels are abnormally high in those with Cushing's syndrome. In addition, the retention of $Na^+$ and water causes high blood pressure. Osteoporosis is another feature.

**Addison's Disease**

The acute form of Addison's disease is caused by a deficiency of glucocorticoid, and the chronic form by deficiency of glucocorticoid and mineralocorticoid.

The underlying cause of the acute condition is mostly atrophy of the adrenal cortex, and sudden withdrawal of glucocorticoid therapy. The chronic condition is a result of tuberculosis of the adrenal cortex, which gets gradually damaged because of the infection.

Persons with Addison's disease have a low blood sugar level and are susceptible to stress due to the deficiency of glucocorticoids. The mineralocorticoid deficiency causes hyponatraemia, hyperkalaemia and acidosis, and also brings down the ECF volume. An excess of ACTH causes diffuse pigmentation of the skin and mucous membrane.

**Aldosteronism**

This disorder is due to an excess of aldosterone. Its primary cause is tumour of the zona glomerulosa of the adrenal cortex. The secondary cause is an increased level of angiotensin II in the liver or kidney, or heart disease.

The features of this disorder are hypokalaemia

and muscle weakness, retention of sodium and water, hypertension and alkalosis.

**Virilizing Tumours of Adrenal Cortex**

The adrenal cortex secretes small amounts of male and female sex hormones. This assumes great importance when tumours of the gland start secreting certain sex hormones in excess.

The excessive secretion of androgen produces precocious puberty in prepubertal boys and the development of male sexual characteristics (beard, moustache, muscular body and breaking of voice) in adult females (masculinization).

This condition is called the adrenogenital syndrome. It may be caused by a partial block in the synthesis of glucocorticoids, which, in turn, increases the secretion of ACTH and stimulates further production of the sex hormones.

Estimation of urinary 17-keto steroids (metabolite), is a measure of adrenal androgenic activity.

## ADRENAL MEDULLA

The adrenal medulla forms about 20 per cent of the adrenal gland. It receives a profuse supply of blood, coming from the cortex. This is essential for the synthesis of the medullary hormones as the blood supplies the necessary cortisol.

The cells of the adrenal medulla are called chromaffin cells as they display an affinity for chromic acid (stain). They are actually postganglionic sympathetic neurons without any processes. The preganglionic sympathetic neurons end on these cells and secretion occurs when there is sympathetic stimulation.

The adrenal medulla secretes three catecholamines—epinephrine, norepinephrine and dopamine.

In humans, the chief source of epinephrine in the plasma is the adrenal medulla, while that of norepinephrine is the postganglionic sympathetic nerve endings. The physiological importance of circulating dopamine is not clear.

### Synthesis of catecholamines

Catecholamines are synthesized from tyrosine, an amino acid, in the following steps:

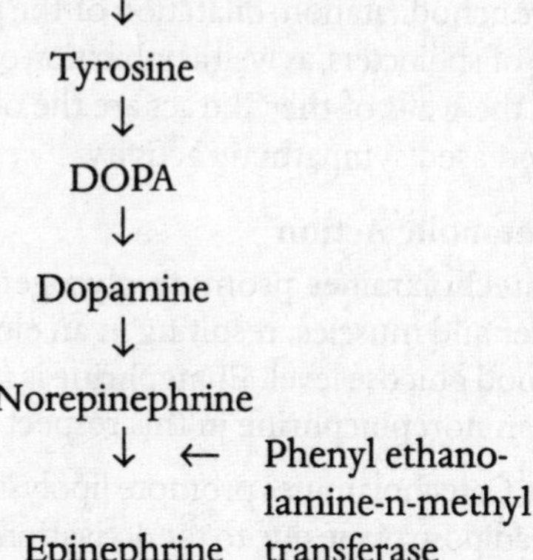


The enzyme phenyl ethanolamine-n-methyl transferase is present in the adrenal medulla but not in the postganglionic sympathetic neurons and its activity is enhanced by glucocorticoids.

The concentration of epinephrine in the plasma is about 30 picograms/ml, and the plasma norepinephrine concentration is about 300 picograms/ml. Both are variable. Catecholamines are degraded by monoamine oxidase (MAO), an enzyme that causes oxidation, and catechol-O-methyl transferase (COMT), which causes methylation.

Free catecholamines are excreted through the urine as such and so are their metabolites. The main metabolite is vanilyl mandelic acid (VMA).

### Action

The effects of two of the catecholamines are brought about by their action on two types of receptors, alpha ($\alpha$) and beta ($\beta$). Norepinephrine excites the $\alpha$ receptors. The effect of epinephrine depends on the type of receptor present in the organ. The catecholamines act in the following ways.

**Supplementation of Sympathetic Activity**

The adrenal medulla is supplied by preganglionic sympathetic fibres. Therefore, its secretions supplement those produced by sympathetic activity (by about 20 per cent).

An increase in sympathetic activity increases cardiac activity, for example, epinephrine raises the heart rate and cardiac output, hence a rise in blood pressure, for example, norepinephrine increases peripheral resistance and the blood pressure. Bronchodilatation, dilatation of the pupils, toning up of sphincters, as well as inhibition of contractions of the walls of the GI tract are the other effects of increased sympathetic activity.

**Metabolic Action**

Catecholamines promote glycogenolysis in the liver and muscles, resulting in an elevation of the blood glucose level. Epinephrine is more effective than norepinephrine in this respect.

Catecholamines promote lipolysis. This occurs in adipose tissue due to the activation of hormone-sensitive lipase, which is activated by catecholamines. They also have calorigenic action, increasing the production of heat in the body in the presence of thyroxine and glucocorticoids.

**Mental Alertness**

Catecholamines increase mental alertness by lowering the threshold of the neurons of the reticular activating system. This is useful during emergencies for the 'fight or flight' response, which causes generalized activation of the sympathetic system.

The stress response or sympathetic alarm reaction is brought about by various types of stresses which increase the secretion of ACTH cortisol via CRH. In an emergency (i.e., a life-threatening situation), a person has to fight the enemy or flee from the dangerous situation. These responses are known as the 'fight or flight' reaction. An increase in the secretion of catecholamines raises the blood pressure and blood flow to the skeletal muscles, improving their performance. This is also supplemented by mental alertness and a higher blood sugar level.

Calorigenesis and hyperglycaemia help fight stress caused by exposure to cold and hypoglycaemia, respectively. The adrenal medulla, however, is not essential for life, in spite of its physiological role as the sympathetic nervous system can produce adequate responses in an emergency.

*Applied physiology*: Phaeochromocytoma is a tumour of the adrenal medulla. It causes increased secretion of catecholamines and the patient suffers from hypertension. An estimation of the VMA level in the urine indicates the amount of catecholamines secreted in the body.

CHAPTER

42

# Endocrine Pancreas

The endocrine part of the pancreas is formed by islets of Langerhans cells, which are scattered among the pancreatic exocrine acini. There are about 1 to 2 million of these and they receive a profuse supply of blood. The islets are innervated by the vagal and sympathetic fibres, and are composed of four types of cells—α, β, δ and F (Fig. 42.1).

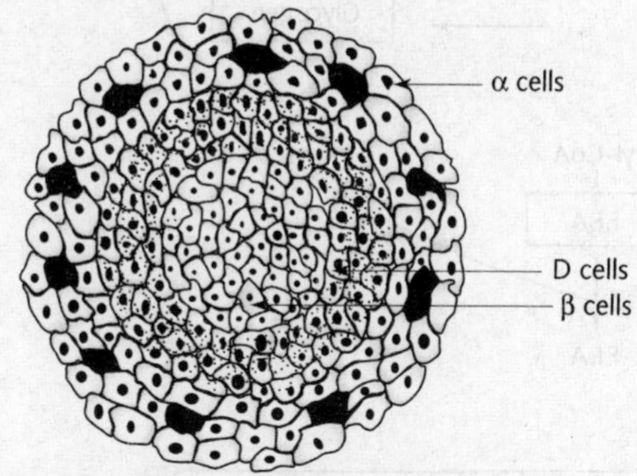


**Fig. 42.1:** Cells of endocrine pancreas

**Table 42.1:** Hormones secreted by Langerhans cells

| Cells | % of total | Secretion |
|---|---|---|
| β | 70% | Insulin |
| α | 20% | Glucagon |
| δ | 5% | Somatostatin |
| F | few | Pancreatic polypeptide |

Insulin and glucagon are involved mainly in the regulation of the blood glucose level. The physiological significance of somatostatin and pancreatic polypeptide is not known clearly.

## INSULIN

Insulin is a polypeptide containing fifty-one amino acids, arranged in two chains linked by disulphide bridges. There are slight variations in the amino acid sequence of the insulin secreted by different species. It is antigenic in other species. Beef insulin is the least antigenic in humans and is, therefore, used to treat diabetes mellitus.

Insulin is synthesized in the β cells of the islets of Langerhans as a large precursor molecule called proinsulin. Its synthesis is stimulated by hyperglycaemia.

Insulin is stored as an insulin-zinc complex in the granules of the β cells. The daily output of insulin is about 40 units per day. The stimuli causing its release are hyperglycaemia, certain amino acids and glucagon.

### Action

Although most of the body tissues are sensitive to insulin, the hormone's main target tissues are skeletal muscle, adipose tissue and the liver.

**Metabolism**

Insulin affects carbohydrate, protein as well as lipid metabolism.

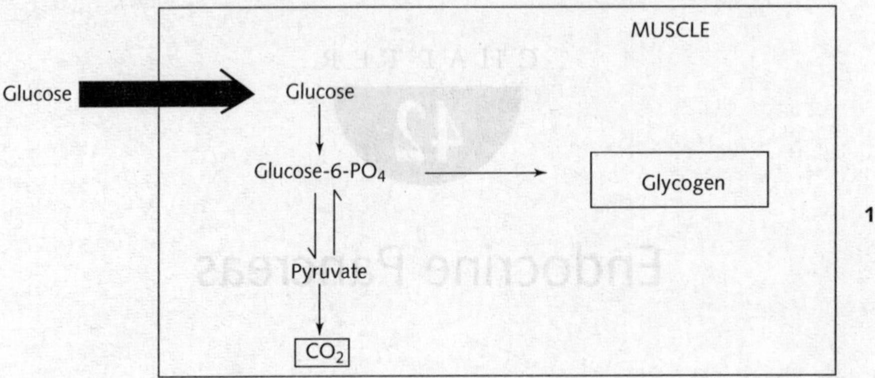


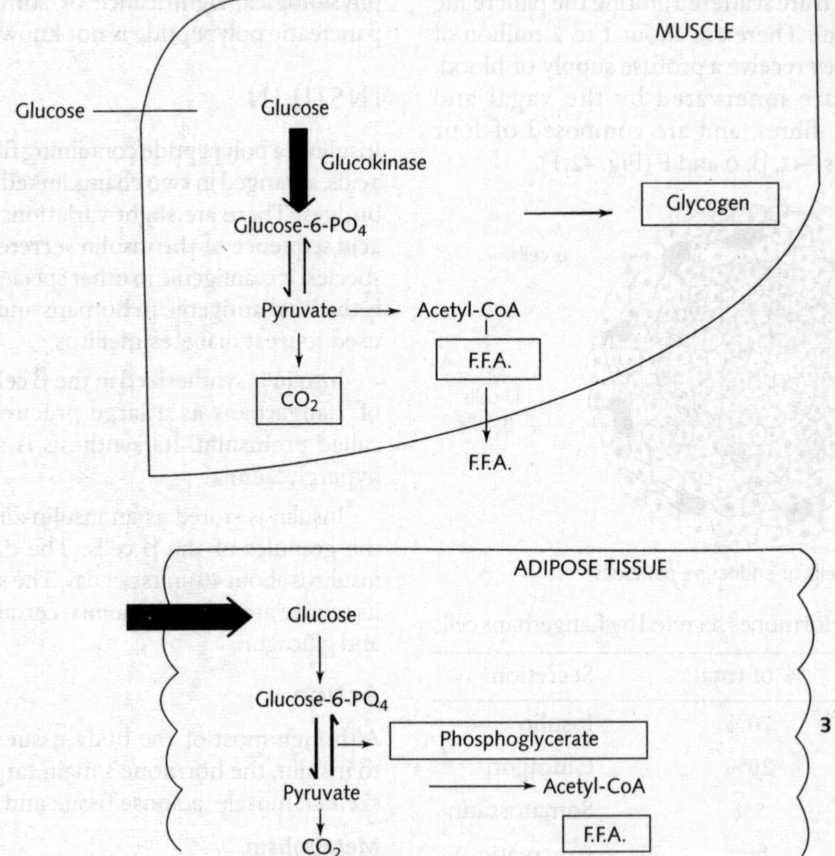


**Fig. 42.2:** Action of insulin on the carbohydrate metabolism: 1. skeletal muscle, 2. in liver, 3. in adipose tissue

*Carbohydrate metabolism*: Insulin increases the transport of glucose into the cells of the skeletal muscle and adipose tissue by enhancing the activity of glucose transporters (carriers) in the cell membrane. These are responsible for facilitated diffusion.

In the liver, insulin has no action on the cell membrane. The transport of glucose into the liver cells occurs freely, independent of insulin. The brain, intestinal mucosa, kidneys and RBCs are also not dependent on insulin for the transport of glucose.

Insulin promotes peripheral utilization of glucose for the production of energy. Glucose is converted to glucose-6-$PO_4$ by the enzyme hexokinase in the skeletal muscle and adipose tissue, and by glucokinase in the liver. This brings down the concentration of glucose in the liver cells, thereby increasing the transport of glucose into them. Glucose-6-$PO_4$ then enters the glycolytic pathway.

Insulin also promotes glycogenesis (i.e., the conversion of glucose to glycogen) by enhancing the activity of the enzyme glycogen synthetase in the skeletal muscle and liver, and plays a part in its storage (Fig. 42.2). Further, it inhibits glycogenolysis by inhibiting the enzyme phosphorylase, and inhibits neoglucogenesis in the liver by inhibiting the enzymes necessary for the process.

By these actions, insulin brings up the level of glycogen deposited in the liver, and less glucose is poured into the circulation. Thus, the overall effect of insulin on carbohydrate metabolism is a fall in the blood sugar level, that is, hypoglycaemia.

*Lipid metabolism*: Insulin inhibits hormone-sensitive lipase and the mobilization of FFAs, thereby lowering the FFA level in the blood, its utilization and the formation of ketone bodies.

It also stimulates the synthesis of FFAs and triglycerides as a result of the entry of more glucose into the adipose tissue. However, most of the triglyceride synthesis occurs in the liver since the amount of glucose transported to the liver is ten times the amount transported to the adipose tissue. When the glycogen stores are saturated, the excess glucose is used for the synthesis of fatty acids. These are transported as chylomicrons to the adipose tissue. Here, insulin enhances the activity of lipoprotein lipase, which favours the uptake of fatty acids. The latter are stored as triglycerides (Fig. 42.3) after their esterification with phosphoglycerate.

Through these actions, insulin regulates the use of glucose or FFAs for the production of energy. After a carbohydrate-rich meal, the secretion of insulin goes up and glucose is used primarily for the production of energy in muscles. Between meals, when the blood glucose level and insulin secretion decrease, lipolysis occurs and FFAs are used for the production of energy.

*Protein metabolism*: Insulin induces the transport of amino acids into cells, particularly in the liver and muscles, and gives a boost to protein synthesis. Further, it prevents catabolism of proteins, and

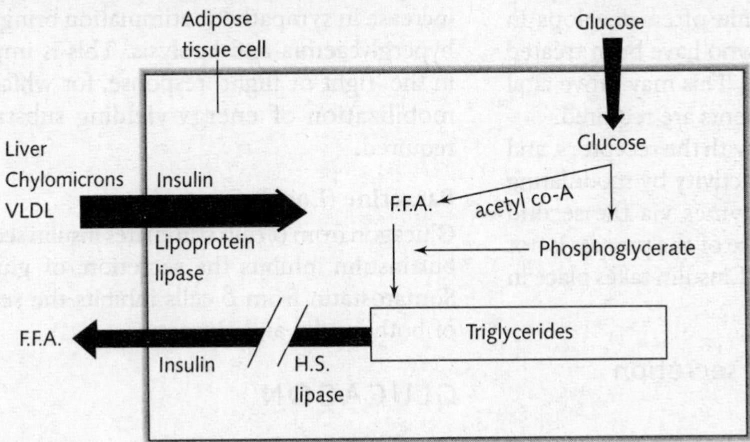


**Fig. 42.3**: Action of insulin on fat metabolism

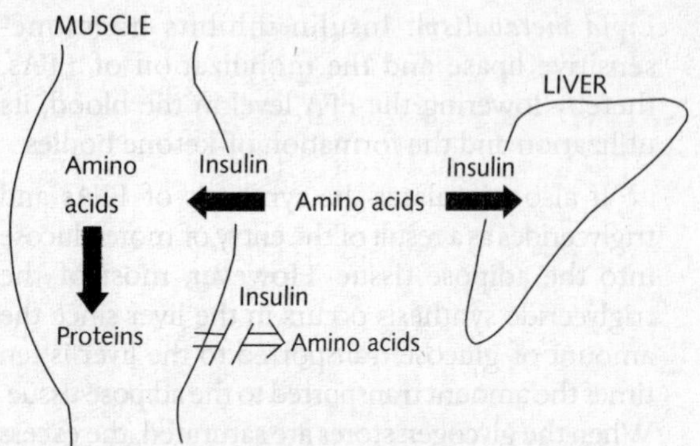


Fig. 42.4: Action of insulin on protein metabolism

inhibits neoglucogenesis in the liver by depressing the activity of the enzymes involved in the process (Fig. 42.4).

The overall effect of insulin on protein metabolism is anabolic.

### Other Action

Insulin plays a role in growth and development, as well as in the transport of ions.

*Growth and development*: The anabolic action of insulin is as important as that of growth hormone for the promotion of normal growth. Proper growth and development require the presence of both hormones, in addition to plenty of nutrients.

*Ion transport*: Insulin induces the transport of $K^+$ from the ECF into the skeletal muscle and hepatic cells. Hence, hypokalaemia often develops in diabetic acidosis patients who have been treated with large doses of insulin. This may prove fatal and so potassium supplements are required.

Insulin acts by binding with the receptors, and brings about intracellular activity by modulating the action of specific enzymes via the second messenger. The exact nature of the process is not known. The degradation of insulin takes place in the liver and kidneys.

## Regulation of insulin secretion

### Blood Glucose Level

This is the most important factor regulating the secretion of insulin. The rate of its secretion is the lowest at the normal fasting blood glucose level (80–120 mg%). As the blood glucose level increases beyond this, it stimulates the β cells to secrete insulin. When it falls below this level, the secretion of insulin is cut off. Thus, there is a negative feedback mechanism for the regulation of insulin secretion.

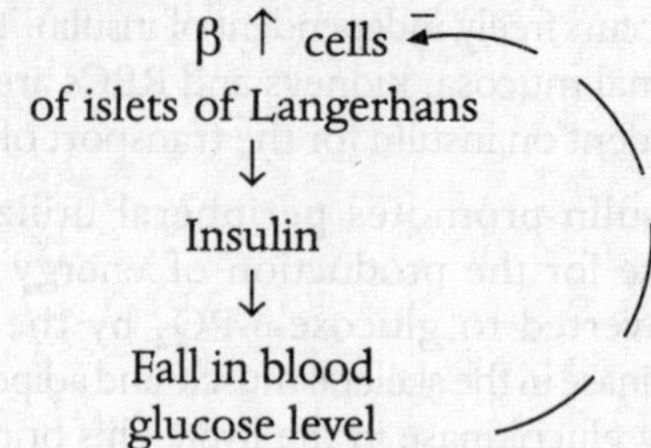


### Amino Acids; Gastrointestinal Hormones

Some amino acids in the plasma, such as arginine and lysine, stimulate the secretion of insulin, which, therefore, increases after a protein-rich meal.

Gastrointestinal hormones, such as gastric inhibitory polypeptide (GIP), gastrin and CCK-PZ, increase the secretion of insulin. These hormones are secreted in high amounts after a meal. Of them, GIP is the most important.

### Autonomic Nervous System

Vagal (parasympathetic) stimulation increases insulin secretion, while sympathetic stimulation brings it down. During stress, therefore, the increase in sympathetic stimulation brings about hyperglycaemia and lipolysis. This is important in the 'fight or flight' response, for which rapid mobilization of energy-yielding substrates is required.

### Paracrine (Local) Control

Glucagon from α cells stimulates insulin secretion, but insulin inhibits the secretion, of glucagon. Somatostatin from δ cells inhibits the secretion of both insulin and glucagon.

## GLUCAGON

Glucagon is a polypeptide containing twenty-nine amino acids. It is secreted mainly by the α cells of the islets of Langerhans. It is also produced by certain cells of the gastric and intestinal mucosa.

Hypoglycaemia and epinephrine stimulate the secretion of glucagon. Insulin and somatostatin inhibit it.

## Action

The liver is the principle target organ for the action of glucagon. Glucagon promotes glycogenolysis in the liver by boosting the activity of phosphorylase. It has no effect on the skeletal muscles, unlike epinephrine.

It also inhibits glycogenesis by inactivating the enzyme glycogen synthetase. It promotes neoglucogenesis by enhancing the activity of the enzymes required for the process. The effect of these actions is to increase the blood sugar level, that is, hyperglycaemia.

In large doses, glucagon promotes lipolysis and the formation of ketone bodies. It also has a calorigenic effect.

The degradation of glucagon occurs in the liver.

## Regulation of secretion

When the blood glucose level falls below the normal range (80–100 mg%), it is the most potent stimulus for the secretion of glucagon. A rise in the blood glucose level (above the normal range) inhibits the release of glucagon. Hence, its secretion is regulated by the blood glucose level via a negative feedback mechanism.

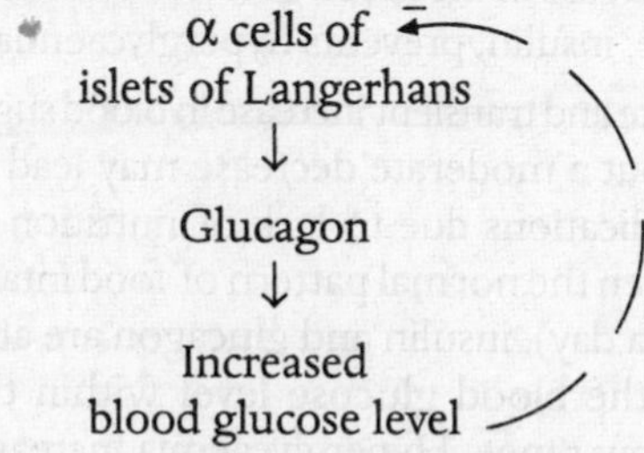


The secretion of glucagon increases following a protein-rich meal.

# REGULATION OF BLOOD GLUCOSE LEVEL

The blood sugar level is normally maintained within a particular range. After an overnight fast, it should be between 80 to 120 mg%. Therefore, the fasting level on an average is about 100 mg%.

After a large meal rich in carbohydrates or following oral intake of glucose, the blood sugar level goes up to about 120–150 mg% (post-prandial level), but never above 180 mg%. It returns to the normal baseline within 2 hours (due to the prompt secretion of insulin). When plotted on a time scale, the response is called the 'glucose tolerance curve' (Fig. 42.5).

## Importance of regulation

Glucose is the only nutrient used by the brain, retina and germinal epithelium of the gonads. The maintenance of their nutrition requires the maintenance of the blood glucose level within a normal range.

*Blood sugar pool*: The total amount of glucose

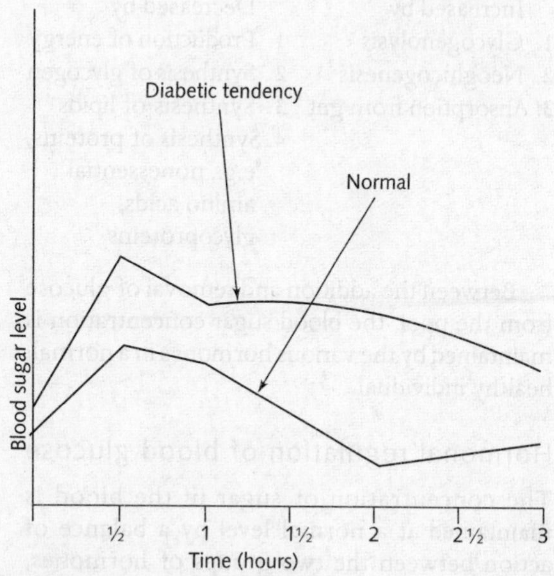


**Fig. 42.5:** Glucose tolerance test

present in the body at any moment forms the blood glucose pool, which is measured by the blood sugar level. Various body tissues take up glucose as per their requirements from this pool. Glucose is used for the production of energy as well as various substances.

Normally, glucose is added to the pool through absorption from the gut. This also happens through glycogenolysis and neoglucogenesis, which take place mainly in the liver during fasting. The glucose from the liver can maintain the body's need for glucose for 3 to 4 hours. The liver, therefore, acts as a storage vault, storing glucose as glycogen when it is in excess and supplying glucose by breaking down glycogen whenever required. The liver is thus the main organ responsible for maintaining the blood glucose level (Fig. 42.6).

Maintenance of blood sugar pool

| Increased by | Decreased by |
|---|---|
| 1. Glycogenolysis | 1. Production of energy |
| 2. Neoglucogenesis | 2. Synthesis of glycogen |
| 3. Absorption from gut | 3. Synthesis of lipids |
| | 4. Synthesis of proteins, e.g., nonessential amino acids, glycoproteins |

Between the addition and removal of glucose from the pool, the blood sugar concentration is maintained by the various hormones in a normal, healthy individual.

## Hormonal regulation of blood glucose

The concentration of sugar in the blood is maintained at a normal level by a balance of action between the two groups of hormones, hyperglycaemic and hypoglycaemic, that is, those which increase and decrease the blood sugar, respectively.

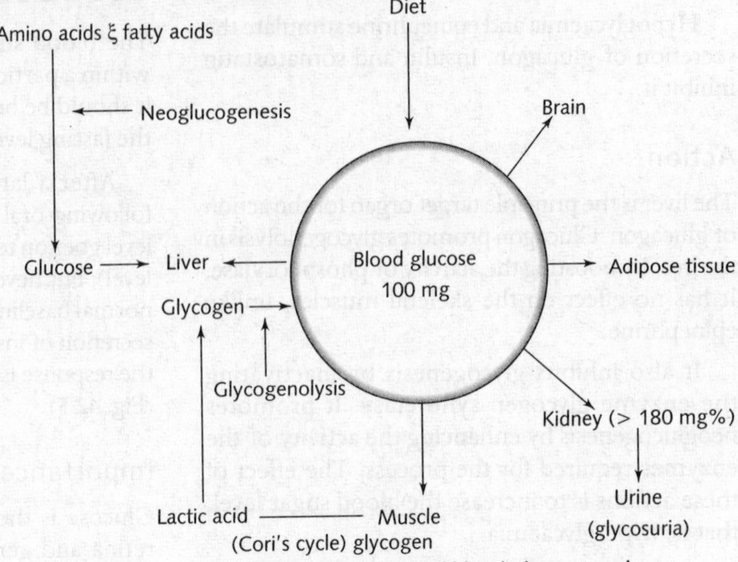


**Fig. 42.6:** Maintenance of blood glucose pool

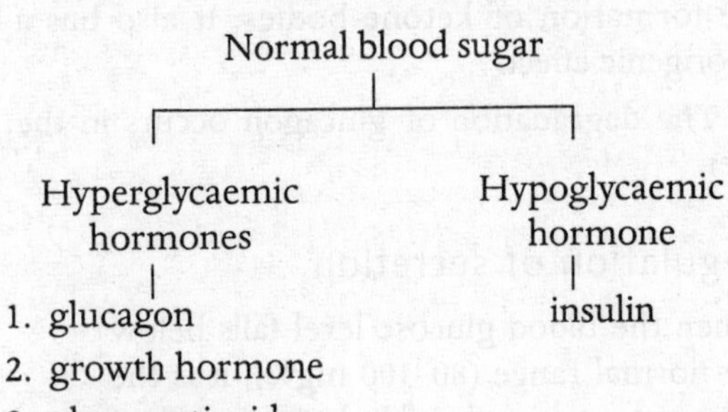


During starvation or between meals, the hyperglycaemic hormones are secreted. These prevent a significant decrease in the blood glucose level. Only one hormone, insulin, prevents hyperglycaemia.

A moderate and transient increase in blood sugar is harmless, but a moderate decrease may lead to serious complications due to lack of nutrition to the brain. Given the normal pattern of food intake (2 to 3 meals a day), insulin and glucagon are able to maintain the blood glucose level within the normal, narrow range. Hyperglycaemia increases the secretion of insulin but decreases that of glucagon. On the other hand, hypoglycaemia increases glucagon secretion but decreases insulin secretion.

## Applied physiology

### Diabetes Mellitus

This is a fairly common metabolic disorder caused by a deficiency of insulin. It may be of juvenile onset (also known as insulin-dependent diabetes) or maturity onset (or non-insulin-dependent diabetes).

The features of each type are listed below.

| *Juvenile onset* | *Maturity onset* |
|---|---|
| 1. Occurs before 40 years of age. | 1. Occurs after 40 years of age. |
| 2. Caused by absolute deficiency of insulin. | 2. Caused by relative deficiency of insulin. |
| 3. The patient is usually lean. | 3. The patient is usually obese. |
| 4. Keto-acidosis is common. | 4. Keto-acidosis is not common. |
| 5. Insulin therapy is essential. | 5. Insulin therapy is not essential. |

Hyperglycaemia is caused by a reduced utilization of glucose, and increased neoglucogenesis and glycogenolysis. When the blood glucose level exceeds 180 mg% (renal threshold), glucose appears in the urine. This is known as glycosuria. In polyuria, osmotic diuresis occurs due to the presence of glucose in the urine.

Another abnormal feature is polydipsia, in which there is increased thirst, caused by the excretion of large volumes of urine, which results in dehydration and depletion of electrolytes. Decreased utilization of glucose causes polyphagia, which increases the intake of food.

Muscle weakness occurs due to increased breakdown of protein and weight loss, while keto-acidosis is caused by increased lipolysis, and can result in coma and death.

### Treatment

Diabetes can be treated by a high-protein, low-fat and low-carbohydrate diet.

Exercise is advised as it promotes the entry of glucose into the cells. Certain oral drugs increase the secretion of insulin by stimulating the β cells of the pancreas that are still functioning. These drugs are useful in maturity-onset diabetes. The administration of insulin is one of the most important measures.

# Reproductive System

CHAPTER

43

# General Considerations

The function of the reproductive system is the propagation of the species. Reproduction is the joint action of the male and female reproductive system. Each system produces a gamete which carries the genetic material of the individual. The female reproductive system has the additional responsibility of maintaining the embryo within it (i.e., the womb) in the early stage, and to nourish the newborn baby by lactation.

The male gamete is called the spermatozoon (sperm) and the female, the ovum (egg). The sperm and ovum fuse to form the zygote, which develops into a new individual.

*Sex differentiation*

Whether the zygote will develop into a male or a female is determined by the presence or absence of the Y chromosome in it. If the Y chromosome is present, the zygote develops into a male, and if not, a female. Normally, the presence of this chromosome leads to the development of male gonads and subsequently, other male characteristics. The absence of the Y chromosome leads to the development of female gonads and other female characteristics.

*Parts of the reproductive system*

The reproductive system consists of sex organs which are present at the time of birth, though in a rudimentary form. Their growth and maturation takes place during puberty. They consist of the primary sex organs or gonads (ovaries in the female and testes in the male), as well as the accessory sex organs, through which the gametes are transported.

## PUBERTY

Puberty is the period of life when the endocrine and gametogenic functions of the gonads develop for the first time, causing the growth and maturation of the sex organs to such an extent that reproduction is possible.

These changes, which lead to adulthood, occur gradually through a period of life known as adolescence. Emotional changes also occur during this period.

In girls, the onset of puberty is between the ages of 10 to 14 years and in boys, 14 to 18 years.

### Cause of puberty

After birth, the gonads remain quiescent up to adolescence, though all the factors necessary for their activity are present throughout. This is because until puberty, the hypothalamus is extremely sensitive to the low level of sex hormones secreted by the adrenal cortex, which inhibit it (the hypothalamus). Thus, this prevents the secretion of releasing factors from the hypothalamus and gonadotrophic hormones from the anterior pituitary.

The development of the hypothalamus and

limbic cortex (concerned with emotions) occurs during puberty. This abolishes the hypersensitivity of the hypothalamus to the low level of sex hormones, so it starts secreting gonadotrophic hormones.

The gonadotrophic hormones act on the gonads (ovaries and testes), making them grow and mature. This is followed by the secretion of sex hormones—oestrogen and progesterone in the female, and testosterone in the male. These act on the various body tissues to bring about the development of the secondary sex characteristics.

The level of sex hormones in the plasma controls the release of releasing hormones from the hypothalamus via a negative feedback mechanism, which, in turn, controls the level of sex hormones in the blood. The latter maintain the secondary sex characteristics (Fig. 43.1).

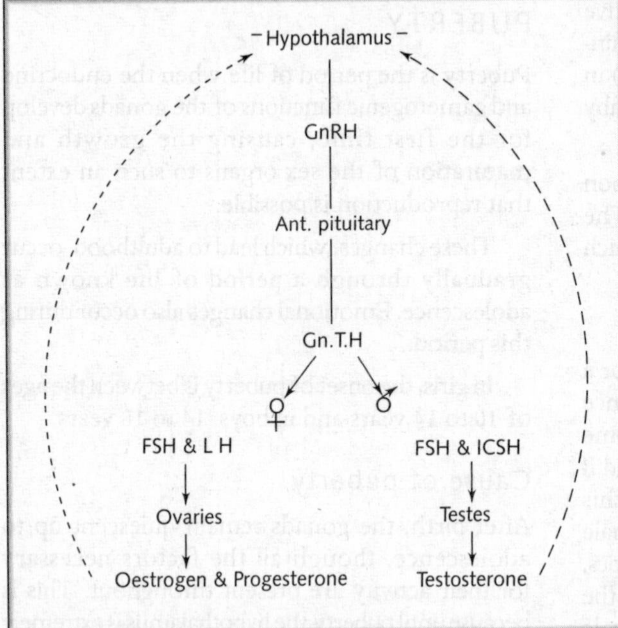


Fig. 43.1: Hormonal mechanism of puberty

## SECONDARY SEX CHARACTERISTICS

In females, the secondary sex characteristics include the development of the breasts and the growth of axillary and pubic hair. Females have more scalp hair than body hair. The first menstrual cycle and, is initiated menarche there is a sudden spurt of growth.

Enlargement of the external and internal genitalia and widening of the pelvis are other secondary sexual characteristics in females. There is also deposition of fat in the buttocks, thighs and breasts. This is why a description of the female body includes narrow shoulders, a broad pelvis, diverging hands and converging legs. The development of a high-pitched voice and attraction towards the opposite sex are the other secondary sexual attributes.

In males, the secondary sexual characteristics include breaking (deepening) of the voice due to laryngeal growth and changes in the vocal cords. Enlargement of the external and internal genitalia, as well as the growth of hair in the axillary and pubic regions, face, chest and back are some of the other features. The hair growth is more dense on the body than on the scalp.

There is a sudden increase in the height, more so than in the case of girls. The shoulders broaden and the muscle mass increases. As in the case of girls, there is attraction towards the opposite sex. The behaviour of boys in this stage becomes aggressive.

## REPRODUCTIVE LIFE

This is the period of life after puberty, when a person is capable of reproducing. The length of this period varies from person to person, according to the age of the onset of menopause, which is the end of reproductive life in females. The reproductive life of females is about 35 to 45 years, while that of males is much longer. This is because menopause occurs between 45 to 50 years of age, whereas there is no such clear cut occurrence in the case of males.

During the reproductive period, normal women have a regular reproductive cycle (except when pregnant or lactating), and they have a chance of conceiving.

Menopause is the age at which a woman's reproductive capacity goes on decreasing and ultimately ends. As mentioned earlier, the onset of menopause is 45 ± 5 years. Menopause occurs because as age advances, the number of follicles in the ovaries keeps decreasing. Therefore, in spite of the high level of anterior pituitary gonadotrophins, the level of sex hormones secreted by the ovaries goes on falling, leading to a reversal of all the pubertal changes.

Several changes take place during menopause. For one, the reproductive (menstrual) cycles become prolonged, irregular and ultimately stop. Ovulation (liberation of ova from the ovarian follicles) stops and so does the secretion of sex hormones. The breasts shrink and the axillary and pubic hair become scantier. Sometimes, there is sudden vasodilatation and sweating, known as hot flushes. In some cases, psychological changes occur since a woman may start feeling unwanted and insecure.

# Male Reproductive System

The male reproductive system consists of the primary reproductive organs, the accessory reproductive organs and the external genitalia. The primary reproductive organs consist of a pair of testes, located in the scrotal sac outside the abdominal cavity so that a favourable temperature is maintained. The testes produce spermatozoa and secrete the male sex hormones, that is, androgens.

The accessory reproductive organs consist of the vas deferens, seminal vesicles, ejaculatory ducts, prostate, bulbourethral glands and penis. These constitute the seminal tracts from each testis and also elaborate some secretions. The vas deferens and the duct of the seminal vesicle form the ejaculatory duct, which opens into the prostatic urethra, into which the prostatic glands and bulbourethral glands also open.

The external genitalia are the penis and scrotum. The secondary sex characteristics of males are not directly related to reproduction (Fig. 44.1).

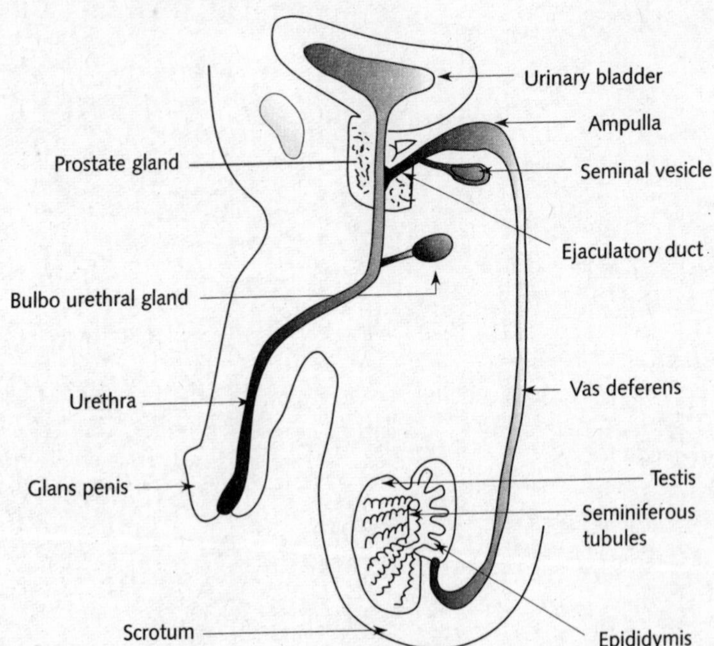


**Fig. 44.1:** The male reproductive system

## SPERMATOGENESIS

This is the process of the formation of spermatozoa and is the primary function of the male reproductive system. Gametogenesis begins at puberty and continues throughout the rest of life. It occurs in the testes.

The testes consist of seminiferous tubules, which contain two types of cells: (i) those in the process of forming sperms, and (ii) large supporting cells, called Sertoli cells, extending from the basement membrane to the lumen of the tubule. Between the seminiferous tubules, in the interstitial connective tissue, there are large polyhedral cells, called Leydig cells (Fig. 44.2).

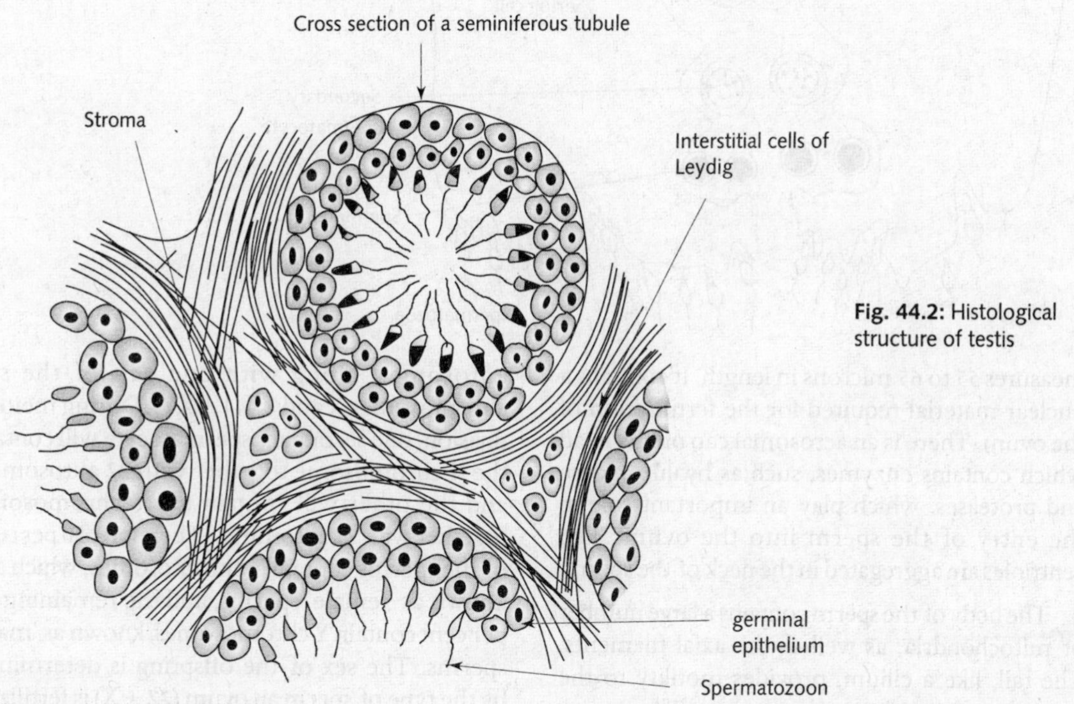


**Fig. 44.2:** Histological structure of testis

### Stages of spermatogenesis

The primordial germ cells of the testes, called spermatogonia A, are situated near the basement membrane of the seminiferous tubule. They behave like stem cells, maintaining a continuous supply of precursors of sperm. These cells undergo continuous mitosis and some of them remain primordial germ cells, while others are differentiated towards the line of future spermatocytes. The latter form cells called spermatogonia B. These pass towards the lumen of the seminiferous tubule, among the Sertoli cells (Fig. 44.3).

The spermatogonia B undergo further mitosis and are converted to large primary spermatocytes, which then undergo meiotic (reduction) division to be converted to two secondary spermatocytes. Each secondary spermatocyte, after a second meiotic division, forms two spermatids. Each of these contains half the number (i.e., 23) of chromosomes or is haploid [i.e., (22 + X) or (22 + Y)], and does not divide further. Each spermatogonium gives rise to 512 spermatids.

The spermatids thus formed are like epithelial cells. They attach themselves to the Sertoli cells, and begin to elongate and mature, that is, differentiate into a spermatozoon. This process is known as spermiogenesis.

A spermatozoon (sperm) consists of a head, neck, body and tail. The head is elliptical and

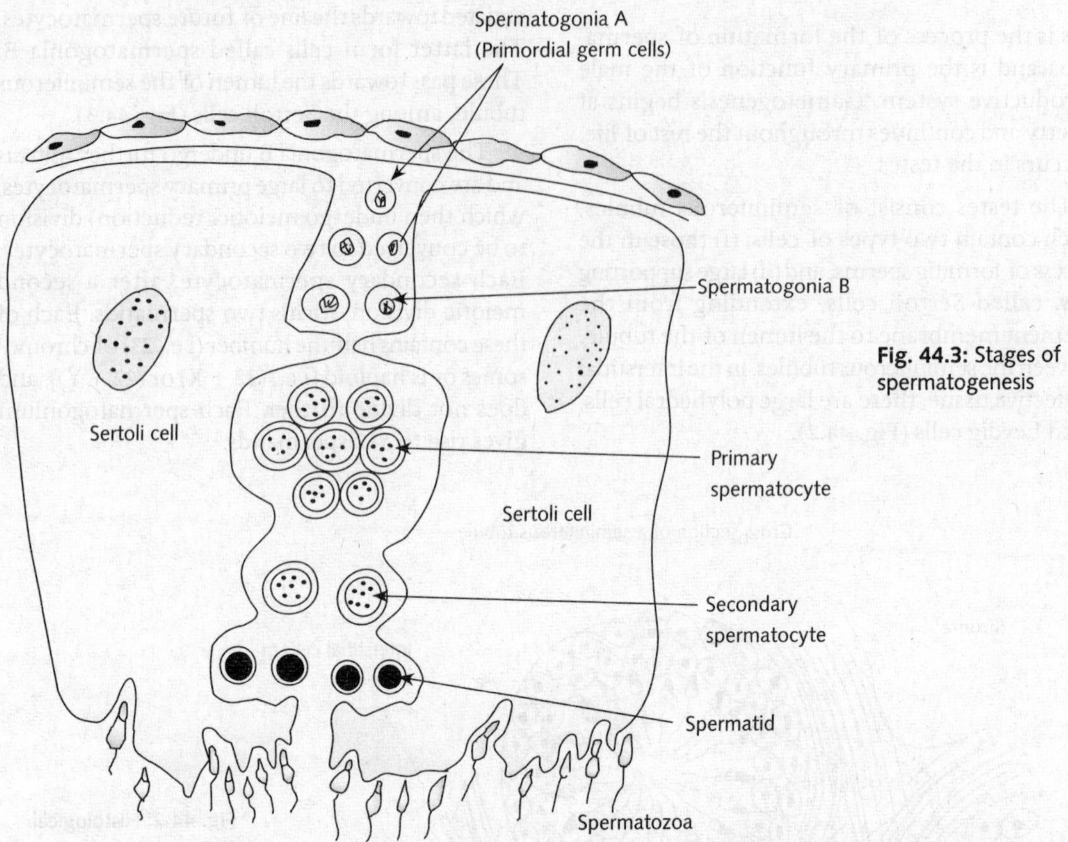


**Fig. 44.3:** Stages of spermatogenesis

measures 55 to 65 microns in length. It contains a nuclear material required for the fertilization of the ovum. There is an acrosomal cap on the head which contains enzymes, such as hyaluronidase and proteases, which play an important role in the entry of the sperm into the ovum. The centrioles are aggregated in the neck of the sperm.

The body of the sperm contains a large number of mitochondria, as well as the axial filaments. The tail, like a cilium, provides motility to the sperm, at a rate of 1–4 mm/minute. The energy for the movement is provided by the mitochondria (Fig. 44.4).

## 'Male' and 'female' sperms

The total number of chromosomes in a cell is 46 (23 pairs). Each primary spermatocyte, like any other cell in the male, contains 22 pairs of autosomes, along with one pair of the sex chromosomes X and Y (44 + XY). During meiotic division, one secondary spermatocyte will contain the X chromosome together with 22 autosomes, and the other will contain the Y chromosome together with 22 autosomes. Therefore, 50 per cent of the sperms contain X chromosomes, which are known as 'female' sperms, and the remaining 50 per cent contain Y chromosomes, known as 'male' sperms. The sex of the offspring is determined by the type of sperm an ovum (22 + X) is fertilized with. The fertilization of the ovum (22 + X) with a male sperm (22 + Y) results in a male offspring (44 + XY), and fertilization with a female sperm (22 + X) results in the formation of a female offspring (44 + XX).

*Transport of sperms*: In the seminiferous tubule, the sperms are not motile. They become motile

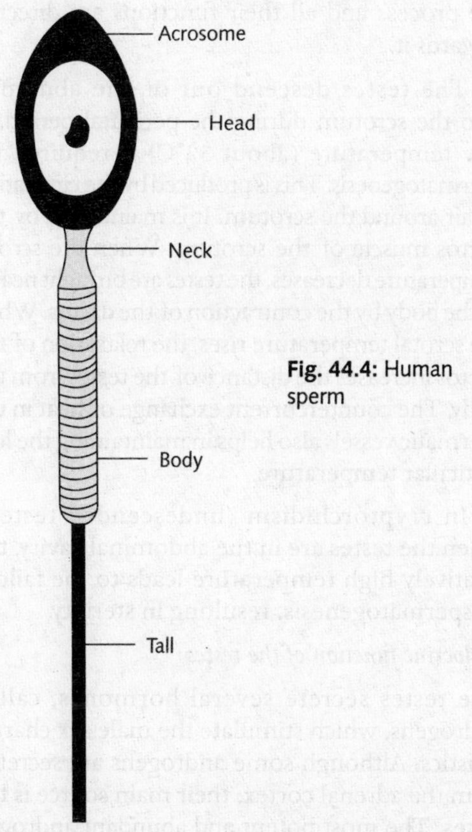

**Fig. 44.4:** Human sperm

during their passage through the epididymis. The sperms move up to the vas deferens due to the positive pressure of the fluid in the seminiferous tubule. This fluid is secreted mainly by the Sertoli cells. Subsequently, the movement is due to the contraction of smooth muscles in the wall of the vas deferens.

## Role of Sertoli cells

The Sertoli cells provide the nutrients, hormones and enzymes necessary for the maturation of spermatids. They also remove excess cytoplasm, as the epitheloid spermatids are gradually converted into long and thin spermatozoa. These are released from the Sertoli cells into the lumen of the seminiferous tubule through a process called spermiation.

The Sertoli cells secrete an androgen-binding protein (ABP), which helps maintain a high concentration of androgens in the seminiferous tubular fluid. This is necessary for the maturation of sperms. The Sertoli cells also secrete a hormone, inhibin, which is polypeptide in nature and inhibits FSH secretion from the anterior pituitary via a feedback mechanism.

The tight junctions between the adjacent Sertoli cells near the basement membrane constitute a blood-testicular barrier, which prevents (i) the passage of proteins and other macromolecules from the blood to the lumen of the seminiferous tubules, and (ii) the passage of the antigenic products of germ cell division and maturation from the seminiferous tubules into the circulation. This prevents the development of immunity against sperms.

## Role of epididymis, seminal vesicles, prostate gland

The epididymis plays a role in the maturation of the sperms, helping them become motile and capable of fertilization. The epididymal secretions required for this are androgen-dependent. The sperms are stored in the epididymis, particularly in its ampulla, for several months.

The seminal vesicles secrete a mucoid material, which contains a large amount of fructose, other nutrients, fibrinogen and prostaglandins. These contribute to about 60 per cent of the total volume of semen.

The prostate gland secretes a thin, milky, acidic fluid that contains citric acid, calcium, acid phosphatase, prefibrinolysin as well as a clotting enzyme. It contributes to about 20 per cent of the total volume of semen.

## Semen

Semen is the fluid ejaculated from the genital tract during the male sexual act. Ejaculation is the process of the ejection of semen, which requires an intact autonomic nervous system. The afferent impulses from the penis lead to reflex contraction of the smooth muscles in the epididymis, vas, seminal vesicles and prostate. There is simultaneous discharge from the accessory glands into the urethra. Then, by contraction of the bulbocavernosus muscle, the semen is ejected. At the same time, contraction of the urethral sphincter prevents the entry of semen into the urinary bladder and also, micturition during the process.

**Composition and Character**

Semen consists of fluids from the vas deferens, containing sperms, and from the seminal vesicles, prostate gland, mucous glands, and particularly from the bulbourethral gland.

The average volume per ejaculation is 2.5 to 3.5 ml. Semen is a white opalescent fluid, which coagulates immediately but liquefies after 15 to 20 minutes. Clotting facilitates its retention in the vagina for some time. Later on, lysis helps in the free movement of sperms in the female genital tract.

The pH of semen is about 7.4 to 7.5. It is maintained by the phosphates and bicarbonates. Semen is more alkaline than the body fluids due to alkaline prostatic fluid. This is necessary to keep the sperms alive and motile in the female genital tract as the vaginal fluid is acidic.

The normal sperm count varies between 40 and 100 million/ml of semen. Of this, 80 per cent should be normal and motile. When the sperm count is less than 20 million/ml, the person is likely to be infertile, though only one sperm is ultimately required for the fertilization of the ovum.

Semen contains fructose, which is extremely important for the nutrition of the sperms. It also contains prostaglandins, zinc, citric acid and phospholipid, among other things.

## Factors influencing spermatogenesis

FSH is the main gonadotrophin required for spermatogenesis. It helps in the conversion of spermatid to sperm. LH stimulates the Leydig cells to produce testosterone, which is essential for spermatogenesis. A high concentration of testosterone within the seminiferous tubules is essential for the growth, multiplication and maturation of gametes.

Sertoli cells are stimulated by FSH to release various factors which help the process of spermatogenesis. Sertoli cells are of crucial importance for the process and all their functions are directed towards it.

The testes descend out of the abdomen into the scrotum during the perinatal period. A low temperature (about 32°C) is required for spermatogenesis. This is produced by the circulation of air around the scrotum. It is maintained by the dartos muscle of the scrotum. When the scrotal temperature decreases, the testes are brought nearer to the body by the contraction of the dartos. When the scrotal temperature rises, the relaxation of the dartos increases the distance of the testes from the body. The countercurrent exchange of heat in the spermatic vessels also helps in maintaining the low testicular temperature.

In cryptorchidism (undescended testes), when the testes are in the abdominal cavity, the relatively high temperature leads to the failure of spermatogenesis, resulting in sterility.

*Endocrine function of the testes*

The testes secrete several hormones, called androgens, which stimulate the male sex characteristics. Although some androgens are secreted from the adrenal cortex, their main source is the testes. The most potent and abundant androgen is testosterone.

Dehydroepiandrosterone and androstenedione are the other important androgens. These are present in both males and females. They originate from the adrenal cortex. When secreted in small amounts, they have only a negligible masculinizing effect, but have an important anabolic effect in females.

## Testosterone

Testosterone is a steroid hormone, which is synthesized by the interstitial Leydig cells from cholesterol. The steps of synthesis are as shown below.

Cholesterol → Pregnanelone → Progesterone
↓ ↓
Dehydroepiandrosterone → Androstenedione
↓
Testosterone

Most of the testosterone is converted to 17-ketosteroid, which forms one-third of the ketosteroid excreted in urine in an adult male. The rest is from the suprarenal cortex.

**Action**

Testosterone performs a number of important functions.

*Growth of genitalia and accessory sexual organs:* Testosterone promotes the growth of the testes, scrotum and penis during puberty, and produces pigmentation in the external genitalia. It also induces the growth of the epididymis, seminal vesicles, prostate and bulbourethral glands.

*Development of secondary sexual characteristics:* Testosterone promotes the development of the secondary sexual characteristics in boys. These include the growth of the beard, axillary and pubic hair (male pattern), as well as temporal recession of the hair line; breaking of the voice; thickening of the skin; development of the shoulder girdle and muscle mass; spermatogenesis and motility of sperms; and the male sexual drive at puberty (libido), aggressive behaviour and interest in the opposite sex.

*Metabolic action:* Testosterone is strongly anabolic and enhances protein synthesis, preventing its breakdown. It also helps in the retention of $Na^+$, $K^+$, $Ca^{++}$, $PO_4^{---}$ and $SO_4^{--}$, along with water.

*Growth of the body:* Testosterone is responsible for the spurt of growth during puberty. The spurt is caused by the stimulation of GH, protein anabolism and the growth of the bones (in length and thickness). This is followed by epiphyseal closure, which arrests further growth in height.

*Erythropoiesis:* Testosterone boosts the production of erythropoietin, thereby raising the haemoglobin concentration and RBC count in males.

*Prenatal development:* In intrauterine life, testosterone from the foetal testes acts on the foetal brain to aid in the development of the male psyche. It also helps in the growth of the male sex organs in a male foetus. In the absence of testosterone, female sex organs develop.

The descent of the testes during the last two months of foetal life, or soon after birth, also depends on testosterone.

During childhood, the testicular Leydig cells revert to an undifferentiated state, to be reactivated at puberty by the secretion of pituitary gonadotrophins.

*Mechanism of action:* In most of the target cells, testosterone is first converted to dihydrotestosterone, which binds with the cytoplasmic receptors, raising the level of protein synthesis in the cell.

**Regulation of Secretion**

Human chorionic gonadotrophin (HCG), a hormone from the placenta, brings about the secretion of testosterone from the Leydig cells of the foetal testes. After birth, testosterone is not secreted up to adolescence. During adolescence, secretion starts again and continues under the influence of the hypothalamus.

*Hypothalamic control:* The hypothalamus secretes gonadotrophin-releasing hormone (GnRH), which reaches the anterior pituitary through the hypothalamo-hypophyseal portal vessels and stimulates the anterior pituitary to secrete FSH and LH.

The effect of psychological stimuli on gonadal function is exerted via the hypothalamus and is more apparent in females, as can be seen by the fact that the reproductive cycle gets disturbed in stressful conditions.

*Anterior pituitary control:* The anterior pituitary secretes two gonadotrophic hormones, FSH and LH (ICSH in the male), which control the testicular function. FSH controls spermatogenesis and LH controls the secretion of testosterone from the Leydig cells.

## Regulation of spermatogenesis

The exact role of FSH in spermatogenesis is not clear. It seems to control the proliferation and function of Sertoli cells. The secretion of ABP by Sertoli cells also depends on FSH.

LH controls the secretion of testosterone, so it plays an indirect role in spermatogenesis.

Testosterone diffuses freely through the blood-testicular barrier into the seminiferous tubules. Its high concentration in the seminiferous tubular fluid is essential for proper spermatogenesis.

The seminiferous follicular fluid contains a polypeptide called inhibin, which is secreted by the Sertoli cells. Inhibin acts directly on the anterior pituitary and inhibits the secretion of FSH. It is the feedback control of FSH secretion, helping maintain a normal rate of spermatogenesis.

## Regulation of testosterone secretion

LH is required for the initial proliferation of Leydig cells at puberty, and for their continuous secretory activity later on in life.

The plasma level of testosterone inhibits anterior pituitary secretion of LH by acting on the hypothalamus via a negative feedback mechanism, that is, a high level of testosterone in the plasma causes a drop in the secretion of LH (Fig. 44.5).

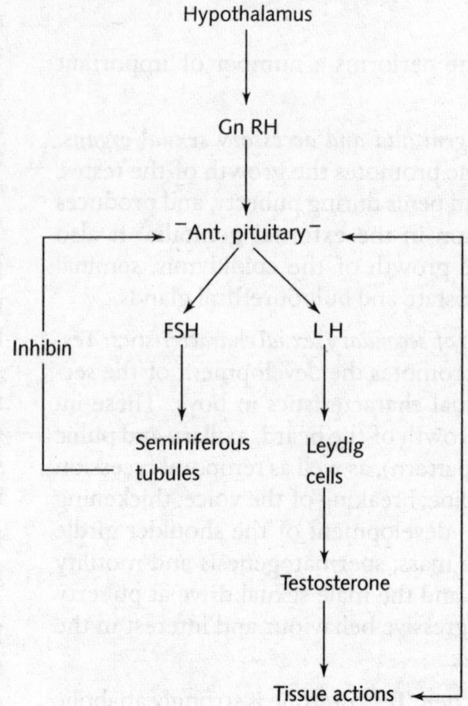


**Fig. 44.5: Regulation of testicular function**

CHAPTER

45

# Female Reproductive System

The female reproductive system consists of the primary reproductive organs, the accessory reproductive organs, the external genitalia and the secondary sexual characteristics.

The primary reproductive organs consist of a pair of ovaries, which produce female gametes (ova). The accessory reproductive organs are the fallopian tubes, uterus and vagina.

The uterus is a hollow structure which maintains the embryo. It consists of two parts: the body and the cervix. The cavity of the uterus communicates above and laterally with a fallopian tube on either side. Below, it opens into the vagina via the cervix. The part of the uterus above the fallopian tubes is called the fundus (Fig. 45.1).

The wall of the uterus consists of three layers. The outermost layer is a peritoneal layer, called the perimetrium. The middle layer, made of smooth muscle, is called the myometrium. This is the thickest layer and plays the most important role during parturition (the process of childbirth).

The innermost mucous membrane, called the endometrium, consists of the epithelium, glands and stroma. The superficial two-thirds of the endometrium is called the stratum functionale. This is supplied by long, coiled spiral arteries. This layer undergoes monthly cyclic changes in preparation for the implantation of a fertilized ovum. The deeper one-third of the endometrium, called the stratum basale, is supplied by short and straight basilar arteries. This layer does not participate in the cyclic changes but is responsible for the regeneration of the endometrium.

The external genitalia are the vulva, with the vaginal opening, the clitoris and the openings of the vestibular glands. The female genital tract opens independently to the exterior, unlike in males, where the genital opens to the exterior through the urethral passage and opening.

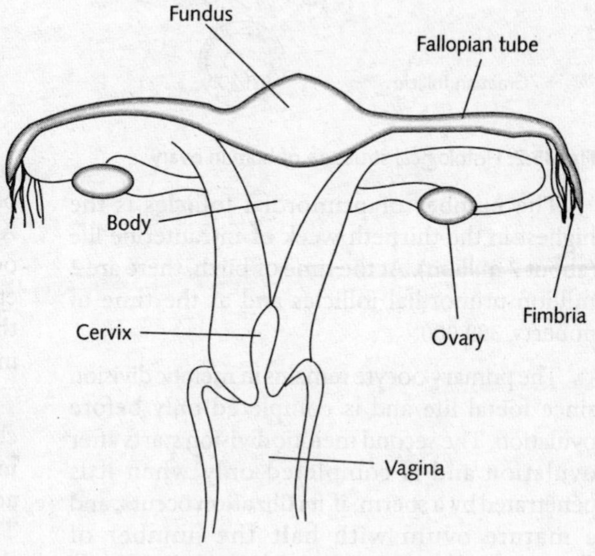


Fig. 45.1: The female reproductive system

The secondary sexual characteristics are not directly related to reproduction, except the development of the breasts (mammary glands), which are meant to nourish the baby.

## GAMETOGENESIS

Gametogenesis is the process of the formation of ova and is the primary function of the female reproductive system. It begins before birth, by 12 weeks of intrauterine life, unlike in males. Gametogenesis occurs in the ovaries.

The outer or cortical portion of the ovary contains the primordial follicles, containing the ova. Each primordial follicle consists of a primary oocyte (the female germ cell), surrounded by a single layer of spindle-shaped cells called granulosa cells (Fig. 45.2).

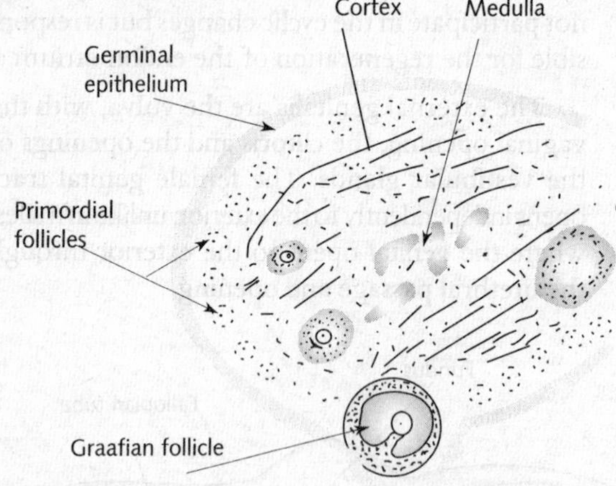


**Fig. 45.2:** Histological structure of human ovary

The number of primordial follicles is the highest in the thirtieth week of intrauterine life (about 7 million). At the time of birth, there are 2 million primordial follicles and at the time of puberty, 300,000.

The primary oocyte remains in meiotic division since foetal life and is completed only before ovulation. The second meiotic division starts after ovulation and is completed only when it is penetrated by a sperm, if fertilization occurs, and a mature ovum with half the number of chromosomes [i.e., 23 (22 + X)] is produced.

## FEMALE REPRODUCTIVE CYCLE

During the reproductive life of a female, in the nonpregnant state, there are cyclic changes involving different organs, particularly those related to reproduction. These cyclic changes are called reproductive cycles and are related to reproductive activities.

The following changes occur in the reproductive cycle. The hypothalamopituitary axis acts cyclically in relation to reproduction. The pulsatile secretion of GnRH and gonadotrophins increases and decreases regularly.

The ovarian cycle is as follows:

Development of Graffian follicle → maturation of ovum → ovulation → formation of corpus luteum → regression of corpus luteum → development of Graffian follicle.

The ovarian cycle is responsible for the regular variations in the secretion of oestrogen and progesterone. These bring about cyclical changes in the related organs.

The uterine cycle is as follows:

Shedding of endometrium (bleeding) → regeneration of endometrium, i.e., proliferative change → secretory change → shedding (bleeding).

This cyclic bleeding is called the menstrual cycle.

The cervical cycle is characterized by alternate changes in the secretions. The secretions become thin and alkaline due to oestrogen, and thick and viscid due to progesterone. As for the vaginal cycle, under the influence of oestrogen, there is cornification of the vaginal epithelium. Under the influence of progesterone, there is proliferation, increased secretion and infiltration by leucocytes.

The oestrogenic phase of the breast cycle is characterized by ductular proliferation. Under the influence of progesterone, there is growth of acini and a slight enlargement of the breasts. There is a slight regression of the breasts when the levels of the hormones decrease.

## OVARIAN CYCLE

The cyclic changes occurring in the ovaries every month can be divided into the follicular phase and the luteal phase.

### Follicular phase

Under the influence of FSH, about twenty primordial follicles start growing and maturing. After about 7 days, only one follicle continues to grow. It reaches maturity, while the rest undergo degeneration or atresia at different stages of development.

The maturation process involves the conversion of follicular cells into granulosa cells, the multiplication of granulosa cells into many layers and the gradual accumulation of fluid within the follicle. With the enlargement of the follicle, a large amount of follicular fluid accumulates and surrounds the ovum from all sides, except at one point. As a result, the ovum, covered by a layer of cells called the corona radiata, remains in contact with the granulosa cells only at a hillock-like area called the cumulus oophorus. A transparent muco-protein envelope, called the zona pellucida, can be seen between the ovum and the corona radiata. This supplies nutrition to the ovum (Fig. 45.3).

The mature follicle is now called a Graffian follicle. It secretes oestrogen and just before ovulation, a small amount of progesterone. It partly bulges out of the surface of the ovary into the peritoneal cavity. The ovarian stroma develops into theca cells, which surround the Graffian

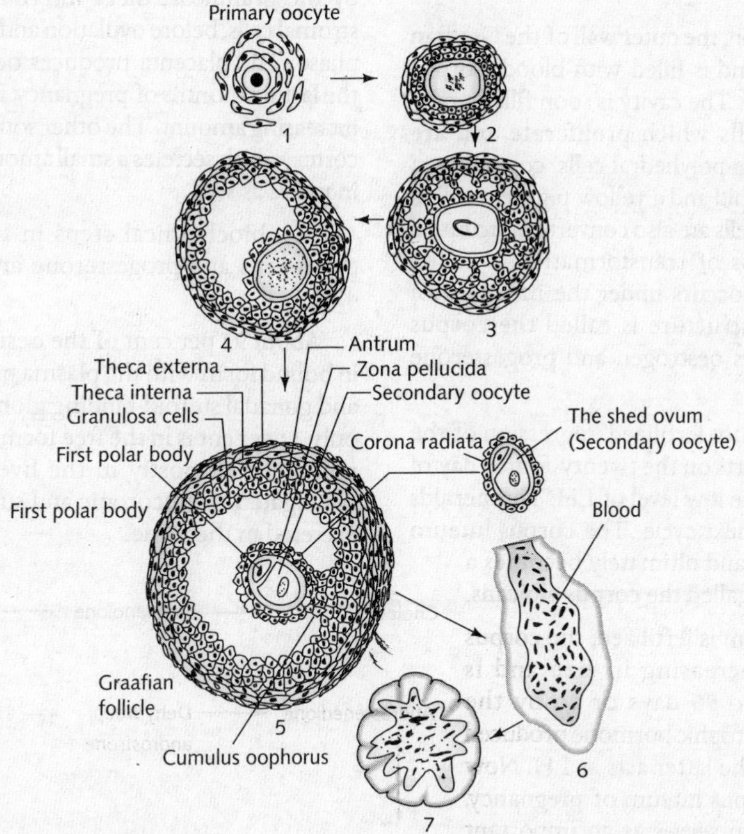


**Fig. 45.3:** Ovarian cycle: 1. Primordial follicle; 2, 3 and 4. Developing follicles; 5. Graffian follicle; 6. Corpus haemorrhagicum; 7. Corpus luteum

follicle. The theca consists of an inner rim of secretory cells, called the theca interna, and an outer rim of fibrous tissue, called the theca externa. Between the theca cells and granulosa cells is a basement membrane.

On about the fourteenth day of the cycle, the distended Graffian follicle ruptures and the ovum, surrounded by the corona radiata, is released into the peritoneal cavity near the open end of the fallopian tube. This process is called ovulation. The rupture may be due to high fluid pressure, ischaemic necrosis, or the proteolytic enzymes released locally.

At the time of ovulation, there is a peak in the secretion of FSH. Just before ovulation, there is a peak in LH secretion (LH surge).

### Luteal phase

Following ovulation, the outer wall of the Graffian follicle collapses and is filled with blood (corpus haemorrhagicum). The cavity is soon filled up by the granulosa cells which proliferate and are modified into large polyhedral cells, containing a large amount of lipid and a yellow pigment called lutein. The theca cells are also converted into luteal cells. This process of transformation is called luetinization and occurs under the influence of LH. The whole structure is called the corpus luteum. It secretes oestrogen and progesterone (Fig. 45.3).

If the ovum is not fertilized, regression of the corpus luteum starts on the twenty-fourth day of the cycle due to the low level of LH. This heralds the onset of the next cycle. The corpus luteum becomes inactive and ultimately becomes a white scar tissue, called the corpus albicans.

When the ovum is fertilized, the corpus luteum keeps increasing in size and is maintained up to 90 days or so by the chorionic gonadotrophic hormone produced by the placenta. The latter acts as LH. Now known as the corpus luteum of pregnancy, the corpus luteum serves as an important source of oestrogen and progesterone. Thus, it is essential for maintaining pregnancy in the early stage, until the placenta takes over the function.

## THE OVARIAN HORMONES

The female sex hormones secreted by the ovaries are oestrogens and progesterone. Both are steroids.

### Oestrogens

There are three types of oestrogens, namely, oestradiol, oestrone and oestriol. Oestradiol, the chief oestrogen secreted by the ovary, is the most potent and is responsible for most of the functions of oestrogens.

Oestrogens are secreted by the ovaries, placenta and adrenal cortex. In the ovaries, they are secreted by the granulosa, theca interna, and luteal and stromal cells, before ovulation and in the mid-luteal phase. The placenta produces oestrogens during the last six months of pregnancy, in a progressively increasing amount. The other source is the adrenal cortex, which secretes a small amount of oestrogens in males as well.

The biochemical steps in the synthesis of oestrogens and progesterone are shown in Fig. 45.4.

About 97 per cent of the oestradiol circulates in bound form with the plasma proteins, albumin and gonadal steroid-binding globulin (GBG), and only 3 per cent is in the free form. Oestrogens are metabolized mostly in the liver, and are then conjugated to glucoronic and sulphuric acid and excreted in the urine.

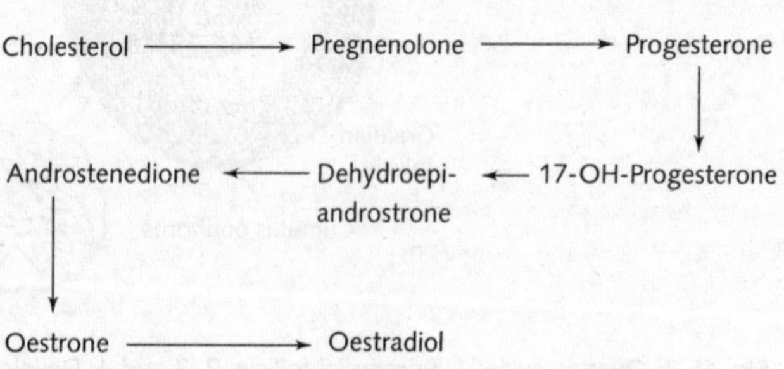


**Fig. 45.4:** Biosynthesis of female sex hormones

### Action

Oestrogens have several important actions, which are described in this section.

*Reproductive system:* The chief target organs of oestrogens are the organs of reproduction. Oestrogens promote the growth and development of the external and internal genitalia and the mammary glands at puberty, as well as their subsequent maintenance in the functional state.

They are responsible for the generalized development and growth of the uterus during puberty and the growth of the uterus during pregnancy. They bring about endometrial changes during the proliferative phase of the menstrual cycle. Oestrogens increase the muscle mass and contractile proteins in the uterus, and also make the myometrium responsive to oxytocin.

Oestrogens promote the development of the fallopian tubes, enhance the activity of both the secretory as well as ciliated cells of the epithelium of the tubes, and also promote contractility of the smooth muscles. This increases the motility of the tubes which, in turn, helps in the transport of the ovum towards the uterus.

Oestrogens boost cervical secretion and make it thin and alkaline. This facilitates the movement of sperms into the uterine cavity. Due to the influence of oestrogens, the cervical mucus (secretion) appears to have a fern-like pattern under the microscope.

Oestrogens are responsible for the growth of the vagina, thickening of the mucosa, cornification of the vaginal epithelium, as well as vaginal acidity. They also have a local effect in helping in the growth of the ovaries and in oogenesis.

At puberty, oestrogens promote proliferation of the stroma and the deposition of fat in the breasts, which are thus enlarged. During pregnancy, they cause rapid growth of the breasts, and also promote proliferation of ductal tissue and pigmentation of the areola. High doses of oestrogen prevent lactation.

Oestrogens produce many other effects on the body, such as the deposition of fat in the subcutaneous tissues of the breasts, buttocks and thighs. The development of a high-pitched voice, as well as narrow shoulders and broad hips are the other secondary sex characteristics produced by oestrogens. The other features are the growth of more scalp hair and less body hair. The growth of pubic and axillary hair is adrenal androgen-dependent, but the typical pattern of pubic hair is oestrogen-dependent.

*Other action:* Oestrogens are responsible for the spurt in growth caused by the growth of the bones in girls during adolescence. They are also responsible for epiphyseal closure, which limits the growth in the height of females. Oestrogens prevent osteoporosis.

Oestrogens lower the plasma cholesterol level and hence, prevent coronary artery disease. They promote protein synthesis and are anabolic, though less so than androgens. They cause salt and water retention in the body. Further, oestrogens are responsible for the female type of behaviour, and also increase the libido in females.

Oestrogens act by increasing mitosis and promoting the synthesis of specific proteins in the target cells.

## Progesterone

The sources of progesterone are the ovaries, placenta and adrenal cortex. In the ovaries, it is produced by the corpus luteum during the second half of the menstrual cycle, as well as the first three months of pregnancy. Very little progesterone is secreted in the follicular phase, before ovulation.

The placenta produces progesterone during the last six months of pregnancy, in a progressively increasing amount. The adrenal cortex is the other source, and it produces a small amount of progesterone in males as well.

The biosynthesis of progesterone can be described thus:

Cholesterol → Pregnanelone → Progesterone

About 98 per cent of the progesterone is bound to plasma proteins, mainly albumin, and 1 to 2 per cent is in the free form. Progesterone is reduced to pregnanediol in the liver. The latter is further conjugated with glucoronic acid to be excreted in the urine.

**Action**

Progesterone has a variety of actions, which are described in this section.

*Reproductive system:* In the oestrogen-primed endometrium, progesterone brings about endometrial changes during the secretory phase of the menstrual cycle. It makes the endometrium suitable for embedding the zygote. In the myometrium, it brings down excitability by decreasing the number of oestrogen receptors.

Progesterone is needed for the formation of the placenta. It helps maintain pregnancy by lowering the sensitivity of the myometrium to oestrogens and oxytocin. A lack of progesterone produces menstrual bleeding and termination of pregnancy, for example, abortion.

Progesterone increases secretions from the fallopian tubes for the nourishment of the zygote. It also thickens the cervical secretion, thus preventing the entry of sperms. Unlike oestrogens, it does not appear to have a fern-like pattern under the microscope. Thus, the presence of a fern-like pattern in the first half of the ovarian cycle and its disappearance in the second half is taken as a strong indication of ovulation having occurred.

Progesterone increases the secretion of vaginal mucus. It can stop ovulation. In the oestrogen-primed mammary glands, it causes growth of the alveoli and prepares them for lactation.

*Other action:* Progesterone has a thermogenic effect. The basal body temperature is 1 to 2°C higher in the luteal phase of the ovarian cycle than in the follicular phase. Clinically, the basal body temperature is measured early in the morning, before the patient leaves bed, to determine the day of ovulation. This information is important in cases of infertility, when a woman wants to conceive.

Progesterone causes the retention of water and electrolytes.

## MENSTRUAL CYCLE

The periodic discharge of blood from the female genital tract is called menstruation. The regular repetition of events from one menstruation to the next is called the menstrual cycle. This uterine event is the most important in the reproductive cycle of a female.

The periodicity and duration of the bleeding is usually constant in a particular female. The duration of the cycle is usually 28 ± 4 days, and that of bleeding, 4 days.

The menstrual cycles begin at puberty (10 to 14 years) and end at menopause (45 to 50 years). Therefore, menstrual cycles occur throughout the reproductive life of a woman, except during pregnancy and lactation.

### Phases of menstrual cycle

Conventionally, the first day of the bleeding is considered to be the first day of the menstrual cycle. The endometrial changes may be divided into three phases—the menstrual phase (first to fourth day), the proliferative phase (fifth to fourteenth day), and the secretory phase (fifteenth to twenty-eighth day) (Fig. 45.5). For the sake of convenience, the menstrual phase is described last.

**Proliferative Phase**

The proliferative phase starts after the cessation of menstruation and coincides with the follicular phase of the ovarian cycle. Its duration is about 10 days, but varies widely. Under the influence of oestrogens secreted by the developing follicle, the glandular epithelial cells proliferate and re-epithelize the endometrial surface. During this period, the simple tubular glands grow and growth of the blood vessels also occurs. The stromal cells and surface epithelial cells proliferate. The rest of the endometrium grows again from the stratum basale. It grows in thickness from 2 mm to 4 mm at the end of the proliferative phase. Ovulation indicates the end of the phase.

**Secretory Phase**

This phase lasts for about 14 days and is usually constant. It starts after ovulation and extends up

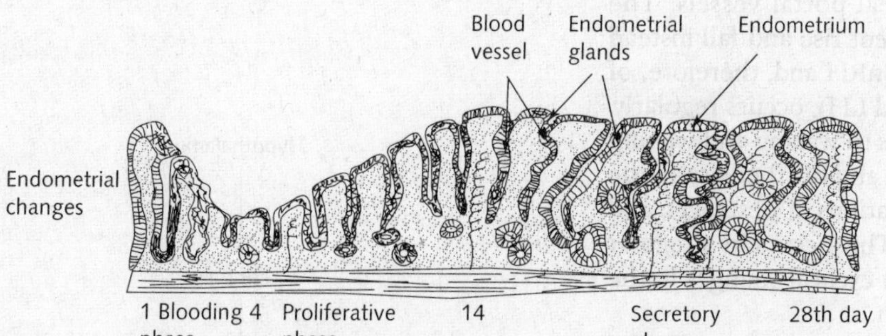


Fig. 45.5: Endometrial changes during menstrual cycle

to the next period of bleeding. It coincides with the luteal phase of the ovarian cycle, when the corpus luteum secretes both oestrogens and progesterone. The oestrogens promote further proliferation of the endometrial stroma. Progesterone produces a marked enlargement and thickening of the endometrial glands. These grow in length and diameter, become coiled and tortuous, and secrete mucus and endometrial fluid. The endometrium becomes highly vascularized. The long, coiled arteries of the stratum functionale become more spiral and dilated, and form perpendicular columns through the mucosa. The stromal cells become oedematous. Prominent corkscrew-shaped glands and an increase in vascularity are the two features characteristic of this phase. The endometrium becomes 4 to 6 mm thick by the end of this phase, which is indicated by vaginal bleeding.

**Menstrual Phase**

If the ovum is not fertilized, the corpus luteum regresses from the twenty-fourth day of the cycle and its involution causes a sharp decline in the plasma levels of oestrogen and progesterone. The stratum functionale shrinks without hormonal support. The spiral arteries become more coiled and their spasm stops the bloodflow. This results in hypoxia and necrosis of the endometrium, as well as haemorrhage due to the subsequent dilatation of the arterioles. The necrosis and shedding of the endometrium occurs in small patches, spread over a period extending from 3 to 5 days (Fig. 45.6).

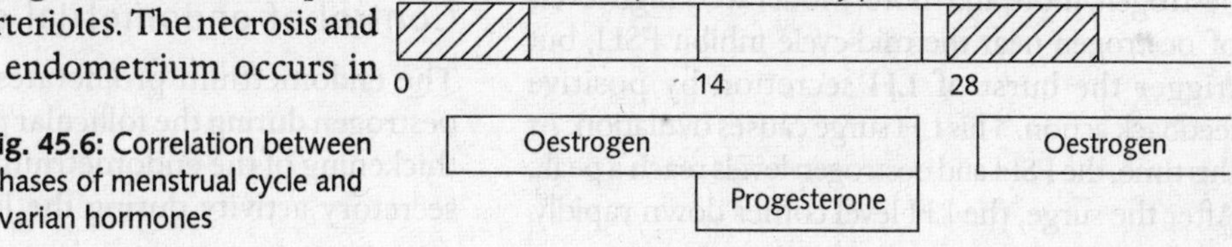


Fig. 45.6: Correlation between phases of menstrual cycle and ovarian hormones

The hormonal changes seem to produce large quantities of prostaglandins in the endometrium. The latter produce vasospasm and necrosis of the endometrium, as well as contractions of the myometrium. This helps to expel the necrotic material.

The menstrual blood is primarily arterial in origin. It normally does not clot because of the fibrinolysins released along with the necrotic endometrial tissue. The volume of menstrual blood is about 70 ml (i.e., about 35 ml of blood and another 35 ml of serous fluid). The blood also contains mucus, stripped bits of endometrium and unfertilized ovum.

## HORMONAL CONTROL OF REPRODUCTIVE CYCLE

The hypothalamo–pituitary–gonadal axis and feedback actions of the oestrogens and progesterone are responsible for the regulation of the reproductive cycle.

**Hypothalamic Control**

The hypothalamus regulates the secretion of both FSH and LH by a single hormone, GnRH, which reaches the anterior pituitary through the hypothalamo-hypophyseal portal vessels. The pulsatile secretion (frequent rise and fall instead of steady secretion) of GnRH and, therefore, of gonadotrophins (FSH and LH), occurs regularly. The biological clock leads to waxing and waning of the GnRH pulses. FSH and LH then act on the ovary to bring about variations of oestrogen and progesterone secretion. This occurs in a regular manner and brings about cyclical changes in the ovaries and endometrium.

**Feedback Control**

The ovarian hormones influence the secretion of gonadotrophins by the anterior pituitary through feedback control, acting directly on the anterior pituitary and through the hypothalamus.

Depending on the relative plasma concentrations of oestrogens and progesterone, they can exert both positive and negative feedback action. Moderately high levels of plasma oestrogens inhibit the release of FSH (negative feedback effect), but promote the release of a large amount of LH (positive feedback effect). High levels of oestrogens and progesterone inhibit the secretion of both FSH and LH (negative feedback effect) (Fig. 45.7).

## Control of ovarian cycle

The lifespan of the corpus luteum (about 10 days) is genetically predetermined. When the corpus luteum degenerates at the end of the ovarian cycle (in the absence of fertilization), the lowered levels of plasma oestrogen and progesterone bring about an increase in the secretion of FSH due to a minimum feedback effect on the hypothalamus. The secretion of GnRH also increases. FSH initiates the next ovarian cycle.

The development of the ovarian follicle begins and as it matures, the ovary starts secreting more oestrogen. This initially has a positive feedback effect, increasing the secretion of FSH and hence, oestrogen, more and more. Moderately high levels of oestrogen near the mid-cycle inhibit FSH, but trigger the burst of LH secretion by positive feedback action. This LH surge causes ovulation. At this time, the FSH and oestrogen levels reach a peak. After the surge, the LH level comes down rapidly.

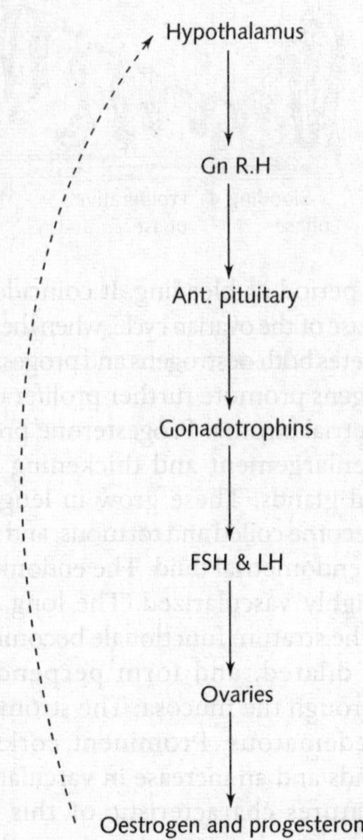


**Fig. 45.7:** Hypothalamic control of reproductive cycle

The corpus luteum is formed after ovulation and it secretes oestrogen and progesterone. Initially, the plasma oestrogen level drops but rises once again to a moderate degree during the luteal phase, when the progesterone level, too, has risen considerably. The high levels of oestrogen and progesterone inhibit the release of both FSH and LH from the anterior pituitary. Hence, unless pregnancy occurs, the corpus luteum degenerates and the next cycle begins once again (Fig. 45.8).

## Control of endometrial cycle

The endometrium proliferates by the action of oestrogen during the follicular phase. The further thickening of the endometrium and the rise in its secretory activity during the luteal phase occur due to oestrogen and progesterone. As a result, it becomes capable of providing nourishment and suitable for implantation of the fertilized ovum.

If fertilization does not occur, the corpus luteum degenerates, leading to a sharp decline in the plasma oestrogen and progesterone levels. The withdrawal of hormonal support leads to necrosis of the superficial endometrium as well as menstrual bleeding (Fig. 45.8).

If the ovum is fertilized and implanted, the secretion of chorionic gonadotrophin maintains the corpus luteum in the secretory state. Consequently, the endometrium grows further and develops to form the decidua.

*Hormonal control of ovarian and menstrual cycle*

Stimulation of ovaries by FSH
↓
Oestrogen secretion by ovaries
↓
Release of FSH by oestrogen
↓
Secretion of more oestrogen by ovaries
↓
LH surge by high level of oestrogen
↓
Ovulation
↓
Formation of corpus luteum
↓
High level of oestrogen and progesterone
↓
Inhibition of FSH and LH

| Fertilization (–) | Fertilization (+) |
|---|---|
| ↓ | ↓ |
| Regression of corpus luteum | Maintenance of corpus luteum by chorionic gonadotrophin |
| ↓ | ↓ |
| Decreased oestrogen and progesterone | Increased oestrogen and progesterone |
| ↓ | ↓ |
| Menstruation | Formation of decidua |

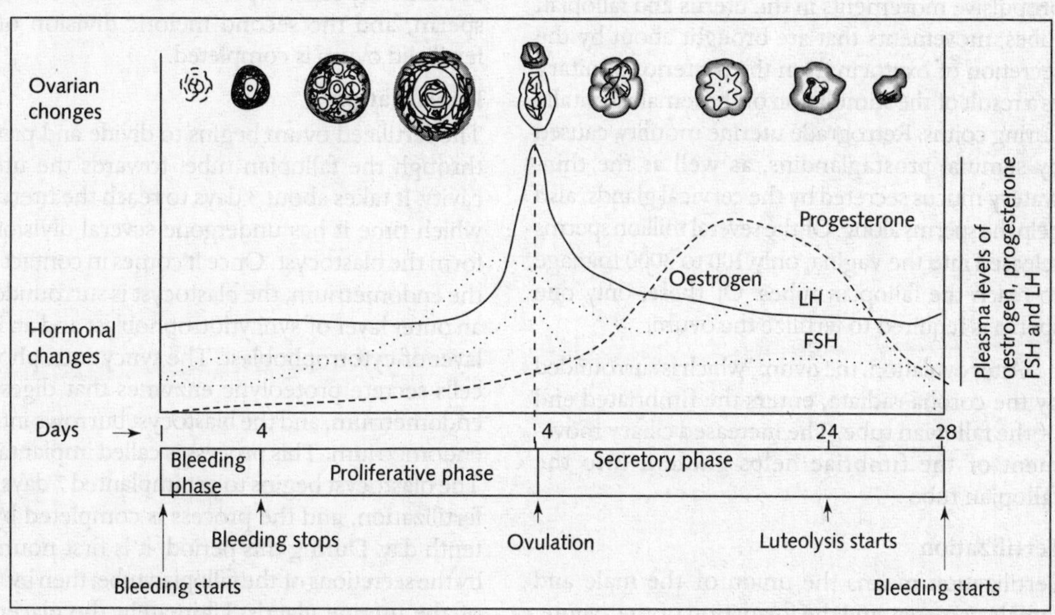


**Fig. 45.8:** Control of ovarian and endometrial cycle

CHAPTER 46

# Pregnancy, Lactation, Contraception

Pregnancy or conception consists of the fertilization of the ovum resulting to the growth of the foetus.

**Transport of Sperms and Ova**

During coitus, sperms are released in the upper part of the vagina. They reach the lateral one-third of the fallopian tube within 30 minutes. The rapidity of sperm transport is due to several factors, such as sperm motility. Sperms travel at a velocity of 1 to 4 mm per minute. They are assisted by the propulsive movements in the uterus and fallopian tubes, movements that are brought about by the secretion of oxytocin from the posterior pituitary as a result of the stimulation of the female genitalia during coitus. Retrograde uterine motility, caused by seminal prostaglandins, as well as the thin, watery mucus secreted by the cervical glands, also help the sperms along. Of the several million sperms released into the vagina, only 100 to 3000 manage to reach the fallopian tubes. Of these, only one sperm is required to fertilize the ovum.

After ovulation, the ovum, which is surrounded by the corona radiata, enters the fimbriated end of the fallopian tube. The increased ciliary movement of the fimbriae helps guide it into the fallopian tube.

**Fertilization**

Fertilization means the union of the male and female gametes, and the formation of the zygote. The ovum is viable for 6 to 24 hours after it has been shed from the ovary. The sperms can survive for 1 to 2 days in the female genital tract. Therefore, pregnancy can occur only if sexual intercourse takes place from one day before to one day after the ovulation.

Fertilization occurs in the ampulla of the fallopian tube. The penetration of the ovum is aided by the proteolytic enzymes present in the acrosome of the head of the sperm. Soon after the entry of one sperm, the change in the molecular structure of the zona pellucida prevents the entry of another sperm, and the second meiotic division of the fertilized ovum is completed.

**Implantation**

The fertilized ovum begins to divide and proceed through the fallopian tube, towards the uterine cavity. It takes about 3 days to reach the uterus, by which time it has undergone several divisions to form the blastocyst. Once it comes in contact with the endometrium, the blastocyst is surrounded by an outer layer of syncytiotrophoblast and an inner layer of cytotrophoblast. The syncytiotrophoblast cells secrete proteolytic enzymes that digest the endometrium, and the blastocyst burrows into the endometrium. This process is called implantation. The blastocyst begins to get implanted 7 days after fertilization, and the process is completed by the tenth day. During this period, it is first nourished by the secretions of the fallopian tube, then by those of the uterine glands. Ultimately, the placenta is formed. It consists of the maternal blood sinuses.

The chorionic villi are bathed in these. The chorionic villi are the cords of the trophoblastic cells in the endometrium forming the foetal part. The placenta connects the embryo with the mother.

## FUNCTIONS OF PLACENTA

### Hormone secretion

The placenta secretes several hormones into the maternal circulation. These hormones play an important role in foetal physiology as well.

**Human Chorionic Gonadotrophin (HCG)**

This is the most important placental hormone in the early part of pregnancy. It is a glycoprotein secreted by the cytotrophoblast.

HCG secretion starts as early as 10 days after fertilization, that is, just after the implantation of the blastocyst in the endometrium. The secretion increases rapidly to its peak level at about 50 to 60 days, then gradually declines to a low level between 12 to 16 weeks. Finally, it ceases just before delivery (parturition).

HCG is excreted by the kidney and its presence in the urine can confirm pregnancy within 10 days of conception.

The most important function of HCG is to prevent involution of the corpus luteum and maintain it in the early part of pregnancy. In this way, HCG is similar to LH, structurally and functionally. In fact, the corpus luteum gets even more enlarged and secretes large amounts of oestrogen and progesterone, which are required for the development of the decidua and myometrium.

HCG serves an additional function in the male foetus. It promotes the proliferation of Leydig cells in the foetal testes, as well as the secretion of testosterone.

Testosterone is essential for the development of the male sex organs in early embryonic life, as well as for the descent of the testes from the abdomen into the scrotum in the later stages of gestation.

**Oestrogens**

After the first three months of pregnancy, the placenta becomes the chief site of the synthesis of oestrogen. The latter is synthesized from dehydroepiandrosterone, from the foetal adrenal cortex, and enters the maternal circulation. The secretion of oestrogen increases progressively throughout the later months of pregnancy.

Oestrone is the major oestrogen involved in human pregnancy. In the mother, it is metabolized into oestriol. It is excreted in the urine after conjugation with glucoronic acid.

Oestrone promotes the growth of both the endometrium and myometrium of the uterus and breasts. It stimulates the proliferation of foetal tissues and causes relaxation of the pelvic ligaments. The latter facilitates the passage of the baby from the birth canal.

**Progesterone**

The secretion of progesterone, too, increases progressively during the last six months of pregnancy, and is essential for the pregnancy. The hormone disappears some hours before the end of pregnancy.

It is synthesized from cholesterol from the mother. Following synthesis, it passes to the mother as well as the foetus. It is used for the synthesis of corticosteroids in the foetal adrenal cortex.

In the mother, the initial (1 to 3 months) development of the decidua and maintenance of the pregnancy is facilitated by the progesterone secreted by the corpus luteum. In the subsequent (4 to 9) months, however, it is the progesterone secreted by the placenta that is essential for the maintenance of pregnancy, as it decreases the spontaneous contractions of the uterine myometrium and antagonizes the oestrogen. It also causes alveolar growth in the breasts and prepares them for lactation.

**Human Placental Lactogen (Human Chorionic somato-mammotrophin)**

This is a very useful hormone for pregnancy. It is responsible for the final maturation of the mammary glands, and also mobilizes growth hormone. Human placental lactogen promotes growth of the foetus as well.

## Other functions of placenta

**Respiratory**

The placenta acts as the foetal lung. Respiratory gases such as $O_2$ and $CO_2$ are transferred between the maternal and foetal blood. Oxygen goes from the mother to the foetus, and $CO_2$ from the foetus to the mother.

The mean $PO_2$ of the maternal blood in the placenta is about 50 mmHg, in contrast to 100 mmHg in the alveoli of the lungs. However, this does not really affect the transport of $O_2$, as the foetal RBCs contain foetal haemoglobin (HbF), which has greater affinity for $O_2$ and there is a higher Hb concentration in the foetal blood.

**Nutritive, Protective, Excretory**

The placenta provides all the nutritive needs of the foetus. It supplies the fetus with glucose, FFAs, amino acids and electrolytes.

Immunoglobulins are transferred from the mother to the foetus through the placenta. These provide immunity. The placenta forms a protective barrier and prevents the entry of harmful substances into the foetus.

The placenta transfers waste products, such as urea, uric acid and creatinine, form the foetus into the maternal circulation.

# PREGNANCY TESTS

There are many pregnancy tests which help diagnose pregnancy. All these tests are based on the presence of HCG in the urine or serum.

The biological tests used earlier consisted of injecting the mother's urine into immature female mice, virgin rabbits or male toads. The presence of HCG in the urine results in ovulation in immature female mice and virgin rabbits, and in the release of sperms in the male toads.

The biological tests have been replaced by an immunological test recently, as the latter is more sensitive and convenient and gives immediate results. In the immunological test, the woman's urine sample is first mixed with anti-serum against HCG. Next, latex particles coated with HCG are added. The absence of flocculation is taken as evidence of pregnancy, since the HCG antibodies have been neutralized by the HCG present in the urine. In the case of a urine sample from a non-pregnant female, the HCG antibodies produce flocculation of the HCG-coated latex particles.

This test can give positive results just 2 weeks after conception, that is, just when the menstrual period is missed and suspicion of pregnancy arises.

# MATERNAL CHANGES DURING PREGNANCY

Various physiological changes during pregnancy make the mother's body suitable for the continuation of pregnancy and for successful reproduction. The progressive growth of the foetus imposes various types of extra demands on the mother's body. These additional demands are met by tremendous adaptations in all the organ-systems of the body. These changes are described in this section.

## Reproductive system

**Uterus**

The uterus increases in weight and size in proportion to the size of the embryo developing inside it. There is both hyperplasia and hypertrophy of the myometrium, and also of the endometrium. The uterine wall becomes thicker initially, but becomes thin towards late pregnancy due to stretching of the muscle fibres. The muscle fibres form an interlacing network around the uterine blood vessels, so their contraction after delivery of the placenta arrests haemorrhage. The uterus initially goes through weak and irregular contractions, but these become regular and stronger towards the term.

The cervix becomes soft and there is an increase in its secretions as the glands proliferate.

**Ovary**

Ovulation stops due to a lack of pituitary gonadotrophins. These are inhibited by high levels of oestrogen and progesterone, which are secreted first by the corpus luteum, then by the placenta. Throughout pregnancy and the initial six weeks postpartum, the ovarian and menstrual cycles remain suspended.

The birth canal widens due to relaxation of the pelvic ligaments.

**Mammary Glands**

The breasts start getting enlarged early in pregnancy. Due to the rise in the secretion of oestrogens and progesterone, hyperplasia of the ductal and alveolar tissue, as well as the myoepithelial cells, occurs. Pigmentation of the nipples and areola takes place. Prolactin, together with placental lactogen, also play an important role in the final maturation of the mammary glands.

**Weight Gain**

In a normal pregnancy, the mother gains 10 to 12 kg. Of this, the foetus accounts for 3 kg. The rest is due to the weight of the uterus, placenta, amniotic fluid, blood volume and fat.

The rise in the secretion of oestrogen, progesterone, aldosterone and ADH causes retention of salt and water.

**Blood and Cardiovascular System**

The blood volume increases by about 25 per cent, and haemodilution and anaemia occur. The number of red cells and white blood cells increases. There is a fall in the total plasma protein concentration due to a drop in the concentration of albumin. However, the concentration of globulin and fibrinogen increases and this, in turn, raises the ESR.

The cardiac output increases by 30 per cent. The blood pressure remains normal, though the blood volume and cardiac output go up. This is because the peripheral resistance falls as a result of the action of progesterone on the vascular smooth muscle.

**Other Changes**

As for the respiratory system, there is an increase in the tidal volume and pulmonary ventilation. The vital capacity falls and oxygen utilization goes up.

In early pregnancy, some women suffer morning sickness, nausea and vomiting. Constipation, heart burn and acidity are common. The skin undergoes certain changes, such as excessive pigmentation on the face, nipples and areola of the breasts on the and midline of the abdomen.

There is a rise in the secretion of HCG, oestrogen, progesterone, thyroxine, parathormone, cortisol, prolactin and oxytocin. In pregnancy, the BMR goes up by 25 per cent. There is protein anabolism and positive nitrogen balance. There is deposition of fat and the level of glucose in the blood may become high. Further, urination becomes more frequent. Slight albuminuria and glycosuria may occur due to abnormal glucose tolerance.

The pregnant woman develops a waddling gait due to laxity of the pelvic joints.

## PARTURITION

Parturition is the process by which the products of conception (the foetus and placenta) are expelled from the uterus per vaginum.

The average duration of human pregnancy is 284 days, from the first day of the last menstrual period. Throughout pregnancy, the myometrium is practically quiescent. Towards the end of the normal duration of pregnancy, it becomes progressively more excitable. The onset of parturition (labour) may start any time between the thirty-seventh to fortieth week of gestation.

At the onset of labour, mild contractions of the myometrium begin. These become progressively stronger over the next 10 to 12 hours. Ultimately, the uterine contractions become so powerful that the baby, as well as the other products of conception, are expelled. The hormonal mechanisms involved are described below.

**Oestrogen–Progesterone Ratio**

Oestrogen increases the excitability of the uterine muscle, while progesterone decreases it. Throughout pregnancy, both hormones are secreted in large amounts by the placenta. However, in the last few weeks of pregnancy, the secretion of oestrogen exceeds that of progesterone, increasing the oestrogen–progesterone ratio to such an extent that the uterus begins to contract.

**Oxytocin**

The high level of oestrogen in the plasma increases the number of oxytocin receptors. The oxytocin concentration in the maternal plasma goes up only in the later stages of labour, when the cervix begins to dilate. However, the rise in the number of oxytocin receptors may cause contractions of uterine muscle even at the normal plasma oxytocin level.

Spinal reflexes and voluntary contraction of the abdominal muscles during labour help in the expulsion of the baby.

## LACTATION

After parturition, lactation occurs to provide nutrition to the newborn baby. This is a process of milk output from the mammary glands. It involves the growth and development of the mammary glands during pregnancy, and the secretion and ejection of milk.

### Growth and development of mammary glands during pregnancy

Although the mammary glands begin to develop during puberty and the breasts start getting enlarged gradually due to the action of oestrogen secreted during each ovarian cycle, it is only during the first pregnancy that the glandular tissue develops fully. It is during pregnancy that the glands become ready for milk secretion. This is due to the increased amount of oestrogen and progesterone secreted by the placenta during the last six months of pregnancy.

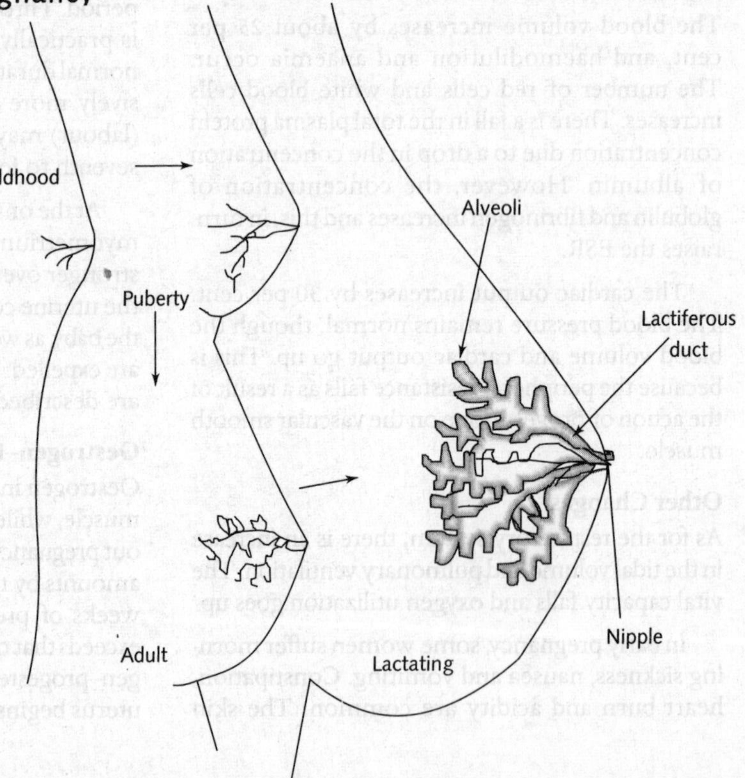


Fig. 46.1: Development of mammary gland

Oestrogen promotes further development of the stroma and duct systems, as well as the deposition of fat in the breasts. Progesterone, acting along with oestrogen, produces marked glandular development. Elevated levels of prolactin and chorionic somatomammotrophin also promote glandular hyperplasia. The secretion of prolactin goes up ten-fold during pregnancy. The prior activity of oestrogen, progesterone and other hormones, such as cortisol, GH, thyroxine and insulin, is required for the final maturation of the mammary glands and the secretion of milk. However, prolactin cannot lead to the production of milk in the presence of high levels of oestrogen and progesterone (Fig. 46.1).

### Secretion of milk

This is the process of the production of milk. It involves (i) the initiation of secretion (lactogenesis) and (ii) the maintenance of secretion (galactopoiesis).

The secretion of milk starts when the circulating progesterone and oestrogen secreted by the placenta during pregnancy decline sharply following the expulsion of the baby and placenta. As a result, the lactogenic effect of prolactin becomes prominent and within 2 to 3 days of delivery, a large amount of milk begins to be secreted. The low level of oestrogen probably helps by inhibiting the release of prolactin-inhibitory factor (PIF) from the hypothalamus, thereby increasing the secretion of prolactin. Prolactin secretion increases effectively during breast-feeding.

Galactopoiesis is mainly a function of prolactin, but the presence of other hormones, such as GH, thyroxine, insulin and cortisol, is also necessary.

## Ejection of milk

This means the expulsion of the formed milk from the gland. The ejection of milk becomes possible due to the suckling action by the baby, the contraction of the myoepithelial cells by the oxytocin secreted by the suckling reflex, and the continuous production of milk, which creates a positive pressure, pushing the milk out. The process is also facilitated by the rise in prolactin secretion, which is caused by suckling.

## Suckling reflex

This is a neuroendocrine reflex, that is, one limb of the reflex arc is formed by the neural system and the other by the endocrine system. Suckling by the baby stimulates the nerve endings in the nipple. Nerve impulses are then carried by the afferent nerves to the hypothalamus. Oxytocin, which is formed in the hypothalamus, is released through the posterior pituitary into the circulation, from where it reaches the mammary gland. It then causes contraction of the myoepithelial cells surrounding the alveoli. This results in the ejection of milk into the ducts and finally, out of the nipple into the baby's mouth. The suckling reflex also raises the secretion of prolactin, which leads to inhibition of ovulation in the lactating mother (Fig. 46.2).

## Milk

Mother's milk is ideally suited for newborn babies as it has more lactose, less protein (particularly casein) and a lower mineral content than cow's milk. The large amount of casein present in cow's milk is difficult to digest and the newborn's kidneys are unable to handle large loads of electrolyte.

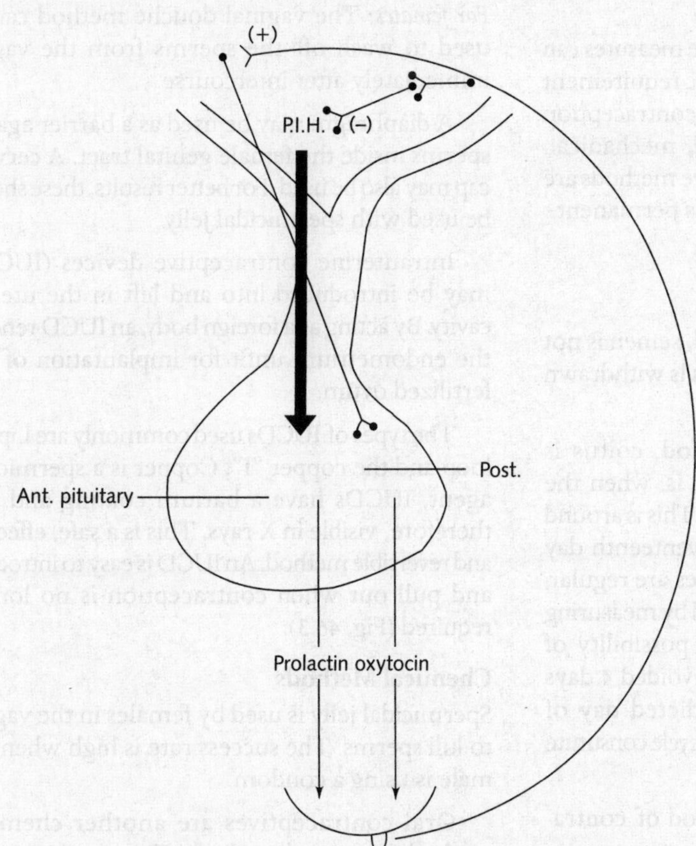


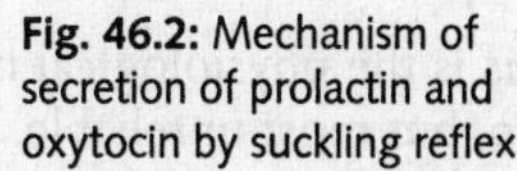

**Fig. 46.2:** Mechanism of secretion of prolactin and oxytocin by suckling reflex

A few days after parturition, breast milk is known as colostrum. It is thicker and yellowish, and contains a lot of proteins and NaCI and less lactose and $K^+$. Colostrum is an important source of antibodies for the neonate. This is particularly important as the newborn's own defense mechanism is not fully developed.

## CONTRACEPTION

Contraception means the prevention of conception in spite of the coital act and, thus, prevention of reproduction.

The various agents or methods used to prevent pregnancy are called contraceptives. These are used not only to limit the size of the family, but also to space the pregnancies since a cycle of pregnancy–lactation followed by another pregnancy can affect or damage the health of both the mother and the child.

One or more of the contraceptive measures can be advised, according to the specific requirement of each couple. The methods of contraception may be classified as physiological, mechanical, chemical and surgical. The first three methods are temporary, while the last method is permanent.

### Physiological Methods

These include the following.

*Withdrawal method:* By this method, semen is not deposited in the vagina as the penis is withdrawn before ejaculation.

*Safe-period method:* By this method, coitus is avoided in the unsafe period, that is, when the chance of conception is the highest. This is around the time of ovulation (tenth to seventeenth day of the cycle). If the menstrual cycles are regular, the day of ovulation can be predicted by measuring the basal body temperature. The possibility of pregnancy is very low if coitus is avoided 4 days before and 3 days after the predicted day of ovulation. The remaining days of the cycle constitute the safe period.

This is the physiological method of contraception, but most unreliable.

Safe period                                        Safe period

1        10     14     17                28

Unsafe period

Days of menstrual cycle

### Mechanical Methods

There are different mechanical methods for males and females.

*For males:* The use of a condom or rubber sheath is probably the most widely accepted method of contraception. A condom acts as a mechanical barrier that prevents the entry of sperms into the female genital tract.

Condoms are very effective, simple and cheap. They also prevent the spread of sexually transmitted diseases (STDs), such as AIDS, hepatitis B, syphilis and gonorrhoea.

*For females:* The vaginal douche method can be used to wash off the sperms from the vagina immediately after intercourse.

A diaphragm may be used as a barrier against sperms inside the female genital tract. A cervical cap may also be used. For better results, these should be used with spermicidal jelly.

Intrauterine contraceptive devices (IUCDs) may be introduced into and left in the uterine cavity. By acting as a foreign body, an IUCD renders the endometrium unfit for implantation of the fertilized ovum.

The types of IUCDs used commonly are Lippy's loop and the copper 'T'. Copper is a spermicidal agent. IUCDs have a barium coating and are, therefore, visible in X-rays. This is a safe, effective and reversible method. An IUCD is easy to introduce and pull out when contraception is no longer required (Fig. 46.3).

### Chemical Methods

Spermicidal jelly is used by females in the vagina to kill sperms. The success rate is high when the male is using a condom.

Oral contraceptives are another chemical method (hormonal method). They are hormonal

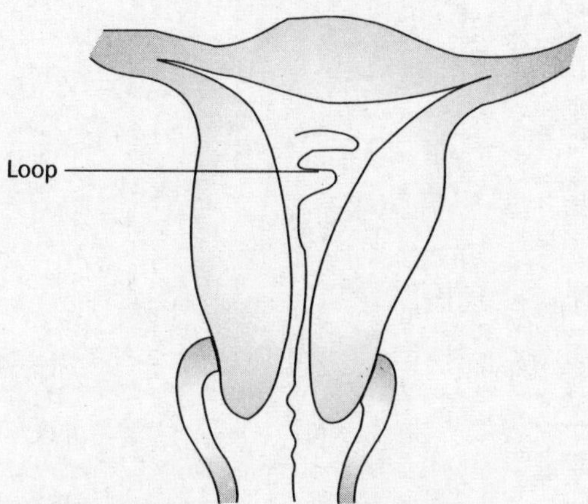


Fig. 46.3: Intrauterine contraceptive device

preparations used orally by females. They are made of synthetic oestrogen and progesterone and are given for 21 days in each 28-day cycle. They probably act by: (i) inhibiting the LH surge and, therefore, ovulation, (ii) making the cervical mucus hostile to sperm penetration, and (iii) making the endometrium hostile to the zygote, preventing its implantation.

These pills are easy to take. Only a small dose of hormone is required, and the method is 100 per cent safe, provided that no dose is missed. However, oral contraceptives are not free from side-effects, such as thrombotic disorders, hypertension and malignancy.

**Surgical Methods**

Vasectomy may be performed in males. In this operation, the vas deferens is cut and ligated. As for females, tubectomy may be performed. In this procedure, the fallopian tubes are cut and ligated. Both operations are almost completely irreversible and the potency of the ducts cannot be restored with certainty, if required at some later stage. Vasectomy is a relatively simpler operation and does not interfere with the sexual performance of a male.

# Excretory System

CHAPTER 47

# The Kidneys: Functions and Functional Anatomy

Cell metabolism results in the formation of various end-products which must be eliminated from the body, as they are of no use to the body and their accumulation can disturb the chemical balance. The removal of these toxic and unwanted materials (waste products) from the body is known as excretion.

There are different organs of excretion for the elimination of different types of substances. These are the kidneys, lungs, GI tract and skin. The kidneys are responsible for the excretion of solid, water-soluble and nonirritant substances. The lungs excrete $CO_2$ and volatile substances. Fatty substances, heavy metals and drugs are excreted from the GI tract, while dead cells, hair and nails are excreted by the skin.

This chapter deals with the kidneys, which are essential for life. The removal of both the kidneys leads to death. However, if one kidney is removed, the other kidney can cope with the extra workload and the person can survive.

The kidneys are the main organs of excretion, but excretion is not the main and sole function of the kidneys.

## FUNCTIONS OF KIDNEY

One of the major functions of the kidney is homeostasis, that is, maintenance of the internal environment (ECF). This includes: (i) maintenance of the water balance and hence the volume of the ECF and blood, as well as blood pressure, (ii) maintenance of the electrolyte balance (e.g., $Na^+$, $K^+$, $Ca^{++}$, $Cl^-$ and $HCO_3^-$), and (iii) maintenance of the acid–base balance.

The kidney is also responsible for the formation of urine and the excretion of waste products, particularly those arising from protein metabolism (e.g., urea, uric acid and creatinine). It has an endocrine function as well. It secretes two hormones—erythropoietin, which stimulates the production of RBCs, and renin, which helps regulate the blood pressure and secretion of aldosterone.

The kidney is involved in the formation of certain new substances, such as ammonia from the amino acid glutamine, prostaglandins and bradykinin. It helps in vitamin D metabolism and hence, the formation of bones and teeth. It activates vitamin D through the conversion of 25-HCC into 1,25-DHCC (calcitrol), which facilitates the absorption of calcium from the intestine.

## FUNCTIONAL ANATOMY

### Gross structure

There are two kidneys, one on either side of the vertebral column. Each kidney is surrounded by a fibrous capsule and there is a concavity, called the hilum, on its medial side. From here, the ureter leaves and blood vessels, nerves and lymphatics enter.

The cut surface of the kidney shows that the kidney substance consists of a reddish cortex on the outside and a pale medulla, containing 10 to 15 cone-shaped masses called the pyramids, on the inside. The apices of the latter are directed towards the hilum and they open into the pelvis of the kidney, from where the ureter begins. The urine formed in the kidney is carried by the ureters to the urinary bladder. It is stored here temporarily and is excreted to the outside from time to time through the urethra (Fig. 47.1).

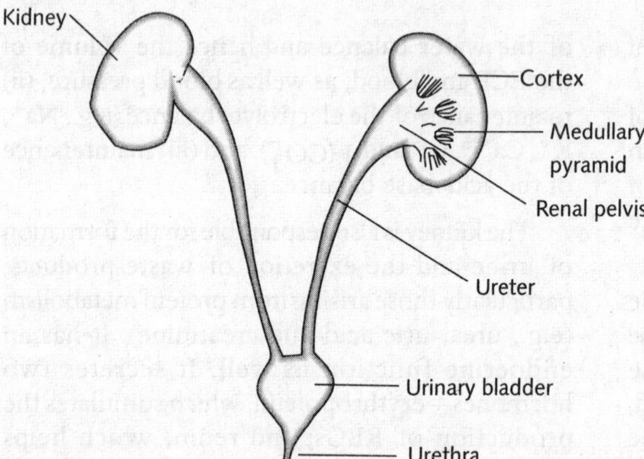


**Fig. 47.1: Functional anatomy of the urinary tract**

## Microscopic structure

Each kidney consists of about 1.2 million nephrons. A nephron is a structural and functional unit of the kidney, that is, it is the smallest part is capable of forming urine and functioning independently. The functions of the kidney mean the sum of the functions of the nephrons.

A nephron consists of a Malpighian body (corpuscle) and a renal tubule. The Malpighian corpuscle consists of a glomerulus and the Bowman's capsule.

The glomerulus, a lobulated tuft of capillaries, invaginates the Bowman's capsule, so that its capillaries get covered with the epithelium of the visceral layer of the Bowman's capsule on all sides.

The visceral epithelium is fused with the adventitia of the afferent and efferent arterioles, which enter and leave the glomerulus, respectively. Blood flows into the glomerulus through the afferent arteriole, which breaks up into capillaries that reunite to form the efferent arteriole. The afferent arteriole divides into 5 to 8 branches, and each branch divides into 3 to 6 capillary loops, forming a lobule. The total number of capillaries in the glomerulus varies between 25 and 50. As a result of this, a large surface area is available for the process of filtration. The function of the glomerulus is filtration.

The Bowman's capsule is the expanded upper end of the renal tubule. It contains a glomerulus, which is tightly packed into it. It is lined by a flat epithelium with a visceral and a parietal layer. The space between these two layers is continuous with the lumen of the tubule. The function of the Bowman's capsule is to collect the filtrate (Fig. 47.2).

The renal tubule continues from the Bowman's capsule, partly convoluted and partly straight. The first, convoluted part of the renal tubule is called the proximal convoluted tubule (PCT). It is lined by cuboidal cells, the luminar border of which has a large number of microvilli that provide a large surface area for the process of reabsorption. The cells contain many mitochondria which provide energy for the transport process. The functions of the PCT are reabsorption and secretion.

The second, straight part of the renal tubule is called the loop of Henle (LH). It consists of a thick, descending segment, followed by a thin descending segment, forming a loop. There is a thin ascending segment in the medulla. This is followed by a thick ascending segment which enters the cortex once again. The thin segment of the loop of Henle is lined by thin, flat epithelium. The structure and function of the thick descending and ascending segments are similar to those of the PCT and DCT (distal convoluted tubule), respectively. The function of the thin segment of Henle's loop is concentration of urine.

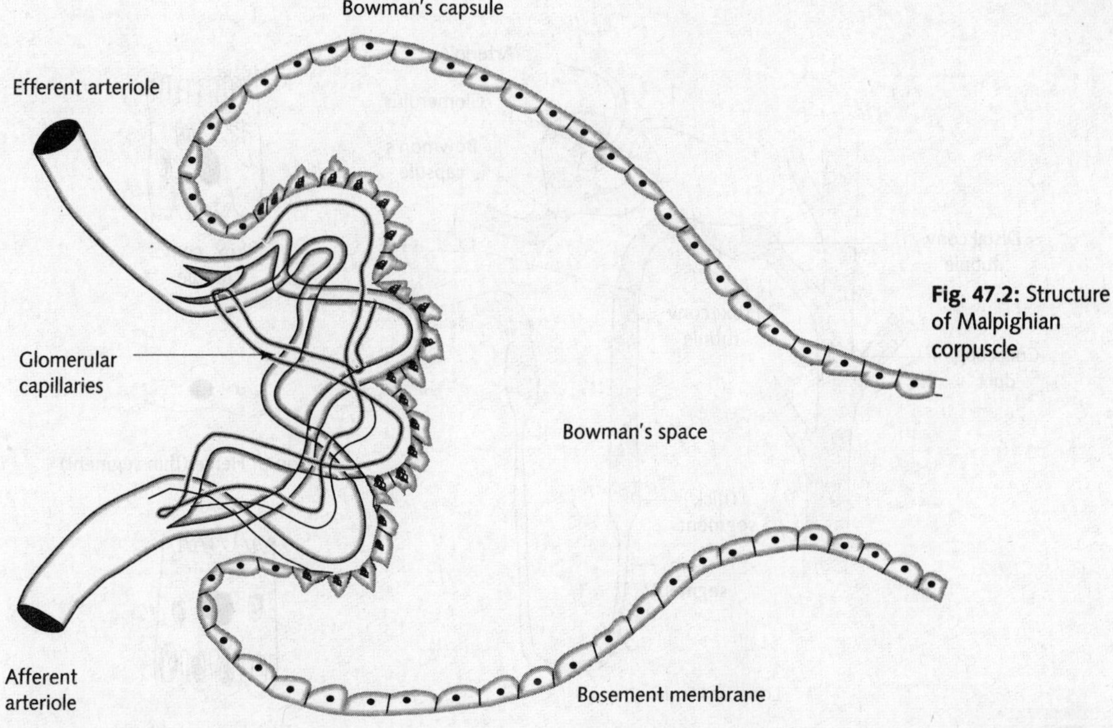


**Fig. 47.2:** Structure of Malpighian corpuscle

The third part of the renal tubule, called the distal convoluted tubule (DCT), is convoluted. Its structure is similar to that of the PCT, but it contains fewer mitochondria and has fewer microvilli. Its function, like the PCT, is reabsorption and secretion, but to a lesser extent.

A number of DCTs communicate with the collecting tubule (CT) and a number of collecting tubules open into the duct of Bellini. The latter passes from the cortex to the medulla, and terminates at the apex of one of the pyramids (Fig. 47. 3a).

The nephrons are of two types, according to their position in the kidney: cortical and juxtamedullary (Fig. 47.3b).

**Table 47.1:** Comparison of two types of nephrons

| | Cortical nephrons | Juxtamedullary nephrons |
|---|---|---|
| 1. Location | Glomerulus, PCT and DCT in the cortex, tip of Henle's loop in the outer medulla | Glomerulus at the cortico-medullary junction, PCT and DCT in the outer medulla, tip of Henle's loop in the inner medulla |
| 2. Incidence | 85% | 15% |
| 3. Length of Henle's loop | Short | Long |
| 4. Efferent arteriol | Narrower than afferent arteriole | Same as afferent arteriole |
| 5. Function | Filtration | Concentration of urine |

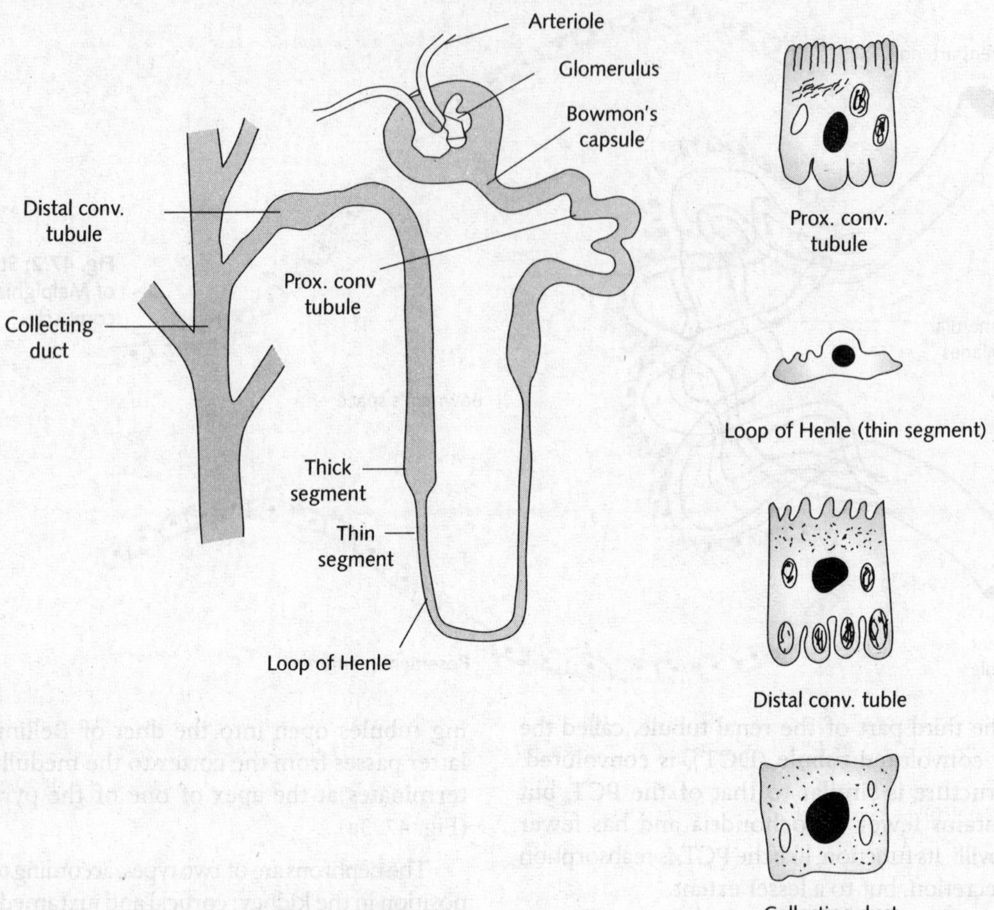


**Fig. 47.3 (a):** Structure of nephron

## RENAL CIRCULATION

The functioning of the kidney depends on its blood supply. The renal artery is a major branch arising directly from the aorta. It subdivides progressively into smaller branches. The smallest branches are called the interlobular arteries, each of which gives off a series of short and wide afferent arterioles. Each afferent arteriole breaks into a bunch of glomerular capillaries, which form a network called the glomerular capillary network (GCN). These join together again, forming the efferent arterioles. An efferent arteriole is long and thin, and carries blood away from the glomerulus. It divides into another set of capillaries, which surround the renal tubule (mainly the PCT and DCT), forming a network called the peritubular capillary network (PCN) in the cortical glomeruli.

The diameter of the efferent arterioles of the juxtamedullary glomeruli is similar to that of the afferent arterioles. The efferent arterioles form a special type of peritubular capillaries, called the vasa recta, instead of forming a network. The vasa recta are relatively straight and long, and closely follow the course of the loop of Henle. They have a descending and an ascending limb, forming hairpin loops along the sides of the loop of Henle.

The peritubular capillaries in the cortex and

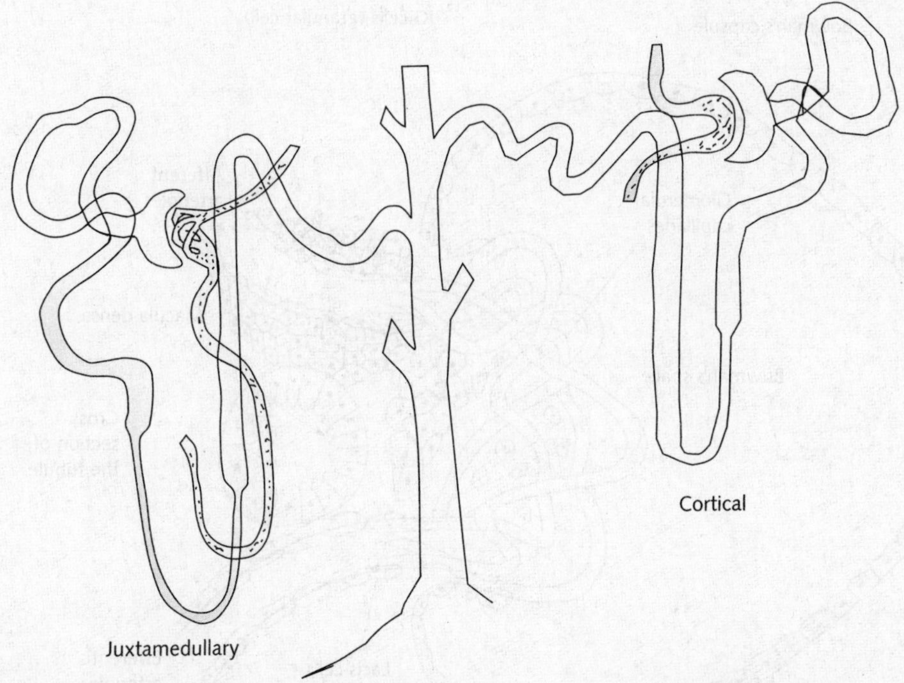


**Fig. 47.3 (b):** Types of nephrons

the vasa recta in the medulla ultimately drain into the renal vein.

*Innervation of renal blood vessels:* Renal vessels have rich sympathetic innervation. During rest, sympathetic discharge is at the lowest level but during stress, such as severe exercise or haemorrhage, it can increase markedly, causing renal vasoconstriction.

### Renal Blood Flow (RBF) and its Regulation

The normal renal blood flow is 1250 ml/minute (i.e., 25 per cent of the cardiac output). Approximately 90 per cent of this blood flows through the renal cortex, while 10 per cent flows through the medulla. The low volume of blood flowing through the medulla is important for the mechanism of concentration of urine. This is maintained constant between a blood pressure range of 70 mmHg to 200 mmHg (Systolic). This phenomenon is known as autoregulation of the renal blood flow. It may be observed in a denervated kidney, but can be abolished by a smooth muscle relaxant, such as papaverine. The autoregulation of the blood flow is an intrinsic mechanism which maintains the renal blood flow and involves the juxtaglomerular apparatus of the kidney.

The renal blood flow is strongly affected by extrinsic regulatory factors, such as sympathetic discharge and angiotensin II. An erect posture and haemorrhage bring about renal vasoconstriction through these two mechanisms. Sympathetic discharge affects the afferent arterioles, while angiotensin II acts on the efferent arterioles.

## JUXTAGLOMERULAR APPARATUS (JGA)

The juxtaglomerular apparatus is formed by the DCT at its junction with the ascending limb of Henle's loop and the afferent arteriole of the parent nephron. This is possible because the DCT comes to lie in the angle formed by the afferent and efferent arterioles, making close contact with them (Fig. 47.4).

Certain changes are seen at the site of contact. The cells of the DCT that are in contact with the afferent arteriole become big, tall, columnar and densely packed, to form maccula densa (crowded

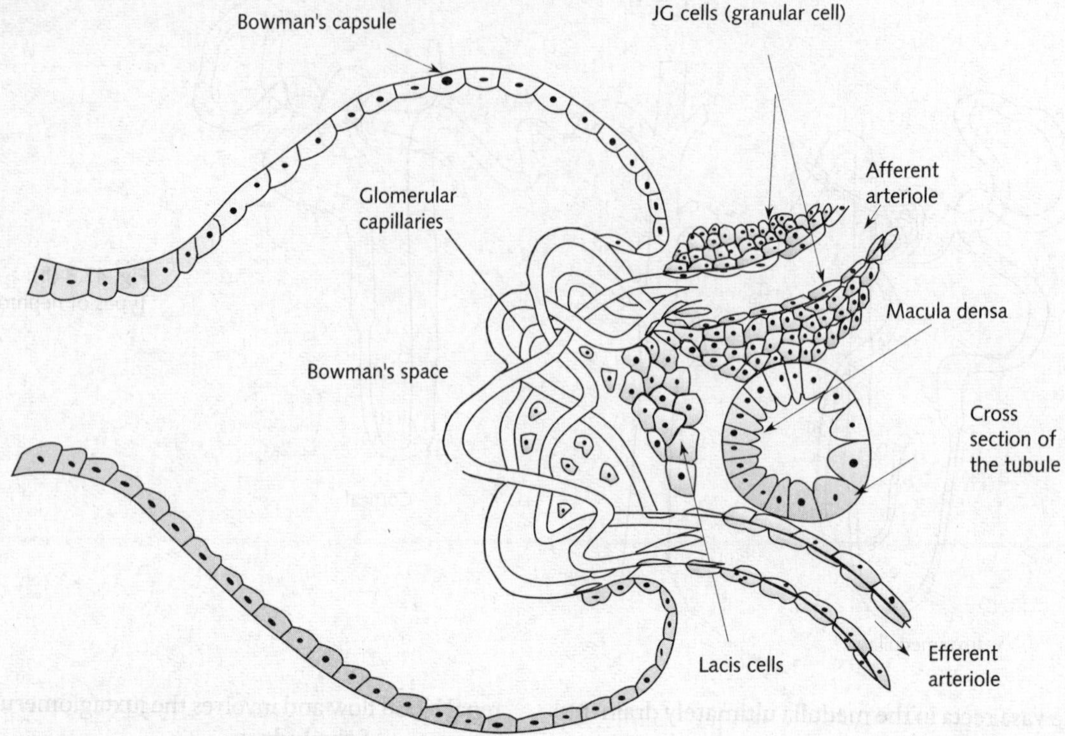


Fig. 47.4: Juxtaglomerular apparatus

spots). Further, the cellular elements of the tunica adventitia and media of the afferent arteriole become more numerous and hypertrophied, to form a thickened part called the polar cushion or polkissen.

At the site of contact, the smooth muscle cells of the afferent arterioles become swollen and modified, and contain granules of renin. These are called juxtaglomerular cells.

The cells between the maccula densa and polkissen are called messengia cells (or Lacis cells). They play an important role in the functioning of the juxtaglomerular apparatus.

## SECRETIONS

The secretions of the JGA are erythropoietin and renin. The secretion of erythropoietin is stimulated by hypoxia. That of renin is stimulated by renal ischaemia, which is caused by a decrease in the blood volume, blood pressure and renal blood flow.

The mechanism of action of renin can be represented as follows:

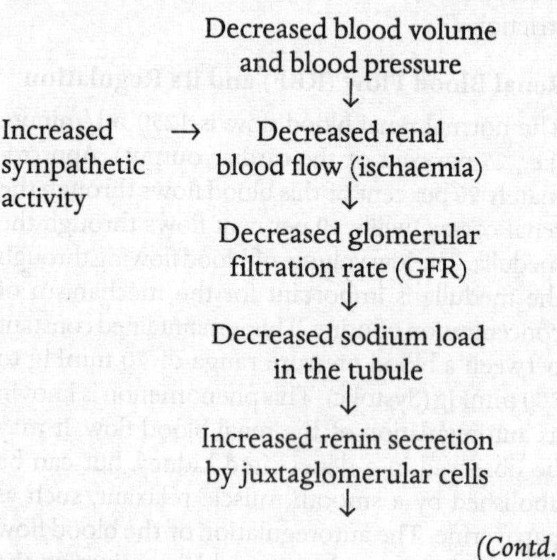


*(Contd.)*

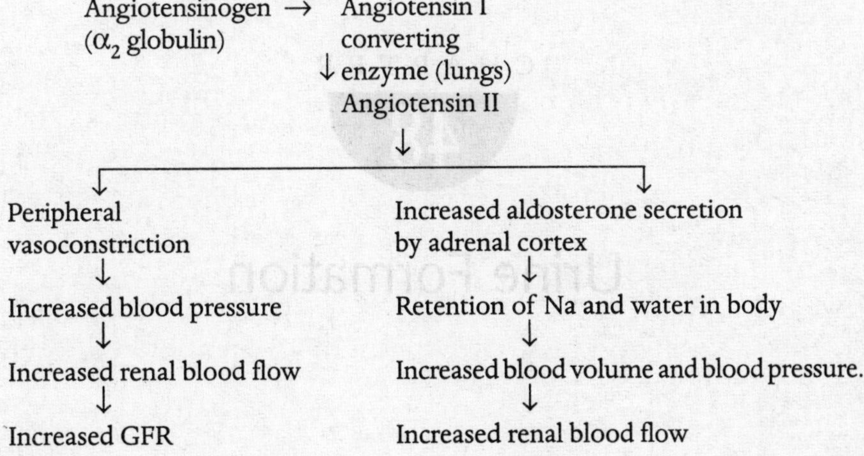


## FUNCTIONS OF JGA

1. Maintenance of the renal blood flow and glomerular filtration rate. Hence, it ensures adequate excretion of solutes.
2. Maintenance of the systemic blood pressure.
3. Homeostasis is another function. It maintains the water balance, and thus, the volume of the ECF and blood. It also maintains the electrolyte balance (e.g., of $Na^+$ and $Cl^-$) in the ECF.
4. Erythropoiesis, or the formation of new red cells, is a very important function of JGA.

CHAPTER

48

# Urine Formation

Urine is formed in two stages. First, ultrafiltrate is formed by the process of glomerular filtration. The ultrafiltrate is then modified into urine by the processes of tubular reabsorption and secretion.

The ultrafiltrate is formed in the glomerulus. The glomeruli act as ultrafilters, filtering a colloid and the cell-free, fluid part of the blood into the Bowman's capsule. Hence, the filtrate consists of plasma minus the plasma proteins.

The composition of the filtrate depends on the permeability characteristics of the filtering membrane, the structure of which facilitates filtration.

## THE FILTERING MEMBRANE

This is the intervening structure between the blood in the glomerular capillary and the capsular space. It is thin and porous, and consists of the three layers described below.

*Layer of capillary endothelial cells:* This layer is thin and consists of flat endothelial cells. It has a pore size of 160 Å, which is larger than in capillaries elsewhere. Hence, this layer is more permeable.

*Basement membrane:* This is a membrane between the capillary endothelium and the epithelium of the visceral layer of the Bowman's capsule. It is made of a meshwork of glycoprotein and mucopolysaccharides. Its pore size is 110 Å.

*Epithelium of visceral layer of Bowman's capsule:* This consists of specialized, flat epithelial cells, called podocytes. The body of podocytes rests on pods or legs, each of which has foot processes or pedicels. These stand on the basement membrane in an interdigitating manner. The gaps between the pedicels are called slit pores, the size of which is 70 Å (Fig. 48.1).

In spite of its tremendous permeability, the glomerular membrane allows only the selective passage of molecules. It does not allow plasma protein molecules to pass through. On the border line, there is albumin, with a molecular weight

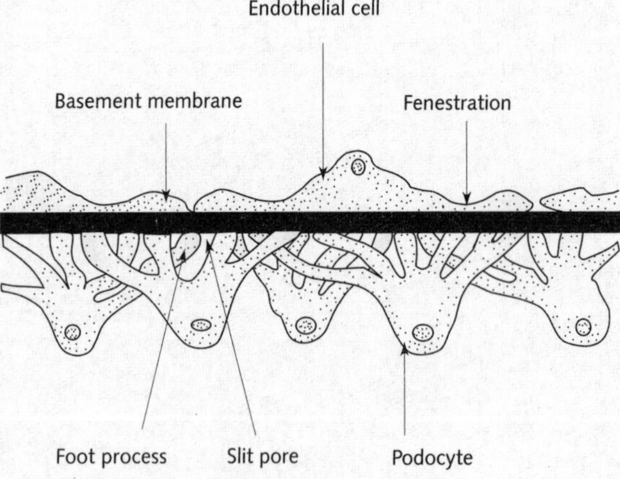


**Fig. 48.1:** The filtering membrane

of 70,000. This is why albumin may appear in the urine in very small amounts (practically absent). Substances which have a higher molecular weight cannot pass through the membrane. Therefore, as soon as the permeability of the filtering (glomerular) membrane increases, as in renal disease, albumin is the first protein to appear in urine. Its appearance in urine (albuminuria) is, therefore, a very sensitive kidney function test. Haemoglobin, which has a molecular weight of 68,000, cannot pass through since it is located within RBCs. A small amount of haemoglobin which may be free due to the normal destruction of RBCs binds with globulin. Haemoglobin appears in the urine only in case of excessive destruction of RBCs.

Substances with a diameter of less than 40 Å can pass through with the greatest ease. The passage of the molecule across the glomerular filter is determined not only by the molecular size, but also by its electrical charge. A positively charged particle passes more easily than a negatively charged particle of the same size.

## MECHANISM OF FILTRATION

Filtration occurs due to the physical forces acting on the filtering or glomerular membrane. The glomerulus is a capillary network of high pressure, which is caused by the differences between the diameters of the afferent and efferent arterioles. The latter offers greater resistance of the flow of blood.

The capillary hydrostatic pressure favours filtration, while the plasma colloid osmotic pressure and intracapsular pressure oppose filtration. The osmotic pressure of the filtrate in the Bowman's capsule is almost zero as normally, no proteins are filtered into it. The capillary hydrostatic pressure is about 45 mmHg. The plasma colloid osmotic pressure is about 25 mmHg, while the capsular hydrostatic pressure is about 10 mmHg.

The effective (net) filtration pressure (EFP) is, therefore, equal to the capillary hydrostatic pressure minus the sum of the plasma colloid osmotic pressure and the capsular hydrostatic pressure.

$$\text{Hence, EFP} = 45 - (25 + 10) = 10 \text{ mmHg}$$

The permeability of the glomerular capillaries is approximately 50 to 100 times greater than that of capillaries elsewhere. Hence, the volume of glomerular filtrate is much higher than that of filtrate from other systemic capillaries.

### Glomerular filtration rate (GFR)

The GFR is the amount of filtrate formed by all the nephrons in both kidneys per minute. Its normal value is 125 ml/min. (i.e., 180 l/day).

The GFR is influenced by the effective filtration pressure, the permeability of the glomerular membrane and the number of active glomeruli. The most important factor is the EFP.

**Effective Filtration Pressure**

The GFR varies directly with the EFP, which varies directly with the capillary hydrostatic pressure and inversely with the plasma colloid osmotic pressure and capsular hydrostatic pressure. The capillary hydrostatic pressure varies according to the systemic blood pressure, the diameter of the afferent and efferent arterioles, as well as sympathetic activity.

*Systemic blood pressure:* The renal blood flow and GFR are maintained constant in the blood pressure range of 80–200 mmHg (Systolic). Above and below this range, the GFR increases and decreases, respectively.

*Diameter of afferent and efferent arterioles:* Constriction of the afferent arteriole decreases the capillary hydrostatic pressure and hence the EFP and GFR. On the other hand, constriction of the efferent arteriole increases the capillary hydrostatic pressure, EFP and GFR. However, prolonged constriction of the efferent arteriole brings down the GFR by raising the colloid osmotic pressure of plasma due to sluggish glomerular circulation and filtration of fluid into the Bowman's capsule.

*Sympathetic activity:* Strong sympathetic stimulation, as in haemorrhagic shock, decreases the renal blood flow and GFR. A drop in the colloid osmotic pressure of plasma (e.g., in burns) and an increase in the capsular hydrostatic pressure, as in ureteric obstruction, brings down the GFR.

### Permeability of Glomerular Membrane and Number of Active Glomeruli

Anoxia increases the permeability of the glomerular membrane, thereby raising the GFR.

Normally, the number of active glomeruli is not an important factor. In renal disease, when some of the glomeruli are destroyed, the GFR decreases.

## Measurement of GFR

The GFR is measured by the clearance test. If a substance present in the plasma is freely filtered by the glomerulus and neither absorbed nor secreted into the tubule, then the amount of substance excreted per minute would be equal to the amount of substance filtered. Inulin is used to measure the GFR.

$$\text{Amount excreted} = \underset{(U)}{\text{Urinary concentration of substance}} \times \underset{(V)}{\text{Urine volume per minute}}$$

$$\text{Amount filtered} = \underset{(P)}{\text{Plasma concentration of substance}} \times \text{GFR}$$

As amount excreted = amount filtered,

$$U \times V = P \times GFR$$

$$GFR = \frac{U \times V}{P} = \text{Clearance of the substance}$$

Therefore, the clearance of a substance is the volume of plasma (in ml) that is completely cleared of the substance per minute.

If a substance is filtered, secreted, but not reabsorbed, its value is more than the GFR, and that substance for example, Para Amino Hippuric acid (PAH) is used to find the plasma flow and hence, the renal blood flow.

# MODIFICATION OF ULTRAFILTRATE INTO URINE

The modification of the ultrafiltrate into urine takes place in the renal tubules. The renal tubules have several functions, such as the conservation of nutrients, concentration and dilution of urine, maintenance of the acid–base balance and formation of ammonia.

As the glomerular filtrate passes through the PCT, loop of Henle, DCT and collecting ducts, it is subjected to various reabsorptive and secretory processes, which are described below.

## Tubular reabsorption

This is a process by which various substances are transferred from the tubular fluid into the peritubular capillaries across the tubular epithelium. The substances wanted by the body are reabsorbed and unwanted substances are left behind. Different substances are reabsorbed to different extents, depending on their importance in the body.

Substances of nutritive value are completely reabsorbed. These include glucose, amino acids, electrolytes and vitamins. The reabsorption takes place mostly in the PCT, by active transport.

Water is almost completely reabsorbed in various segments of the nephron. Salts are reabsorbed to a certain extent, while the reabsorption of waste products like urea, uric acid, sulphates and phosphates is the lowest (e.g., 50 per cent of the urea and uric acid is reabsorbed). Creatinine is not reabsorbed at all.

## Tubular secretion

The process of tubular secretion is just the opposite of that of tubular reabsorption. Thus, substances from the peritubular capillaries (e.g., $H^+$, $K^+$ and $NH_3^+$) are added to the tubular fluid. Besides these natural substances, certain drugs and iodinated contrast media may also be secreted by the cells of the PCT. Uric acid (organic substance) and $K^+$ (inorganic substance) can be both reabsorbed and secreted (Fig. 48.2).

Due to the removal and addition of certain substances, the ultrafiltrate is modified and goes through quantitative change, qualitative changes, and tonicity changes.

### Quantitative Changes

The total amount of glomerular filtrate formed per day is 180 l, but the output of urine per day is

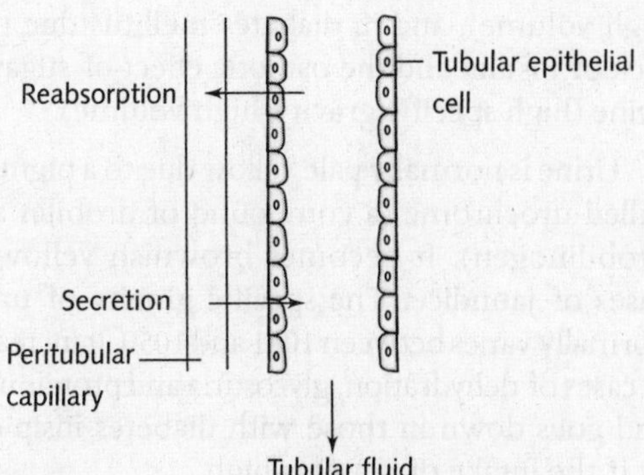


**Fig. 48.2:** Tubular reabsorption and secretion

only 1 to 1.5 l. Thus, about 99 per cent of the water is reabsorbed from the glomerular filtrate, allowing only 1 per cent to be excreted out.

Of the amount of water that is reabsorbed, about 75 per cent is absorbed in the PCT. This is accompanied by the absorption of salts like NaCl. The absorption of water is compulsory and is hence called obligatory reabsorption. It occurs by a passive mechanism along the osmotic gradient, created secondary to the active reabsorption of Na. About 20 per cent of the water is absorbed in the DCT. This amount varies according to the needs of the body, and the process is known as facultative reabsorption. This is also passive and is controlled by ADH from the posterior pituitary. A rise in the secretion of ADH increases the permeability of the DCT to water by increasing the pore size. This, in turn, causes more water to be reabsorbed.

It also increases the reabsorption of water by the collecting ducts.

## Qualitative Changes

An important change is the complete removal of glucose from the tubular fluid, provided the blood glucose level is normal. This is why there is normally no glucose in the urine. However, if the blood glucose level exceeds 180 mg% (renal threshold), it appears in the urine (glycosuria), as the renal tubules have a fixed upper limit for the reabsorption of glucose. This is called the tubular maximum for glucose (TmG). The TmG is approximately 375 mg/min. Those with diabetes mellitus have glycosuria owing to hyperglycaemia.

Renal glycosuria occurs even in those with a normal glucose level if there is a congenital tubular defect (low Tm value for glucose).

The electrolyte concentration of the urine changes according to the need to maintain their concentration in plasma. Most of the salts are reabsorbed in the PCT. Fewer are absorbed in the DCT. Their absorption is controlled by hormones. For example, aldosterone from the adrenal cortex increases the reabsorption of $Na^+$ and decreases that of $K^+$. The reabsorption of calcium and phosphate is reciprocal and is controlled by the parathyroid hormone.

The reabsorption of $Cl^-$ occurs passively, and is accompanied by the reabsorption of $Na^+$. The reabsorption of $HCO_3^-$ occurs as $CO_2$ (Fig. 48.3). The other qualitative change is the addition of $H^+$, $K^+$ and $NH_3^+$.

## Tonicity Changes

Changes occur in the osmotic pressure of the tubular fluid, depending on the relative amounts of Na and water present in different segments of the tubule. If the amount of Na exceeds that of water, the fluid becomes hypertonic. If the amounts are equal, it becomes isotonic and if the amount of Na is less than that of water, it becomes hypotonic. For example, in the PCT, the fluid is

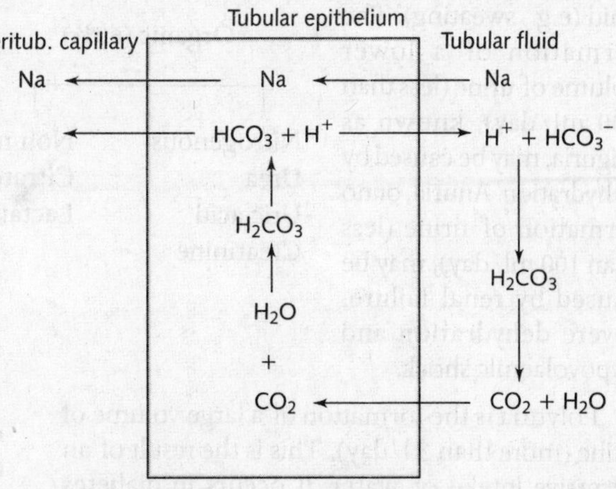


**Fig. 48.3:** Reabsorption of bicarbonate

isotonic with the plasma, it is hypertonic in the descending limb of the Loop of Henle, hypotonic in the ascending limb of the Loop, and hypertonic or hypotonic in the DCT and CT, depending on the presence or absence of hormone ADH, respectively. The osmolality of plasma is 300 milliosmols/l, whereas that of the urine can vary from 70 milliosmols/l to 1200 milliosmols/l. Thus, urine can be concentrated or diluted according to the body's need to maintain the water balance. If plenty of water is available, dilute urine is excreted and if not, concentrated urine is excreted. The maintenance of the water balance helps maintain the osmolality of body fluids.

Thus, as a result of qualitative, quantitative and tonicity changes, the glomerular filtrate is modified and converted to urine.

## URINE

The composition and rate of formation of urine are subjected to diurnal variations. They are also influenced by the diet and muscular activity. Hence, a 24-hour urine sample is used for analysis.

### Characteristics

The normal volume of urine is 0.5 to 2.5 l/day. Physiologically, it varies with the intake of fluids as well as nonrenal loss of fluid (e.g., sweating). The formation of a lower volume of urine (less than 400 ml/day), known as oliguria, may be caused by dehydration. Anuria, or no formation of urine (less than 100 ml/day), may be caused by renal failure, severe dehydration and hypovolaemic shock.

Polyuria is the formation of a large volume of urine (more than 3 l/day). This is the result of an excessive intake of water. It occurs in diabetes insipidus due to a lack of ADH (low specific gravity, high volume), and in diabetes mellitus due to a lack of insulin and the osmotic effect of sugar in urine (high specific gravity, high volume).

Urine is normally pale yellow due to a pigment called urochrome (a compound of urobilin and urobilinogen). It becomes brownish yellow in cases of jaundice. The specific gravity of urine normally varies between 1001 and 1050. It increases in cases of dehydration, glycosuria and proteinuria, and goes down in those with diabetes insipidus or if the intake of water is high.

If the fixed specific gravity of urine is 1010, it indicates chronic renal disease and the failure of both the concentration and dilution mechanisms.

Urinary pH is normally 6.5, that is, it is slightly acidic. The normal range is 5 to 7.5. The urine becomes alkaline in those who have vegetarian food, following a meal (alkaline tide) and hyperventilation. It becomes acidic in those who have high-protein diets (nonvegetarian food).

### Constituents

The normal constituents of urine are as shown below.

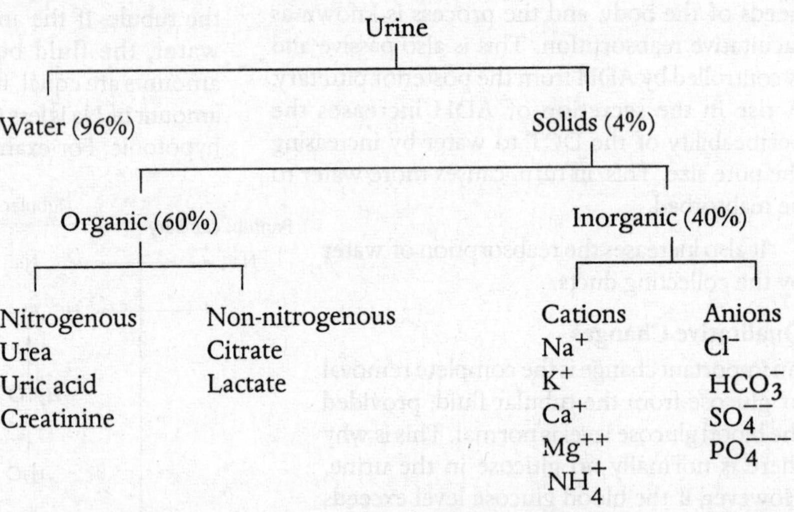


In certain conditions, glucose, protein or blood may be found in the urine. These are abnormalities of a chemical nature.

The presence of glucose in the urine is called

glycosuria. It may be caused by hyperglycaemia, and occurs in those with diabetes mellitus. A low renal threshold or TmG causes renal glycosuria, while a large carbohydrate meal gives rise to alimentary glycosuria. Endocrine glycosuria occurs as a result of increased secretion of hormones, for example, growth hormone, cortisol and thyroxine, and lactosuria is observed in lactating women.

The presence of protein (usually albumin) in the urine is called proteinuria. It may be caused by renal disorders, pregnancy, congestive cardiac failure, anaemia or prolonged standing.

The presence of blood in the urine makes the urine appear red and is called haematuria. It may be due to acute glomerulonephritis, renal stone, injury or malignancy. Bilirubin appears in the urine in patients with jaundice, while ketone bodies appear in the urine in ketosis due to diabetes mellitus and prolonged starvation.

Urine may have certain microscopic abnormalities. For example, casts may appear in it. These are solidified protein substances shaped like renal tubules. Casts are of several types, for example, hyalin casts, granular casts with fragmented epithelial cells, RBC casts with RBCs, or WBC casts with pus cells.

If more than ten pus cells are seen in the urine in the high-power field, infection is indicated. The other microscopic abnormalities include the presence of epithelial cells, RBCs (as in haematuria), and crystals of oxalate.

# Concentration, Dilution and Acidification of Urine

## CONCENTRATION AND DILUTION OF URINE

The maintenance of the osmolality of body fluids is one of the most important functions of the kidney. The volume of urine excreted per day may vary from 500 ml to several litres. When the plasma osmolality is high, a small volume of urine, containing a high concentration of solutes (highly concentrated urine), is excreted. When the plasma osmolality is low, a large volume of urine with a low concentration of solutes (dilute urine) is excreted.

The kidney's ability to concentrate or dilute urine is related to two factors—hyperosmolality of the medullary interstitium and the level of ADH in the plasma.

### Hyperosmolality of Medullary Interstitium

The osmolality of the cortical interstitial fluid is approximately 300 milliosmoles/l. That of the renal medullary interstitium increases from 300 milliosmoles/l in the cortex, to 1200 milliosmoles/l at the tip of the pyramid (Fig. 49.1).

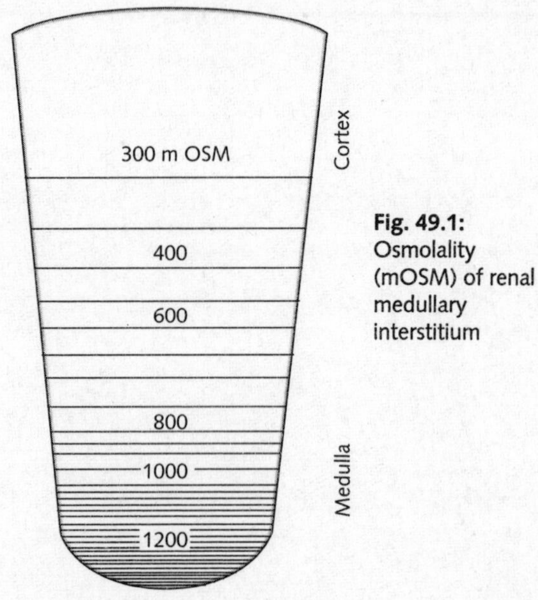


**Fig. 49.1:** Osmolality (mOSM) of renal medullary interstitium

### Level of ADH in Plasma

The glomerular filtrate has an osmolality of 300 milliosmols/l. In the PCT, the fluid remains iso-osmotic, although 70 per cent of the solutes are absorbed, as a similar proportion of water also accompanies the solutes passively.

The descending limb of the loop of Henle is permeable to water but relatively impermeable to solutes. Therefore, water moves out into the hyperosmolar interstitium and the fluid in the descending limb becomes progressively hyperosmolar.

In the ascending limb of Henle's loop, the active transport of NaCl progressively decreases the osmolality of the tubular fluid, which becomes 100 milliosmols/l by the time it reaches the DCT. Subsequent changes in the osmolality of the tubular fluid depend on the presence or absence of ADH.

## Role of ADH

A small volume of concentrated urine is formed in the presence of ADH. An increase in the plasma osmolality, such as that produced by dehydration, stimulates the secretion of ADH from the posterior pituitary. ADH increases the permeability of the DCT and collecting ducts to water, resulting in the passive reabsorption of water from the tubular fluid. Hence, the osmolality of the tubular fluid in the DCT increases to 300 milliosmoles/l (equal to the osmolality of the cortical interstitium).

As the fluid passes along the collecting ducts, it becomes increasingly concentrated as water is progressively reabsorbed into the hyperosmolar medullary interstitium. The urinary osmolality may go up to 1200 milliosmoles/l and the urinary volume reduced to 0.3 ml/min., when enough ADH is present in the plasma.

In the absence of ADH, a large volume of dilute urine is formed (diuresis). A decrease in the plasma osmolality, such as that produced by drinking a large amount of water, results in the inhibition of ADH secretion from the posterior pituitary. Therefore, the DCT and collecting ducts become impermeable to water, but NaCl reabsorption continues. Most of the fluid reaching the DCT is excreted. Due to the reabsorption of NaCl in the collecting ducts, the osmolality of the tubular fluid drops further, from 100 milliosmoles/l to as low as 70 milliosmoles/l. This is known as water diuresis (Fig. 49.2).

Depending on the status of the water in the body and the plasma osmolality, considerable variations normally occur in the rate of urine flow as well as urine osmolality during different parts

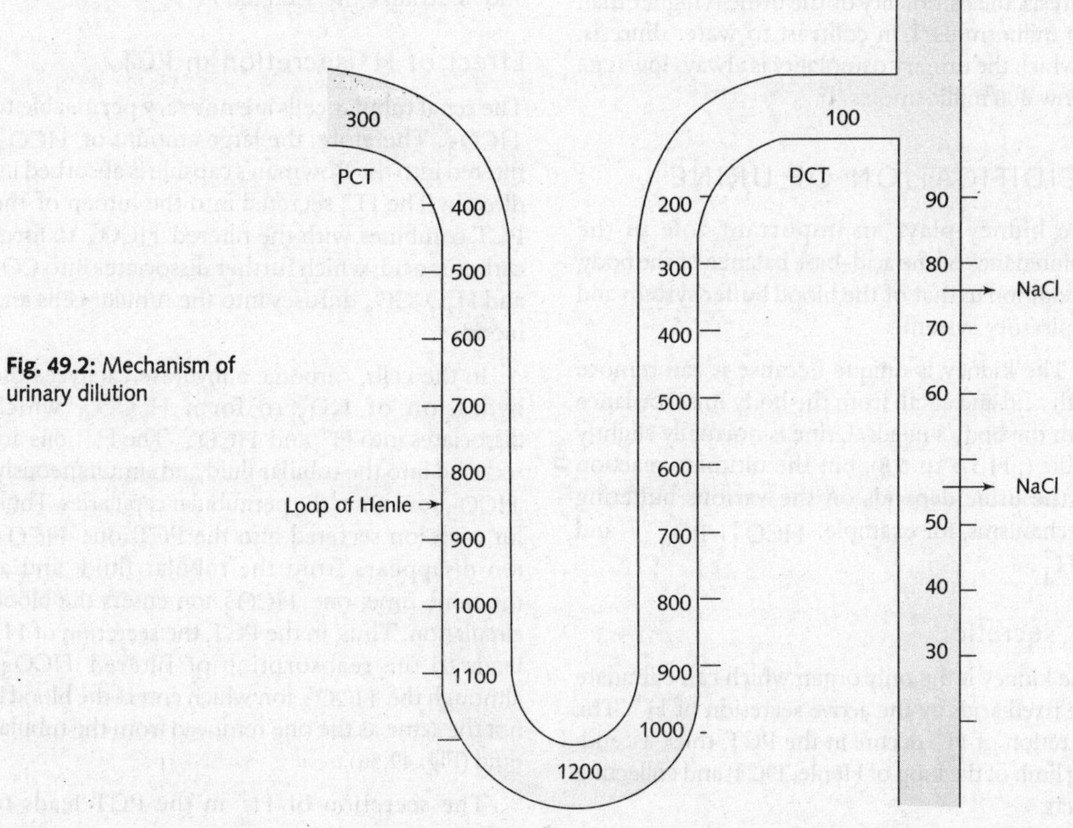


**Fig. 49.2:** Mechanism of urinary dilution

of the day. This is brought about by variations in the plasma ADH concentration, which can produce proportionate changes in the permeability of the collecting ducts to water. After an overnight fast, the morning urine samples tend to be relatively more concentrated.

The normal volume of urine is about 1.5 l a day. The excretion of urinary solutes such as NaCl, $K^+$ and urea, requires a certain minimum amount of urinary water. The minimum volume of urine necessary to contain the excreted solutes at maximum urinary concentration is known as the obligatory urine volume. This is about 500 ml/day.

The presence of a larger amount of solutes in the renal tubular fluid can also raise the volume of the urinary excretion of water because of an osmotic effect. This is known as osmotic diuresis. For example, an excess of glucose in the tubular fluid, as in diabetes mellitus, produces polyurea. In osmotic diuresis, the osmolality of the urine is higher than 300 milliosmols/l, in contrast to water diuresis, in which the urinary osmolality is always low (i.e., below 300 milliosmoles/l).

## ACIDIFICATION OF URINE

The kidney plays an important role in the maintenance of the acid–base balance of the body, in addition to that of the blood buffer system and respiratory system.

The kidney is unique because it can remove both acid and alkali from the body in accordance with the body's needs. Urine is normally slightly acidic (pH 5.5 to 6.8), but the ultimate reaction of the urine depends on the various buffering mechanisms, for example, $HCO_3^-$, $PO_4^{---}$ and $NH_4^+$.

### $H^+$ secretion

The kidney is the only organ which can eliminate the fixed acids by the active secretion of $H^+$. The secretion of $H^+$ occurs in the PCT, thick ascending limb of the loop of Henle, DCT and collecting ducts.

The $H^+$ ions secreted in the kidney are formed in the tubular cells by the hydration of $CO_2$, in the presence of the enzyme carbonic anhydrase.

$$CO_2 + H_2O \xrightarrow{CA} H_2CO_3 \rightarrow H^+ + HCO_3^-$$

The $HCO^-_3$ goes into the blood and $H^+$ is secreted by an $Na^+$–$H^+$ exchange, mostly in the PCT. Thus, during the secretion of $H^+$, $HCO_3^-$ is generated and it replaces the $HCO_3^-$ lost while buffering the fixed acids.

In the distal nephron, $H^+$ ions are also secreted against $Na^+$ but the main mechanism of $H^+$ production is the ATP-driven proton pump, which can increase the level of $H^+$ in the tubular fluid to a thousand times the plasma concentration.

The secretion of $H^+$ in the renal tubule can continue only if free $H^+$ is immediately buffered in the tubular fluid. In the PCT, the filtered $HCO_3^-$ buffers the secreted $H^+$. In the DCT and collecting ducts, $Na_2HPO_4$ and $NH_3$ act as buffers and neutralize the secreted $H^+$.

### Effect of $H^+$ secretion in PCT

The renal tubular cells are not very permeable to $HCO_3^-$. Therefore, the large amount of $HCO_3^-$ filtered into the Bowman's capsule is absorbed indirectly. The $H^+$ secreted into the lumen of the PCT combines with the filtered $HCO_3^-$ to form carbonic acid, which further dissociates into $CO_2$ and $H_2O$. $CO_2$ diffuses into the tubular cells and blood.

In the cells, carbonic anhydrase catalyzes the hydration of $CO_2$ to form $H_2CO_3$, which dissociates into $H^+$ and $HCO_3^-$. The $H^+$ ions are secreted into the tubular fluid and simultaneously, $HCO_3^-$ ions enter the peritubular capillaries. Thus, for each ion secreted into the PCT, one $HCO_3^-$ ion disappears from the tubular fluid, and at the same time, one $HCO_3^-$ ion enters the blood circulation. Thus, in the PCT, the secretion of $H^+$ leads to the reabsorption of filtered $HCO_3^-$, although the $HCO_3^-$ ion which enters the blood is not the same as the one removed from the tubular fluid (Fig. 49.3a).

The secretion of $H^+$ in the PCT leads to

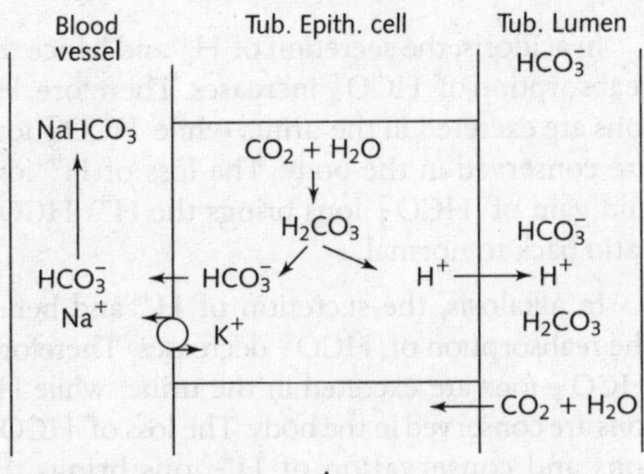


**Fig. 49.3(a):** Fate of $H^+$ secretion in the kidney: role of bicarbonate buffer

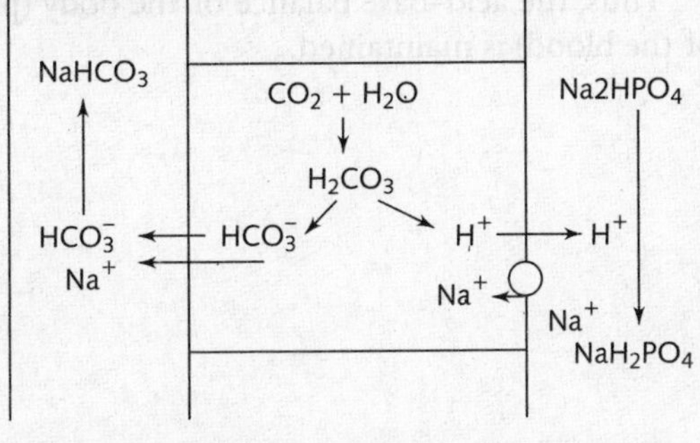


**Fig. 49.3(b):** Fate of $H^+$ secretion in the kidney: role of phosphate buffer

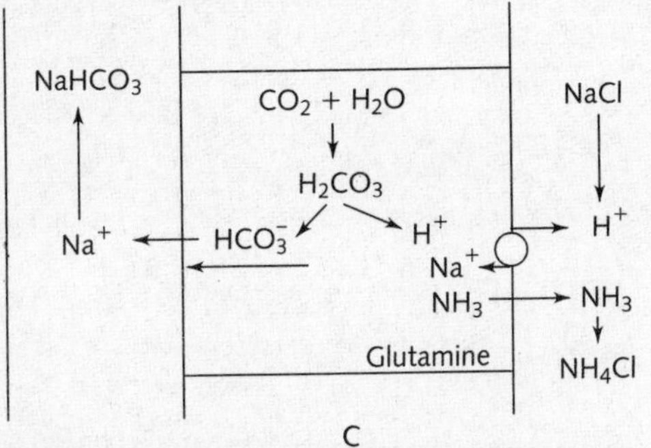


**Fig. 49.3(c):** Fate of $H^+$ secretion in the kidney: role of ammonia buffer

almost total reabsorption of the filtered $HCO_3^-$. Although the tubular cells secrete over 4000 meq of $H^+$ per day, most of it is used for reabsorption of $HCO_3^-$. Only 60 meq of $H^+$ ions are excreted from the body—with phosphate buffer and with ammonia—making the urine acidic. Thus, the role of $HCO_3^-$ is to buffer $H^+$ ions which are added to the body as a result of metabolism (metabolic acids). There is practically no change in the pH of the tubular fluid.

If the amount of $HCO_3^-$ in the tubular fluid is more than normal, as in alkalosis, all the $HCO_3^-$ cannot be neutralized and the excess amount is excreted in the urine, making it alkaline.

## Effect of $H^+$ secretion in the distal tubular segments

### Role of Phosphate Buffer

Phosphate buffers consist of a mixture of $Na_2HPO_4$ (basic phosphate) and $NaH_2PO_4$ (acidic phosphate). They are not effective in the blood, but are very effective in kidney as they get concentrated in the tubular fluid secondary to the reabsorption of water.

The $H^+$ ions secreted into the distal tubule combine with $Na_2HPO_4$ to form $NaH_2PO_4$ and $Na^+$, which is reabsorbed in exchange for the $H^+$ secreted. $NaH_2PO_4$ is excreted in the urine.

$$Na_2HPO_4 + H^+ \rightarrow NaH_2PO_4 + Na^+$$

As a result, the $NaH_2PO_4$ present in the urine determines the titrable acidity of urine (Fig. 49.3b).

If the number of $H^+$ ions secreted in the tubular fluid is above normal, as in acidosis, all the $H^+$ cannot be neutralized and the pH of the urine goes down to 4.5. Beyond this, the secretion of $H^+$ stops (limiting the pH) and the ammonia mechanism is utilized.

### Role of Ammonia Secretion

Ammonia ($NH_3$) and ammonium ions ($NH_4^+$) constitute another important buffer system in the tubular fluid.

Ammonia is synthesized mainly in the tubular cells of the DCT and collecting ducts from glutamine (60 per cent). The remaining amount is synthesized from the amino acids, glycine and alanine (40 per cent). Ammonia is lipid-soluble and diffuses into the tubular lumen. There, it immediately binds with $H^+$ to form ammonium ($NH_4^+$), a nondiffusible ion.

$$NH_3^+ + H^+ \rightarrow NH_4^+$$

Ammonium is excreted in the urine mostly as

$NH_4Cl$ (Fig. 49.3c). This cannot be accounted for in the titrable acidity.

The importance of $NH_3$ as a urinary buffer lies in the fact that it is not limited, like the phosphate buffer, to glomerular filtration. Hence, in chronic acidosis (diabetic or respiratory), the secretion of ammonia keeps increasing and the excretion of $NH_4^+$ may go up ten-fold, compared to the five fold increase in excretion with the phosphate buffer.

## Applied physiology

The $H^+$: $HCO_3^-$ ratio increases in acidosis, while it decreases in alkalosis. Acidosis and alkalosis can have respiratory or metabolic causes.

In acidosis, the secretion of $H^+$ and hence the reabsorption of $HCO_3^-$ increases. Therefore, $H^+$ ions are excreted in the urine, while $HCO_3^-$ ions are conserved in the body. The loss of $H^+$ ions and gain of $HCO_3^-$ ions brings the $H^+$: $HCO_3^-$ ratio back to normal.

In alkalosis, the secretion of $H^+$ and hence the reabsorption of $HCO_3^-$ decreases. Therefore, $HCO_3^-$ ions are excreted in the urine, while $H^+$ ions are conserved in the body. The loss of $HCO_3^-$ ions and conservation of $H^+$ ions brings the $H^+$: $HCO_3^-$ ratio back to normal.

Thus, the acid–base balance of the body (pH of the blood) is maintained.

CHAPTER

50

# Micturition

Once the urine is formed by the processes of filtration, reabsorption and secretion, it enters the ureters, which carry it to the urinary bladder. Here, it is stored temporarily and voided from time to time. The periodic emptying of the urinary bladder is called micturition.

## PHYSIOLOGICAL ANATOMY OF URINARY BLADDER

The urinary bladder consists of the body and the trigone. The body expands during filling. Its wall is made of an involuntary muscle, called the detrusor. The trigone is a triangular area bounded by two ureteric openings and one urethral opening. The proximal end of the urethra is guarded by an internal sphincter, which is involuntary and remains tonically contracted. The distal end is guarded by an external sphincter, which is under voluntary control.

*Nerve supply*: Intact innervation is essential for the normal and complete evacuation of the urinary bladder. The urinary bladder, internal sphincter and proximal urethra are supplied by the autonomic nervous system.

The sympathetic supply comes from the $L_1$ and $L_4$ segments of the spinal cord, through hypogastric nerves. These contain afferent fibres, carrying the sensation of pain, and efferent fibres, which cause contraction of the internal sphincter and relaxation of the detrusor muscle, resulting in filling of the urinary bladder. Hence, the sympathetic nerves are known as the nerves of 'filling and feeling'.

The parasympathetic supply comes from the $S_2$, $S_3$ and $S_4$ segments of the spinal cord, through pelvic nerves. They contain afferent fibres, which carry the sensation of distension, and efferent fibres, which cause contraction of the detrusor muscle and relaxation of the external sphincter, resulting in emptying of the urinary bladder. Hence, the parasympathetic nerves are called the nerves of emptying.

The distal urethra and external sphincter are supplied by somatic nerves coming from the $S_2$, $S_3$ and $S_4$ segments of the spinal cord, through the pudendal nerves.

## THE PROCESS OF MICTURITION

The urinary bladder is first progressively filled with urine, until the tension in its wall rises to a threshold or critical level, at which the micturition reflex is initiated. This either results in micturition or produces a conscious desire to micturate.

### Filling of Bladder

As the urinary bladder gets filled with urine, several changes are seen in the intravesical pressure. When the volume of urine in the bladder is between 0 and 100 ml, there is a proportionate rise in the pressure. When it is between 100 and 400 ml, there is not much of a rise in the intravesical pressure.

This is due to stretching of the elastic smooth muscle fibres in the bladder wall, which is known as adaptation. As a result of this, the bladder can hold urine for some time. This helps in the storage function of the bladder.

The micturition reflex is initiated when the volume of urine reaches about 400 ml, and a conscious desire to evacuate the bladder is felt. Micturition can be inhibited voluntarily by higher nervous control when the volume is between 400 and 800 ml. Beyond 800 ml, micturition occurs involuntarily and the intravesical pressure falls (Fig. 50.1).

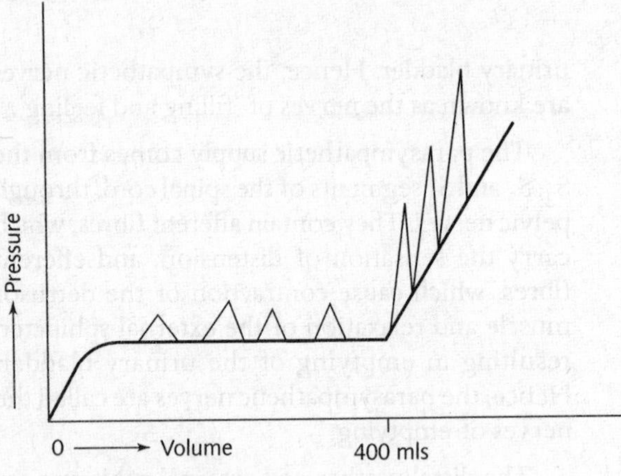


Fig. 50.1: Cystometrogram

**Emptying of Bladder**

When the volume of urine reaches about 400 ml (threshold), the micturition reflex is initiated due to a sharp increase in the intravesical pressure. The stretch receptors in the bladder wall are stimulated due to distension. Afferent impulses are carried by the pelvic nerves to the sacral segments ($S_2$, $S_3$, $S_4$) of the spinal cord, which is the centre for the micturition reflex. Efferent impulses from the centre are carried to the bladder, causing contraction of the detrusor. This stretches the bladder wall further as the stretch receptors are arranged in a series. The afferent impulses go to the spinal cord and the efferent impulses come back to the bladder, causing further contraction of the detrusor. The micturition reflex is, thus, self-regenerative, that is, the initial contraction of bladder results in a strong contraction and an increase in the intravesical pressure, which leads to relaxation of the internal sphincter.

In suitable circumstances, the external sphincter is relaxed voluntarily and micturition occurs. Otherwise, fatigue sets in and the detrusor muscle relaxes. The next reflex begins a few minutes later and is much stronger because the bladder is now more full. If micturition is still inhibited voluntarily, the bladder goes on filling and when the volume of urine exceeds 800 ml, micturition occurs involuntarily. The external sphincter is mechanically forced open, in spite of voluntary inhibition.

## Control by the brain

The cerebral cortex is the motor area which inhibits micturition and, therefore, exerts voluntary control. In infants, there is no voluntary control and hence, the bladder empties automatically as soon as it fills.

The inhibitory control is exerted by tonic contraction of the external sphincter. In suitable circumstances, the cerebral cortex facilitates the sacral micturition centre and inhibits the external sphincter, causing its relaxation.

The midbrain has an inhibitory centre, and the pons has a facilitatory centre. Micturition is basically a spinal cord reflex, but is facilitated or inhibited by the supraspinal centres.

The act of micturition involves first the contraction of the detrusor, chest muscles and abdominal muscles, which increase the intra-abdominal pressure. Next, the sphincters, and internal, external and perineal muscles are relaxed. Another factor that comes into play is the learned ability to control external sphincter.

Thus, micturition involves coordinated activity of both the somatic and autonomic nervous systems.

Applied physiology: In acute transection of spinal cord, voluntary micturition is completely abolished. Retention of urine occurs. In the course of time, reflex micturition occurs.

# CHAPTER 51

# Skin

The skin covers the surface of the body. Our contact with the environment is through the skin. Although it is an excretory organ, its other functions are more important.

## STRUCTURE

The skin consists of two layers: the epidermis and dermis (Fig. 51.1).

### The epidermis

The epidermis is the outer layer and has no blood vessels. It is made of stratified squamous epithelium, which is arranged in the following layers from superficial to deep:

1. Stratum corneum: This consists of dead cells containing keratin, but no nuclei. The superficial cells are shed off continuously.
2. Stratum lucidum: This is a homogeneous layer of flattened cells containing eleidin, the precursor of keratin.
3. Stratum granulosum: The cells of this layer contain granules of keratohyaline.
4. Stratum spinosum: This layer is made of prickle cells, the surfaces of which contain spine-like processes. These cells move upward, forming the above layers.
5. Stratum germinativum: This layer is made of cells situated on the basement membrane in a single layer. The cells undergo mitosis and move upward. Melanocytes are present in this layer.

### The dermis

The dermis is the inner layer. It is divided into a superficial papillary layer and a deeper reticular layer.

The papillary layer consists of papillae that project into the epidermis. They contain blood vessels, lymphatics and nerve endings. The reticular layer consists of reticular and elastic fibres, fat and loose areolar tissue. It also contains sebaceous glands, hair follicles and sweat glands.

The colour of the skin depends on the amount of melanin pigment present in it. The more the pigment, the darker the colour. The amount of blood flow also determines the colour of the skin. A good flow of blood imparts a pink colour to the skin and if the blood flow is low, the skin looks pale. The thickness of the skin also influences its colour.

## SWEAT GLANDS

Sweat glands are present all over the skin, except in the eardrums, lips, etc. They are present in the dermis of the skin and are ectodermal in origin. They consist of an initial coiled, secretory portion in the dermis, the active secretion of which is called sweat. This is carried to the surface by the straight portion above the dermis. The modified

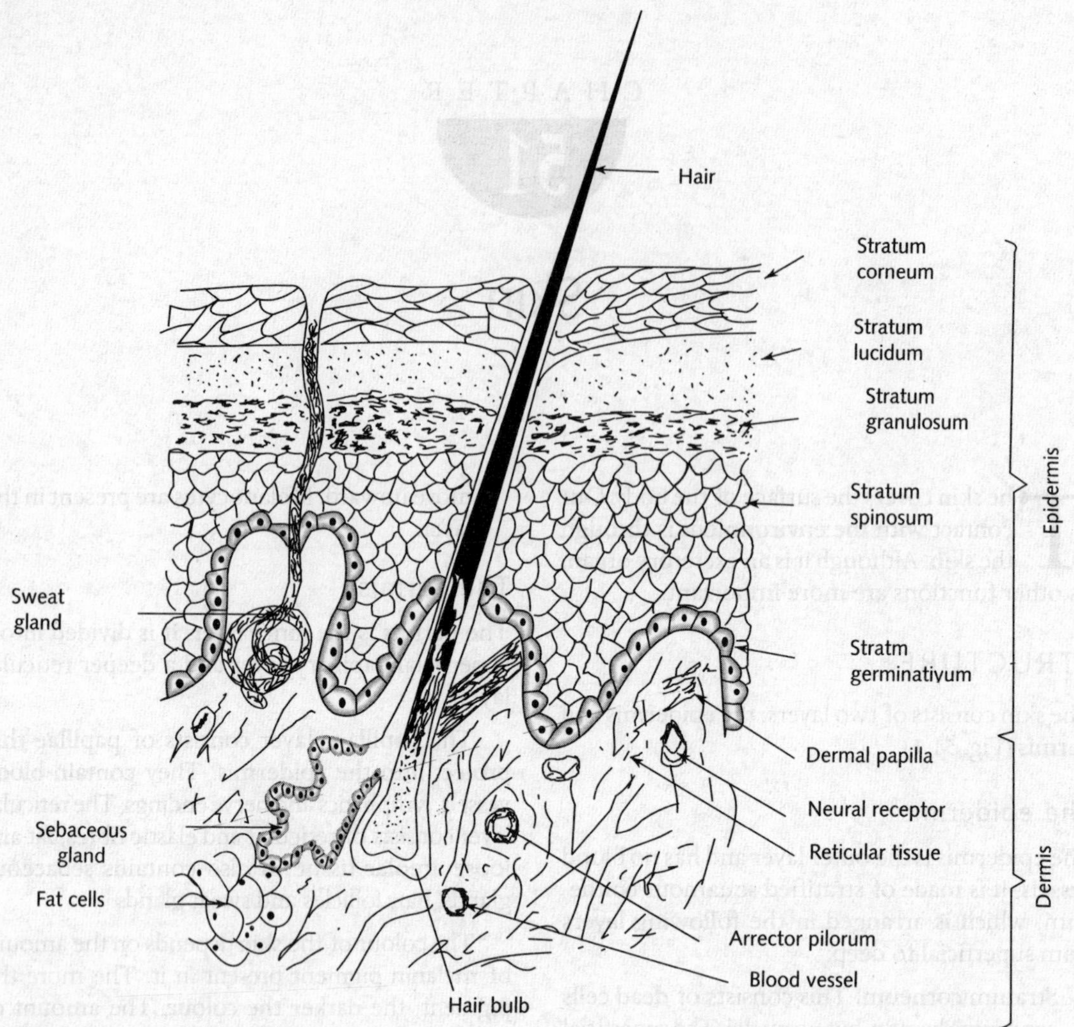


**Fig. 51.1:** Structure of skin

smooth muscle cells (myoepithelial cells) around the basal portion help in eliminating sweat by their contraction.

Sweat glands are of two types—apocrine and eccrine. The differences between the two types are listed in Table 51.1.

**Table 51.1:** Comparison of two types of sweat glands

| | *Apocrine* | *Eccrine* |
|---|---|---|
| 1. Mode of secretion | Apical part of cell disintegrates. | The cell remains intact, only the secretion comes out. |
| 2. Incidence | Greater in lower animals. | Greater in human beings. |

| | | | |
|---|---|---|---|
| 3. | Distribution | Not uniform; present in selected regions, e.g., axilla, pubic region, nipple and areola of breast. | Uniform throughout the body; maximum in palms, soles, neck and forehead. |
| 4. | Size | Large | Small |
| 5. | Opening | Into the hair follicle. | On the surface of the skin, in a sweat pit. |
| 6. | Nature of secretion | Thick, viscid and has a characteristic odour due to bacterial decomposition. | Thin, watery, colourless and odourless. |
| 7. | Control of secretion | Hormonal: Starts at puberty and decreases in old age according to secretion of sex hormones. | Nervous: Anatomically sympathetic but physiologically parasympathetic or cholinergic. |
| 8. | Functions | Sexual attraction to opposite sex. | Excretion, maintenance of water, salt, pH and, most important, regulation of body temperature. |

## FUNCTIONS OF SKIN

The skin performs several functions, an important one being protection. This includes protection from excessive gain or loss of water from the tissues (i.e., water-proofing function). It also provides the deeper structures with protection from injury. These functions are carried out by the horny layer of the epidermis.

Sebum, an oily secretion from the sebaceous glands of the skin, protects a person from infection. Sebum has antibacterial and antifungal properties. The melanin pigment in the skin provides protection from the damaging effects of ultraviolet rays.

Some of the sensations we feel are through the skin, which contains the nerve endings, that is, receptors for the sensations of touch, pain and temperature. The skin is also responsible for the excretion of heavy metals, salts and metabolites, like urea, which are excreted through sweat. Further, vitamin D is synthesized from ergosterol in the skin, by ultraviolet rays.

Fat, water, glucose and about 500 ml of blood are stored in the skin. The latter acts as a reservoir which can be translocated to the vital organs in shock. The skin absorbs fat-soluble vitamins and lipid-soluble materials, like steroids, when these are applied over it.

Sebum, sweat and milk are secreted from the skin. Further, by regulating the formation and evaporation of sweat, the skin helps maintain the water balance of the body. It also helps maintain the acid–base balance. Sweat is acidic in nature and in acidosis, sweating increases.

An important function of the skin is that it gives diagnostic signs of vitamin deficiency, malnutrition, dehydration, ageing and infectious diseases. The regulation of the body temperature is the most important function. The is carried out by the control of heat loss from the body. The skin regulates heat loss in the following ways:

1. Radiation: Heat is given to the surrounding air, provided the temperature of the body is higher than that of the air.
2. Conduction: Heat is conducted to the objects in contact with the body, for example, clothing.
3. Convection: The conduction of heat is facilitated by the movement of heated air in currents. The heated air in contact with the body is replaced by cooler air.
4. Evaporation: Water is evaporated from the skin surface through insensible perspiration and sweating.

*Insensible perspiration:* This is the continuous diffusion of water molecules through the skin and respiratory membrane, of which we are not aware. The loss of water (about 500 ml/day) and, therefore, of heat loss from the body is fixed. The evaporation of 1 l of water produces a loss of 580 kcal from the body.

*Sweating:* Sweat is an active secretion of the sweat glands, of which we are aware or conscious. The loss of water (0–a few thousand ml/day) and hence, heat loss from the body is variable, according to the need of the body. The mechanism of sweating is, therefore, more important than insensible perspiration.

5. Vasodilatation: Vasodilatation of the skin arterioles brings heated blood from the deeper parts of the body to the surface. This increases sweating and heat loss from the body through all the mechanisms described earlier.

# Muscle and Nerve

# The Muscle

The muscle is an excitable tissue. It is characterized by its ability to contract, which allows it to shorten and generate force following an action potential.

*Classification:* The muscles in our body have been classified into three types: skeletal muscle, cardiac muscle and visceral or smooth muscle. Certain details pertaining to each type are given in Table 52.1.

**Table 52.1:** Comparison of different types of muscles

| | *Skeletal muscle* | *Cardiac muscle* | *Visceral or smooth muscle* |
|---|---|---|---|
| 1. Location | Attached to the skeleton | In the wall of heart | In the wall of visceral organ |
| 2. Cross-striations | Present | Present | Absent, hence called smooth muscle |
| 3. Nerve supply | Somatic | Autonomic | Autonomic |
| 4. Control | Under will, i.e., voluntary | Not under will, i.e., involuntary | Not under will, i.e., involuntary |
| 5. Function | Movement of joints | Movement of blood, i.e., circulation | Movement of contents, i.e., mixing or propulsion |

The composition of muscles may be represented as shown below.

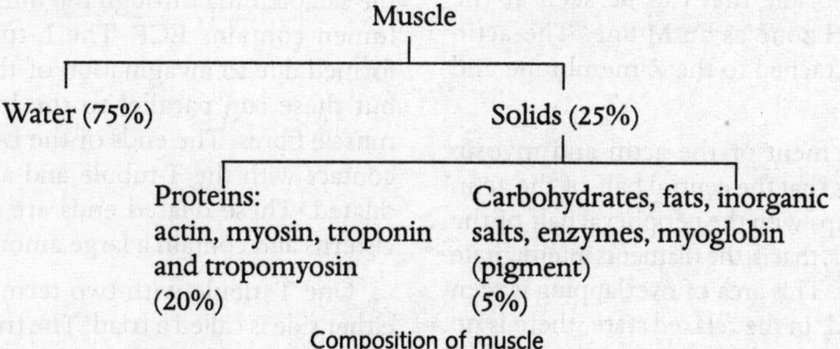


Composition of muscle

## SKELETAL MUSCLE

Skeletal muscles constitute about 40 per cent of the body weight. Most skeletal muscles begin and end in fibrous tendons, by which they are attached to the bones.

A skeletal muscle consists of numerous skeletal muscle cells or fibres, which run parallel to each other along the length of the muscle. They are arranged in bundles, with the help of fibrous tissue.

The muscle fibres are cylindrical in shape and of variable thickness and length. Under the light microscope, a muscle fibre is seen to have an outer cell membrane, called the sarcolemma, and the protoplasm, called the sarcoplasm. The latter contains mitochondria, the sarcotubular system and myofibrils, which possess actin and myosin (contractile proteins). Cross-striations, caused by alternate dark and light bands, are also seen across the length of muscle fibres.

Under the electron microscope, each muscle fibre is seen to have a large number of myofibrils that are placed parallel to each other. Each myofibril contains alternate dark (A) and light (I) bands. At the centre of the I-band is a dark line called the Z-line, and at the centre of the A-band is a lighter H-zone. The portion between the two successive Z-lines, called a sarcomere, is the structural and functional unit of the muscle fibre. It consists of an A-band, with half an I-band on either side.

The A-band is made of about 1500 thick myosin filaments, while the I-band is made of about 3000 actin filaments. The former are kept in position by a thin membrane that can be seen at the centre of the H-zone as an M-line. The actin filaments are attached to the Z-membrane and are thin.

The arrangement of the actin and myosin filaments shows that the central half of the actin filaments overlaps with the peripheral half of the myosin filaments, that is, the filaments interdigitate with each other. This area of overlapping is seen as a dark A-band. In the relaxed state, there is no overlapping of filaments in the central portion of myosin, and the gap is seen as an H-zone. The peripheral parts of the actin filaments do not overlap with the myosin filaments and this area forms the light band, with a dark Z-line at the centre (Fig. 52.1).

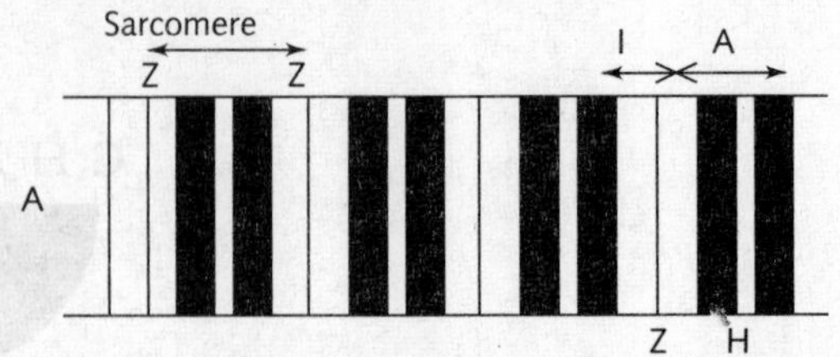


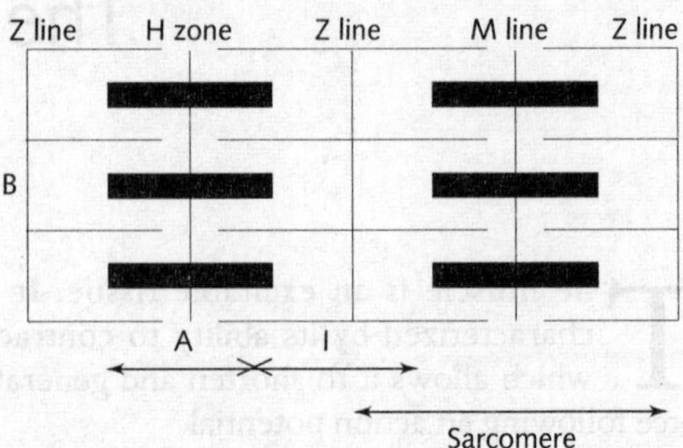


**Fig. 52.1:** Structure of a skeletal muscle cell (fibre): A. under phase contrast microscope, B. under electron microscope

### Sarcotubular System

The sarcotubular system consists of membranous tubular and vesicular structures that surround the individual myofibril in the sarcoplasm. These are called transverse (T) tubules and longitudinal (L) tubules.

The T-tubules are formed by invagination of the sarcolemma through the muscle fibre. Their lumen contains ECF. The L-tubules, too, are formed due to invagination of the sarcolemma, but these run parallel to the long axis of the muscle fibres. The ends of the L-tubule come in contact with the T-tubule and are expanded or dilated. These dilated ends are called terminal cisterns and contain a large amount of $Ca^{++}$.

One T-tubule with two terminal cisterns on either side is called a triad. The triads are situated at the A–I junctions (Fig. 52.2).

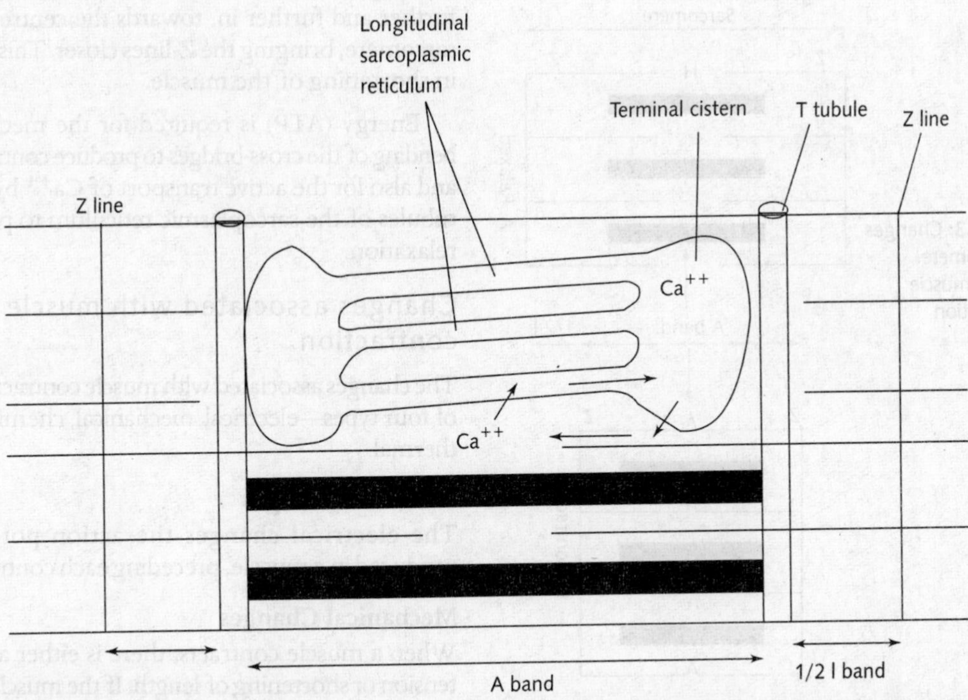


**Fig. 52.2:** The sarcotubular system

## Excitation–Contraction Coupling

When a muscle is adequately stimulated by a large motor nerve fibre, action potential develops. This spreads over the sarcolemma and then through the T-tubules. When it reaches the triad, the permeability of the terminal cisterns for $Ca^{++}$ increases and $Ca^{++}$ ions are released into the sarcoplasm. The $Ca^{++}$ ions diffuse into the myofibrils, causing the contraction of each sarcomere and hence, shortening of the muscle. The muscle remains contracted as long as the sarcoplasmic $Ca^{++}$ concentration is high. However, after a few milliseconds, the $Ca^{++}$ pump operating at the L-tubule decreases the $Ca^{++}$ concentration very rapidly and the muscle relaxes. From the L-tubule, $Ca^{++}$ ions diffuse to the terminal cisterns, to be stored until another stimulus reaches the T-tubules.

# Mechanism of muscle contraction

Various changes are observed in each sarcomere during muscle contraction. The H-zone disappears, but the width of the A-band remains unchanged. The width of the I-band decreases and the Z-lines come close to each other.

These changes indicate that the length of the myosin and actin filaments do not change during muscle contraction, but shortening of the muscle occurs due to the sliding of the actin filaments over the myosin filaments. The former overlap with the central portion of the latter and buckle, thereby decreasing the length of the sarcomere (Fig. 52.3).

## Mechanism of Sliding

The thick or the myosin filament is made of myosin molecules, each of which has an outgrowth process called the head. During contraction, the heads get attached to the actin molecules of the thin filament, so that the myosin and actin filaments are now physically connected with each other. These connecting links, called cross-bridges, pull the actin filaments towards the centre of the sarcomere. The myosin head also contains ATPase enzyme.

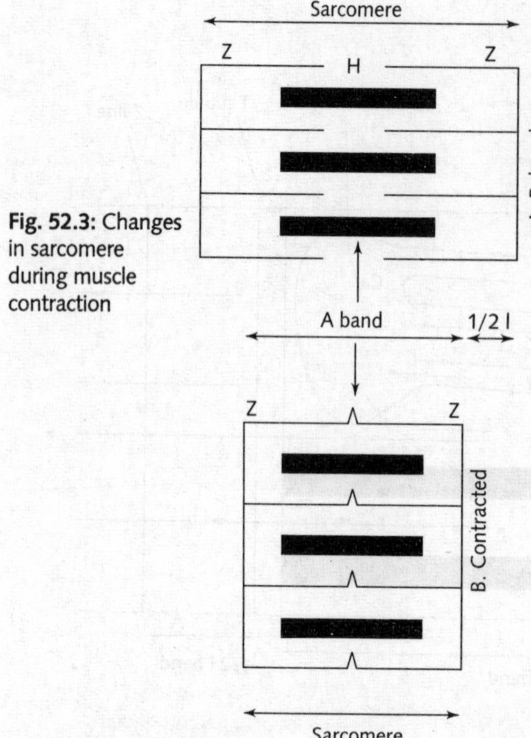


**Fig. 52.3:** Changes in sarcomere during muscle contraction

The thin or the actin filament is made of actin, tropomyosin and troponin molecules. The actin molecules possess binding sites for the myosin heads at regular intervals. The tropomyosin molecules cover these active sites and the troponin molecules hold the tropomyosins in position, so that the latter can cover the active sites.

When $Ca^{++}$ binds to troponin, the tropomyosin molecules are released and they move away slightly to expose the active sites on the actin filament. The myosin heads attach themselves to the exposed binding sites, forming cross-bridges which bend immediately. The ATP attached to the cross-bridges splits into ADP, and the energy released is used for the bending of cross-bridges. The inward bending of cross-bridges makes the actin filaments slide inwards. Almost immediately, the myosin heads release the actin filament, bind with another ATP molecule and return to the perpendicular position with respect to the body of the myosin filament. By repeated binding, bending and release, the actin filaments are pulled further and further in, towards the centre of the sarcomere, bringing the Z-lines closer. This results in shortening of the muscle.

Energy (ATP) is required for the mechanical bending of the cross-bridges to produce contraction, and also for the active transport of $Ca^{++}$ by the L-tubules of the sarcoplasmic reticulum to produce relaxation.

## Changes associated with muscle contraction

The changes associated with muscle contraction are of four types—electrical, mechanical, chemical and thermal.

### Electrical Changes

The electrical changes the action potentials produced in a muscle, preceding each contraction.

### Mechanical Changes

When a muscle contracts, there is either a rise of tension or shortening of length. If the muscle is free to shorten, for example, if it is attached to a small load, the contraction is called isotonic. However, if the muscle is attached to a heavy load, it may develop a large amount of tension but be unable to shorten. This is called isometric (same length) contraction.

In the intact body, if a weight is lifted off the ground, it involves isotonic contraction of the flexor muscles of the forearm (e.g., the biceps). Since external work is being done, a greater amount of energy is used in isotonic contraction than in isometric contraction. Postural muscles contract isometrically. Thus, the muscles can perform various movements and do external work.

The duration of an action potential in the skeletal muscle is approximately 5 milliseconds and the refractory period, during which it does not respond to a second stimulus, is shorter still. The duration of a mechanical response (simple muscle twitch) is 30 to 50 milliseconds. Hence, if the skeletal muscle is stimulated at short intervals, an action potential results, provided that each second stimulus falls after the refractory period produced by the previous stimulus. Each action potential results in the contraction of the muscle.

At a slower rate of stimulation, the muscle undergoes repetitive contractions, separated by partial relaxation. This response is called incomplete tetanus or clonus. At a higher frequency of stimulation, fusion of contractions occurs since the second stimulus falls in the contraction period of the previous stimulus. Thus, the muscle remains in a sustained state of contraction, called complete tetanus (Fig. 52.4). The tension produced during a tetanic response is greater than that produced in a simple muscle twitch.

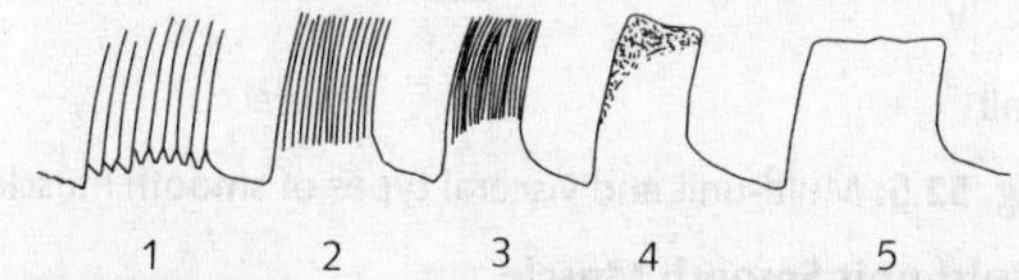


**Fig. 52.4:** Effect of increase in frequency of stimulation of skeletal muscle—1–4: partial tetanus; 5: complete tetanus

The length of the muscle which produces the maximum tension is known as the optimum length. During isometric contraction, the tension develops in proportion to the number of cross-bridges formed between the actin and myosin filaments.

On different occasions, a skeletal muscle may be required to generate widely different degrees of power. The gradation of muscular power is achieved mainly by the activation (i.e., recruitment) of varying numbers of motor units.

The axon of a spinal motor neuron divides into a number of branches and each branch supplies a single muscle fibre. A motor neuron and all the muscle fibres innervated by it constitute a motor unit. The number of muscle fibres in a motor unit varies. The muscles involved in fine, graded and precise movements (e.g., muscles of the eyeballs and fingers) have a large number of muscle fibres.

In addition, a rise in the frequency of discharge in the motor unit helps increase the muscular power. Normally, however, muscles are stimulated at a subtetanic discharge rate. Asynchronous (out of phase with each other) discharge in different motor units of muscles converts jerky responses into smooth muscle contractions.

### Chemical Changes

Various chemical changes take place in the muscle during and after contraction. The first change is the hydrolysis of ATP. This reaction supplies energy to the muscle. ATPs are synthesized within the muscle fibres, both from the Embeden–Mayerhof (EM) pathway and the TCA cycle.

All muscle fibres are not identical in this respect, and may be divided into two types—red fibres and white fibres. A muscle containing more white fibres is called white muscle and looks pale as it has no myoglobin. These muscles are rapid in their action and are also called fast muscles. They derive their ATP requirement from glycolysis (anaerobic), so they cannot continue contracting for a long time. The muscles moving the fingers of the hand are of this type. The red muscle is made of red fibres, which mainly contain plenty of myoglobin. This type is slow in action and is also called slow muscle. It derives its energy requirements from the TCA cycle (aerobic). Therefore, red muscles can continue to act for a prolonged period. The postural muscles are of this type.

Lactic acid is also produced as a result of muscle contraction. It is normally produced from pyruvic acid, following glycolysis, in fast muscles. It is produced in slow muscles, too, when the $O_2$ supply cannot keep pace with the demand. The lactic acid is disposed mainly through the Cori's cycle.

### Thermal Changes

When a skeletal muscle shortens, only 20 to 25 per cent of the energy input is converted into muscular work. The rest is converted to heat. During isometric contraction, no external work is done and all the energy is converted into heat. The production of heat in the muscle is increased not only during contraction (initial heat), but also subsequently (recovery heat), due to metabolic processes that restore the muscle to the pre-exercise level.

## Energy for muscle contraction

The immediate source of energy for muscle contraction is ATP. ATP is hydrolysed to ADP and energy is released. ATP is resynthesized from ADP by creatine phosphate.

$$ATP \longrightarrow ADP + P$$

$$ADP + CP \longrightarrow ATP + C$$

These two high-energy phosphates can provide energy for some time, after which they need to be resynthesized. ATP is provided by the mitochondria. ATP then converts the creatine into CP. Therefore, both ATP and CP are replenished by metabolism within the cell. The major fuel for the formation of ATP, particularly in red muscles, is the free fatty acids. Muscle glycogen comes into the picture later, when the contraction is prolonged and exhaustive. In the case of white muscles, glycogen is the main source.

### Role of Myoglobin

Myoglobin is an iron-containing porphyrin pigment, similar to haemoglobin. It becomes saturated with $O_2$ even at a very low arterial $PO_2$ and releases it at an extremely low tissue $PO_2$. During severe and sustained muscular contraction, when the blood supply to the muscle decreases, the muscle can extract some $O_2$ from myoglobin. Thus, myoglobin acts as a small but important store of $O_2$ for the muscle.

### $O_2$-debt Mechanism

During heavy exercise, the supply of $O_2$ to the muscle may be insufficient for the oxidation of pyruvic acid through the citric acid cycle. However, pyruvate is converted to lactate by certain mechanisms and this prevents the blockade of glycolysis. At the end of exercise, the lactate that has diffused into the circulation gets converted to pyruvate when sufficient $O_2$ becomes available, so that it can be oxidized to $CO_2$ and $H_2O$ in the liver and cardiac muscle, or be converted to glycogen in the liver. Thus, during heavy exercise, the body goes into $O_2$ debt, which is paid back during rest. The consumption of $O_2$ does not come back to the pre-exercise level until all the excess lactate has been metabolized.

## SMOOTH MUSCLE

Smooth muscle cells are smaller than skeletal muscle cells and are characterized by the absence of cross-striations. Smooth muscle is of two types—multi-unit smooth muscle and visceral smooth muscle (Fig. 52.5).

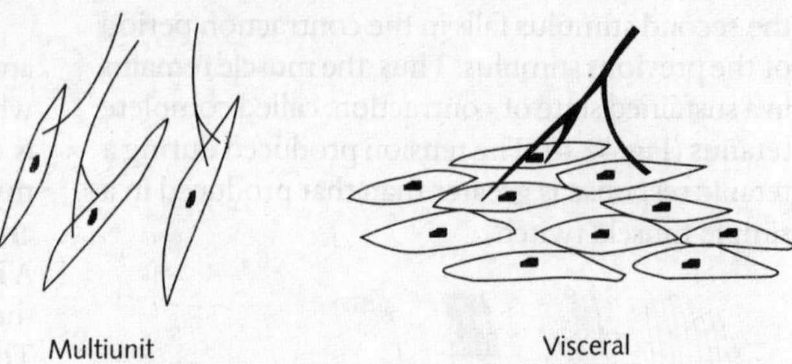


**Fig. 52.5:** Multi-unit and visceral types of smooth muscle

### Multi-unit Smooth Muscle

In this type, the smooth muscle is composed of discrete muscle cells, each innervated by individual neurons (e.g., ciliary muscle and the muscle of the iris). Such fibres are capable of contracting independently and can produce discrete and finely graded contractions. They contract mainly in response to neural stimuli.

### Visceral Smooth Muscle

In this type, the muscle cells are arranged in sheets and bundles. They are in close contact with each other and there are gap junctions between them. Therefore, these cells are excited simultaneously and contract together. Most of the viscera contains this type of smooth muscle, which contracts spontaneously in the absence of extrinsic innervation.

## Electrophysiology

The resting membrane potential (RMP) of smooth muscle is not steady but fluctuates between –30 mV and –60 mV. It shifts towards –30 mV with activity. The low value of the RMP is due to the relatively low intracellular $K^+$ concentration. Superimposed on this RMP are action potentials with prolonged plateaus, lasting for several milliseconds. These account for prolonged periods of contraction of the smooth muscle. Slow wave and spike potentials are seen in the smooth muscles of the gut.

## Factors affecting smooth muscle activity

Stretching of the visceral smooth muscle leads to the development of spike potentials and contraction, even in the absence of extrinsic innervation.

Most of the visceral smooth muscles have dual autonomic innervation, that is, sympathetic and parasympathetic fibres which have antagonistic actions. However, parasympathetic (cholinergic) fibres may be excitatory to the smooth muscle fibres of the intestine and urinary bladder, and inhibitory to the sphincters of the GI tract and urinary bladder. Similarly, sympathetic (noradrenergic) fibres may cause contraction of the smooth muscle fibres of the sphincters of the GI tract and urinary bladder, but relaxation of the bronchial smooth muscles. These differences depend on the type of specific receptors present on the surface of the muscle cells.

Smooth muscle activity is also affected by the state of the local tissue. A lack of $O_2$, excess of $CO_2$ and low pH cause relaxation of the smooth muscle in the arterioles. The hormones, epinephrine, norepinephrine, vasopressin, oxytocin, angiotensin II, serotonin and histamine, influence smooth muscle contraction. Excitation or inhibition occurs according to the type of receptors present on the cells.

CHAPTER 53

# The Nerve

The nervous system is made of nervous tissue, which consists of the neurons and neuroglial cells. A neuron is the basic unit of nervous tissue and is excitable. It is specialized to perform the functions of reception, integration and transmission of information in the body.

There are 10 to 15 times more neuroglial cells than neurons. They are not directly involved in the transfer of information, but they form a supporting structure and do not play an important role in the overall functioning of the nervous system. They are of three types: microglial cells, astrocytes and oligodendrocytes (Fig. 53.1).

*Microglial cells*: These are the scavenger cells of the nervous tissue. They are activated by injury or the inflammatory process. They migrate to the area of injury to become phagocytic macrophages and clean the cellular debris.

*Astrocytes:* These are found throughout the central nervous system (CNS). They are small cells with extensive branching processes. Astrocytes appear to produce substances which are trophic to neurons. They can also take up $K^+$ and neurotransmitters, such as glutamate and gamma aminobutyric acid (GABA), released by neural activity into the interstitial fluid. The processes of astrocytes surround the cerebral capillaries closely and form a blood–brain barrier.

*Oligodendrocytes:* These are responsible for the production and maintenance of the myelin sheath around the axons in the CNS.

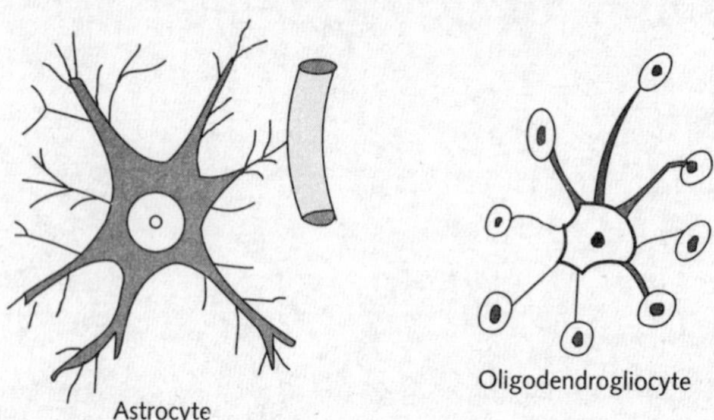


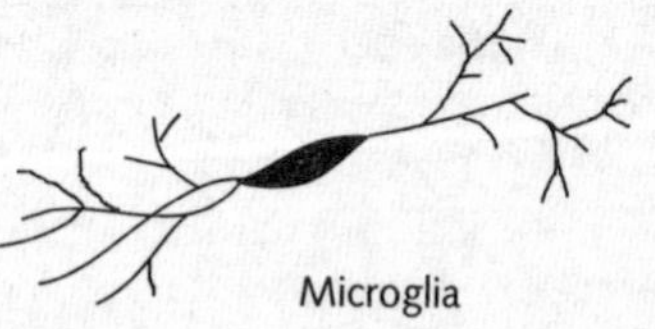


**Fig. 53.1:** Neuroglial cells

## THE NEURON

A neuron consists of a cell body (soma) and its processes (nerve fibres or nerves) (Fig. 53.2).

The cell body contains a nucleus, nucleolus, Nissl granules (RNA material), Golgi apparatus, mitochondria and neurofibrils, but no centrosomes. Hence, neurons once destroyed

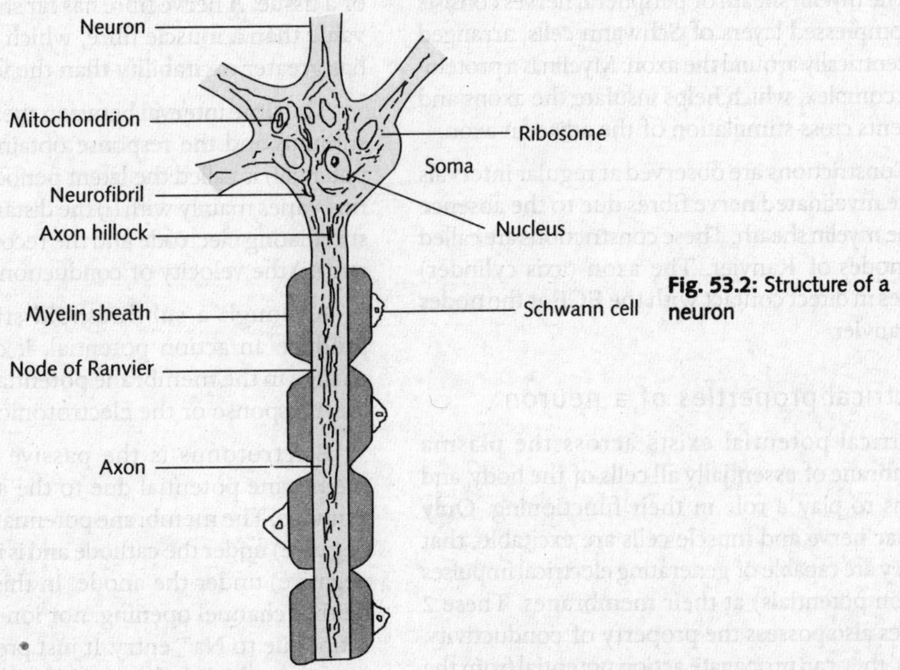

**Fig. 53.2:** Structure of a neuron

cannot be regenerated and are replaced by neuroglia. The neuron cell bodies synthesize neuro-transmitters which are transported along the axon to the nerve terminals. The cells bodies are located within the grey matter of the CNS. Some masses of nerve cell bodies, called ganglia, are also present outside the CNS, for example, dorsal root ganglia.

The processes of the cell body are of two types—dendrites and axons. There are many dendrites. A dendron (singular for dendrites) is short and branches extensively. It is afferent in nature, that is, it brings impulses to the cell body.

An axon is a single, long process and is efferent in nature, that is, it carries impulses away from the cell body. It originates from the thickened area of the cell body, called the axon hillock. The first unmyelinated portion of the axon is called the initial segment. The axon terminates by dividing into a number of branches, the ends of which are enlarged (terminal knobs), making contact with the muscle (neuromuscular junction) or another neuron (synapse).

The axon may either constitute a part of the long tract of the CNS, forming the white matter, or leave the brain or spinal cord as a peripheral nerve fibre. On leaving the grey matter, the axon may acquire a thick myelin sheath, to become a myelinated fibre; if not, it is an unmyelinated fibre (Fig. 53.3).

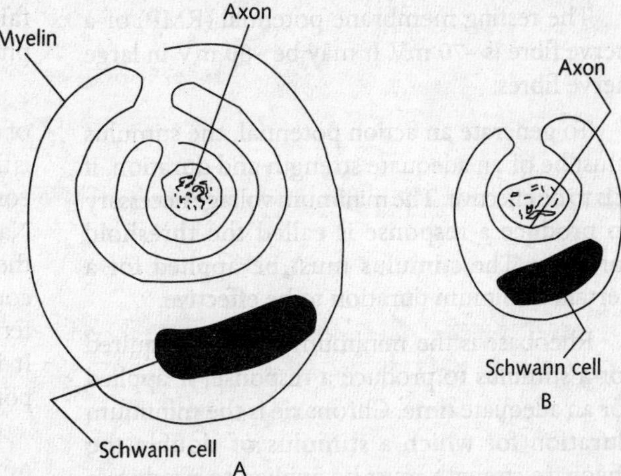

**Fig. 53.3:** T.S. of a nerve fibre: A. myelinated, B. unmyelinated

The myelin sheath of peripheral nerves consists of compressed layers of Schwann cells, arranged concentrically around the axon. Myelin is a protein-lipid complex, which helps insulate the axons and prevents cross-stimulation of the adjacent axon.

Constrictions are observed at regular intervals in the myelinated nerve fibres due to the absence of the myelin sheath. These constrictions are called the nodes of Ranvier. The axon (axis cylinder) comes in direct contact with the ECF at the nodes of Ranvier.

## Electrical properties of a neuron

Electrical potential exists across the plasma membrane of essentially all cells of the body, and seems to play a role in their functioning. Only cardiac nerve and muscle cells are excitable, that is, they are capable of generating electrical impulses (action potentials) at their membranes. These 2 tissues also possess the property of conductivity. Thus, they can propagate action potential from the point of generation to the rest of the membrane.

**Excitability**

Excitability is the ability to respond to a stimulus, which is a change in the environment. An excitable tissue may be stimulated electrically, mechanically or chemically. Electrical stimulation is used for experimental purposes since it is more physiological and its duration and intensity can be controlled.

The resting membrane potential (RMP) of a nerve fibre is –70 mV. It may be –80 mV in large nerve fibres.

To generate an action potential, the stimulus must be of an adequate strength and duration, if it is to be effective. The minimum voltage necessary to produce a response is called the threshold intensity. The stimulus must be applied for a certain minimum duration to be effective.

Rheobase is the minimum strength required for a stimulus to produce a response, if applied for an adequate time. Chronaxie is the minimum duration for which a stimulus of double the rheobase strength must be applied to produce a response. Chronaxie is the index of the excitability of a tissue. A nerve fibre has far shorter chronaxie value than a muscle fibre, which indicates that it has greater excitability than the former.

The time interval between the application of a stimulus and the response obtained (here action potential) is called the latent period. The latent period varies mainly with (i) the distance between the stimulating electrode and the recording electrode, and (ii) the velocity of conduction of the nerve.

Although a subthreshold stimulus fails to produce an action potential, it does produce a change in the membrane potential, known as the local response or the electrotonic potential.

Electrotonus is the passive change in the membrane potential due to the application of a stimulus. The membrane potential is lowered (less negative) under the cathode and is increased (more negative) under the anode. In this stage, there is neither channel opening, nor ion movement and is not due to $Na^+$ entry. It just precedes the local response which is due to $Na^+$ entry.

The local response is a change in membrane potential with the active participation of the membrane. It occurs due to the entry of $Na^+$ in the nerve fibre after the channels have opened. It follows the electrotonic change and takes the membrane potential towards the firing level.

The threshold stimuli must rise to their peak intensity rapidly. Stimuli of slowly rising strength fail to produce an action potential due to a phenomenon called accommodation.

Action potential is the most important property of nerve fibres. The action potential in a nerve fibre is the mechanism of transfer of a message for neural communication. It develops due to an explosive $Na^+$ entry and once produced, it is conducted along the fibre without any change in size. When it is conducted towards the cell body, the conduction is termed antidromic, and when away, orthodromic. It is an 'all or none' phenomenon and action potentials are not summated.

An action potential, if produced, is produced fully and never partially. The size of the action potential formed in a particular fibre is always the same in amplitude and duration, whatever the strength of the stimulus above the threshold intensity, provided other conditions remain constant. This property of nerve fibre is known as the 'all or none' law.

During an action potential, the excitability of a neuron is reduced. The application of another stimulus, whatever its strength, during the phase of depolarization or early repolarization fails to produce any response. This is known as the absolute refractory period (ARP). The later part of the repolarizing phase and the phase of hyperpolarization are known as the relative refractory period (RRP), since the threshold of stimulation is elevated and a relatively stronger stimulus is required to evoke another action potential. Most of the $Na^+$ channels opened during the action potential remain inactivated during the ARP and many of them return to normalcy during the RRP.

**Conductivity**

Conductivity is the ability to conduct the action potential. Action potentials formed in the nerve fibres are conducted at various speeds, depending on the type of nerve fibre. The velocity of conduction is higher in myelinated fibres. It also depends on the diameter of the fibre. The thicker the fibre, the higher the velocity of conduction. A conducted action potential is called a nerve impulse. An action potential is conducted by the active participation of the membrane.

## Propagation of nerve impulse

### In Unmyelinated Nerve Fibre

A cell membrane is polarized at rest. If a threshold stimulus is applied in the middle of the nerve fibre, a narrow segment develops an action potential. Now this depolarized segment (A) acts as a current sink for the adjacent segments (B and C) on either side of segment A. The current is drawn off to such an extent that the membrane potential in segments B and C decreases to the firing level, and an action potential is fired in the two segments. By this time, segment A undergoes repolarization. Next, segments B and C act as a current sink for segments D and E, respectively, producing electronic depolarization and an action potential. In this way, an impulse originating at A spreads on either side, until it reaches the ends of the muscle fibre. An impulse travels only in the forward direction (Fig. 53.4).

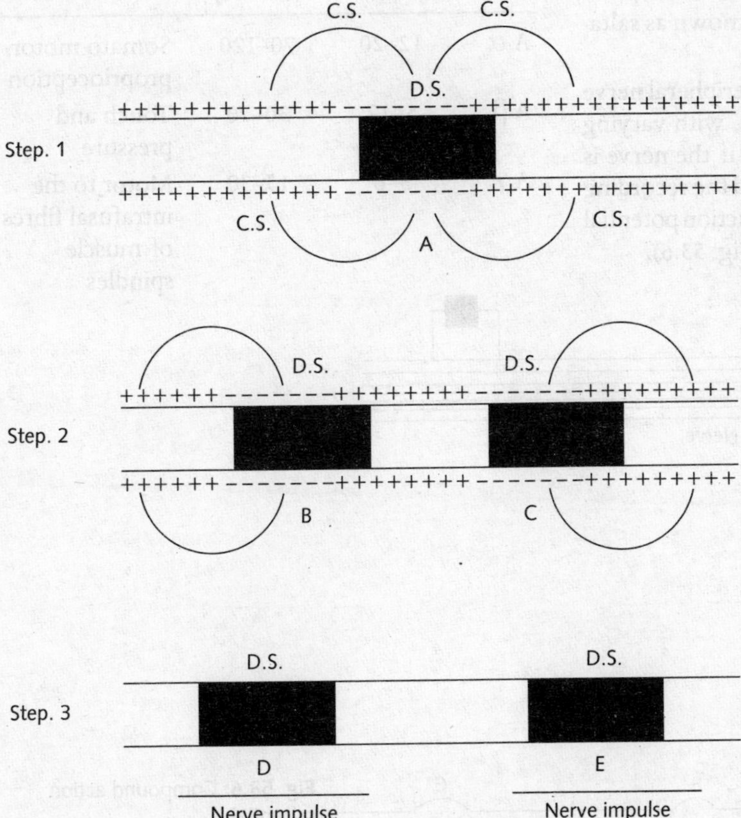


**Fig. 53.4:** Mode of conduction of a nerve impulse in an unmyelinated nerve fibre: DS—depolarized segment, CS—current sink

**In Myelinated Nerve Fibre**

The impulse is propagated basically in the same manner as in unmyelinated nerve fibres, except that action potentials develop only at the nodes of Ranvier. One depolarized node of Ranvier causes an action potential in the next node, and so on. Since an impulse jumps from node to node, its propagation is much faster than in an unmyelinated nerve fibre. When a nerve impulse is conducted in this manner, it is known as saltatory conduction (Fig. 53.5).

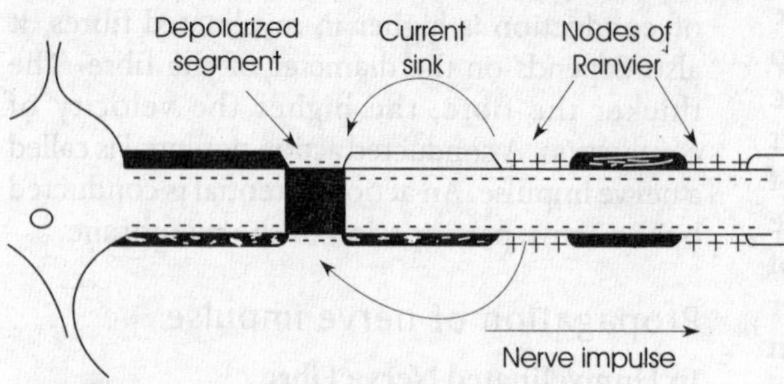


**Fig. 53.5:** Mode of conduction of a nerve impulse in a myelinated nerve fibre

*Action potential in a mixed nerve:* A peripheral nerve contains a large number of axons, with varying thresholds of stimulation. Hence, if the nerve is stimulated by a strong stimulus and the recording electrode is placed at a distance, an action potential with multiple peaks is observed (Fig. 53.6).

There are three main peaks, called A, B and C. Peak A contains four components, α, β, γ and δ. The record is called the compound action potential. It is produced by the summation of the individual action potentials of axons with varying conduction velocities.

## CLASSIFICATION OF NERVE FIBRES

According to the velocity of conduction, mammalian nerve fibres have been classified into three groups, A, B and C. Type A fibres are thickly myelinated, Type B thinly myelinated, and Type C unmyelinated. Different types of nerve fibres, their diameters, conduction velocities and functions are listed in Table 53.1.

**Table 53.1:** Classification of Nerve Fibres

| Group | Diameter (μm) | Conduction velocity (m/sec) | Function |
|---|---|---|---|
| A α | 12–20 | 70–120 | Somato motor, proprioception |
| A β | 5–12 | 30–70 | Touch and pressure |
| A γ | 3–6 | 15–30 | Motor to the intrafusal fibres of muscle spindles |

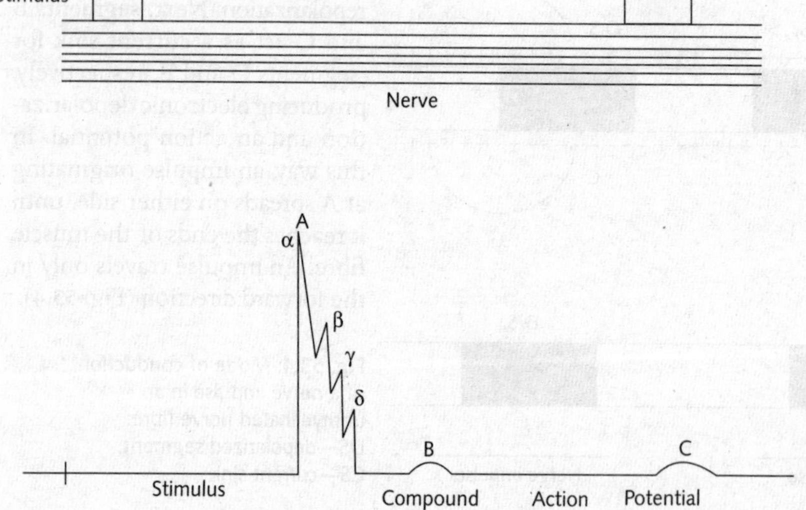


**Fig. 53.6:** Compound action potential

| | | | |
|---|---|---|---|
| A δ | 2–5 | 12–30 | Pain, touch, temperature |
| B | 1–3 | 3–15 | Preganglionic autonomic |
| C | < 1 | < 3 | Pain, temperature, post-ganglionic sympathetic |

Type A and B fibres are more susceptible to the effects of hypoxia and pressure, while type C fibres are more susceptible to the effects of local anaesthetics. These factors can block the conduction of nerve impulses.

The sensory fibres are classified as shown in Table 53.2.

**Table 53.2:** Classification of Sensory Fibres

| Group | Receptors | Fibre type |
|---|---|---|
| Ia | Annulo-spiral endings in muscle spindles | A α |
| Ib | Golgi tendon organ | A α |
| II | Flower spray endings in muscle spindles, touch, pressure | Aβ |
| III | Touch, pain, temperature | A δ |
| IV | Pain | C |

## NERVE INJURY

The effects of injury to a peripheral nerve depend on the degree and type of damage. The injury may vary from mild pressure for a limited period to crush injury, leaving the endoneurial tubes intact, or even complete severing of nerve, involving endoneurial tubes.

Mild pressure or a pull results in only a transient loss of function. If the nerve has been crushed, degenerative changes occur, not only in the whole axon distal to the site of injury, but also in the proximal segment and the cell body of the neuron involved (Fig. 53.7).

Degenerative changes in the cell body are characterized by the disintegration of Nissl granules into dust (chromatolysis) and their disappearance, within 48 hours. The cell becomes swollen and the neurofibrils also disappear. The recovery begins within 40 days and is completed by 80 days. The cell appears normal and ready for regrowth of the proximal stump. If the injury occurs very close to the cell body, the neuron may degenerate and atrophy.

In degenerative changes in the proximal segment, the part of the axon between the cell body and the site of injury degenerates up to the first node of Ranvier next to the site of injury. This is called retrograde degeneration. The changes are similar to those in the distal segment.

The segment distal to the site of injury degenerates completely and the process is called Wallerian degeneration. The axis cylinder breaks up into a number of fragments within a few days. The myelin sheath is converted to lipid droplets. The macrophages in the endoneurium remove the debris by phagocytosis. The Schwann cells divide by mitosis to form cords of cells, which fill the endoneurial tube and can make up a gap up to 3 mm. The growth of the Schwann cells is from the distal stump towards the central cut end. If the gap is greater, it is filled up with scar tissue.

The stage of degeneration, which lasts for about 30 days, is followed by a stage of regeneration. Complete recovery can take several months to 1 year.

### Regeneration

The proximal segment which survives after degeneration starts growing when the cell recovers. The axon elongates and its branches extend towards the distal endoneurial tube, at a rate of 2 mm/day, guided by the strands of Schwann cells. Eventually, each endoneurial tube contains an axon up to the muscle or sensory receptor, as the case may be. Initially, the regrown fibre is thin and unmyelinated. It later thickens and myelination starts, continuing up to 1 year.

Hence, recovery is better when a nerve is crushed with intact endoneurial tube than when it

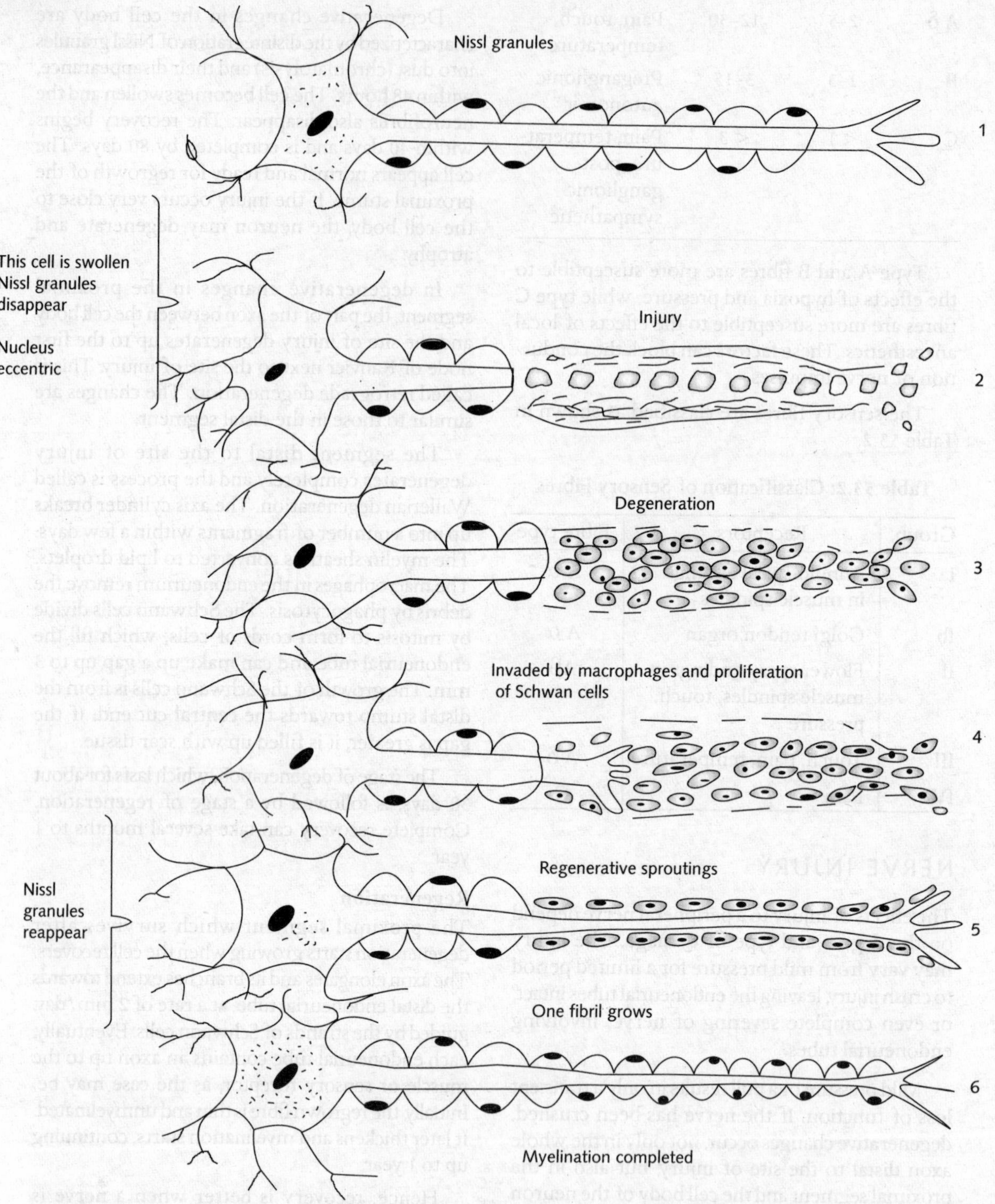


**Fig. 53.7:** Changes following nerve injury (see text)—degeneration and regeneration in a nerve fibre

is severed completely along with endoneurial tube and cut ends are separated.

## NEUROMUSCULAR JUNCTION

The neuromuscular junction is the junction between a motor nerve and a muscle cell, through which the nerve can communicate with the muscle. It is also called the myoneural junction. It differs according to the types of nerves and muscles involved. In the case of a skeletal muscle, the junction is as described below (Fig. 53.8).

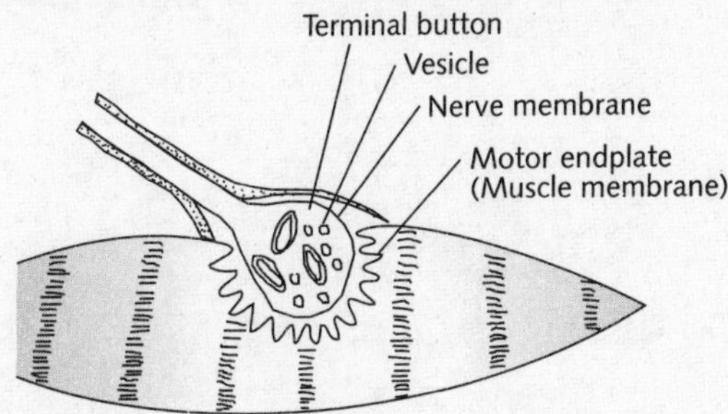


**Fig 53.8:** Myoneural junction

As a branch of motor nerve approaches the muscle fibre, it loses its myelin sheath and divides into a number of branches (axon terminals), each of which supplies one muscle fibre. The end of the terminal is swollen like a bulb (terminal button), which invaginates the sarcolemma and fits into the depression on the muscle cell. At the site of contact, the sarcolemma is modified to form a thickened region, called the motor end plate, which contains receptors for acetylcholine. Here, the sarcolemma is thrown into folds. This increases the area of the end plate, so that it can accommodate a sufficient number of acetylcholine receptors for the transmission of the impulse. It is also rich in the enzyme cholinesterase. The space inside the junction between the nerve membrane and the muscle membrane is called the synaptic cleft.

The terminal buttons have a large number of vesicles (about 300,000), which contain and store the neurotransmitter acetylcholine. They also have mitochondria, which provide energy for the synthesis of acetylcholine.

## MECHANISM OF NEUROMUSCULAR TRANSMISSION

The sequence of events occurring in neuromuscular transmission is as follows. First, the nerve impulse reaches the axon terminal, causing its depolarization. Voltage-gated $Ca^{++}$ channels in its membrane open up, increasing its permeability $Ca^{++}$. Next, $Ca^{++}$ ions from the synaptic cleft enter the terminal button and bind to the vesicles containing acetylcholine, causing their exocytosis.

The acetylcholine released from the vesicles crosses the synaptic cleft to bind with specific receptors on the motor end plate. As a result, the permeability of the motor end plate to $Na^{++}$ increases several thousand times due to the opening of the acetylcholine-gated channels. The influx of $Na^{++}$ into the motor end plate produces a local depolarizing potential, called the end plate potential (EPP). The characteristics of EPP are:

1. It can be graded, that is, does not follow the 'all or none' law,
2. It is not propagated, and
3. It can be summated.

An EPP of 30 mV is sufficient to generate action potentials on either side of the end plate by the current sink mechanism.

Action potentials once generated are conducted away from the motor end plate on either side. The final step is excitation–contraction coupling, resulting in muscular contraction.

### Removal of the Neurotransmitter

The EPP is shortlived. Within a few milliseconds of its release from the terminal button, acetylcholine is removed from the synaptic cleft, mostly due to its destruction by cholinesterase into acetic acid and choline. This returns the motor end plate to its resting polarity and it is now ready to respond to the next stimulus.

*Applied physiology:* Complete skeletal muscle relaxation, which is required during surgical operations, is achieved by giving a drug, curare, which acts by competing with acetylcholine for the receptor sites on the motor end plate.

Myasthenia gravis is a disorder of neuromuscular transmission. It is characterized by weakness and rapid onset of fatigue in the skeletal muscles. Death may occur due to respiratory paralysis. This is due to the formation of antibodies against acetylcholine receptors, which results in the failure of neuromuscular transmission.

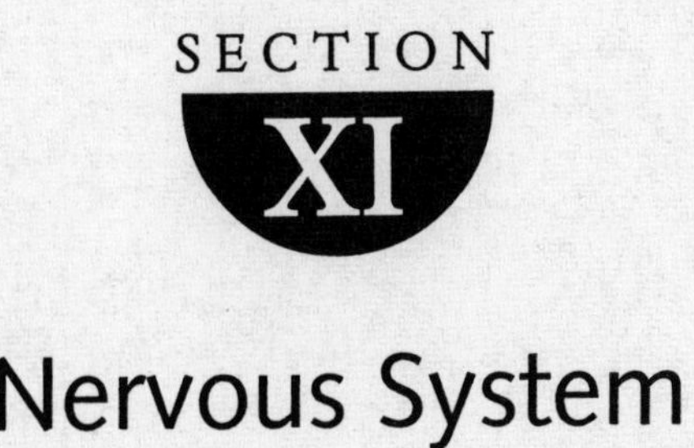


# Nervous System

# Classification and Functions of the Nervous System

The nervous system, together with the endocrine system, controls and coordinates various functions of the body. The body has to make adjustments according to the changes in its internal and external environments. These adjustments are essential for the maintenance of homeostasis, as well as for existence.

Of these two intercellular communication systems (the nervous system being neural and the endocrine system chemical), neural communication is far superior to chemical communication. This is because it is speedy and specific (fast and discrete), and is also involved in the coordination of various specialized functions of the body.

The nervous system can be classified anatomically, according to its different structures, and physiologically, according to its functions.

**Anatomical**

The anatomical structure of the nervous system can be represented as shown in Fig. 54.1.

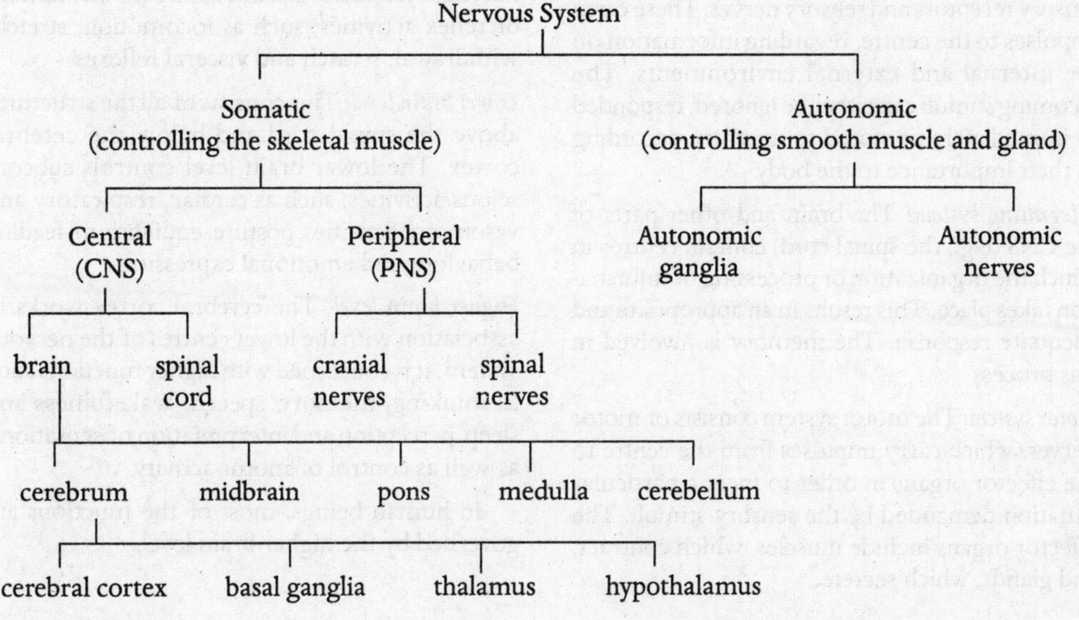

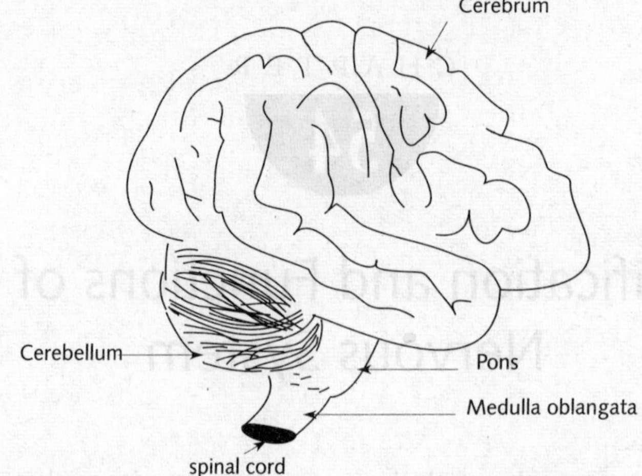


**Fig. 54.1:** Parts of the CNS

**Functional**

The nervous system functions like a computer and has three parts. The first is the afferent, input or sensory system, which receives stimuli. The second is the centre or integrating system, which integrates stimuli and processes information to determine a response. The third part is the efferent, output or motor system, which is responsible for responses to various stimuli.

*Sensory system:* The sensory system consists of sensory receptors and sensory nerves. These carry impulses to the centre, regarding information on the internal and external environments. The incoming stimuli can either be ignored, responded to immediately or stored as memory, according to their importance to the body.

*Integrating system:* The brain and other parts of the CNS (e.g., the spinal cord) contain centres in which the organization or processing of information takes place. This results in an appropriate and adequate response. The memory is involved in this process.

*Motor system:* The motor system consists of motor nerves, which carry impulses from the centre to the effector organs in order to meet a particular situation demanded by the sensory stimuli. The effector organs include muscles, which contract, and glands, which secrete.

## FUNCTIONING OF NERVOUS SYSTEM

The nervous system functions at three levels. The lowest level is the spinal cord level, which is responsible for routine functions. The middle or lower brain level looks after the vital functions, while the highest or higher brain level is responsible for special or higher functions.

*Spinal cord level:* The spinal cord acts as a link (connection) between the peripheral and central nervous systems. It is also a centre for involuntary or reflex activities, such as locomotion, stretch, withdrawal, scratch and visceral reflexes.

*Lower brain level:* This consists of all the structures above the spinal cord and below the cerebral cortex. The lower brain level controls subconscious activities, such as cardiac, respiratory and vasomotor activities, posture, equilibrium, feeding behaviour and emotional expression.

*Higher brain level:* The cerebral cortex works in association with the lower centres of the nervous system. It is concerned with higher functions such as thinking, memory, speech, wakefulness and sleep, perception and interpretation of sensations, as well as control of motor activity.

In human beings, most of the functions are governed by the higher brain level.

CHAPTER

55

# Cerebrospinal Fluid

The cerebrospinal fluid (CSF) is the fluid present in the ventricles (cavities) of the brain, central canal of the spinal cord and subarachnoid space around the brain and spinal cord.

## Formation, Circulation and Absorption

CSF is produced continuously by an active secretory process in the epithelial cells covering the blood vessels of the choroid plexus, in the two lateral ventricles and the third and fourth ventricles. It passes from the two lateral ventricles to the third ventricle through the foramina of Monroe. From the third ventricle, it passes to the fourth ventricle via the aqueduct of Sylvius. It then passes to the central canal of the spinal cord, which is long and narrow, and also into the subarachnoid space around the brain and spinal cord, through two lateral foramina of Luschka and a central foramen of Magendie. The CSF thus circulates internally and externally around the brain and spinal cord (Fig. 55.1).

The CSF is reabsorbed continuously into the subdural sinuses, mainly the superior sagittal sinus, by the arachnoid villi through a passive process (Fig. 55.2). It is transferred to the blood because the hydrostatic pressure in the ventricles is higher than that in the venous sinuses. Diffusion also results in the transfer of the CSF into the blood.

## Functions

The CSF protects the brain from injury as it surrounds the brain from all sides and is also present inside. The brain floats in CSF, so that the dependent part of the brain is not subjected to its own weight. The CSF also acts as a cushioning and protects the delicate tissue of the brain from jolts resulting from blows to the skull.

The CSF provides a pathway for the removal of some materials, such as epinephrine, 5-HT and certain drugs, from the brain. It also provides nutrition to the brain.

Since the brain lies in the rigid cranium, the CSF provides space for the brain when it swells owing to disease. It also provides room for the cerebral blood flow to increase, as some of the CSF leaves through the blood. In other words, a decrease in the volume of CSF allows for an increase in the volume of the brain or cerebral blood volume.

## Character and Composition

The volume of the CSF is about 120 to 150 ml. It is clear and may contain some cells. Its pH is less than that of plasma. The CSF contains proteins (20 to 40 mg%), glucose (45 to 80 mg%) and chloride (720 to 750 mg%). It also contains other constituents present in the plasma.

## Lumbar Puncture

Lumbar puncture is the procedure by which CSF is extracted from the subarachnoid space for study. The subject is made to lie on his/her side and a needle is inserted between the third and fourth lumbar spine (below the termination of the spinal

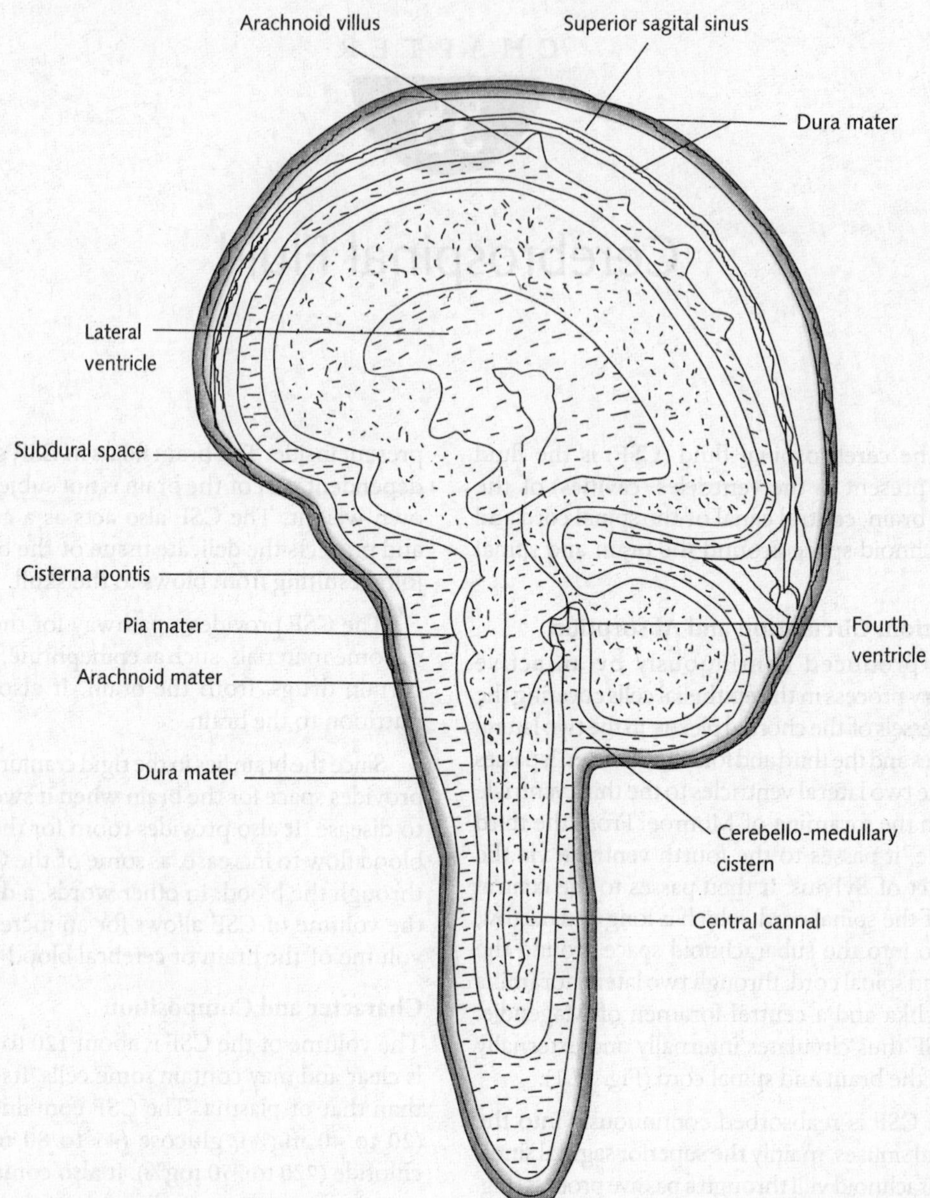


**Fig. 55.1:** The ventricles and meninges of the brain

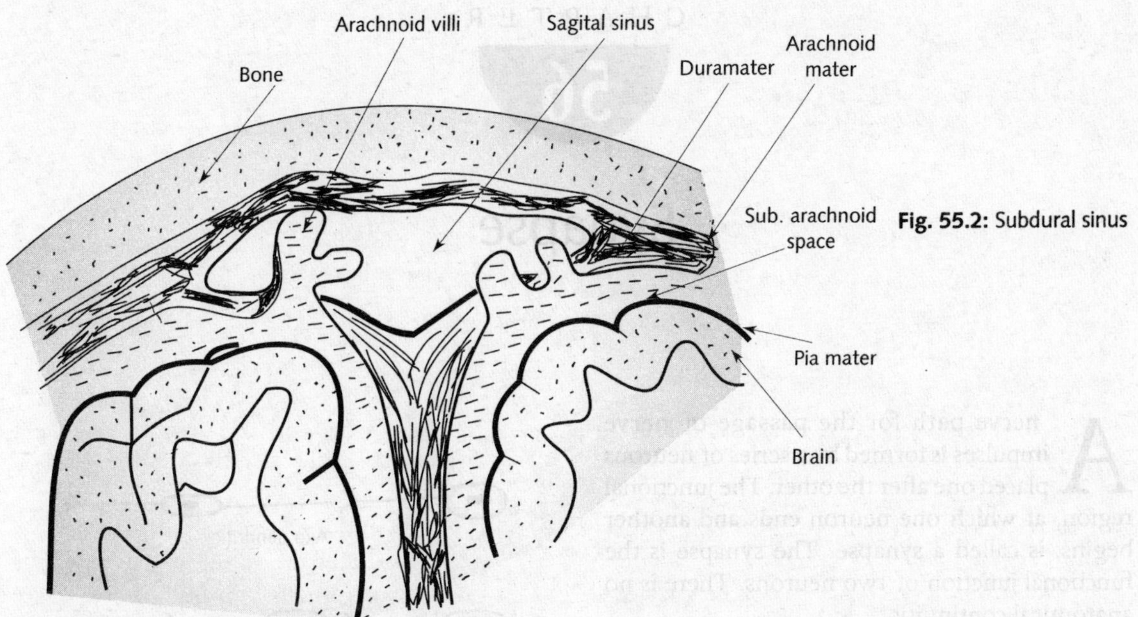


**Fig. 55.2:** Subdural sinus

cord). By connecting the needle to a manometer, the CSF pressure can also be measured.

The normal CSF pressure is about 10 to 12 cm of water, when the subject is in a supine position. It rises when there is an increase in the formation of CSF, as in inflammatory conditions like meningitis. The pressure also goes up very high if there is an obstruction to the flow of CSF and this may result in hydrocephalus (an excess of water in the cranial cavity).

## BLOOD–BRAIN BARRIER

It is not possible for all the constituents of blood to enter the brain ECF because the walls of the capillaries supplying the brain form a barrier, called the blood–brain barrier. This is formed mainly by the tight junctions between the endothelial cells and the foot processes of the astrocytes covering the cerebral capillaries. No substance is completely excluded, but various substances are transferred at different rates. Only $O_2$, $CO_2$, water and some drugs diffuse across the cerebral capillaries freely. All the other constituents of plasma may take 3 to 30 times longer to diffuse (e.g., various ions).

*Blood–CSF barrier*: This is identical in function with the blood–brain barrier, and lies between the capillaries of the choroid plexus and the CSF in the ventricles. The barrier is provided by the tight junctions between the ependymal cells, since the capillaries of the choroid plexus are fenestrated.

*Brain–CSF barrier*: This barrier is weak and is used to inject certain drugs into the brain via the CSF through a lumbar puncture.

*Importance:* The blood–brain barrier helps maintain the constancy of the environment of the neurons in the CNS. Even a minor change in the electrolyte composition around the neurons seriously affects their functioning. The blood–brain barrier also protects the brain from the endogenous and exogenous toxins circulating around it, or neurotransmitters produced outside the brain.

Antibiotics which can diffuse freely through the blood–brain barrier are given to treat cerebral infections.

CHAPTER

# Synapse

A nerve path for the passage of nerve impulses is formed by a series of neurons placed one after the other. The junctional region, at which one neuron ends and another begins, is called a synapse. The synapse is the functional junction of two neurons. There is no anatomical continuity.

## TYPES OF SYNAPSES

A neuron carrying impulses towards a synapse is called a presynaptic neuron, and one carrying impulses away is called a postsynaptic neuron. The axon of the presynaptic neuron loses its myelin sheath and breaks into a number of fine terminals, which have a close relationship with the dendrites or the cell body of the postsynaptic neuron. Accordingly, synapses are of three types: (i) axondendritic (about 80 per cent), (ii) axosomatic (about 20 per cent), and (iii) axoaxonic (rare) (Fig. 56.1).

The morphological features and functional properties of all synapses are the same.

The mechanism of neuronal contact at the synapse is variable. There are different types of synaptic terminals. One is the button type. In the majority of synapses, the presynaptic axon terminal swells to form a knob, before making contact with a postsynaptic neuron. Synaptic terminals can also be of the intertwining or wavy type, basket or net type, and direct type.

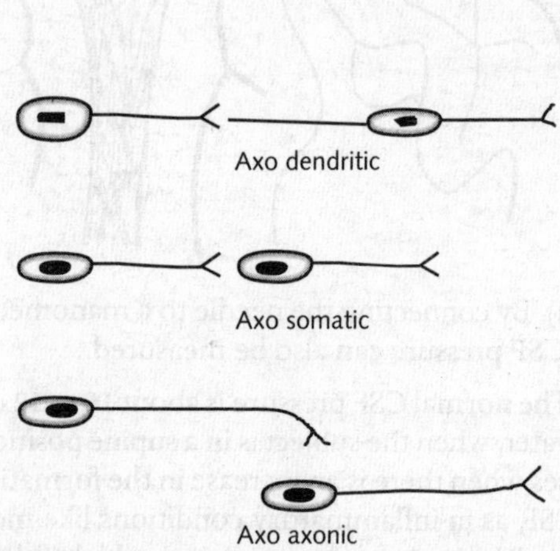


**Fig. 56.1:** Types of synapses

The wavy and basket types are found in the cerebellum and autonomic ganglia, while the direct type is found in the cerebral cortex.

### Histology of Synaptic Knob

Electron microscopy has shown that there is no anatomical or protoplasmic continuity between two neurons, but there is a gap or a narrow extracellular space between the presynaptic and postsynaptic membranes. This gap, called the synaptic cleft, is about 200 to 300 Å (μm) in width. It prevents the direct transmission of action potential across it.

The synaptic knob contains mitochondria, which provide energy (ATP) for the synthesis of neurotransmitters. Multiple vesicles are clustered near the presynaptic, Membrane storing of the neurotransmitter (i.e., the chemical synthesized in the nerve terminal, which acts as a synaptic transmitter). There are three types of vesicles. One type is spherical and it stores packets of acetylcholine. The second type has a dense core and stores adrenergic transmitters, while the third is flat and stores inhibitory neurotransmitters (Fig. 56.2).

The amount of neurotransmitter is enough for the transmission of a few impulses.

## FUNCTIONS OF SYNAPSE

The synapse transmits or conducts nerve impulses.

It acts as a safety valve and modulates neuronal activity. For example, a weak impulse may be blocked or amplified into a strong impulse. An incoming impulse may be changed to many outgoing impulses by the synapse. In addition, an impulse may be dispersed in all directions, or integrated with those from other neurons, to form complex patterns.

The basis of the modulator function is the arrangement of the synapses. Two phenomena are observed in this context—convergence and divergence. In the former, multiple neurons, with their axons, synapse with a single postsynaptic neuron, which, therefore, acts as a neural integrator and helps in the processing of information. The number of synaptic knobs on a single cell body is variable and may be as high as 6000.

In divergence, a single neuron, with the branches

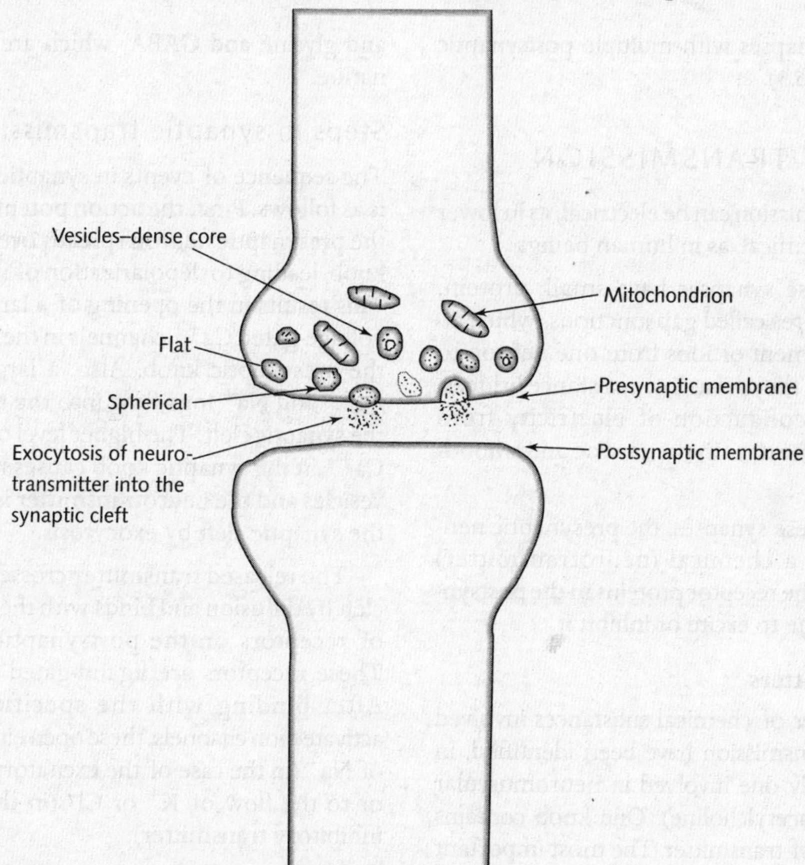


Fig. 56.2: Synapse (Histology of synaptic knob)

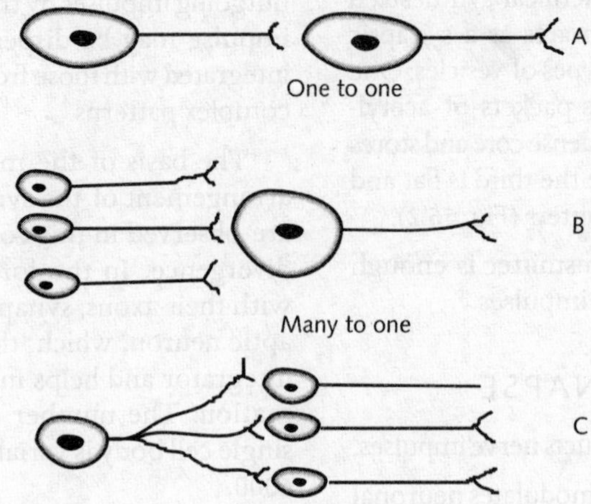


**Fig. 56.3:** Arrangement of neurons at synapse, showing convergence (B) and divergence (C)

of its axon, synapses with multiple postsynaptic neurons (Fig. 56.3).

## SYNAPTIC TRANSMISSION

Synaptic transmission can be electrical, as in lower animals, or chemical, as in human beings.

*Electrical:* These synapses have small, protein, tubular structures called gap junctions, which allow free movement of ions from one neuron to the next. Thus, they act as low-resistance bridges, allowing the conduction of electricity from one cell to the next, as in the cardiac and smooth muscles.

*Chemical:* In these synapses, the presynaptic neuron produces a chemical (neurotransmitter) which acts on the receptor proteins in the postsynaptic membrane to excite or inhibit it.

### Neurotransmitters

A large number of chemical substances involved in synaptic transmission have been identified, in contrast to only one involved in neuromuscular transmission (acetylcholine). One knob contains only one type of transmitter. The most important chemical neurotransmitters include acetylcholine and norepinephrine, which are excitatory in nature, and glycine and GABA, which are inhibitory in nature.

### Steps in synaptic transmission

The sequence of events in synaptic transmission is as follows. First, the action potential arriving in the presynaptic neuron spreads over the synaptic knob, leading to depolarization of its membrane. This results in the opening of a large number of voltage-gated $Ca^{++}$ channels in the membrane of the presynaptic knob. Also, a large number of $Ca^{++}$ and $Na^{+}$ ions flow into the terminal from the synaptic cleft. The higher level of intracellular $Ca^{++}$ in the synaptic knob causes rupture of the vesicles and the neurotransmitter is released into the synaptic cleft by exocytosis.

The released transmitter crosses the synaptic cleft by diffusion and binds with the large number of receptors on the postsynaptic membrane. These receptors are ligand-gated ion channels. After binding with the specific chemically activated ion channels, these open either to the flow of $Na^{+}$ (in the case of the excitatory transmitter), or to the flow of $K^{+}$ or $Cl^{-}$ (in the case of the inhibitory transmitter).

Depending on the ion and the direction of the movement of the ions, the membrane potential of the postsynaptic neuron changes towards either depolarization or hyperpolarization. This change in the membrane potential, called the synaptic potential, creates the signal in the postsynaptic neuron. Synaptic potential may be either excitatory or inhibitory.

**Excitatory Postsynaptic Potential (EPSP)**

If the change in potential in the postsynaptic membrane is towards depolarization, it is called EPSP. The RMP of the soma of the postsynaptic neuron is –65 mV. The rapid influx of positively charged $Na^+$ ions into the interior of the neuron neutralizes part of the negativity of the RMP, which becomes –45 mV. Thus, in this case, the EPSP is +20 mV.

The EPSP is localized. It can be graded and does not obey the 'all or none' law (i.e., the stronger the stimulus, the greater the response).

The EPSP can be summated. There are two types of summation, temporal and spatial. In the former, small EPSPs formed in quick succession in the same membrane are added up to become effective. Spatial summation means the addition of multiple EPSPs, produced simultaneously on the same postsynaptic membrane from different synaptic knobs.

Inhibition is described in a later section as a special property of the synapse.

After summation, the EPSP reaches a firing level and an action potential is produced. It begins in the axon hillock, that is, the initial segment of the axon, since it has a large number of voltage-gated $Na^+$ channels. Once the action potential is formed, it travels along the axon and also, backwards over the soma, but not beyond.

**Removal of Neurotransmitter from Synaptic Cleft**

Within 1 to 2 milliseconds, the action of the chemical transmitter is terminated, causing closure to the ion channels. This is a result of the removal of the neurotransmitter from the synaptic cleft. The neurotransmitter is removed in the following ways:

1. By the diffusion of the transmitter into the surrounding fluid.
2. By enzymatic destruction within the cleft, for example, the destruction of acetylcholine by the enzyme cholinesterase, which is present in the cleft, bound to the proteoglycan matrix.
3. By the re-uptake of the transmitter into the presynaptic terminal itself, for example, the re-uptake of norepinephrine into the presynaptic terminal of the sympathetic nervous system.

## PROPERTIES OF SYNAPTIC TRANSMISSION

Synaptic transmission has the property of one-way conduction. The transmission of an impulse at a synapse occurs from a presynaptic neuron to a postsynaptic neuron and only in one direction, as against transmission in the nerve, which is in both directions. One-way conduction takes place because only the presynaptic neuron has vesicles.

Synaptic delay is another feature of synaptic transmission. A certain amount of time elapses during the transmission of an impulse from a presynaptic neuron to a postsynaptic one. This delay occurs because of the time required for the release and action of the chemical transmitter. For one synapse, the delay is about 0.5 milliseconds. Hence, the number of synapses along a particular nerve path can be calculated from the total conduction time.

As the presynaptic neuron is stimulated at a rapid rate, the impulse discharge from the postsynaptic neuron progressively decreases and ultimately stops. This feature is known as fatigue. Fatigue is a protective mechanism against excess neuronal activity and occurs because of exhaustion of the neurotransmitter.

Inhibition is a unique property of the synapse. If, due to synaptic transmission, the potential of the postsynaptic membrane is carried towards hyperpolarization, it is called the inhibitory postsynaptic potential (IPSP). The RMP of the soma of the postsynaptic neuron is –65 mV. An increase in the efflux of $K^+$ and influx of $Cl^-$ leads

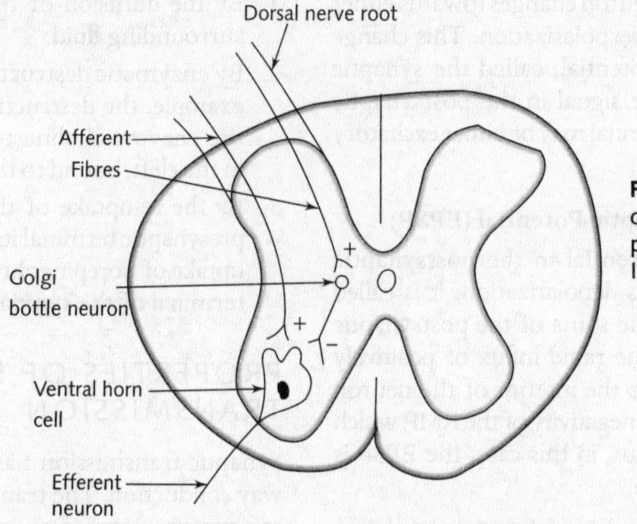


**Fig. 56.4:** Arrangement of neurons involved in production of EPSP or IPSP

to hyperpolarization of the membrane, and the membrane potential becomes –70 mV. Thus, in this case, the IPSP is –05 mV.

The IPSP, like the EPSP, is a local response that can be summated. IPSPs are caused by transmitters such as GABA and glycine. Hyperpolarization of the postsynaptic membrane carries the membrane potential away from the firing level and thus, causes inhibition.

The afferent fibres in the root of the dorsal nerve have mostly EPSP-producing terminals. The interneurons (Golgi-bottle neurons) between the dorsal and ventral horn cells produce IPSP. The dorsal root fibres stimulate the Golgi-bottle neuron by releasing an excitatory transmitter. The Golgi-bottle neuron releases glycine, which produces an IPSP in the ventral horn cells. Due to the Golgi-bottle neuron, one group of neurons is stimulated while another is inhibited by the same afferent stimulus. This explains reciprocal inhibition (Fig. 56.4).

In reciprocal inhibition, an afferent stimulus activates a group of muscles and simultaneously inhibits the antagonistic muscles, resulting in a smooth and coordinated movement. An example is the movement of a joint due to stimulation of the flexor and simultaneous inhibition of the extensor muscle.

Synaptic transmission is particularly susceptible to the effects of excess $H^+$ and a lack of $O_2$ (hypoxia). The latter decrease synaptic transmission.

CHAPTER

57

# Sensory System

## RECEPTOR ORGANS

The sensory system carries information from the periphery to the CNS. This information is received by receptor organs, which form the first structure in the sensory pathway. Receptor organs are the specialized endings of the afferent or the sensory nerves.

Receptor organs receive information about the external and internal environments through different kinds of stimuli, such as mechanical, chemical, thermal and electromagnetic. They act as transducers, converting these stimuli into an electrical action potential, which is carried by special sensory pathways to different regions of the cerebral cortex. The cerebral cortex converts this electrical form of energy into the original modality (principal type) of sensation.

According to the site of stimulus, receptor organs can be classified into the following types:

1. Telereceptors: These are receptors for stimuli whose source is situated away from the body, for example, receptors for light and sound.
2. Exteroceptors: These receive stimuli which are outside the body but in contact with the skin. Some examples are receptors for touch, temperature and pressure.
3. Enteroceptors: These are receptors for stimuli situated within the body, for example, visceral sensations.
4. Proprioceptors: These receive stimuli arising in the deeper structures, for example, the joints, muscles and tendons.

According to the type of stimulus, receptors can be classified into the following:

1. Mechanoreceptors: These are for mechanical stimuli, for example, touch, pressure and vibration.
2. Chemoreceptors: These receive chemical stimuli, for example, taste and smell.
3. Thermoreceptors: These receive thermal stimuli, for example, cold and warmth.
4. Osmoreceptors: These are for changes in the osmolality of the ECF.
5. Nociceptors: These receptors receive the stimulus of pain.
6. Electromagnetic receptors: These receive electromagnetic stimuli.

### Morphology and electrophysiology of receptor organs

**Morphology**

The afferent nerve loses it myelin sheath and gets converted into a specific receptor organ. Receptor organs are of many different morphological types. For example, there are free nerve endings, which are the peripheral endings of a sensory nerve. They do not have any obvious special structure in them. Receptors for pain are free nerve endings.

Then there are expanded nerve endings, which are nerve endings thickened to form specialized structures, such as Merckel's disc for touch and Ruffini end bulbs for warmth.

Another morphological type comprises the encapsulated endings. These are nerve endings covered with multilamellar capsules, for example, Krause's end bulb for cold, Pacinian corpuscles for pressure and Meissner's corpuscles for touch.

Specialized cells are another type. Here, the nerve ending is attached to a cell which acts as a receptor. Rods and cones (for light) and hair cells in the cochlea (for sound) are some examples.

In the sense organs, the receptor cells, along with other cells, form a group, for example, taste buds for gustation (Fig. 57.1).

**Electrophysiology**

The electrophysiology of the receptor organ is studied in Pacinian corpuscles since they are large and can be easily isolated, microdissected and

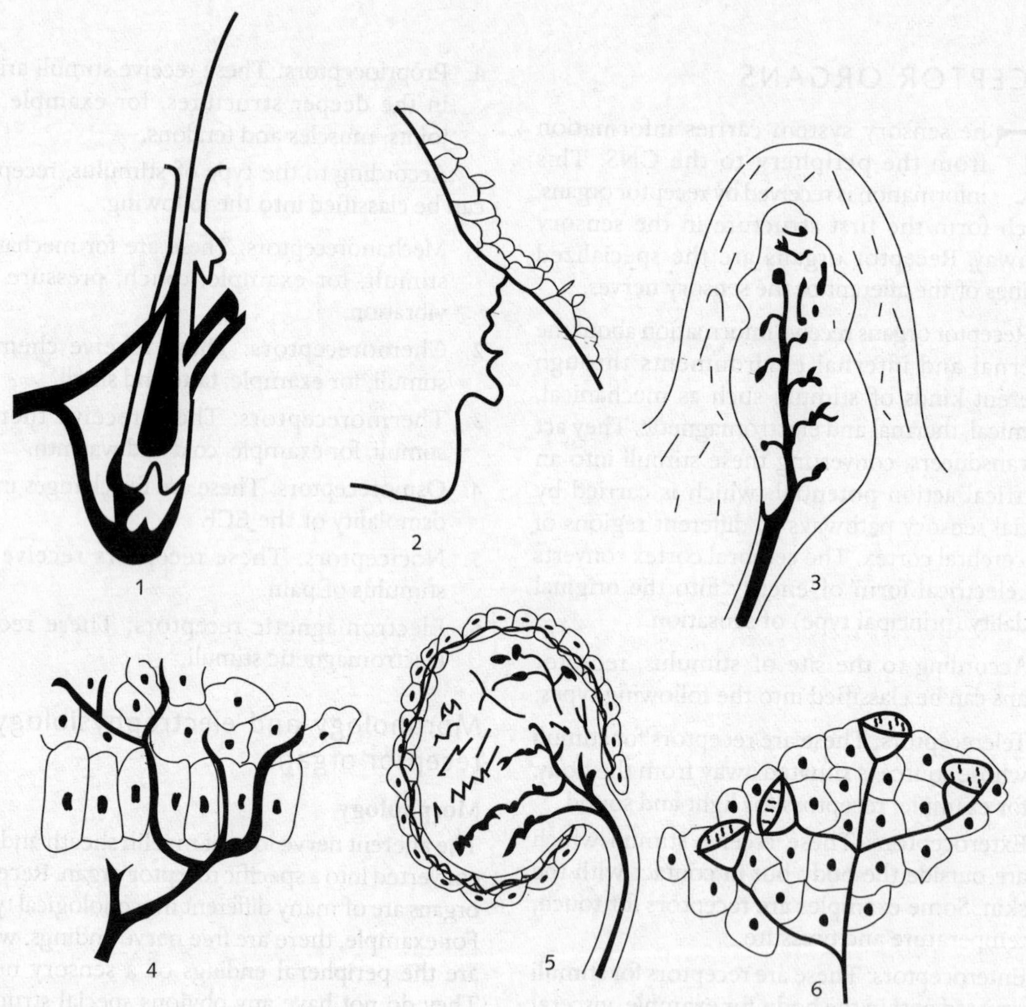


**Fig. 57.1:** Morphology of receptor organs: 1. Hair bulb ending, 2. Ruffini ending, 3. Meissner's corpuscle, 4. Free nerve ending, 5. Krause's end bulb, 6. Merckel's disc

studied with microelectrodes. In this receptor, the end of the sensory nerve, including the first node of Ranvier, is enclosed by concentric lamellae made of fibrous tissue. There is fluid between the lamellae (Fig. 57.2a).

Recording electrodes are placed on the sensory nerve and the nerve ending is stimulated by the application of pressure on the corpuscle. The distortion of the nerve ending increases the permeability of its membrane to $Na^+$ (Fig. 57.2b). The $Na^+$ influx changes the membrane potential towards depolarization. The change, produced in the unmyelinated nerve ending, is called the receptor or generator potential. The receptor potential also depolarizes the first node of Ranvier within. The generator potential has the following characteristics:

1. It is localized.
2. It can be graded and does not obey the 'all or none' law.
3. It can be summated.

When the generator potential reaches a threshold value (10 mV), an action potential is produced in the sensory nerve ending. The latter is then propagated down the nerve. The greater the pressure applied, the greater the generator potential produced above the threshold value, and the higher the frequency of the action potential in the sensory nerve.

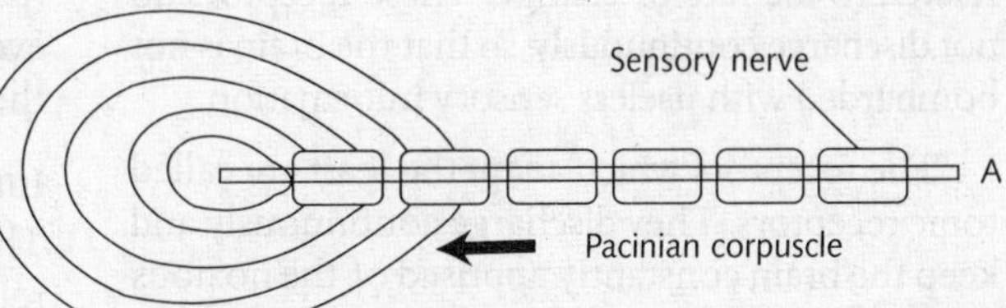


Fig. 57.2(a): Pacinian corpuscle and mechanism of adaptation

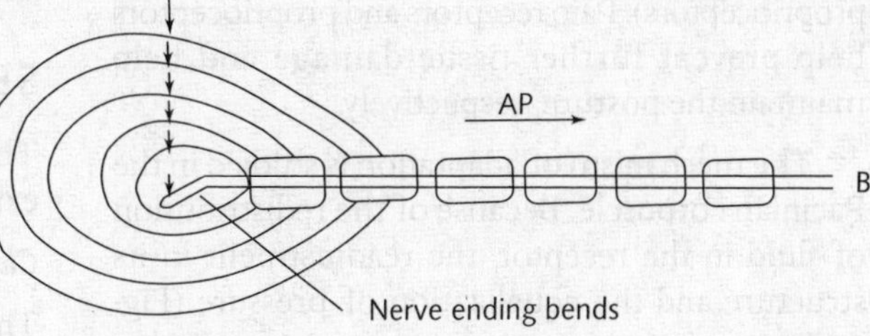


Fig. 57.2(b): Pacinian corpuscle and mechanism of adaptation

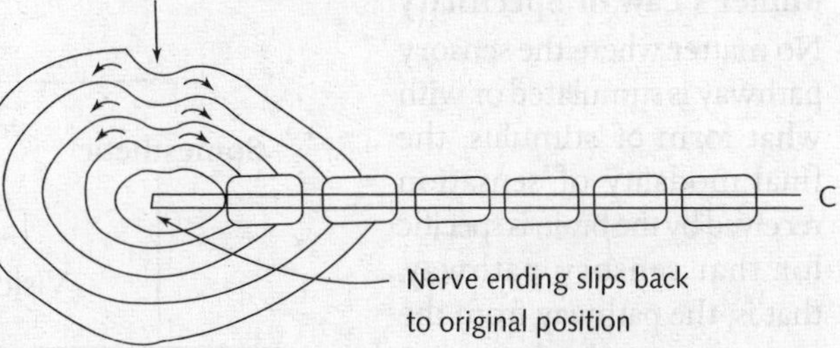


Fig. 57.2(c): Pacinian corpuscle and mechanism of adaptation

## Properties of receptor organ

### Differential Sensitivity

Each receptor organ responds to a specific stimulus. For example, Meissner's corpuscles respond to touch and Pacinian corpuscles to pressure. However, although a receptor organ has the maximum sensitivity to the stimulus for which it is designed, it may respond to other stimuli to a lesser extent. For example, rods and cones respond mainly to light and respond to a lesser extent to pressure on the eyeball.

### Adaptation

This is an important property of receptors. When a stimulus of constant strength is applied continuously, the discharge rate from the receptor decreases progressively and in some cases, may cease completely. If the strength of the stimulus is changed, the receptor starts responding again. This property is displayed by mechanoreceptors. When we wear glasses, we can feel them on our nose, but after some time, we do not notice them. This is due to the adaptation of the receptors, which cease to report the presence of the glasses.

Some receptors, such as those for touch (Meissner's corpuscles) and pressure (Pacinian corpuscles), adapt more rapidly. Thermoreceptors adapt to a moderate degree, while pain receptors and proprioceptors adapt the least. The sensory receptors which adapt are called phase receptors. These respond in phases, that is, when a change is actually taking place. The rate of discharge is directly related to the rate of change. These receptors do not discharge continuously, so that the brain is not bombarded with useless sensory information.

The receptors which adapt the least are called tonic receptors. They discharge continuously and keep the brain constantly apprised of the noxious stimuli arising from tissue damage (e.g., pain receptors), as well as the position of different parts of the body and their relation to each other (e.g., proprioceptors). Pain receptors and proprioceptors help prevent further tissue damage and help maintain the posture, respectively.

The mechanism of adaptation is studied in the Pacinian corpuscle. Because of the redistribution of fluid in the receptor, the readjustment in its structure and the equalization of pressure (Fig. 57.2c).

**Muller's Law of Specificity**

No matter where the sensory pathway is stimulated or with what form of stimulus, the final modality of sensation received by the brain is specific for that sensory pathway, that is, the pathway from the sensory receptor to the sensory cortex (brain). The integrity of the pathway is essential for an accurate interpretation of the type of sensation. For example, if a vibrating tuning fork is hit on a bony projection, it gives a sense of vibration, but to the ear, it gives a sensation of sound. The stimulation of the pain pathway gives a sensation of pain, though the stimulus may be heat, crushing or electricity.

**Law of Projection**

Regardless of the point at which the sensory pathway is stimulated, the conscious recognition of the stimulus is always projected to the location of the receptor organs. For example, pain arising from an amputated stump due to pressure on the nerve terminals is perceived as arising from the nonexistent part of the limb, like the toes or fingers (phantom-limb). In other words, the sensation evoked in the brain is projected to the area where the receptors used to be.

**Intensity Discrimination**

The recognition of the intensity of a stimulus is related to the rate of impulse discharge in the sensory fibre. The magnitude of sensation felt is proportionate to the log of the intensity of the stimulus. This is known as Weber–Fechner's law.

## SENSATIONS

The awareness of a change in the internal or external environment is called a sensation.

*Classification*

The classification of sensations can be represented as shown below.

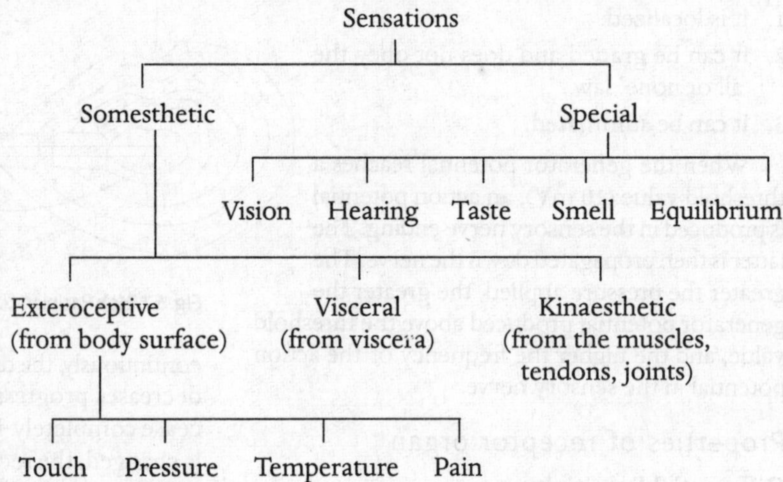


### Somesthetic sensations

As shown in the flow chart above, somesthetic sensations are of three types—exteroceptive, visceral and kinaesthetic.

**Exteroceptive**

The exteroceptive sensations consist of touch, pressure, temperature and pain.

*Touch and pressure*: Many types of receptors are involved in the detection of tactile sensation. An example is Meissner's corpuscles, located in the non-hairy part of the skin and hair end organs (basal nerve fibre with vertical filaments around the base of the hair follicle). These are the most rapidly adapting receptors. Merckel's disc and Ruffini end organs are other examples. These receptors adapt slowly.

Pacinian corpuscles, located in the subcutaneous tissue and around the joints, are also exteroceptive. They adapt rapidly and respond to deep pressure.

The tactile receptors are unevenly distributed in the body. They are crowded in some areas, as in the tips of the fingers, nose and tongue, the lips, nipples, areola of the breast and genital parts. They are sparsely distributed in other places, such as the back and abdomen. Hence, tactile discrimination (the identification of two points simultaneously stimulated, as two separate points) is superior in the areas where receptors are crowded.

Tactile sensation involves tactile localization, tactile discrimination and the identification of the texture and consistency of the object.

*Temperature:* The receptors involved in the sensation of temperature are Krause's end bulbs (for cold), Ruffini nerve endings (for warmth) and free nerve endings (for both).

The number of cold receptors is 3 to 10 times higher than that of heat receptors in all parts of the body. There are large number of thermoreceptors in the lips, and a moderate amount in the fingertips. The skin of the trunk has the lowest number of thermoreceptors.

Thermoreceptors respond to the temperature of the subcutaneous tissue surrounding them, and not to the environmental temperature as such. The cold receptors respond to temperature ranging from 10 to 40°C, and the warmth receptors, 30 to 50°C. The stimulation of these receptors to different degrees helps a person detect fine gradations of temperature. The free nerve endings respond to extremes of temperature. Since extremes produce tissue damage, a sensation of pain rather than temperature is produced.

Thermoreceptors show a moderate degree of adaptation. They are better at registering the rate of change of temperature than steady temperature. This is why cold and heat are felt maximally when the temperature is falling or rising.

*Pain:* Most ailments produce pain, and the knowledge of pain helps in the diagnosis of various diseases.Pain is an unpleasant sensation involving the emotions and is correlated with a protective reflex.

The sensation of pain warns the body of tissue damage, so that remedial action can be taken by the brain. This is done by either the removal of the painful stimulus, or by the withdrawal of the affected area from the stimulus. A lack of the sensation of pain is seen in patients with diabetic neuropathy, who thus end up ignoring small injuries which later develop into large wounds.

Pain may be of the acute, sharp or fast type, or the chronic, dull or slow type. Table 57.1 gives information on both types of pain.

**Table 57.1:** Acute and Chronic Pain

| | *Acute pain* | *Chronic pain* |
|---|---|---|
| 1. Nature | Pricking, piercing, lightening, excruciating | Throbbing, aching, burning |
| 2. Onset | Sudden | Slow |
| 3. Duration | Short | Long |
| 4. Localization | Better | Poor |
| 5. Transmission | By fast-conducting nerve fibres (Aδ) | By slow-conducting nerve fibres (C) |
| 6. Purpose | Protection through immediate withdrawal effect | Protection through resting the part since it keeps the person alert |

The receptors for pain are free nerve endings. These are located throughout the body, barring the brain. They are stimulated by nociceptive stimuli, which can be caused by any kind of energy that is strong enough to damage the tissue (e.g., mechanical, thermal, chemical and electromagnetic).

Tissue damage leads to the release of chemical substances from the tissue. These substances stimulate the free nerve endings to produce pain. Bradykinin, serotonin, $K^+$, acids, AMP, ADP, substance 'P' and prostaglandins are some of the chemical substances released. The pain receptors are tonic receptors and remain active as long as the stimulus is present.

The threshold for pain is the same for all individuals, irrespective of age, sex or environment. However, the reaction to pain differs from individual to individual.

Pain is perceived at the subcortical level (i.e., the thalamus). The cerebral cortex helps interpret the quality and localization of pain.

Visceral pain: Superficial pain is accurately localized, while deep and visceral pain is poorly localized. The latter is also associated with autonomic reactions, such as nausea and sweating.

Localized tissue damage in the viscera does not produce pain but pain results due to diffuse visceral inflammation, distension of the hollow viscera and ischaemia.

Referred pain: Visceral pain does not remain localized to the organ where it is produced. It is, instead, referred to a distant part of the body, a part which is a somatic structure. For example, pain due to myocardial ischaemia is referred to the left shoulder and arm. Pain is usually referred to a structure which has the same embryonic origin as its site of production. Both areas are innervated by a common neural (spinal) segment. For example, testicular pain is felt in the abdomen since both the testes have descended from the abdomen.

The mechanism of referred pain is the convergence of the pain pathways from the visceral and the somatic structures. Therefore, a disorder in the viscus is interpreted as arising from the somatic structure (Fig. 57.3).

Referred pain helps in the diagnosis of several diseases. A physician can determine which organ is diseased as he/she knows about the regions to which pain is usually referred.

Applied physiology: A reduced or increased threshold of pain causes certain abnormal conditions,

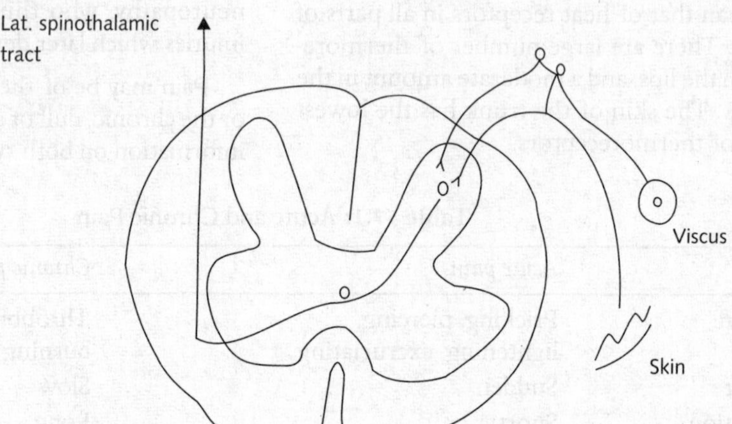


**Fig. 57.3:** Mechanism of referred pain

such as hyperalgesia and analgesia. In hyperalgesia, the pain receptors are abnormally sensitive because of a decreased threshold. Even a normal, light touch can produce pain around the injured part.

In analgesia, the pain receptors are less sensitive than normal due to an increased threshold. A drug which decreases pain, for example aspirin, is called an analgesic.

Anaesthesia is a condition characterized by the total absence of pain.

## Visceral and proprioceptive sensations

Visceral sensations are the sensations of pain and stretching. Visceral pain has been described earlier. The sensation of stretching can be felt in all the hollow viscera. It may be due to gas, liquids or solids. The mechanoreceptors (stretch receptors) are responsible for it.

Proprioceptive sensations are concerned with the physical state of the body, for example, the sense of position, tendon and muscle sensations, deep pressure and the sense of equilibrium. The sense of position includes the sense of static position, as well as conscious recognition of the rate of movement of different parts of the body.

The receptors for the sense of position are located in the joint capsules and the ligaments around the joints. Some examples are the Ruffini end organs, Pacinian corpuscles, muscle spindles and Golgi-tendon organs.

# TRANSMISSION OF SENSATIONS

For the purpose of perception, a sensation needs to be carried to a part of the CNS called the sensorium. Some sensations are sensory or conscious (we can feel them), while others are nonsensory or unconscious, but all sensations are utilized by the CNS for its activity. Sensations are initiated at the receptors, carried by the sensory nerves to the spinal cord, and then by sensory nerve tracts to the higher level of the CNS. The somesthetic sensations are carried to the cerebral cortex via the thalamus.

## Sensory nerves

Although each type of sensation has its own importance, some sensory signals must be carried to the brain rapidly, while others may be carried slowly. For example, information from the muscle and joint receptors is carried very fast because the position of muscles and joints changes practically every second while running. Some critical sensory signals, such as tactile localization and discrimination, are also carried rapidly. Such information is carried by fast-conducting, thick, myelinated 'A' type of nerve fibres. The sensation of dull chronic pain is carried slowly by thin, unmyelinated 'C' type of fibres.

A spinal nerve forms a link between the periphery and the spinal cord. It is attached to the spinal cord by the posterior and anterior nerve roots. The former is also called the dorsal root. All the sensory fibres enter the CNS through the dorsal root or it's cranial equivalent. These fibres are both myelinated and unmyelinated, and are of various types. The cell bodies of the fibres are situated in the dorsal root ganglion (DRG). On entering the cord, the dorsal root divides into two bundles. The medial division contains thicker fibres (group I and II fibres), which carry the sensations of touch and proprioception. The sensation proceeds upward in the posterior column. Collaterals of these fibres enter the dorsal horn to provide a pathway for reflex action.

The lateral division contains thinner fibres (belonging to groups III and IV), which carry the sensations of pain and temperature. These fibres end on the posterior horn cells. On entering the spinal cord, they form Lissauer's tract and give collaterals to spinal grey matter.

The anterior root, also called the ventral root, is made of motor fibres. These are $\alpha$, $\gamma$ and preganglionic autonomic fibres (Fig. 57.4).

The fact that afferent fibres enter the spinal cord through the posterior root and efferent fibres come out through the anterior root is known as Bell–Megendie's law. The area of skin supplied by the afferent fibres of a single dorsal root (spinal cord segment) is called a dermatome.

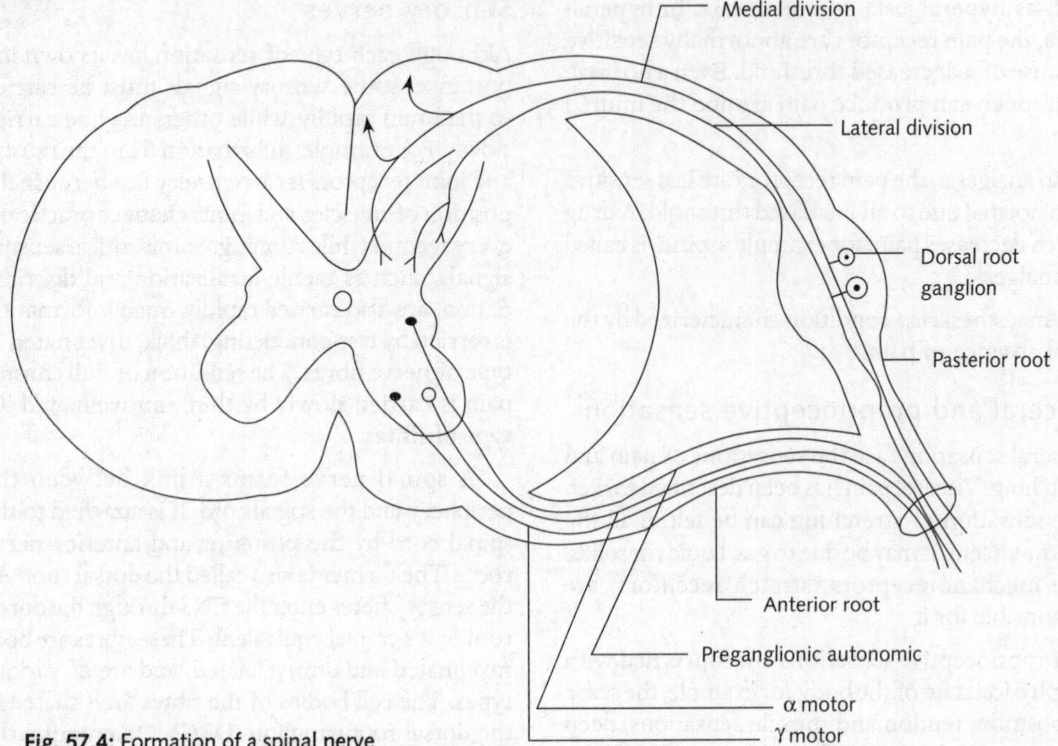


Fig. 57.4: Formation of a spinal nerve

## Spinal cord

The centre of the spinal cord contains grey matter and its periphery contains white matter.

### Grey Matter

Grey matter is made of nerve cells and is arranged in the form of the letter 'H' or the shape of a butterfly. Three projections or horns can be seen in the grey matter: the posterior horn, attached to the posterior root; the anterior horn, attached to the anterior root; and the lateral horn in the thoraco-lumbar region ($T_1$ to $L_3$) and sacral region.

*Posterior or dorsal horn*: The grey matter of the posterior horn has been divided into six laminae on the basis of its cytoarchitecture. Its neurons are sensory in nature and are arranged in the following groups:

1. Substantia gelatinosa of Rolando (SGR): These are located at the tip of the posterior horn. They are formed by laminae II and III.
2. Nucleus proprius: This comprises the largest group.
3. Clarke's column cells: These cells are located anteromedially to the nucleus proprius.
4. Visceral afferent nucleus: This is located at the base of the posterior horn, in the thoraco-lumbar region ($T_1$ to $L_3$).

*Lateral horn*: The lateral horn contains motor nuclei, the axons of which form preganglionic fibres of the autonomic nervous system.

*Anterior horn*: The anterior horn contains α and γ motor nuclei. The former, also called lower motor neurons, are large and form about 60 per cent of the neurons in this horn. Their axons supply the extrafusal (regularly contracting) muscle fibres of the skeletal muscles.

The γ motor neurons are small and comprise about 30 per cent of the neurons in the anterior horn. They supply the intrafusal fibres of the muscle spindle.

In addition, there are plenty of interneurons, which may be excitatory or inhibitory. They

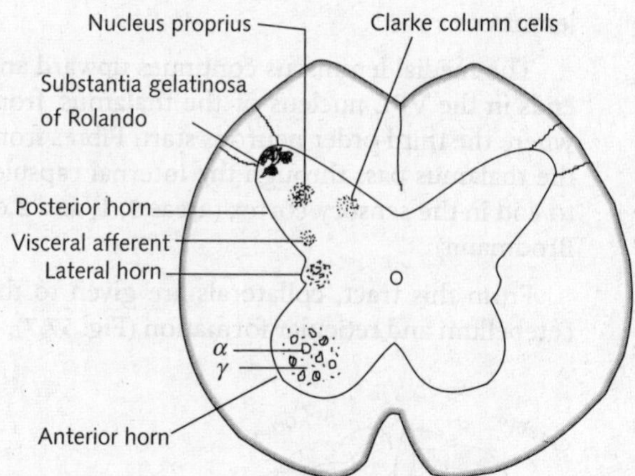


**Fig. 57.5:** Groups of neurons in spinal grey matter

receive inputs from various sources, such as sensory inputs from the periphery and motor inputs from the brain, and modify the activity of mostly the α motor neurons (Fig. 57.5)

## White Matter

The white matter is made of nerve fibres that are arranged in three columns: the posterior column, between the posterior median septum and the posterior root; the lateral column, between the posterior and anterior root; and the anterior column, between the anterior root and anterior median fissure.

The nerve fibres in these columns are arranged in various tracts. A tract is a bundle of fibres which carry impulses in the CNS and have similar functions and destination. A flat tract is called a lemniscus. There are four lemnisci—the spinal, trigeminal, medial and lateral lemnisci. These are the main afferent tracts in the brainstem.

After entering the grey matter of the spinal cord, all the fibres, except those carrying fine touch and sensory proprioception, synapse with one of the groups of neurons in the grey matter.

In the posterior horn, fibres carrying temperature and pain relay in the SGR. Those carrying crude touch relay in the nucleus proprius, and those carrying nonsensory kinaesthetic sensation relay in Clarke's column cells. Fibres carrying visceral pain relay in the visceral afferent nucleus.

In the lateral horn, fibres carrying visceral sensation for visceral reflex relay in lateral horn cells, while in the anterior horn, somatic fibres for stretch reflex relay in anterior horn cells.

The cells of the posterior horn may be broadly classified into two types: (i) local neurons or interneurons and (ii) relay neurons. The former synapse with other neurons within the spinal cord, and are concerned with spinal cord reflexes. Relay neurons, as in the posterior horn, give rise to long fibres which ascend in the sensory tracts of the spinal cord and transmit exteroceptive and proprioceptive information to the brain.

## Sensory Tracts

The major ascending tracts in the spinal cord consist of the dorsal column, anterolateral column and dorsolateral column.

The dorsal column consists of the fasciculus gracilis and cuneatus (tracts of Gall and Burdah), while the anterolateral column consists of the anterior (ventral) and lateral spinothalamic tracts. The dorsolateral column consists of the dorsal and ventral spinocerebellar tracts (Fig. 57.6).

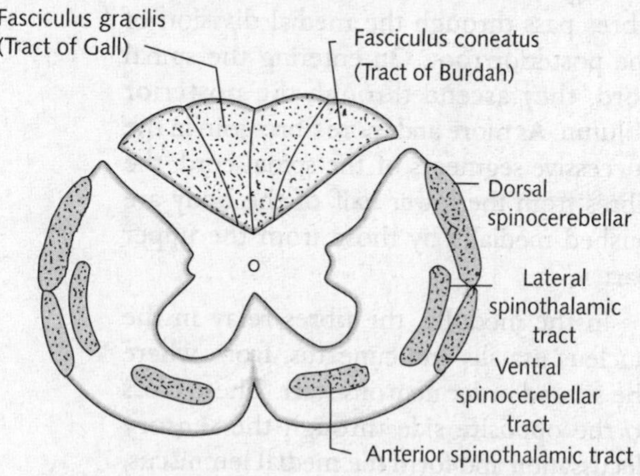


**Fig. 57.6:** Cross-section of spinal cord showing the sensory tracts

## Pathway for touch

The sensation of touch is carried by the anterior spinothalamic tract, as well as the tracts of Gall and Burdah.

### Anterior Spinothalamic Tract

The sensation of crude touch is carried by the C type of nerve fibres, the cell bodies of which are located in the dorsal root ganglion, through the posterior nerve root. The fibres pass through the medial division of the posterior root into the posterior horn of the spinal grey matter. They relay in the nucleus proprius, from where the second-order neurons start. These cross to the opposite side and ascend in the anterior column of the spinal cord, as the anterior spinothalamic tract.

The tract continues in the brainstem as the spinal lemniscus, along with the medial lemniscus, to relay in the ventral posterolateral (VPL) nucleus of the thalamus. From here, the third-order neurons start. From the thalamus, the fibres pass through the internal capsule to the sensory cortex (areas 3, 1 and 2 of Brodmann).

### Tracts of Gall and Burdah

Fine touch, tactile localization and discrimination are carried by A fibres, whose cell bodies are situated in the dorsal root ganglion, through the posterior nerve root. These fibres pass through the medial division of the posterior root. On entering the spinal cord, they ascend through the posterior column. As more and more fibres join in the successive segments of the spinal cord, the fibres from the lower half of the body are pushed medially by those from the upper part.

In the medulla, the fibres relay in the nucleus gracilis and cuneatus, from where the second-order neurons start. These cross to the opposite side through the sensory decussation and form the medial lemniscus. The fibres of the trigeminal lemniscus, carrying the sensation of touch from the face and related structures, join the medial lemniscus.

The medial lemniscus continues upward and ends in the VPL nucleus of the thalamus, from where the third-order neurons start. Fibres from the thalamus pass through the internal capsule, to end in the sensory cortex (areas 3, 1, and 2 of Brodmann).

From this tract, collaterals are given to the cerebellum and reticular formation (Fig. 57.7).

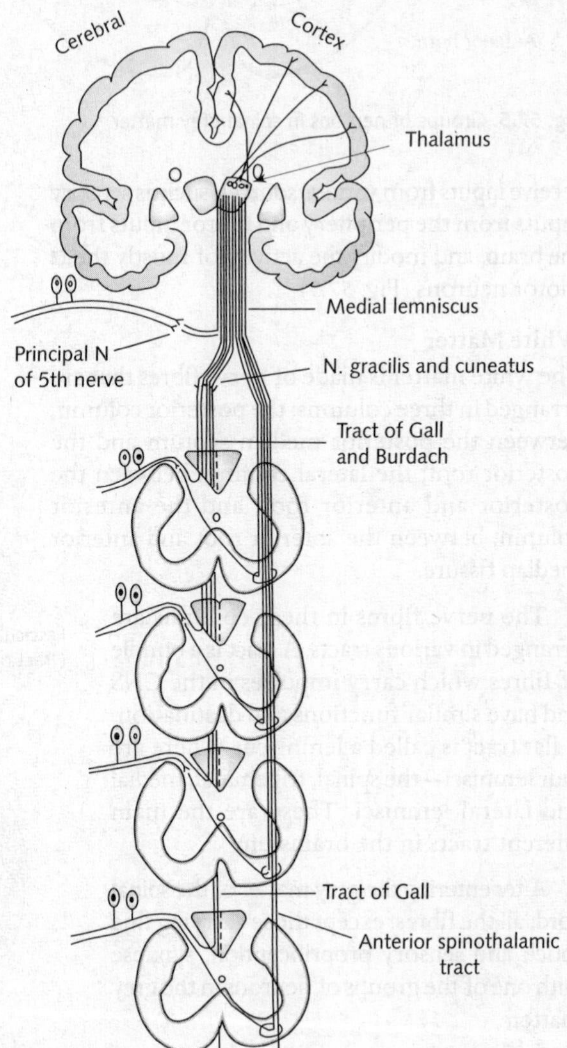


**Fig. 57.7:** Pathway for touch

## Pathway for temperature

The sensations of cold and warmth are carried by the A and C type of nerve fibres through the lateral division of the posterior root. The cell bodies of these fibres are situated in the dorsal root ganglion. On entering the spinal cord, they form Lissauer's tract and relay in the SGR. From here, the second-order neurons start. They cross to the opposite side and ascend in the lateral column of the spinal cord as the lateral spinothalamic tract. Fibres from the lower segments are pushed towards the surface of the spinal cord by fibres from the upper segment. The tract continues in the brainstem and, together with the anterior spinothalamic tract, forms a spinal lemniscus to relay in the VPL nucleus of the thalamus. From the thalamus, the third-order neurons start. These pass through the internal capsule to relay in the sensory cortex (Fig. 57.8).

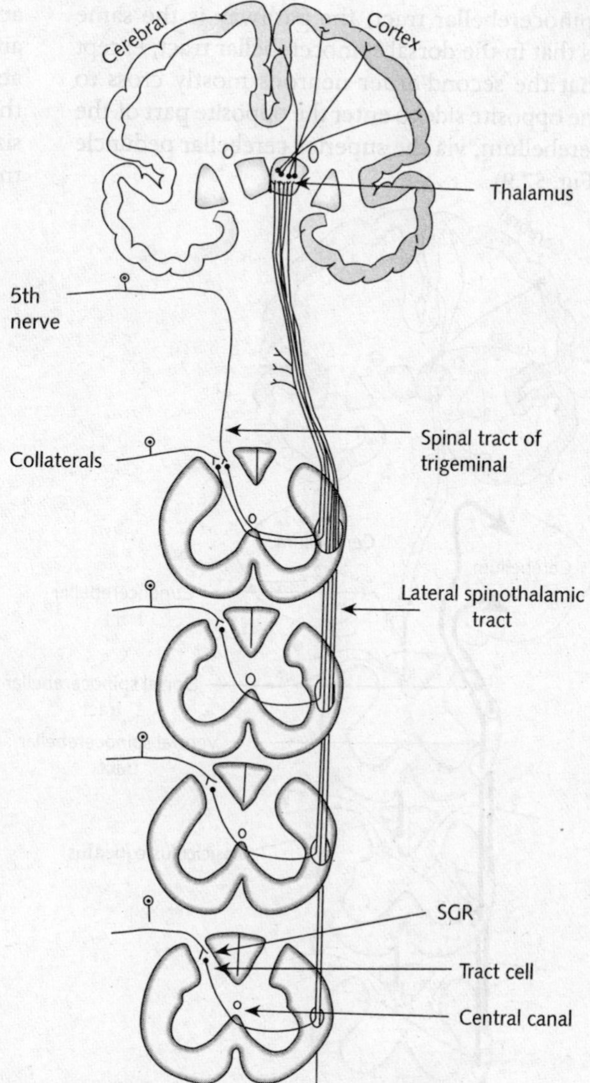


**Fig. 57.8:** Pathway for temperature and pain

## Pathway for pain

The sensation of pain is carried from the receptors by A fibres (fast pain) and C fibres (slow pain), via the posterior root to the spinal cord. Fast pain is carried along with thermal sensations via the lateral spinothalamic tract and thalamus to the sensory cortex (areas 3, 1 and 2).

Slow pain is carried by the same pathway, except that the fibres of the spinal lemniscus reach the thalamus via the reticular formation of the brainstem and relay in its intralaminar nuclei. Fibres from the thalamus, that is, the third-order neurons, reach all the areas of the sensory cortex. This generalized thalamocortical projection or reticular activating system (RAS) is concerned with sleep and wakefulness. Therefore, chronic slow pain produces sleeplessness.

## Pathway for proprioception

Proprioception is carried by the group I and II sensory fibres to the spinal cord. After this, it goes via the tracts of Gall and Burdah, as well as the spinocerebellar tracts (dorsal and ventral).

The tracts of Gall and Burdah carry proprioception to the cerebral cortex for the projection of a conscious image of the body in space. In the dorsal spinocerebellar tract, the sensory fibres enter the spinal cord through the medial division of the posterior root and relay in the Clarke's column cells of the posterior horn. The second-order neurons from these reach the anterior and posterior lobes of the cerebellum on the same side, via the inferior cerebellar peduncle. In the ventral spinocerebellar tract, the pathway is the same as that in the dorsal spinocerebellar tract, except that the second-order neurons mostly cross to the opposite side to enter the opposite part of the cerebellum, via the superior cerebellar peduncle (Fig. 57.9).

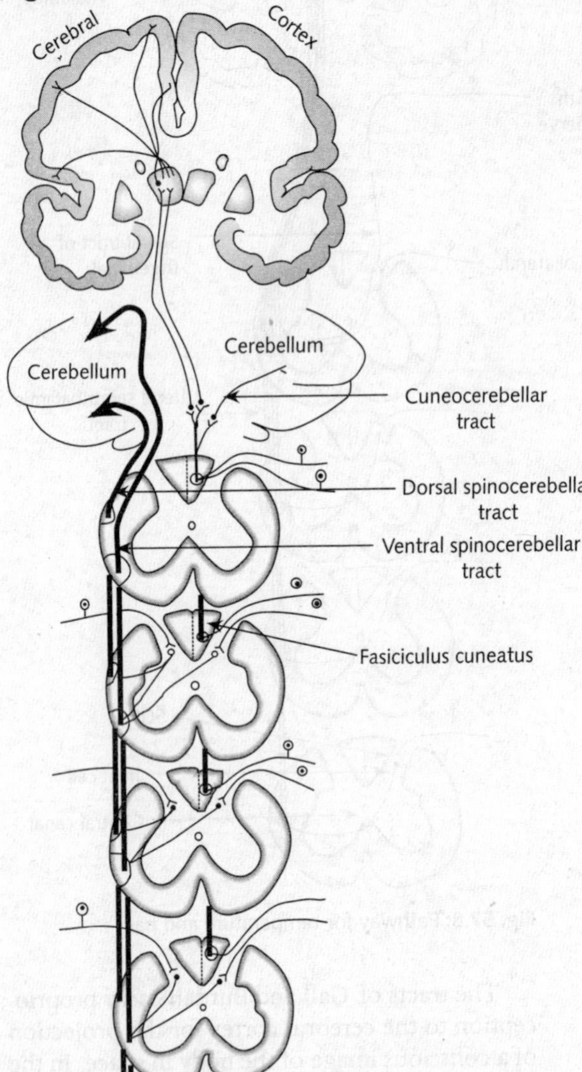


**Fig. 57.9**: Pathway for proprioception

## SYNTHETIC SENSATIONS

In addition to the primary sensations, there are other sensations that result from the simultaneous activity of two or more sensations. Some examples are tickling, itching and stereognosis, which is the ability to identify an object through touch, with the eyes closed. It involves the appreciation of size, shape and texture, that is, of many sensory modalities. It also involves the cerebral cortex and memory. The lemniscal system is essential for stereognosis.

## THE SOMATO-SENSORY CORTEX

Sensory signals from the body are projected to two regions of the cerebral cortex: somato-sensory area I and somato-sensory area II (Fig. 57.10). Somato-sensory area I (areas 3, 1 and 2 of Brodmann) is located in the post-central gyrus of the parietal lobe. It extends from the lateral sulcus to the medial surface of the cerebral hemisphere.

Each side of the cortex receives sensory information only from the opposite half of the body. A distinct topographical representation of the body is present in the cortex. The body is represented upside down in the post-central gyrus. The face is represented at the foot of the gyrus, while the legs and feet are represented at the top, extending on to the medial surface. The size of the cortical areas in which different parts of the body are represented is not proportionate to the size of the body part, but depends on the number of receptors present in that part. The number varies according to the extent to which the part can be used to collect biologically useful sensory information. The higher the number of receptors present in a particular area of the body, the larger the area of cortical representation. Therefore, some parts of the body, such as the lips, tongue and fingers, have proportionately larger areas of representation than areas like the trunk (Fig. 57.11).

Somato-sensory area II is located in the superior wall of the lateral sulcus.

*Functions*: Somato-sensory area I is responsible for the localization, analysis and discrimination of different sensory modalities, the perception of fine touch, proprioception and stereognosis. The perception of pain and temperature occurs in the thalamus, but their localization requires somato-sensory area I. Somato-sensory area II is involved in the process of learning from these sensory modalities.

The somato-sensory association area (areas 5 and 7 of Brodmann) is concerned with the interpretation of these sensations.

*Role of thalamus:* The medial and trigeminal lemniscus terminate in the VPL nucleus of the thalamus. Pain and temperature are perceived at the thalamic level. All other sensations are transmitted to the cerebral cortex by the third-order neurons arising in the thalamus.

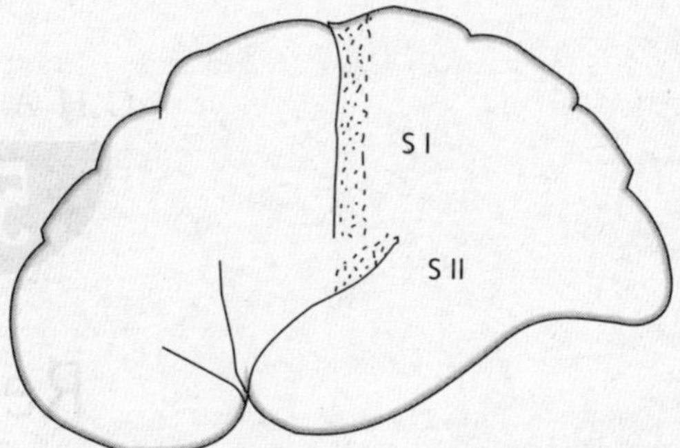


**Fig. 57.10:** Lateral surface of cerebral hemisphere showing the somato-sensory areas

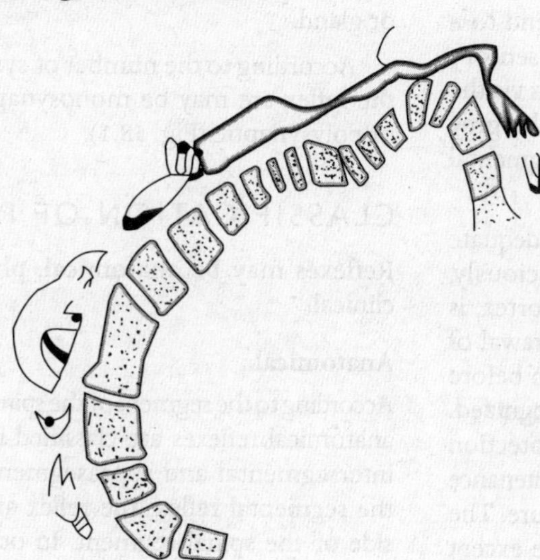

**Fig. 57.11:** The representation of the body in the somato-sensory area 1

CHAPTER

# Reflex

After entering the spinal cord, sensory signals may follow one or both of the following routes. They may ascend to a higher level of the CNS through various sensory tracts and reach the somato-sensory cortex via the thalamus, or may terminate locally in the grey matter of the spinal cord and elicit local segmental responses.

An involuntary motor response to an adequate sensory stimulus that occurs subconsciously, without the mediation of the cerebral cortex, is called a reflex. An example is the withdrawal of the hand after touching a hot plate, even before the intensity of its hotness has been recognized. The reflex action is important for the protection of the body. It is also responsible for the maintenance of the tone of the muscles, as well as posture. The centre for reflex action can be anywhere except the cerebral cortex. It is usually in the spinal cord but may be in the brainstem.

Reflex action is prompt and requires less time than voluntary action, since a smaller number of synapses is required in the path of the former than the latter.

The anatomical basis of reflex action is the reflex arc, which must be intact. It consists of: (i) the receptor organ, (ii) the afferent or the sensory neuron, which carries the sensory stimulus from the receptor organ to the centre, (iii) the centre, (iv) the efferent or motor neuron, which carries motor impulses from the centre to the effector organ, and (v) the effector organ, such as the muscle or gland.

According to the number of synapses present, the reflex arc may be monosynaptic, disynaptic or polysynaptic (Fig. 58.1).

## CLASSIFICATION OF REFLEXES

Reflexes may be anatomical, physiological or clinical.

### Anatomical

According to the segment of the spinal cord involved, anatomical reflexes are classified into segmental, intersegmental and suprasegmental reflexes. In the segmental reflex, the reflex arc involves one side of the spinal segment. In other words, the receptor organ, afferent neuron, efferent neuron and effector organ are located on the same side (ipsilateral) of the spinal segment. An example is the stretch reflex.

In the intersegmental reflex, the reflex arc involves both sides of the spinal segment. That is, the efferent neuron and effector organ are on opposite sides (contralateral) of the receptor organ. An example is the crossed extensor reflex.

In the suprasegmental reflex, the segments above the level of the reflex arc are involved. An example is the postural reflex.

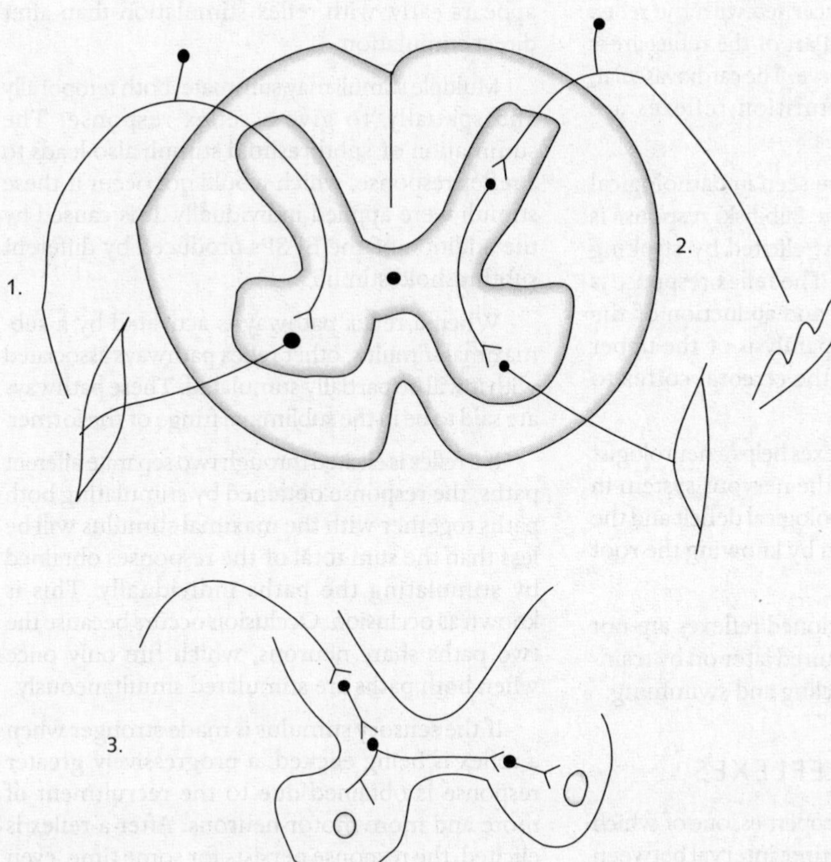


Fig. 58.1: Types of reflex arc: 1. Monosynaptic reflex arc, 2. Disynaptic reflex arc, 3. Polysynaptic reflex arc

**Physiological**

Physiological reflexes are classified into flexor/withdrawal and extensor/stretch reflexes according to their function. Certain details regarding the two types are listed in Table 58.1.

**Table 58.1:**

| *Flexor/withdrawal reflex* | *Extensor/stretch reflex* |
|---|---|
| 1. Nociceptive stimulation causes flexion of the joint and withdrawal of the part of the body. | Stretching of the muscle results in its contraction. |
| 2. Present in flexor muscles. | Present in anti-gravity extensor muscles. |
| 3. Polysynaptic. | Monosynaptic. |
| 4. Gives protection to the body. | Maintains muscle tone and posture. |

**Clinical**

Clinical reflexes are classified into unconditioned and conditioned reflexes according to whether they were present at birth or developed later.

*Unconditioned reflexes*: Unconditioned reflexes are inborn reflexes, which are present at birth. An example is the suckling reflex in a newborn. Unconditioned reflexes may be superficial, deep, visceral or pathological.

Superficial reflexes are elicited by the stimulation of receptor organs that are present superficially in the skin or mucous membrane. Some examples are the conjunctival reflex, abdominal reflex and plantar reflex.

Deep reflexes are elicited by tapping the tendon of a slightly stretched muscle. Some examples are the knee jerk, biceps jerk and ankle jerk.

Visceral reflexes are concerned with the reflex activity of internal organs. Part of the reflex arc is formed by the autonomic nerve. The cardiovascular, gastrointestinal and micturition reflexes are examples of visceral reflexes.

Pathological reflexes are seen in pathological conditions. For example, the Babinski response is an abnormal plantar reflex, elicited by stroking the lateral side of the foot. The reflex response is dorsiflexion of the big toe and abduction of the small toes. This is seen in paralysis of the upper motor neuron type (from the cerebral cortex to the anterior horn cells).

The clinical study of reflexes helps a neurologist gauge the involvement of the nervous system in a disease, the extent of neurological deficit and the approximate site of a lesion by knowing the root value.

*Conditioned reflexes*: Conditioned reflexes are not present at birth but are acquired later on by training. Some examples are cycling and swimming.

## PROPERTIES OF REFLEXES

Reflexes have a number of properties, one of which is synaptic delay. This is the time interval between the application of a stimulus and the response. The interval is greater for reflex stimulation (through the sensory nerve) than direct stimulation (through the motor nerve). The delay occurs because of the time taken by the impulse to traverse the synapse. For a single synapse, the delay is about 0.5 milliseconds. It is longer in the polysynaptic reflex arc than in the monosynaptic reflex arc.

Fractionation is another property of reflexes. The reflex response is always a fraction of the direct response. Fatigue occurs if a reflex is elicited repeatedly. In other words, the response gradually becomes weaker and ultimately disappears. Fatigue appears early, with reflex stimulation than after direct stimulation.

Multiple stimuli may summate, both temporally and spatially, to give a reflex response. The summation of subthreshold stimuli also leads to a reflex response, which would not occur if these stimuli were applied individually. It is caused by the addition of the EPSPs produced by different subthreshold stimuli.

When a reflex pathway is activated by a submaximal stimulus, other reflex pathways associated with it will be partially stimulated. These pathways are said to be in the subliminal fringe of the former.

If a reflex is elicited through two separate afferent paths, the response obtained by stimulating both paths together with the maximal stimulus will be less than the sum total of the responses obtained by stimulating the paths individually. This is known as occlusion. Occlusion occurs because the two paths share neurons, which fire only once when both paths are stimulated simultaneously.

If the sensory stimulus is made stronger when a reflex is being elicited, a progressively greater response is obtained due to the recruitment of more and more motor neurons. After a reflex is elicited, the response persists for some time, even after the stimulus is withdrawn. This happens because of the reverberation of the impulse through the collaterals.

If a strong stimulus is used, the response does not remain localized to that reflex arc but spreads to the neighbouring reflex arc, producing a wider response. This property is known as irradiation. Another property of reflexes is reciprocal innervation/inhibition. When one group of muscles is stimulated reflexly (agonist), the opposite group of muscles (antagonist) is inhibited simultaneously, making the muscle contraction smooth.

CHAPTER

59

# The Motor System

The motor system carries motor (efferent) impulses from the CNS to the whole body. On the basis of information collected from the sensory system, these impulses control the activities of the muscles and glands in order to bring about the changes necessary for the maintenance of homeostasis.

A part of the system also acts under the voluntary effort of the individual and controls the skeletal (voluntary) muscles. The involuntary muscles and glands are controlled by the autonomic nervous system.

The motor impulses coming from the cerebral cortex are carried by descending fibres. Some of these go to the anterior horn cells of the spinal cord (final common path), via the pyramidal system. The rest pass through other subcortical structures, and then via the extrapyramidal system, to reach the final common path. The final common path is the lower motor neuron located in the spinal cord or in the brainstem. The axons of this neuron supply the target organs.

The parts of the nervous system that are involved in motor activities are described in the following sections.

## Cerebral Cortex

The cerebral cortex consists of grey matter which is highly convoluted. The convolutions increase its surface area. The elevations are called gyri and the depressions are called sulci. There are three main sulci, which divide the cerebral cortex into four lobes. These are the central, lateral and parieto-occipital sulci. The four lobes are the frontal, parietal, temporal and occipital lobes (Fig. 59.1).

Histologically, six layers can be identified in 90 to 95 per cent of the cortical surface, which is known as the neocortex. Three types of cells have been identified in this area (Fig. 59.2). These are:

1. Pyramidal cells: These are triangular cells, the bases of which face downwards. They are found in the third and fifth layers. Giant pyramidal or Betz cells are found in the fifth layer of the primary motor cortex.
2. Granule cells: These have small cell bodies, from which dendrites arise in all directions. Granule cells are found in the second and fourth layers. They are best developed in the fourth layer of the primary sensory cortex.
3. Fusiform cells: These are spindle-shaped cells which are found in the sixth layer of the cerebral cortex.

On the basis of histology, Brodmann divided the cortex into a number of areas, each with a distinct morphological feature. The differences in the functions of different Brodmann's areas do not arise from the differences in the cell type, but because of the difference in the afferent and efferent connections of the cells in that area (Fig. 59.3).

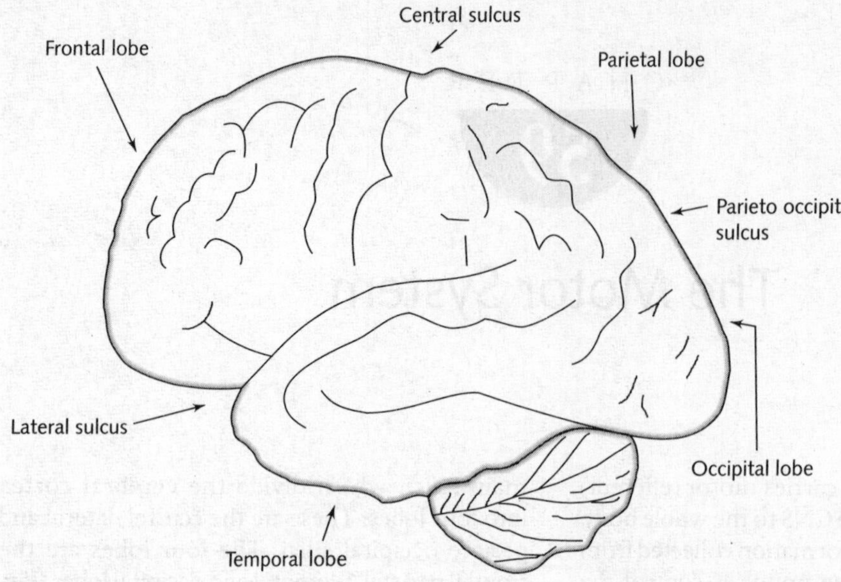


**Fig. 59.1:** Lateral aspect of the cerebral cortex showing the sulci and different lobes

## Motor Cortex

Various parts of the cerebral cortex are involved directly or indirectly in motor activity (Fig. 59.4). These are the primary motor area, the premotor area and the supplementary motor area.

*Primary motor area:* This area is situated in the precentral gyrus, that is, area 4 of Brodmann, and extends on to the medial surface as well.

Each primary motor cortex controls the movements of the opposite side of the body. The whole body is represented upside down. The face is represented at the bottom of precentral gyrus, while the legs and feet are represented on the medial side of the hemisphere. The parts of the body concerned with highly skilled movements, such as the fingers and tongue, have proportionately larger cortical representation (Fig. 59.5). The primary motor area is related to fine and skilful voluntary movements.

*Premotor area*: This area is situated in front of the primary motor area. It consists of Brodmann's area 6 and part of area 8. It is concerned with the coordination of movements, as well as other activities.

*Supplementary motor area:* This area is situated mainly on the medial surface of the cerebral hemisphere. It helps in planning complex movements.

## Sensory Cortex

The parietal cortex is also involved in the performance of some complex movements. It regulates sensory-motor coordination.

## Subcortical Structures

The subcortical structures consist of the basal ganglia and cerebellum. The former are masses of grey matter inside the cerebral hemisphere. They plan movement and help in the programming of movements.

The cerebellum is indirectly concerned with motor activities and is responsible for their coordination. It is also responsible for movements related to equilibrium.

*The descending (motor) tracts in spinal cord* (Fig. 59.6) The fibres controlling the motor activities of the body descend from the motor cortex to the anterior horn cells (motor) of spinal cord, forming descending tracts. These form two systems or pathways: a direct pathway or the pyramidal system and an indirect pathway or the extrapyramidal system.

The pyramidal system consists of the corticospinal tract, lateral and anterior and the extrapyramidal system consists of the multiple tracts. These

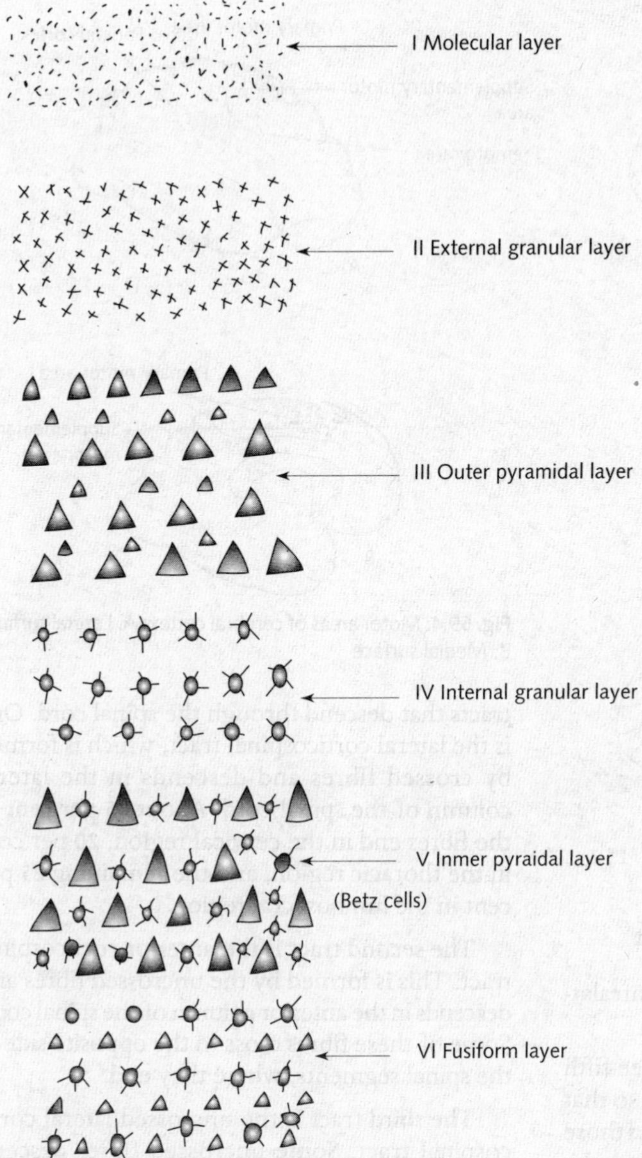


**Fig. 59.2:** Histological structure of cerebral cortex (neocortex)

are Rubrospinal, Reticulospinal, Vestibulospinal, Tectospinal and Olivospinal tracts.

## PYRAMIDAL SYSTEM

The pyramidal or the corticospinal tract is the most important tract through which the motor cortex controls the activity of the anterior horn cells of the spinal cord.

In the primary motor cortex, giant pyramidal or Betz cells in area 4 contribute about 30 per cent of the fibres of the pyramidal tract.

In the premotor and supplementary motor areas, areas 6 and 8 contribute about 30 per cent of the fibres. In the parietal cortex, somato-sensory areas 3, 1 and 2 contribute about 40 per cent of the fibres. Of the total of 1 million fibres, about 90 per cent are thin and 10 per cent are thick.

### Course

The tract originates in the cortex, moves through the cerebral hemispheres to the brainstem, and then to the spinal cord (Fig. 59.7). The tract starts from a wide area. While passing down, the fibres converge and, along with ascending fibres, form a fan-shaped mass of radiating fibres, called the corona radiata. During their passage through the hemispheres, the fibres are twisted through 90°, so the fibres which were placed laterally at the origin are situated anteriorly by the time they reach the internal capsule.

The internal capsule is a compressed V-shaped band of fibres, situated between the thalamus, medially, and the basal ganglia, laterally. The corticospinal fibres occupy the genu (bend) and the anterior two-thirds of the posterior limb of the internal capsule. The sensory and visual tracts are located slightly behind the corticospinal fibres.

The fibres passing through the genu form the corticobulbar tract, the fibres of which end in the motor nuclei of the cranial nerves in the brainstem (5, 7, 9, 10, 11 and 12), mainly on opposite side and some on the same side.

The internal capsule, an important area of the brain, is a common site of vascular lesions (thrombosis) in the elderly. Such lesions produce

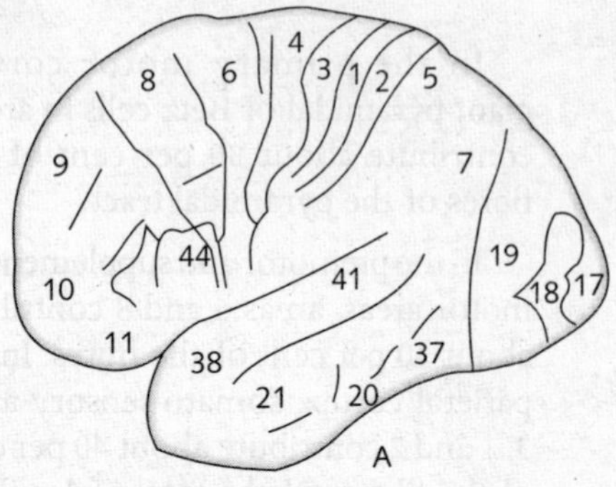


Fig. 59.3: Brodmann's areas of the cerebral hemisphere: A. Lateral aspect, B. Medial aspect

widespread motor disturbances on the contralateral side of the body (hemiplegia).

Next, the fibres occupy the middle three-fifth of the cerebral peduncles and are rotated, so that fibres for the head are situated medially and those for the legs, laterally. They then pass through the ventral side of the pons, and the tract is broken into small bundles by the pontine nuclei.

All the fibres unite again to form compact masses, called pyramids, in the upper half of the medulla. In the lower part of the medulla, about 80 per cent of the fibres cross to the opposite side, while 20 per cent continue on the same side.

In the spinal cord, the fibres group into three

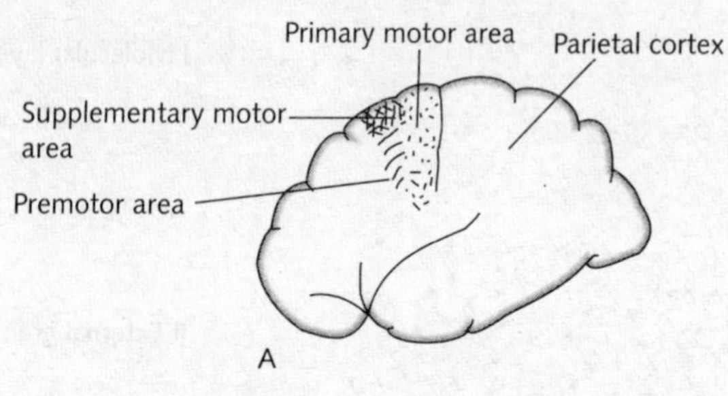


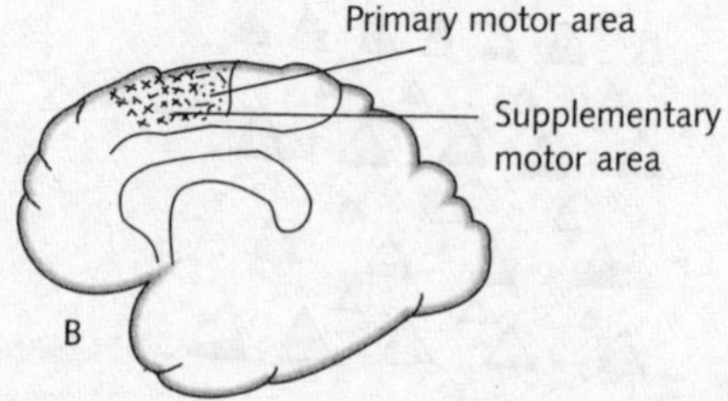


Fig. 59.4: Motor areas of cerebral cortex: A. Lateral surface, B. Medial surface

tracts that descend through the spinal cord. One is the lateral corticospinal tract, which is formed by crossed fibres and descends in the lateral column of the spinal cord. About 55 per cent of the fibres end in the cervical region, 20 per cent in the thoracic region, and the remaining 25 per cent in the lumbosacral region.

The second tract is the anterior corticospinal tract. This is formed by the uncrossed fibres and descends in the anterior column of the spinal cord. Some of these fibres cross to the opposite side in the spinal segments, where they end.

The third tract is the uncrossed lateral corticospinal tract. Some uncrossed fibres descend in the lateral column of the spinal cord, along with the crossed fibres. Therefore, some muscles are bilaterally controlled, from both cerebral hemispheres.

The fibres of the corticospinal tract end on the anterior horn cells, directly or via interneurons.

### Functions

The corticospinal tract is responsible for the execution of fine, skilled voluntary movements.

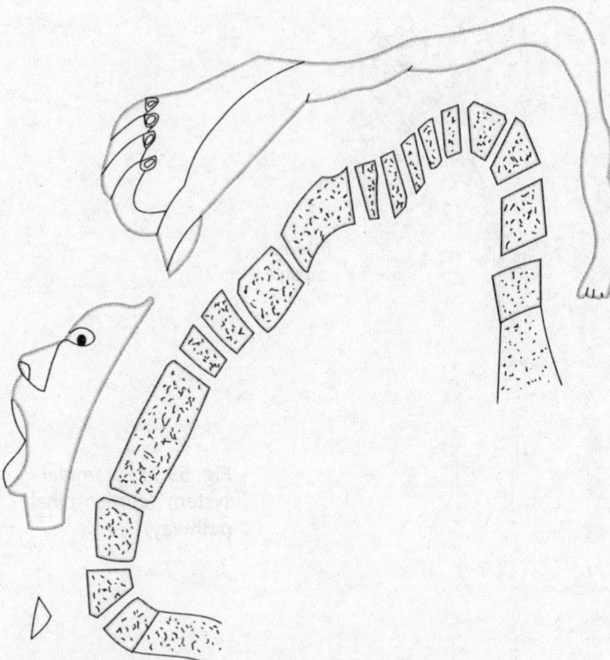

Fig. 59.5: The disposition of the body in the primary motor area

The fibres of the lateral corticospinal tract are involved in the regulation of the distal limb muscles and thus, in fine, discrete movements, such as the fine movements of the fingers.

The fibres of the anterior corticospinal tract control the axial muscles, such as the muscles of the trunk, thereby helping in postural movements. The corticospinal tract facilitates in the tone of muscles.

## EXTRAPYRAMIDAL SYSTEM

The descending fibres from the brain to the spinal cord (except those included in the pyramidal system) form the extrapyramidal system. These fibres relay in various basal ganglia, red nucleus and the brainstem reticular formation, forming rubrospinal, reticulospinal, vestibulospinal, tectospinal and olivospinal tracts. The extrapyramidal tracts constitute multisynaptic pathways, unlike the pyramidal tracts.

### Rubrospinal Tract

This tract arises from the red nucleus in the midbrain and immediately crosses to the opposite side. It goes down the lateral column of the entire spinal cord. The fibres end on the anterior horn cells, via interneurons.

The rubrospinal tract enhances flexor tone and decreases extensor tone.

### Reticulospinal Tracts

These tracts arises from the reticular formation (RF) in the brainstem. The RF is a reticulum of interlacing neurons with complex processes.

The medial reticulospinal tract originates from the pontine RF, while the lateral reticulospinal tract originates from the medullary RF. Each tract ends on the same side, on the anterior horn cells of the spinal cord, directly or via interneurons. Some fibres cross to the opposite side.

The main function of these tracts is to regulate muscle tone. The lateral reticulospinal tract is facilitatory to muscle tone, while the medial one is inhibitory.

### Vestibulospinal Tracts

The lateral and medial vestibulospinal tracts arise from the lateral and medial vestibular nuclei and

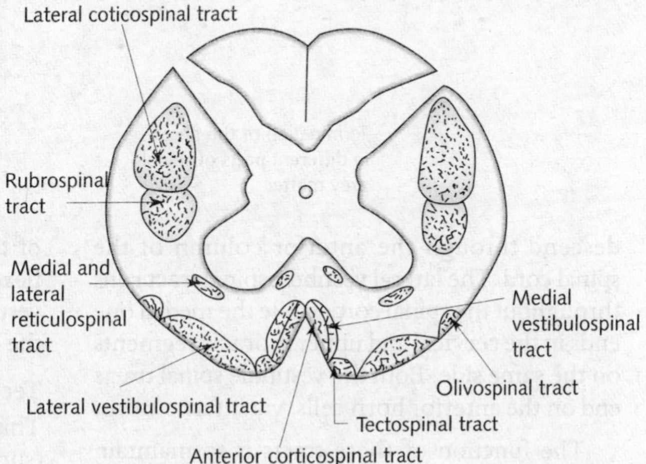


Fig. 59.6: Cross-section of spinal cord showing the descending tracts

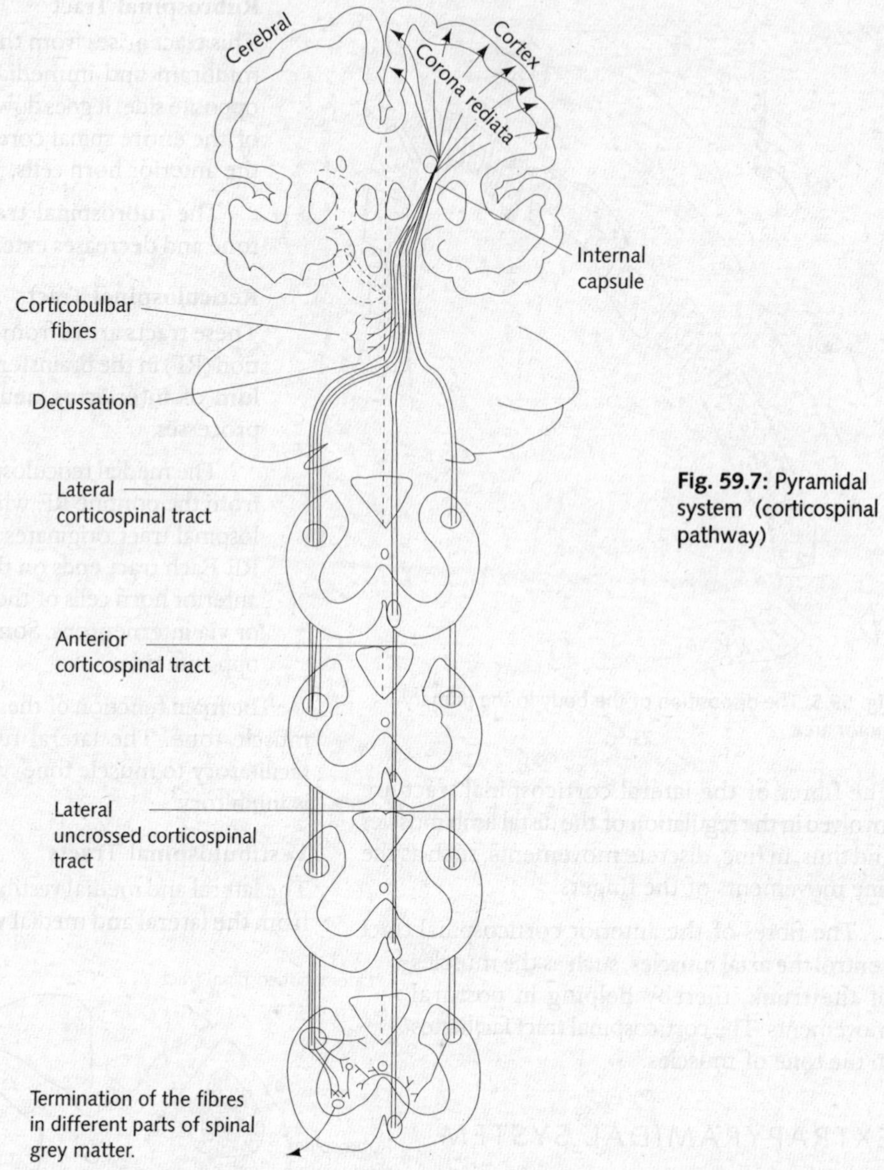


**Fig. 59.7:** Pyramidal system (corticospinal pathway)

descend through the anterior column of the spinal cord. The lateral vestibulospinal tract runs throughout the spinal cord, while the medial one ends in the cervical and upper thoracic segments on the same side. Both the vestibule spinal tracts end on the anterior horn cells, via interneurons.

The function of these tracts is to maintain posture and equilibrium. They increase the tone of the extensor muscles but decrease that of the flexors. Both tracts relay information from the vestibular apparatus and cerebellum, and influence the spinal motor neurons.

### Tectospinal Tract

This tract arises from the tectum of the midbrain (superior colliculi) and immediately crosses to the opposite side. It descends through the anterior column and ends in the cervical segment of the spinal cord, mainly on the interneurons. The tectospinal tract is responsible for the turning of the head towards a sound or an object (auditospinal and visuospinal reflexes), and also due to somatic stimuli.

**Olivospinal Tract**

This tract arises from the olivary nucleus in the medulla, descends in the anterior column down to the cervical segments and ends on the anterior horn cells. The function of the olivospinal tract is not clear, but it is involved in motor activity.

### Functions of extrapyramidal system

The extrapyramidal system is concerned with the regulation of muscle tone and posture. It performs the gross postural movements and provides an appropriate and stable postural background for the muscle activity produced by the pyramidal tracts.

**Table 59.1:** Pyramidal and Extrapyramidal Systems

| | Pyramidal System | Extrapyramidal System |
|---|---|---|
| 1. Phylogenically | Newer system | Older system |
| 2. Myelination | After birth | Before birth |
| 3. Onset of function | 1 to 2 years after birth | Before birth |
| 4. Function | Fine and skilled movements | Gross postural movements |
| 5. Damage results in | Clumsiness and weakness | Spasticity |

## APPLIED PHYSIOLOGY

### Upper and lower motor neuron lesion

Voluntary control over the skeletal muscle requires an intact motor pathway, which consists of two types of neurons, the upper motor neuron (UMN) and the lower motor neuron (LMN).

The cells originating in the corticospinal tract in the cerebral cortex and their axons are known as upper motor neurons. These also include extrapyramidal fibres.

The anterior horn cells (α) and their axons are known as the lower motor neurons. These include cranial motor neurons. The terms 'upper motor neurons' and 'lower motor neurons' serve a useful purpose in the clinical diagnosis of neurological disorders. Lesion of UMN or LMN leads to paralysis (loss of power in the muscles).

### Spinal cord lesions

The spinal cord may be injured for various reasons, in many ways and to varying extents. In each case, the features depend on the extent and type of damage caused to the neural elements.

**Table 59.2:** UMN and LMN lesions

| | UMN Lesion | LMN Lesion |
|---|---|---|
| 1. Site | Higher than anterior horn cells | Anterior horn cells and their axons |
| 2. Cause | Thrombosis in the internal capsule | Nerve injury or anterior poliomyelitis |
| 3. Loss of power | (i) On the opposite side if before crossing; on the same side if after crossing | (i) On the same side |
| | (ii) Involvement of the body parts according to site of lesion | (ii) Segmental |

(Contd...)

(*Table 59.2 contd.*)

| | UMN Lesion | LMN Lesion |
|---|---|---|
| 4. Tone | Hypertonia or spasticity due to simultaneous involvement of extrapyramidal fibres | Hypotonia or flaccidity |
| 5. Reflexes | (i) Superficial—absent<br>(ii) Deep—exaggerated<br>(iii) Babinski sign is positive<br>(iv) Clonus present | (i) Superficial—absent<br>(ii) Deep—absent<br>(iii) Plantar reflex absent if $S_1$ and $S_2$ involved<br>(iv) Clonus absent |
| 6. Muscles | (i) No wasting or atrophy<br>(ii) Contracture absent | (i) Disuse atrophy<br>(ii) Contracture may be present |

**Complete Transection of Spinal Cord**

Car accidents and war injuries may produce spinal cord lesions of varying severity. In cases of complete transection, the following features are seen in different stages, with the passage of time.

*Stage of spinal shock*: This occurs immediately after the injury. There is a complete loss of all sensation and voluntary movement below the level of the lesion. This happens because the spinal cord cannot act in the absence of the commands that it normally receives from the higher level.

During this stage, all the reflexes are abolished, the muscles are flaccid, and the bladder and rectum are paralysed. The blood pressure may fall if the lesion is in the upper thoracic segments. The duration of spinal shock is 2 to 3 weeks.

*Stage of reflex activity*: When the spinal shock passes, autonomic reflex activity is the first to return. The urethral sphincter regains its tone, so that urine can be retained. The vascular tone returns, so the blood pressure goes back to normal.

Among the somatic reflexes, the Babinski sign is the first to appear. Subsequently, deep reflexes appear. The flexor reflexes appear first, followed by the extensor reflexes. There is hypotonia and the stretch reflex is feeble. With proper medical care, the patient may survive for years. Later on, hypertonia and exaggerated deep reflexes may be observed.

*Stage of reflex failure*: If left uncared for, the patient suffers from severe infections and toximea occurs. There is failure of reflexes and death.

**Hemisection of Spinal Cord (Brown–Sequard Syndrome)**

Lesion of one half of the spinal cord may be produced due to an extradural tumour of the spinal cord or a traumatic injury. This is characterized by LMN type of paralysis at the level of the lesion, on the same side. UMN type of paralysis also occurs, and there is loss of fine touch, tactile localization and tactile discrimination on the same side, below the level of the lesion. In addition, there is loss of the sensations of pain, temperature and crude touch on the opposite side, below the level of the lesion.

CHAPTER

60

# The Basal Ganglia and the Cerebellum

## BASAL GANGLIA

The basal ganglia are a group of subcortical grey masses involved in motor activities. They are located in the white matter of the cerebral hemisphere, near its base, hence the name. The basal ganglia consist of the caudate nucleus, putamen, globus pallidus, subthalamic body of Luys and substantia nigra.

Phylogenetically, the caudate nucleus and putamen are of more recent origin and are together called the neostriatum. The globus pallidus is more primitive (Fig. 60.1).

### Connections

The basal ganglia are interconnected with one another and also with other parts of the CNS, to form different circuits (Fig. 60.2). The connections of the basal ganglia are considered under the following three headings.

#### Motor Cortex–Basal Ganglia Circuit

Fibres originating from all parts of the cerebral cortex terminate in the caudate nucleus and the putamen. From the neostriatum, the fibres proceed to the globus pallidus and then to the thalamus. From here, they go to all parts of the motor cortex, particularly to the prefrontal, premotor and supplementary motor cortices, where the planning of movements takes place.

#### Neostriatum–Substantia Nigra Circuit

The neostriatum has a GABA-secreting, inhibitory pathway to the substantia nigra which, in turn, has a dopamine-secreting inhibitory projection on

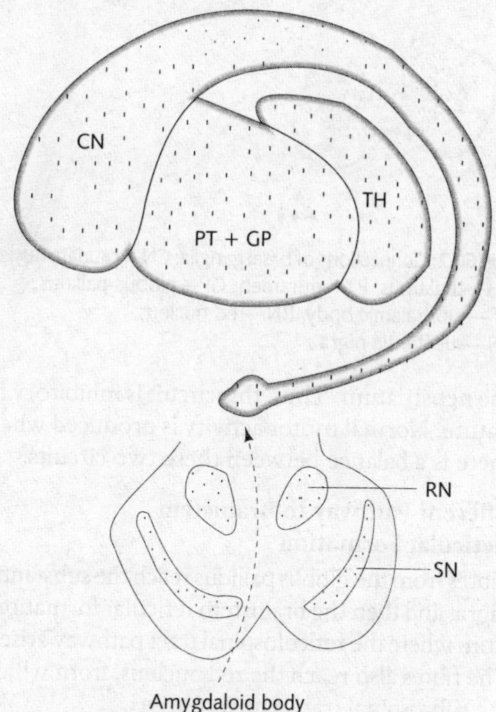


**Fig. 60.1:** Basal ganglia: CN—caudate nucleus, TH—thalamus, PT—putamen, GP—globus pallidus, ST—subthalamic body, RN—red nucleus, SN—substantia nigra

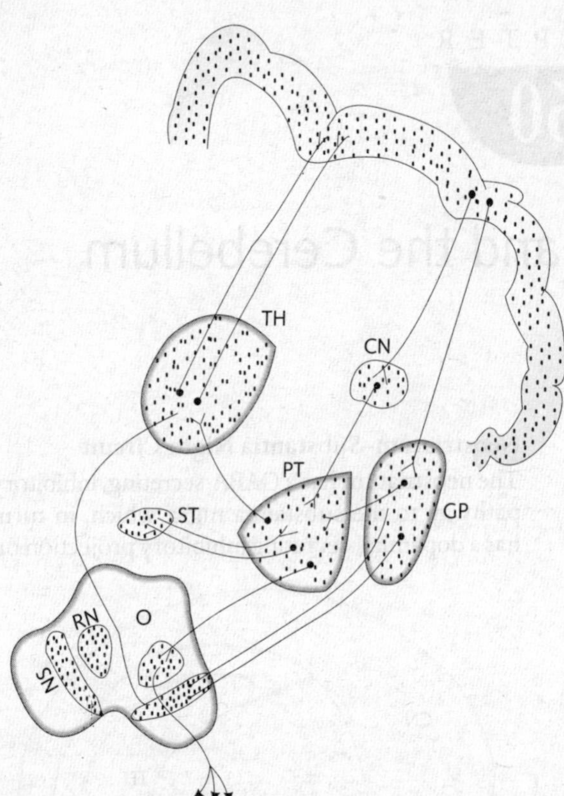


Fig. 60.2: Connections of basal ganglia: CN—caudate nucleus, TH—thalamus, PT—putamen, GP—globus pallidus, ST—subthalamic body, RN—red nucleus, SN—substantia nigra

the neostriatum. Thus, this circuit is inhibitory in nature. Normal motor activity is produced when there is a balance between these two circuits.

**Efferent Pathway to Brainstem Reticular Formation**

Fibres from the globus pallidus reach the substantia nigra, and then the brainstem reticular formation, from where the reticulospinal tract pathway arises. The fibres also reach the red nucleus, from which the rubrospinal tract pathway arises.

## Functions of basal ganglia

The basal ganglia are responsible for planning and programming movements. Neuronal discharge in the basal ganglia begins well before the beginning of movement. They are also involved in the regulation of tone and posture. The cortical inhibitory areas project on to the caudate nucleus which, in turn, projects on the medullary inhibitory reticular formation. The latter inhibits muscle tone.

## Applied physiology

Abnormalities in the functioning of the basal ganglia can be of two types, hyperkinetic and hypokinetic.

*Hyperkinetic*: This is associated with abnormal movements, caused by damage to the neostriatum. One of the abnormalities is chorea, in which there are spontaneous, jerky, irregular and 'dancing' movements. In athetosis, another abnormality, there are slow, writhing movements.

*Hypokinetic*: This is associated with poverty of movements. An example is Parkinson's disease, a disorder observed among middle-aged patients. This disorder is caused by the degeneration of the substantia nigra, which results in a decrease in the secretion of dopamine. It is characterized by the following features:

1. Muscular rigidity of the lead pipe type, due to increased tone in the flexor and extensor muscles.
2. Tremors in the resting state, in contrast to the intention tremors of cerebellar disease. These are involuntary, rhythmic and oscillatory movements of the distal parts of the limb at rest, but disappear with voluntary activity.
3. Mask-like face or lack of facial expression due to the absence of automatic associated movements.

# CEREBELLUM

The cerebellum is called a small brain, but has a large role to play in the motor activity of the CNS. It is situated on the dorsal aspect of the brainstem, to which it is connected by three cerebellar peduncles on either side.

The cerebellum consists of the central vermis and two cerebellar hemispheres on either side. The phylogenetic divisions of the cerebellum are as given below.

*Archicerebellum*: This is the oldest part and consists of the flocculo-nodular lobe. Its main connections are with the vestibular apparatus and hence, it is concerned with the maintenance of the equilibrium of the body.

*Palaeocerebellum*: This appears after the archicerebellum and consists of the rest of the vermis, along with the adjacent medial portions of the hemispheres. It receives proprioceptive impulses from the body and is, therefore, concerned with the regulation of tone and posture.

*Neocerebellum*: This is the newest portion and also, the best developed in humans. It consists of the lateral portions of the cerebellar hemispheres. It interacts with the cerebral motor cortex and in association with it, coordinates movements involving skill. It helps in the planning and programming of movements (Fig. 60.3).

Like the cerebrum, the cerebellum consists of an outer cortex made of grey matter, and inner white matter. Within the white matter, there are four deep cerebellar nuclei: fastigial, globose, emboliformis and dentate. The cortical grey matter has transverse folds, which are thin and regular.

## Connections

### Afferent Connections

The sensory input to the cerebellum is mostly ipsilateral. Proprioceptive impulses reach the cerebellum via the dorsal and ventral spinocerebellar tracts, and the olivocerebellar and cuneocerebellar tracts.

Vestibular impulses reach the cerebellum from the vestibular nuclei via the vestibulocerebellar

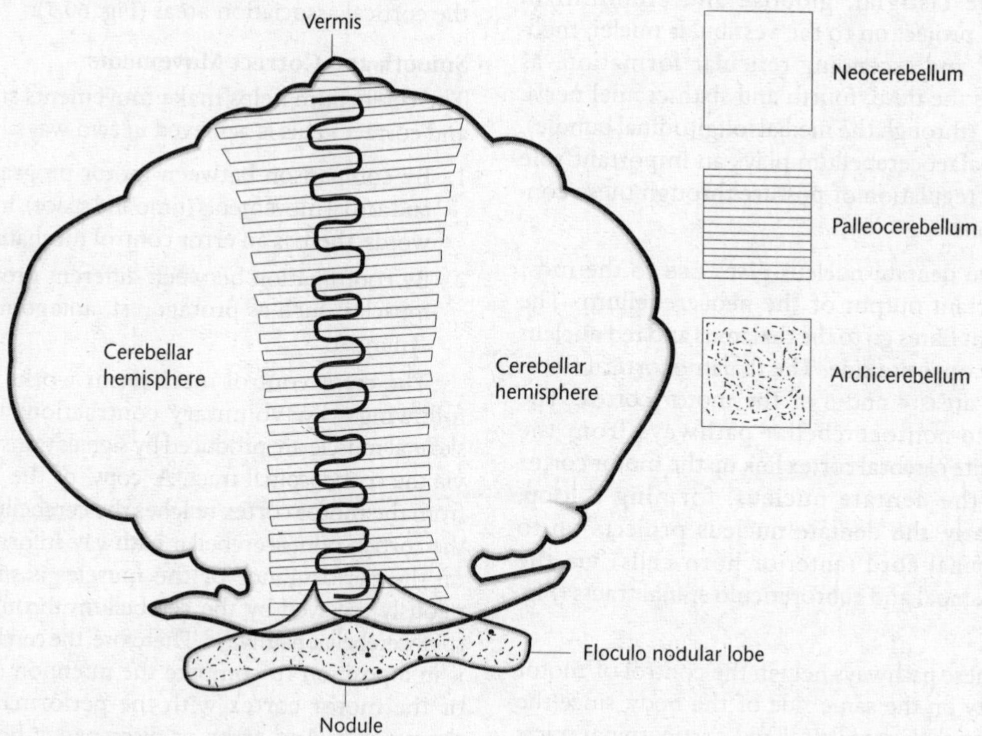


Fig. 60.3: Phylogenic divisions of cerebellum

tract, and visual and auditory impulses reach it from the superior and inferior colliculi via the tectocerebellar tract.

Impulses from the opposite motor cortex and red nucleus reach the cerebellum via the pontocerebellar and rubrocerebellar tracts. Impulses from the brainstem reticular formation reach it via the reticulocerebellar tracts.

All the afferent impulses reach the Purkinje cells of the cerebellar cortex. These cells project on to the deep cerebellar nuclei.

**Efferent Connections**

The axons of the Purkinje cells project on to the four deep nuclei as follows.

The fastigial nucleus receives fibres from the vermis, while the globose and emboliform nuclei receive fibres from the palaeocerebellum. The dentate nucleus receives fibres from the neocerebellum.

The fastigial, globose and emboliform nuclei project on to the vestibular nuclei, medullary and ascending reticular formation, as well as the third, fourth and sixth cranial nerve nuclei (through the medial longitudinal bundle). The palaeocerebellum plays an important role in the regulation of posture through these connections.

The dentate nucleus gives rise to the most important output of the neocerebellum. The efferent fibres go to the thalamus and red nucleus of the opposite side. The thalamocortical fibres reach areas 4 and 6 of the motor cortex. The cortico-pontocerebellar pathways from the opposite cerebral cortex link up the motor cortex with the dentate nucleus, forming a loop. Similarly, the dentate nucleus projects on to the spinal cord (anterior horn cells) via the rubrospinal and rubroreticulo spinal tracts (Fig. 60.4).

These pathways help in the control of motor activity on the same side of the body, since the dentato-thalamocortical and corticospinal tracts cross to the opposite side.

## Functions of cerebellum

**Regulation of Tone and Posture**

The palaeocerebellum receives proprioceptive impulses. It projects on to the alpha as well as gamma motor neurons, through the efferent output to the vestibular nuclei and reticular formation, that is, vestibulospinal and reticulospinal tracts, respectively. Thus, it regulates tone and posture.

**Maintenance of Equilibrium**

The archicerebellum has afferent and efferent connections with the vestibular nuclei. Thus, the vestibular apparatus and the flocculo-nodular lobe of the cerebellum are intimately connected. This helps in the maintenance of equilibrium.

**Planning and Programming of Movements**

Like the basal ganglia, neuronal discharge in the cerebellum begins well before the beginning of a movement. Therefore, it is believed that the cerebellum is also involved in the planning and programming of movements that are initiated in the cortical association areas (Fig. 60.5).

**Smooth and Correct Movements**

The cerebellum helps make movements smooth and correct. This is achieved in two ways:

1. By comparison between motor programmes and actual movements (time and space). In other words, there is an error control mechanism.
2. By coordination between different groups of muscles, such as protagonist, antagonist and synergist.

The error control mechanism works in the following way. Voluntary contractions of the skeletal muscle are produced by signals transmitted via the corticospinal tract. A 'copy' of the 'order' from the motor cortex reaches the cerebellum via the cortico-pontocerebellar pathway. Information on the performance of the muscles is simultaneously received by the cerebellum through the spinocerebellar pathways. Therefore, the cerebellum is in a position to compare the intention (order) of the motor cortex with the performance of the muscle. Any error or discrepancy between the two is corrected by feedback control of the

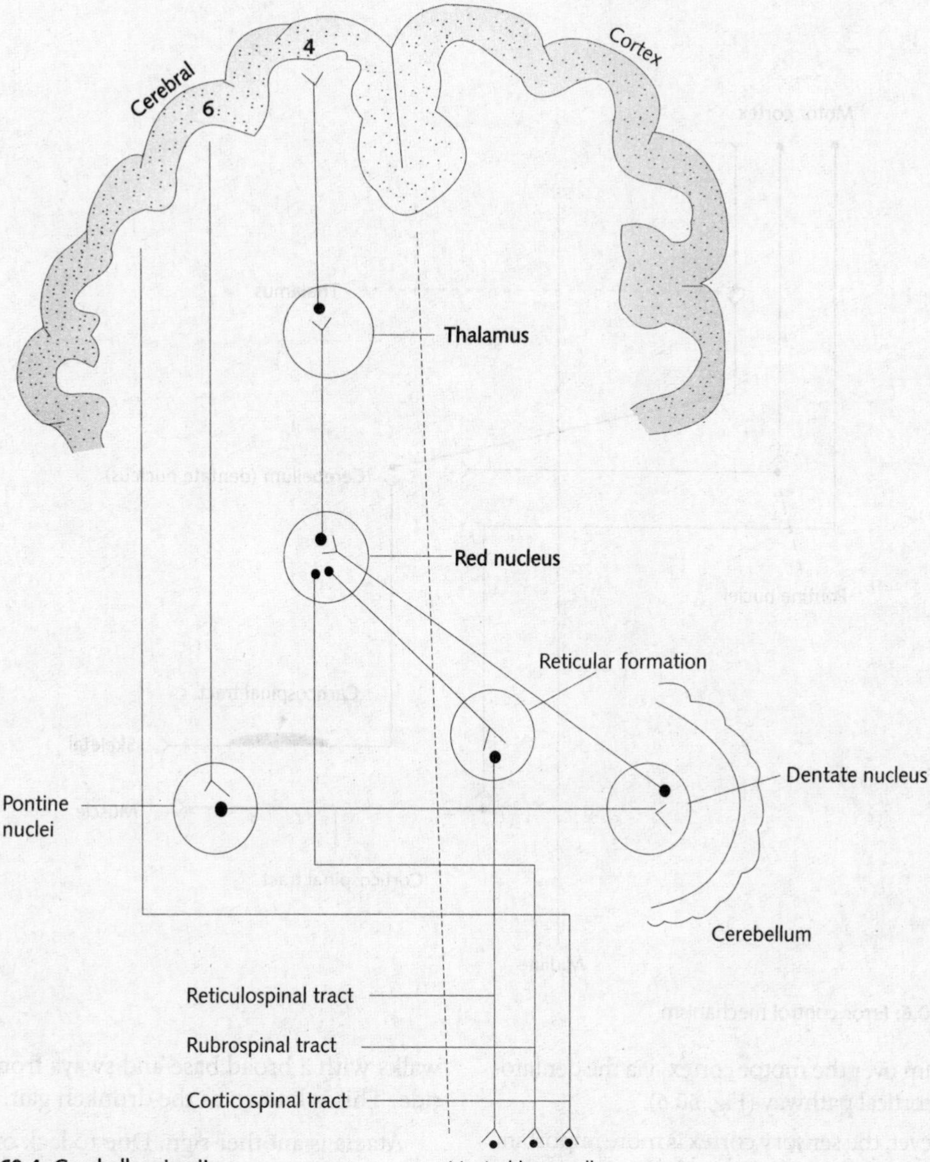

Cerebral
Cortex
4
6
Thalamus
Red nucleus
Reticular formation
Dentate nucleus
Pontine nuclei
Cerebellum
Reticulospinal tract
Rubrospinal tract
Corticospinal tract
Ventral horn cell.


Fig. 60.4: Cerebellar circuits

Cortical association area (idea)
Basal ganglia
Cerebellum
Motor cortex
Muscle (movement)
Palleocerebellum


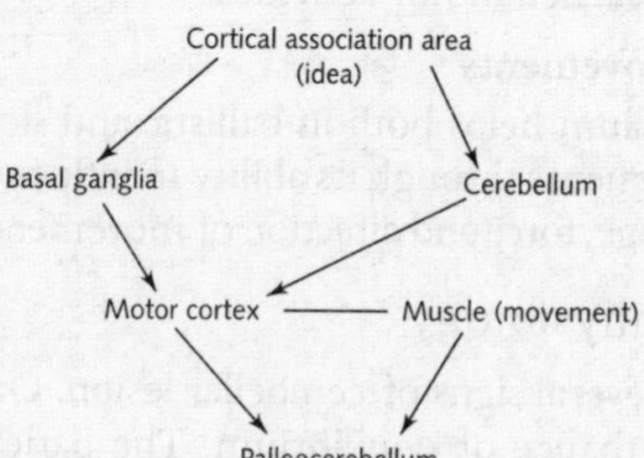

**Fig. 60.5:** Planning and programming of movements

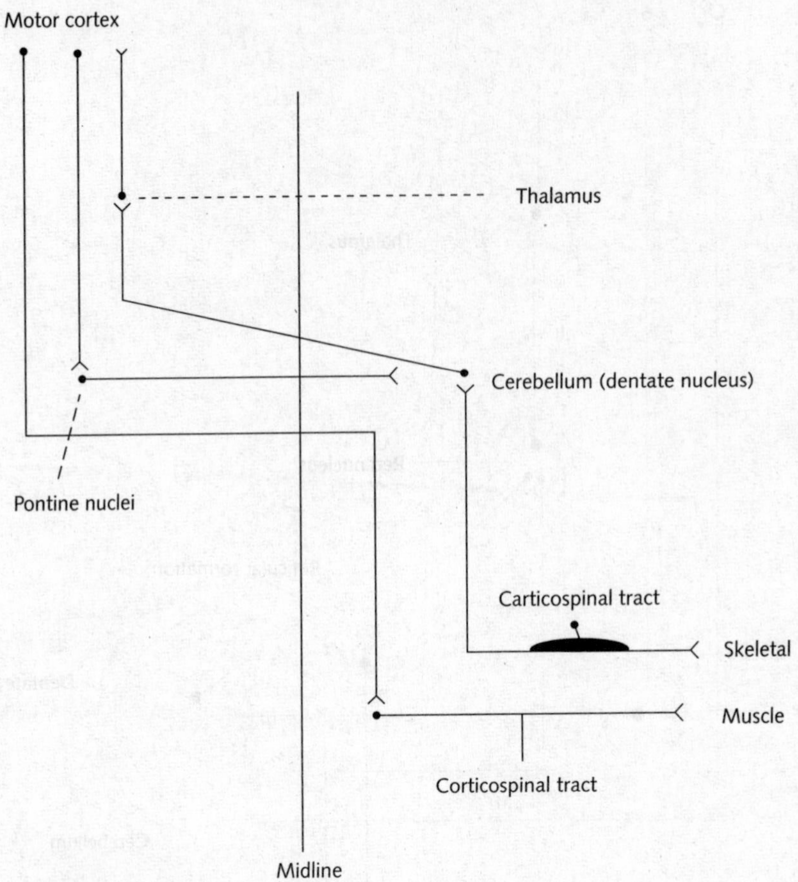


**Fig. 60.6:** Error control mechanism

cerebellum over the motor cortex, via the dentato-thalamocortical pathway (Fig. 60.6).

However, the sensory cortex is more important in the learning of complicated tasks as well as control of learned motor activities.

**Ballistic Movements**

The cerebellum helps both in ballistic and slow ramp movements through its ability to influence the rate, range, force and direction of movements.

## Applied physiology

There are several signs of cerebellar lesion. One is the disturbance of equilibrium. The patient walks with a broad base and sways from side to side. This is known as the drunken gait.

Ataxia is another sign. Due to lack of coordination of movements, the patient fails to walk in a straight line and tends to fall to one side.

Cerebellar lesions cause the decomposition of movements. Due to lack of smooth coordination between different groups of muscles, a smooth movement is completed in steps and not in one go. Cerebellar lesions can also cause adiadochokinesia. The patient fails to perform alternate repetitive movements in quick succession, for example, pronation and supination.

The patient may suffer from intention tremors. Such tremors are present during movement, but not at rest. There may be hypotonia, in which the muscle tone is decreased due to a fall in gamma discharge.

Nystagmus, which is characterized by jerky, oscillatory movements of the eyeballs, is another sign of cerebellar lesion. It is caused by lack of coordination between different extraocular muscles.

The speech may be slurred owing to lack of coordination of the muscles of the tongue and larynx.

CHAPTER

61

# The Thalamus, Reticular Formation, EEG and Sleep

## THE THALAMUS

The thalamus is a large, ovoid, nuclear mass. It is situated at the top of the midbrain and lies on the medial side of the cerebral hemisphere. It forms the medial boundary of the internal capsule and the lateral boundary of the third ventricle.

The thalamic nuclei are divided into mainly three large groups by a vertical, Y-shaped sheath of white matter. The group of nuclei located between the two anterior limbs is called the anterior group, while the groups on either side are called the medial and lateral groups of nuclei.

The medial nuclear mass consists of the intralaminar nuclei, dorsomedial nucleus and midline nuclei.

The lateral nuclear mass can be divided into the dorsal and ventral groups. The dorsal group consists of the lateral dorsal group, lateral posterior group and pulvinar groups of nuclei. The ventral group consists of the ventral anterior, ventral lateral and ventral posterior groups. The ventral posterior nuclei can be divided into ventral-postero lateral (VPL) and ventral-postero medial (VPM).

The lateral and medial geniculate bodies are located in the posterior zone. The sheet of reticular nuclei is located just outside the lateral group and inside the internal capsule (Fig. 61.1).

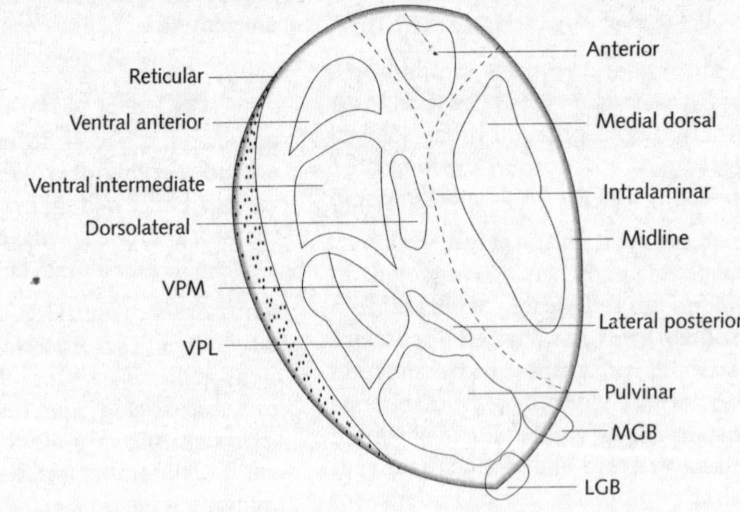


**Fig. 61.1:** Thalamic nuclei

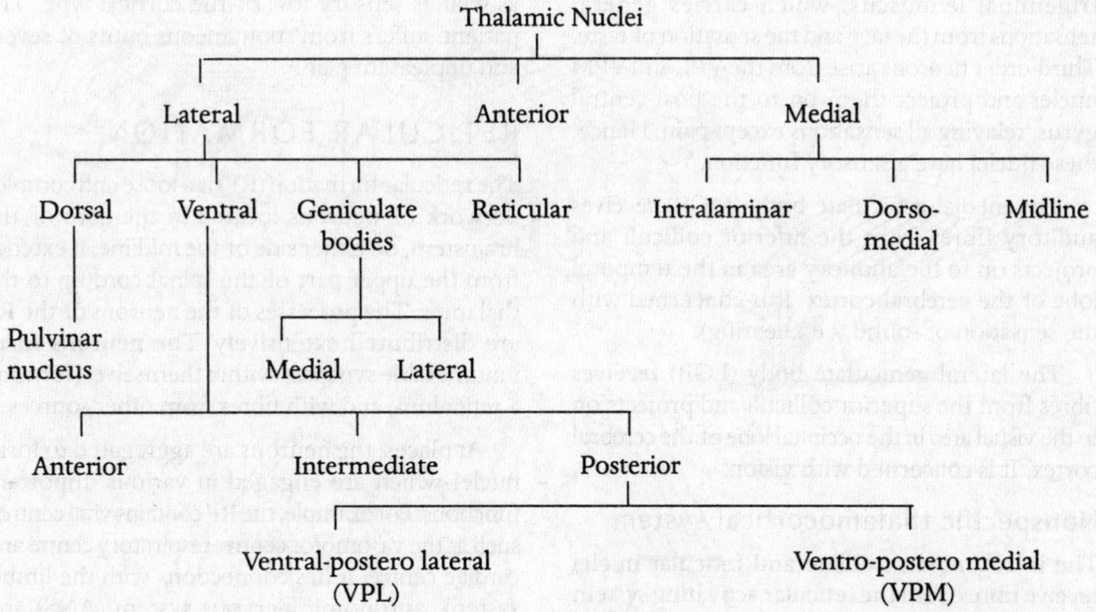


The thalamus has extensive connections with the cerebral hemisphere. If all these are cut off, the loss of cortical function is much greater than that caused by damage to the cerebral cortex alone, since thalamic excitation of the cortex is necessary for almost all cortical activities. Therefore, it appears that the cerebral hemispheres are anatomical and functional outgrowths of the thalamus. This is why together, they are called the thalamocortical system. This system can be divided into two parts:

1. Specific: extending from specific thalamic nuclei to specific parts of the cerebral cortex, for sensory and motor functions.
2. Nonspecific: extending from nonspecific thalamic nuclei to all parts of the cerebral cortex, for alertness.

## Specific thalamocortical system

The anterior thalamic nuclei receive afferents from mamillary bodies through the mamillo-thalamic tract. The nuclei project on to the hypothalamus and cingulate gyrus, that is, they are connected to the limbic system. They are, therefore, concerned with a person's emotions and recent memory.

The medial group of nuclei receive afferents from other thalamic nuclei, the hypothalamus and amygdala, and project on to the prefrontal cortex. They are, therefore, concerned with the integration of all sensations and their correlation with the emotional behaviour of a person.

As for the lateral group of nuclei, the ventral anterior nucleus receives fibres from the cerebellum and basal ganglia. It projects on to the premotor and motor cortex. Hence, it is concerned with motor activities. The ventral lateral nucleus is the chief motor nucleus of the thalamus. It receives dentato-thalamic fibres from the cerebellum, as well as fibres from the basal ganglia. It projects on to the primary motor and premotor cortex (areas 4 and 6). It is concerned with motor activities, that is, the control of movements and posture.

The VPL nucleus receives fibres from the medial lemniscus, which carries fibres from the nucleus gracilis and cuneatus, and the spinal lemniscus, which carries fibres from the anterior and lateral spinothalamic tract. The VPL nucleus projects on to the sensory cortex. It receives general sensations, such as touch, temperature, pain and proprioception, from the trunk and limbs.

The VPM nucleus receives fibres from the

trigeminal lemniscus, which carries general sensations from the face and the sensation of taste. Third-order neurons arise from the VPL and VPM nuclei and project them on to the post-central gyrus, relaying all sensations except pain. Hence, these nuclei have a sensory function.

The medial geniculate body (MGB) receives auditory fibres from the inferior colliculi and projects on to the auditory area in the temporal lobe of the cerebral cortex. It is concerned with the sensation of sound (i.e., hearing).

The lateral geniculate body (LGB) receives fibres from the superior colliculi and projects on to the visual area in the occipital lobe of the cerebral cortex. It is concerned with vision.

### Nonspecific thalamocortical system

The intralaminar, midline and reticular nuclei receive fibres from the reticular activating system and project them on to various areas of the cerebral cortex (generalized thalamocortical projection).

The nonspecific thalamocortical system is concerned with generalized activation of the cerebral cortex and, therefore, with alertness.

### Functions of thalamus

The thalamus is the relay station for all sensory inputs, barring olfaction, to the specific areas of the cortex. It relays general sensations through the VPL and VPM nuclei, and special senses through the LGB and MGB. Each thalamus represents the contralateral side of the body.

The thalamus is the subcortical perception centre for the sensation of pain. It also forms an important link between the basal ganglia and cerebellum on the one hand, and the motor cortex on the other, and is concerned with the control of movements and posture.

The thalamus plays a role in arousal and alertness of the brain as a whole. It is concerned with the emotions as well.

**Applied Physiology**

The thalamic syndrome is produced by thrombosis of the artery supplying the thalamus. It is characterized by muscular weakness, atonia and ataxia, as well as sensory loss of the cortical type. The patient suffers from spontaneous bouts of severe and unpleasant pain.

## RETICULAR FORMATION

The reticular formation (RF) is a loose and complex network of neurons located in the core of the brainstem, on either side of the midline. It extends from the upper part of the spinal cord up to the thalamus. The processes of the neurons of the RF are distributed extensively. The neurons form innumerable synapses within themselves, forming a reticulum, and with fibres from other sources.

At places, the neurons are aggregated to form nuclei which are engaged in various important functions. For example, the RF contains vital centres, such as the vasomotor centre, respiratory centre and cardiac centre. It has connections with the limbic system, autonomic nervous system (ANS) and endocrine system.

The RF has important projections, both descending and ascending. The descending RF consists of reticulospinal tracts for the control of lower motor neurons. Hence, it helps in the regulation of muscle tone and the maintenance of posture. It also has pathways for the control of the vital functions, endocrine regulation and regulation of sensory inputs to the CNS.

The ascending RF is called the reticular activating system (RAS). It sends information to the higher centres via the thalamus. Its fibres relay in the midline and intralaminar nuclei of the thalamus, and project on to all parts of the cerebral cortex. Part of the projection bypasses the thalamus.

The long sensory tracts, while going up the brainstem, give collaterals to the RAS. The latter, therefore, receives inputs from the medial, spinal and trigeminal lemnisci, as well as from the visual, auditory and olfactory systems. These impulses are sent to the whole cortex by the RAS. The RF is thus highly nonspecific as it is activated by any input. It also receives collaterals from the long motor tracts while going down the brainstem. Hence, the RF is in a position to synthesize everything from the incoming impulses (Fig. 61.2).

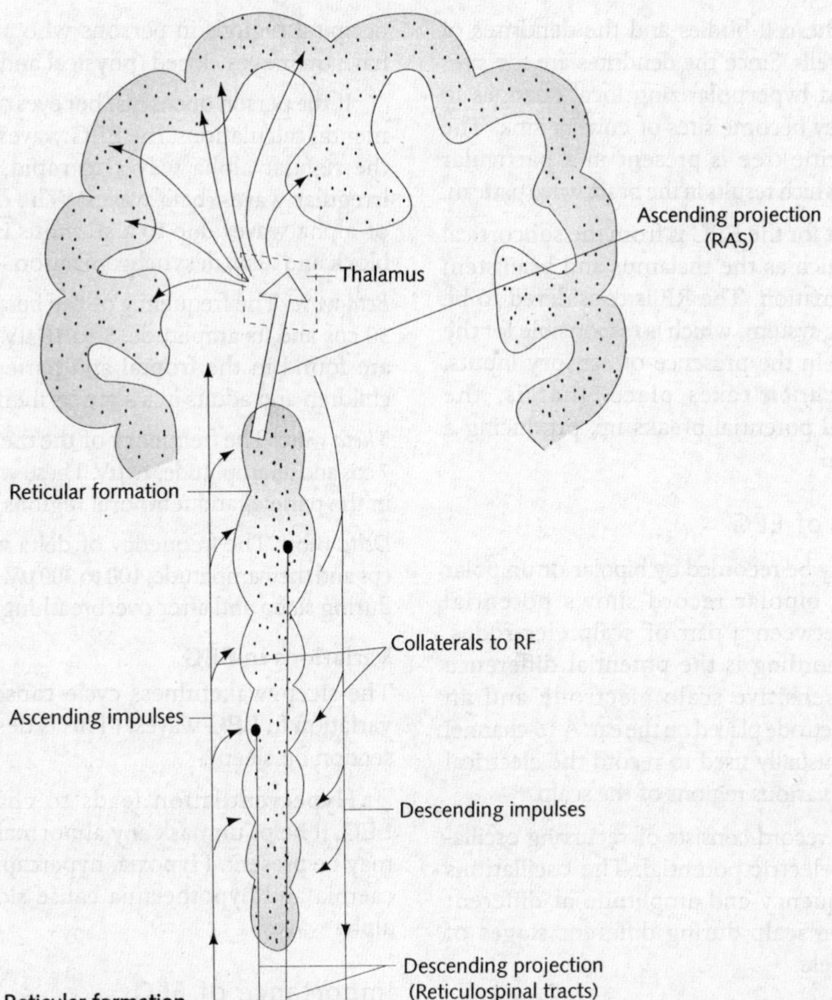


**Fig. 61.2:** Reticular formation

The RAS is responsible for arousal. In other words, it makes the cortex alert about various incoming stimuli. This alertness is important for the functioning of the brain, including sensory perception, thinking, memory and motor activity.

*Functions*: The RF regulates the vital functions, endocrine function and autonomic function. It alerts the brain to various stimuli and is responsible for the control of muscle tone and posture.

## THE ELECTROENCEPHALOGRAM (EEG)

The EEG is a record of the electrical activity of the brain.

The neurophysiological basis of the EEG is not known exactly. The genesis of electric potential in the brain is similar to that of electric potential in any other part of the body, that is, it has an ionic basis. However, the electrical activity in the brain is spontaneous and the changes in permeability are rhythmical. In the EEG, a record of the summated electric potentials from various neurons of the cortical grey matter is obtained. Thus, the EEG is the *synchronization* of small potentials that is represented as waves. The lower the frequency, the better is the synchronization and higher the amplitude of the waves.

The changes in potential recorded as an EEG are believed to result from fluctuating dipoles formed by the cell bodies and the dendrites of the cortical cells. Since the dendrites are the sites of hypo- and hyperpolarizing local changes in potential, they become sites of current sink. The dense dendritic tree is present in a particular orientation, which results in the brain wave pattern.

The input for the EEG is from the subcortical structures, such as the thalamus and brainstem reticular formation. The RF is considered to be the activating system, which is responsible for the brain waves. In the presence of sensory inputs, *desynchronization* takes place, that is, the synchronized potential breaks up, producing a wave pattern.

## Recording of EEG

The EEG may be recorded by bipolar or unipolar methods. A bipolar record shows potential variations between a pair of scalp electrodes. Unipolar recording is the potential difference between a sensitive scalp electrode and an indifferent electrode placed on the ear. A 16-channel polygraph is usually used to record the electrical activity from various regions of the scalp.

The EEG record consists of recurring oscillations in the electric potential. The oscillations differ in frequency and amplitude at different points on the scalp during different stages of mental alertness.

The following waves are seen in the EEG.

*Alpha wave*: The frequency of the alpha wave is 8 to 13 cycles per second (cps) and the amplitude, 50 µV. These waves are found in the parietal and occipital regions in persons who are awake and have their eyes closed (physical and mental rest).

If the person opens his/her eyes or makes some mental calculations, the EEG waves change from the regular alpha waves to rapid, low-voltage, irregular waves (beta waves). The disappearance of alpha waves due to a stimulus is called alpha block and also, desynchronization.

*Beta wave*: The frequency of the beta wave is 14 to 30 cps and its amplitude, 5 to 10 µV. These waves are found in the frontal and parietal regions in children and adults in a state of mental tension.

*Theta wave*: The frequency of the theta wave is 4 to 7 cps and its amplitude, 10 µV. These waves are found in the parietal and temporal regions in children.

*Delta wave*: The frequency of delta waves is 1 to 3 cps and their amplitude, 100 to 300 µV. They are seen during sleep and after overbreathing (Fig. 61.3).

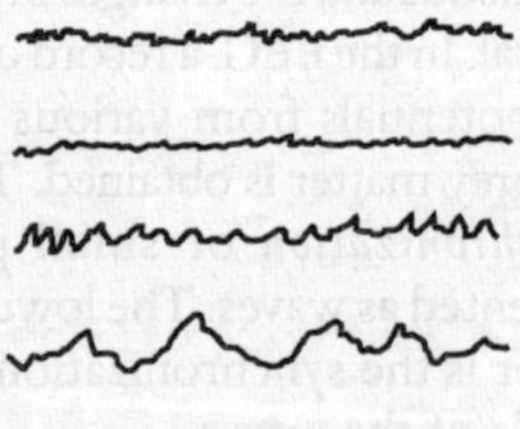

| Waves | Pattern | Frequency (CPS) | Amplitude (MV) |
|---|---|---|---|
| Alpha | | 8 – 13 | 50 |
| Beta | | 14 – 13 | 5–10 |
| Theta | | 4 – 7 | 10 |
| Delta | | 1 – 3 | 100–300 |

**Fig. 61.3:** Fundamental waves seen in EEG

### Variations in EEG

The sleep–wakefulness cycle causes maximum variation in EEG waves. (This is described in the section on sleep).

Hyperventilation leads to changes in the EEG. It helps unmask any abnormal rhythm that may be present. Hypoxia, hypercapnia, hypoglycaemia and hypothermia cause slowing of the alpha waves.

## Importance of EEG

Abnormalities in the EEG patterns may help diagnose a local cerebral pathology. The presence of irregular, slow waves (theta or delta waves) in a localized area of the scalp helps in the diagnosis of brain tumour.

Epilepsy is characterized by fits of uncontrolled and excessive motor activity of a part or the whole of the body. An EEG may not only help diagnose the type of epilepsy, but may also indicate the site of irritating focus in the cerebral cortex. Surgical removal of such a focus may cure the patient of epileptic fits.

Brain death is indicated by a persistently flat EEG record. The EEG is particularly important in cases of organ transplantation. It has been losing its importance as a diagnostic tool since more modern and effective diagnostic procedures, such as MRI and CT scan, are available these days.

## SLEEP

Sleep is a temporary state of unconsciousness of the body. A person can easily be aroused from sleep by the appropriate sensory stimuli. It is, therefore, entirely different from deep anaesthesia and coma, from which a person cannot be aroused by sensory stimuli.

In adults, the sleep-wakefulness cycle follows a 24-hour rhythm. The majority of human beings sleep at night and are awake during the day.

The requirement of sleep is inversely proportional to age. Newborns require 20 to 22 hours of sleep, children 14 to 16 hours, adults 7 to 9 hours, and old people less than 5 hours.

### Types of sleep

Sleep is of two types—slow-wave sleep (SWS) and rapid eye movement (REM) sleep.

#### Slow-wave Sleep (SWS)

Slow-wave sleep has been named so because the EEG waves gradually become slower as sleep proceeds. SWS may be divided into the four stages described below.

*Stage I*: The EEG waves, which are fast and of low amplitude (beta waves) in an alert, wakeful condition, get converted into alpha waves as dozing starts. This sleep is light and the person can be easily aroused.

*Stage II*: In this stage, the EEG shows sleep spindles superimposed on low-voltage background activity like theta waves. Sleep spindles are bursts of high-amplitude, high-frequency waves of short duration. Arousal becomes slightly difficult in this stage.

*Stage III*: The sleep spindles are now superimposed on delta waves. The threshold for arousal goes up further.

*Stage IV*: In this stage, the EEG shows synchronization and slow delta waves. This stage is the most prolonged and arousing a person is more difficult than in the other stages (Fig. 61.4).

Sleep starts with stage I and proceeds stage by stage to stage IV. It then comes back to stage I, which is followed by REM sleep. The successive stages of sleep are as shown below.

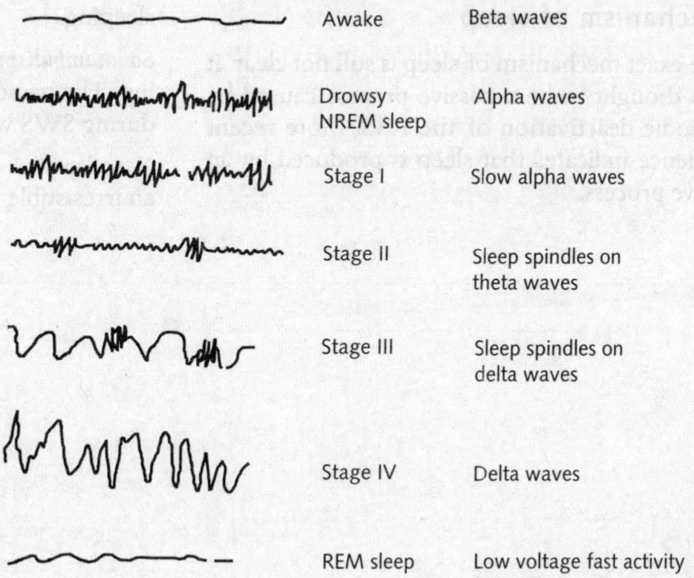

Awake — Beta waves

Drowsy NREM sleep — Alpha waves

Stage I — Slow alpha waves

Stage II — Sleep spindles on theta waves

Stage III — Sleep spindles on delta waves

Stage IV — Delta waves

REM sleep — Low voltage fast activity Beta waves

**Fig. 61.4:** EEG changes in sleep

Stage I → II → III → IV →
III → II → I → REM sleep

The duration of SWS is 90 minutes.

During sleep, the threshold for many reflexes goes up. The Babinski sign may appear. There is a reduction in muscle tone, and the heart rate, blood pressure and respiratory rate fall but remain steady.

**Rapid Eye Movement (REM) Sleep**

REM sleep derives its name from the fact that during this type of sleep, there are bursts of rapid eye movements. It is also called paradoxical sleep because certain signs of wakefulness, such as high-frequency, low-voltage waves on the EEG (beta rhythm), eye movements, and a rise in the heart rate and respiration, are present even though the person is in a deep sleep, as shown by the marked decrease in muscle tone. REM sleep is associated with dreaming. Its duration is about 10 minutes.

Every 80 to 100 minutes of SWS is followed by 5 to 30 minutes of REM sleep. There are 4 to 6 bouts of REM sleep every night. Thus, REM sleep constitutes 20 to 25 per cent of the total sleep time in adults. In infants, it constitutes 25 to 50 per cent of the total sleep.

## Mechanism of sleep

The exact mechanism of sleep is still not clear. It was thought to be a passive process caused by periodic deactivation of the RAS. More recent evidence indicates that sleep is produced by an active process.

Raphe nuclei, which are situated in the lower half of the pons and medulla, are the centres that produce SWS. Nerve impulses spread extensively from these neurons into the RF. They then travel via the thalamus to the neocortex and limbic system. Neurons associated with Raphe nuclei produce serotonin, which produces SWS by the inhibition of the RAS.

The locus ceruleus, which is located in the pontine RF, seems to be responsible for the production of REM sleep. The neurons of the locus ceruleus secrete norepinephrine.

It is also known that a rise in the secretion of epinephrine and norepinephrine results in stimulation of the RAS, alertness and arousal, among other things.

*Importance of sleep*: Sleep is essential for normal physical and mental health. Both the REM and SWS (NREM) types of sleep seem to be required. Sleep-deprived individuals suffer from loss of concentration, memory failure and somatic symptoms, such as weakness and tremors.

**Sleep Disorders**

The following are the common sleep disorders.

*Insomnia*: This is an inability to get sufficient or restful sleep, despite adequate opportunities for sleeping.

*Somnambulism*: This is also known as sleep walking. The person may wander about in the house during SWS without being aware of it.

*Narcolepsy*: A person afflicted by narcolepsy has an irresistible urge to sleep even while working.

CHAPTER 62

# Muscle Tone, Posture and Equilibrium

## MUSCLE TONE

Muscle tone is the partial, sustained state of contraction in the muscle, even in the resting state. It is like a background activity, over which muscle contraction becomes easier and more efficient.

The muscle tone is determined by the activity of the myotatic or stretch reflex. When a muscle is stretched, it contracts against that stretch and the degree of contraction is proportional to the stretch applied. All the deep reflexes, called jerks, are stretch reflexes.

### Reflex arc

The anatomical basis of the stretch reflex is the intact reflex arc, which is monosynaptic. It consists of the receptor organ, the afferent and efferent neurons, the centre and the effector organ.

**Receptor Organ**

The muscle spindles are the sensory receptors which detect the degree and rate of stretch of the skeletal muscle. The degree and rate of stretch affect the length of the muscle. These receptors are spindle-shaped structures that are 1 to 4 mm long and 0.1 to 0.2 mm broad. They lie parallel to and between the muscle fibres, in the fleshy part of the muscle. The muscle spindle is attached to the fibrous covering (endomycium) of the muscle fibre at either end. The number of muscle spindles in a muscle belly varies according to the accuracy of the movements that the muscle is required to perform (Fig. 62.1).

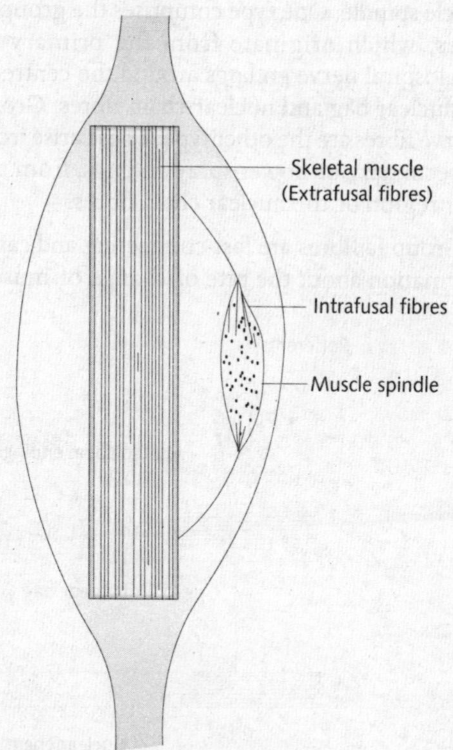


**Fig. 62.1:** Location of muscle spindle

Each muscle spindle contains 3 to 6 modified muscle fibres, called intrafusal fibres. (The ordinary skeletal muscle fibres are called extrafusal muscle fibres). The intrafusal fibres are enclosed in a thin, fibrous capsule, containing lymph sacs. They consist of two striated, contractile poles, which contain actin and myosin and have a central noncontractile part. The striated poles can shorten and stretch. The contraction of the striated poles stretches the central part, where the nuclei are aggregated. Two types of intrafusal fibres can be identified in a muscle spindle. These are nuclear bag fibres and nuclear chain fibres. In the former, the nuclei are gathered together in the central, dilated, bag-like portion, while in the latter, they are arranged in a single chain. The nuclear chain fibres are situated on the sides of the nuclear bag fibre (Fig. 62.2).

**Afferent Neuron**

Two types of sensory neurons arise from the muscle spindle. One type comprises the group Ia fibres, which originate from the primary or annulospiral nerve endings around the centre of the nuclear bag and nuclear chain fibres. Group II nerve fibres are the other type. These arise from the secondary or flower-spray endings, from the polar region of the nuclear chain fibres.

Group Ia fibres are fast-conducting and carry information about the rate of change of muscle length. Group II fibres are slow-conducting and carry information about the absolute length of the muscle.

**Centre**

The anterior horn cells in the spinal cord act as a centre for stretch reflex.

They control the discharge of motor impulses along the efferent neurons ($\alpha$ and $\gamma$) to the skeletal muscle for contraction.

**Efferent Neuron**

Two types of motor neurons arise from the anterior horn cells. These are:

1. The axons of alpha neurons, which are large and supply the extrafusal fibres; and
2. The axons of gamma neurons, which are small and supply the intrafusal fibres (the contractile ends of the muscle spindle).

**Effector Organ**

Both the extrafusal and intrafusal fibres of the skeletal muscle contract due to the activity of the alpha and gamma motor neurons, respectively (Fig. 62.3).

## Mechanism of stretch reflex and muscle tone

Whenever a muscle is stretched, the muscle spindle gets stretched. Next, sensory impulses are carried

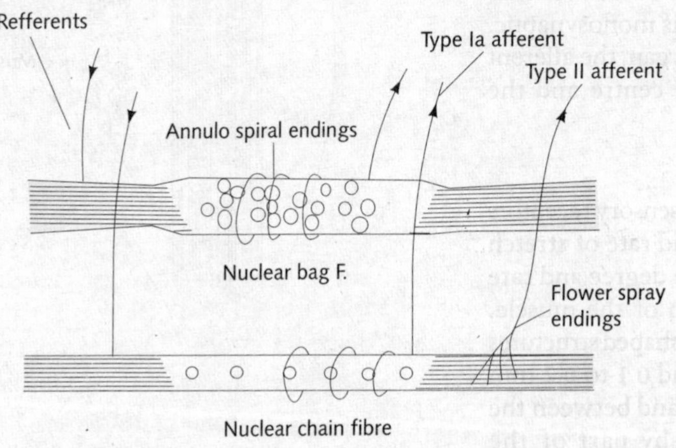


**Fig. 62.2:** Structure and innervation of intrafusal fibres of muscle spindle

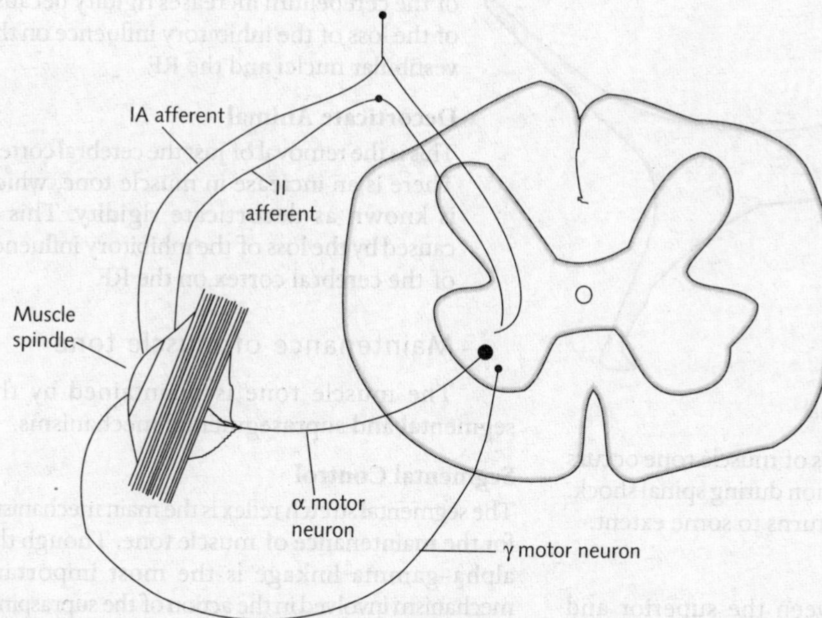


Fig. 62.3: Pathway for a stretch reflex

from the primary and secondary endings to the spinal cord, and the anterior horn cells are stimulated. This causes activation of the alpha motor neuron so that impulses are given to the extrafusal fibres and the muscle contracts. This is a stretch reflex. Then, the muscle length decreases, making the spindle insensitive and the muscle relaxes. To make the spindle sensitive, there is simultaneous activation of gamma motor neurons. This produces contraction of the striated poles of the intrafusal fibres, leading to stretching of the noncontractile central region. Therefore, the increase in gamma discharge produces an increase in the afferent discharge from the muscle spindles. In this way, the tonic discharge from the muscle spindle to the spinal cord via posterior root maintains the tonic activity of the alpha neuron, and resulting continuous tonic signals to the extrafusal fibres, in a state of partial contraction of muscle and tone. This is called alpha-gamma linkage.

The muscle tone is maintained by asynchronous contraction of the motor units. A few contract at a time while the others remain relaxed. Following this, the latter group contracts and the former relaxes. This prevents fatigue of the muscles.

The muscle tone depends on the integrity of the stretch reflex arc. Damage to the afferent and efferent (alpha) neurons results in loss of muscle tone. It also depends on discharge in the gamma motor neurons, which ultimately decide the level of activity of the alpha motor neuron.

## Supraspinal control of muscle tone

Though the spinal reflex arc is the primary determinant of the muscle tone, it is continuously regulated or modulated by impulses coming from the supraspinal centres (the cerebral cortex, basal ganglia and cerebellum). All these together form an integrated pattern. To understand the role of some of the mechanisms by eliminating others, sections of the neural axis are taken at various levels and their effects are noted below the level of section.

The following preparations are produced experimentally:

**Spinal Animal**

A section of the spinal cord is taken at the mid-thoracic level which disconnects the segments below the level of the section from all higher

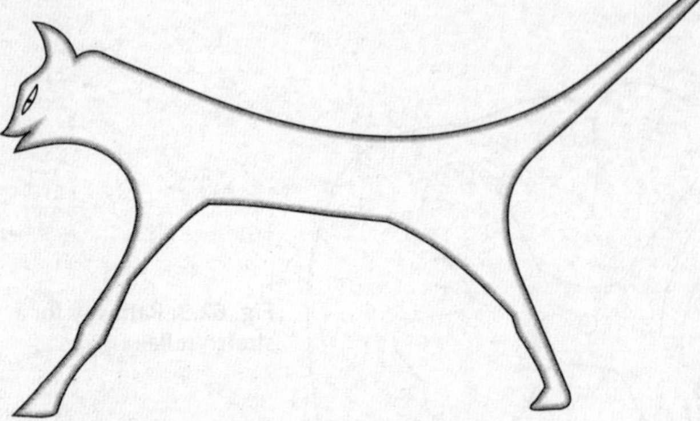

Fig. 62.4: A decerebrate animal

influences. Immediate loss of muscle tone occurs below the level of the section during spinal shock. Later, the muscle tone returns to some extent.

**Decerebrate Animal**

A section is taken between the superior and inferior colliculi of the midbrain. The preparation is called the decerebrate animal, as the influence of the cerebrum is absent.

Spinal shock does not develop, but the muscle tone increases in the antigravity muscles of all four limbs. The animal shows extension of all four limbs, an arched back and extension of the tail (Fig. 62.4). This rigidity is produced by gamma motor discharge, and then through the alpha–gamma linkage. Therefore, it disappears after cutting the posterior root which disrupts the alpha-gamma linkage.

The mechanism of rigidity can be explained as follows. The brainstem reticular formation (RF) has both excitatory and inhibitory areas which influence the muscle tone. The inhibitory axons are driven by the inhibitory areas of the cerebral cortex, basal ganglia and cerebellum. On the other hand, the facilitatory area in the brainstem acts on its own, on the basis of the inputs it gets from the periphery. Due to decerebration, the inhibitory influences from the cerebral cortex and basal ganglia are lost. Therefore, the excitatory areas get the upper hand and the muscle tone increases (Fig. 62.5).

The tone of the extensors increases due to an intact vestibulospinal reflex as well. The removal of the cerebellum increases rigidity because of the loss of the inhibitory influence on the vestibular nuclei and the RF.

**Decorticate Animal**

This is the removal of just the cerebral cortex. There is an increase in muscle tone, which is known as decorticate rigidity. This is caused by the loss of the inhibitory influence of the cerebral cortex on the RF.

## Maintenance of muscle tone

The muscle tone is maintained by the segmental and suprasegmental mechanisms.

**Segmental Control**

The segmental stretch reflex is the main mechanism for the maintenance of muscle tone. Though the alpha–gamma linkage is the most important mechanism involved in the action of the supraspinal influences, direct stimulation or inhibition of the alpha motor neurons also influences the muscle tone.

Inhibitory neurons in the spinal cord play a role in feedback inhibition of the alpha motor neurons. They also decrease the tone of the antagonistic muscle. Further, Golgi tendon organs in the muscle tendon, when stimulated by excessive stretching, decrease the muscle tone by direct inhibition of the alpha motor neurons (negative stretch reflex).

**Suprasegmental Control**

Influences from different parts of the CNS act by affecting the segmental stretch reflex, or by altering the rate of gamma motor discharge, or by directly influencing the alpha motor neurons. These influences are as follows.

*Cerebral cortex*: The cerebral cortex has an inhibitory influence, which is mediated through the extrapyramidal mechanism (rubrospinal, reticulospinal and vestibulospinal tracts). It also influences the alpha and gamma motor neurons directly through the corticospinal pathways.

*Basal ganglia*: These have an inhibitory influence on muscle tone.

*Cerebellum*: The cerebellum inhibits muscle tone,

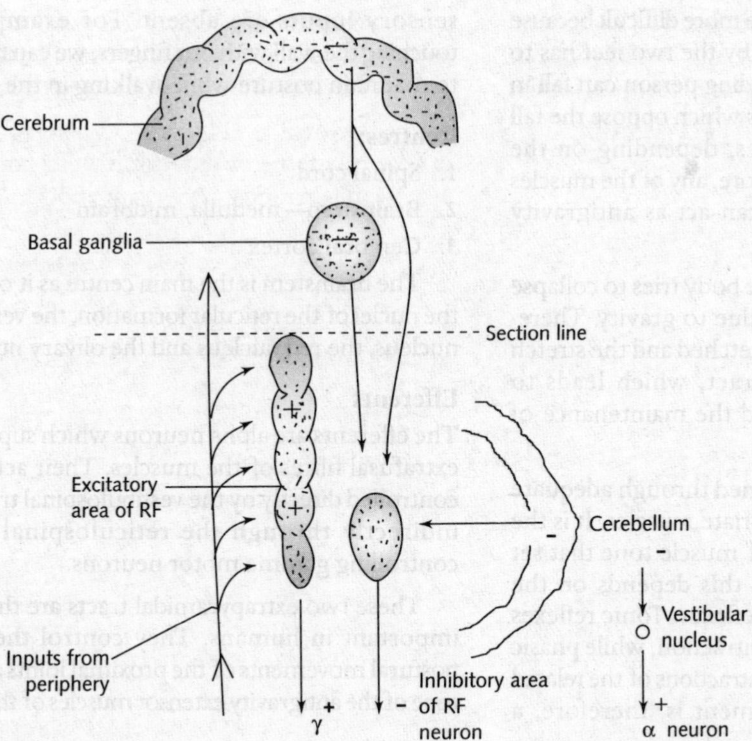


Fig. 62.5: Mechanism of decerebrate rigidity

mainly by its vestibulospinal mechanism and to some extent, via other extrapyramidal mechanisms.

*Brainstem*: The brainstem contains reticular and vestibular nuclei. The reticular nuclei (RF) have both inhibitory and excitatory influences, while the vestibular nuclei have an excitatory influence on the tone in antigravity muscles.

## Applied physiology

The assessment of muscle tone is one of the important components of the clinical examination of a patient with a neurological disorder. The muscle tone is tested by the flexion of a limb at various joints, such as the elbow or knee joint.

An increase in the muscle tone is called hypertonia and a decrease, hypotonia. The former leads to two types of rigidity.

*Clasp-knife rigidity*: Great resistance is offered at the beginning of a passive movement. Once the movement begins, the resistance subsides. This is seen in pyramidal tract (UMN) lesions.

*Lead-pipe rigidity*: Due to the uniform resistance offered, no movement is possible. This is seen in extrapyramidal tract lesions (Parkinson's disease).

In hypotonia, no resistance is offered to passive movement and the muscle is said to be flaccid. It is seen in LMN lesions and cerebellar disease.

## REGULATION OF POSTURE

A specific attitude of the body, in the absence of movement, is called posture. Standing and sitting are two examples. Posture is defined as the orientation of the head in relation to space and the alignment of the body and neck in relation to the head, so that an upright position is maintained.

The posture must be maintained properly in order for equilibrium to be maintained when the body moves (dynamic). Voluntary movements can be performed properly and purposefully if the posture is proper and provides a stable background.

In quadrupeds, the extensor muscles are basically antigravity muscles. In man, the maintenance of an erect posture has become more difficult because the narrow base provided by the two feet has to support a tall body. A standing person can fall in any direction. The muscles which oppose the fall act as antigravity muscles, depending on the direction of the fall. Therefore, any of the muscles of the trunk and limbs can act as antigravity muscles.

In the erect posture, the body tries to collapse and the knees try to flex due to gravity. Therefore, the quadriceps are stretched and the stretch reflex makes them contract, which leads to extension of the knee and the maintenance of an erect posture.

The posture is maintained through adequate contraction of the appropriate muscles. It is the degree and distribution of muscle tone that set a particular posture, and this depends on the various tonic and phasic reflexes. Tonic reflexes cause sustained muscle contraction, while phasic reflexes lead to transient contractions of the related muscles. Postural adjustment is, therefore, a reflex mechanism.

## Reflex arc for postural reflexes

The reflex arc for postural reflexes consists of the receptor organ, afferent neuron, centre, efferent neuron and effector organ.

**Afferents**

Proprioceptive impulses from the muscle spindles present in the muscles of the neck and limbs, as well as from the joints, send continuous information to the brain (sensory) and cerebellum (nonsensory) regarding the sense of position. Proprioceptive impulses from the deeper parts of the soles of the feet are also important for the maintenance of an erect posture.

Vestibular impulses from the vestibular apparatus send information about the direction of action of body weight. Visual impulses from the eyes give an idea of the position of the body with respect to the environment. Vision can maintain posture even in the absence of other afferent impulses.

Tactile impulses from the skin play an important role in the maintenance of posture when all other sensory inputs are absent. For example, by touching the wall with our fingers, we can manage to maintain posture while walking in the dark.

**Centres:**

1. Spinal cord
2. Brainstem—medulla, midbrain
3. Cerebral cortex

The brainstem is the main centre as it contains the nuclei of the reticular formation, the vestibular nucleus, the red nucleus and the olivary nucleus.

**Efferents**

The efferents are alpha neurons which supply the extrafusal fibres of the muscles. Their activity is controlled directly by the vestibulospinal tract and indirectly through the reticulospinal tracts controlling gamma motor neurons.

These two extrapyramidal tracts are the most important in humans. They control the gross postural movements of the proximal joints and the tone of the antigravity extensor muscles of the body.

## Role of centres in CNS

The role of different centres of the CNS in the maintenance of posture is studied in the spinal, decerebrate and decorticate animals.

*Sections*

3. Cerebral cortex / Thalamus → Decorticate animal

Basal ganglia → High

2. Medulla / Spinal cord → Low

(High and Low: Decerebrate animal)

1. Midbrain / Pons → Spinal animal

**Spinal Animal—Role of spinal cord**

Following the stage of spinal shock, when isolated segments regain their reflex activity, the stretch and cross extensor reflexes, as well as the positive and negative supporting reactions can be observed. This indicates that the spinal cord is a centre for these postural reflexes.

*Stretch reflex*: This is the basic mechanism involved in the maintenance of posture. Most of the other mechanisms maintain posture by influencing this reflex directly or indirectly. The stretch reflex appears in the flexor muscles first, since the spinal cord controls the primitive functioning of the body. However, the stretch reflex is very weak and the spinal animal cannot stand unsupported as the supraspinal control is lost.

*Crossed extensor reflex*: This reflex helps maintain posture by causing contraction of the extensors of the opposite side, when the flexors of one side are contracting. This is of great importance during walking.

*Positive supporting reaction*: When the lower limb is supported against gravitational force with the hand, both the flexor and extensor groups of muscles contract simultaneously and the lower limb is converted into a rigid pillar so as to support the body. This helps in the fixing and locking of joints. The limb starts moving along the direction of the fingers of the observer. This is called the magent reaction. It is initiated by the stimulation of the touch, pressure and proprioceptive receptors. It prevents the animal from falling over to that side.

*Negative supporting reaction*: When the extensors of a limb are excessively stretched, the supporting reaction is lost, that is, the limb no longer supports the body weight. The proprioceptors and extensors are involved in the negative supporting reaction, which helps unlock the joint.

### Decerebrate Animal—Role of Medulla and Midbrain

A transection at the upper border of the pons separates the spinal cord, medulla and pons from the rest of the brain (low decerebrate animal).

The following reflexes can be observed in the decerebrate animal:

1. A strong stretch reflex
2. Crossed extensor reflex
3. Positive supporting reaction
4. Negative supporting reaction
5. Tonic neck and labyrinthine reflexes

*Tonic neck and labyrinthine reflexes*: These are tonic reflexes operating at the level of the medulla. Tonic neck reflexes are caused by the stimulation of the muscle spindles in the neck. First, dorsiflexion of the head leads to extension of the forelimbs and flexion of the hind limbs. This gives the appearance of an animal looking over a shelf.

Next, ventroflexion of the head leads to flexion of the forelimbs and extension of the hind limbs, giving the appearance of an animal peeping through a hole in the ground (Fig. 62.6). Rotation of the head then causes the limbs towards the jaw to extend and those towards the skull to flex. Finally, pressure on the seventh cervical vertebra leads to flexion of all four limbs.

Tonic labyrinthine reflexes are caused by the stimulation of the vestibular apparatus by the force of gravity. If a decerebrate animal is placed on its back, all four limbs are extended, but if the vestibular apparatus on one side is destroyed, the limbs on that side remain flexed (Fig. 62.7).

The presence of tonic neck and labyrinthine reflexes indicates that the medulla is the centre for them.

If a section is taken just above the midbrain (high decerebrate animal), the animal can not only stand normally but can also reflexly perform typical quadrupedal walking movements.

The reflexes observed are those present in the low decerebrate animal, as well as righting reflexes. This indicates that the midbrain is the centre for righting reflexes. Righting reflexes are those reflexes that help right or correct the posture from a destabilized position and maintain the body in the normal upright position.

*Righting reflexes*: There are four righting reflexes—the labyrinthine righting reflex, body on head righting reflex, neck righting reflex and body on body righting reflex. The labyrinthine righting reflex helps to keep the head upright if the body is tilted in various ways. It is caused by the stimulation of the vestibular apparatus. The asymmetrical discharge from the two labyrinths causes changes in the tone of the neck muscles, resulting in righting of the head.

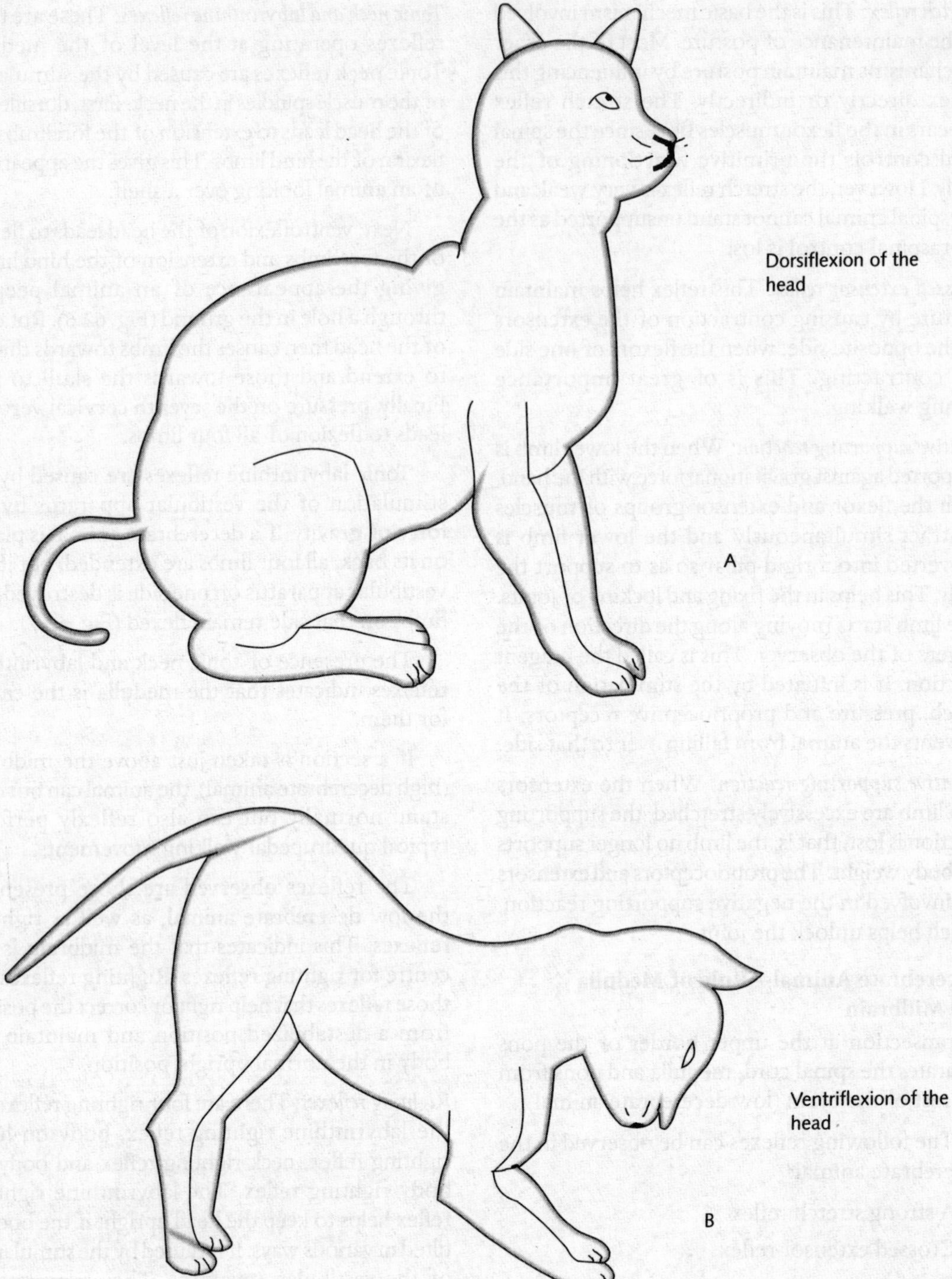


**Fig. 62.6: Tonic neck reflex**

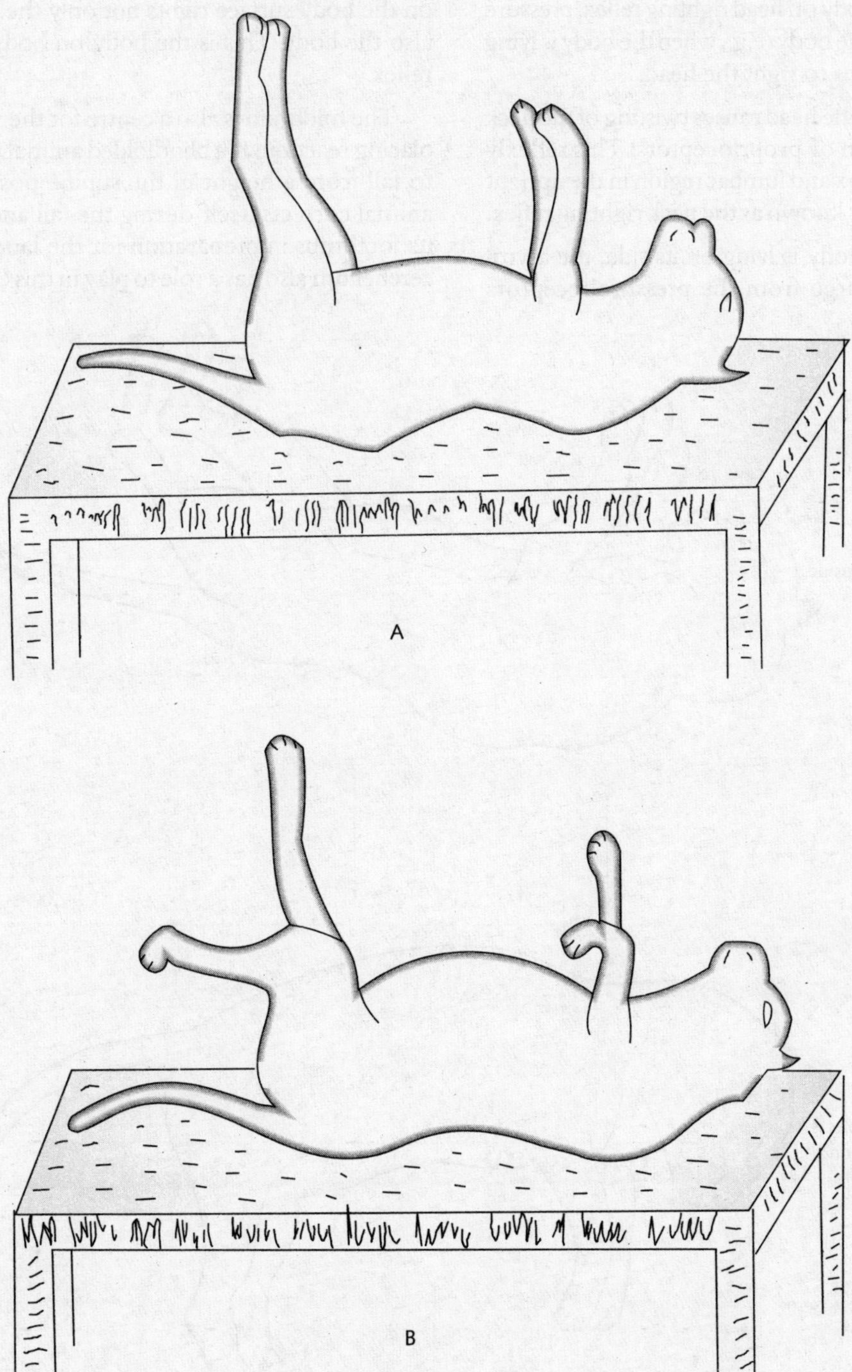


**Fig. 62.7:** Tonic labyrinthine reflex: A. Intact labyrinth, B. Destruction of left labyrinth

As for the body on head righting reflex, pressure on the side of the body (e.g., when the body is lying on its side) helps to right the head.

Righting of the head causes twisting of the neck and stimulation of proprioceptors. This reflexly brings the thorax and lumbar region in the upright position. This is known as the neck righting reflex.

When the body is lying on its side, the asymmetrical discharge from the pressure receptors on the body surface rights not only the head, but also the body. This is the body on body righting reflex.

The midbrain is also a centre for the vestibular placing reaction. If a blindfolded animal is allowed to fall from a height in the supine position, the animal corrects itself during the fall and extends its forelimbs in preparation for the landing. The cerebellum also has a role to play in this (Fig. 62.8).

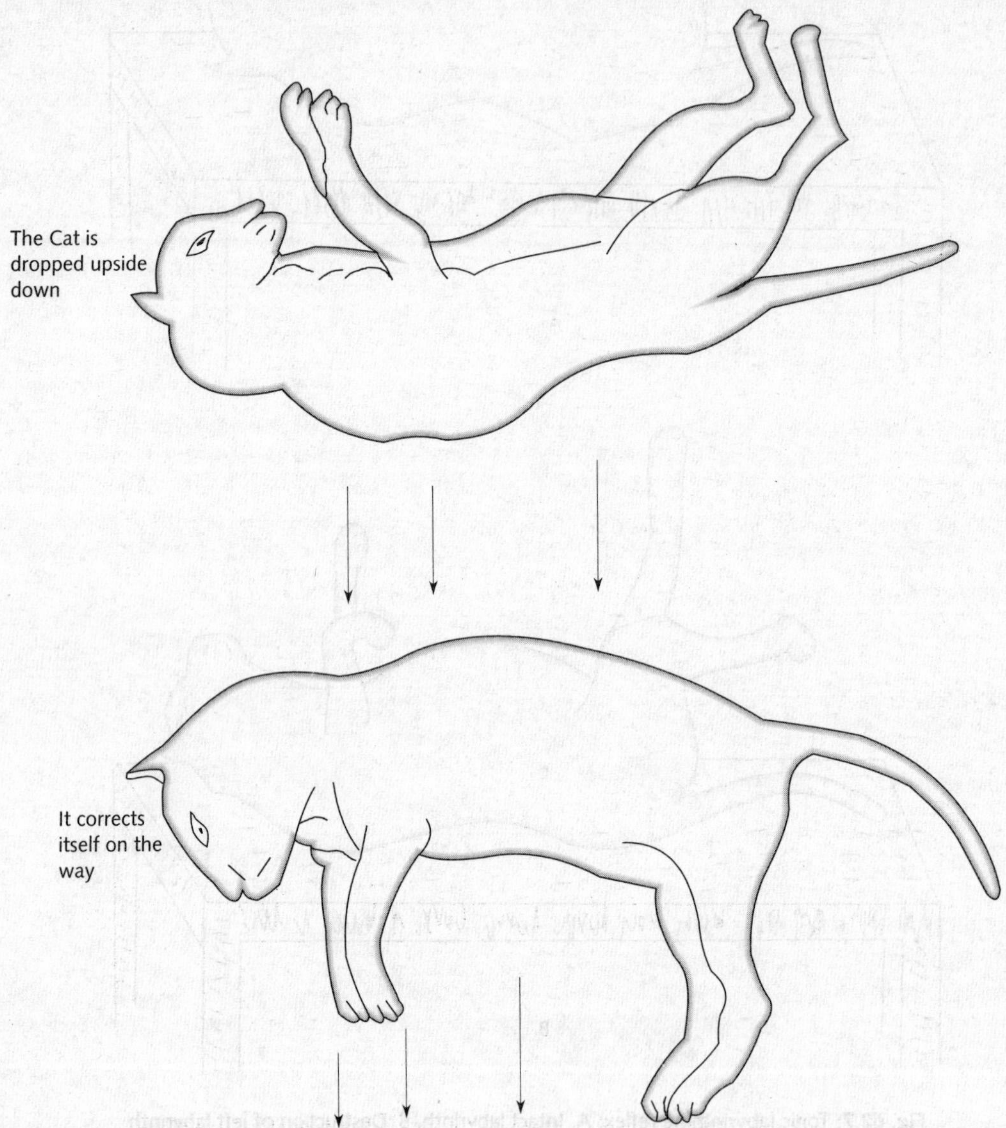
The Cat is dropped upside down
It corrects itself on the way

**Fig. 62.8:** Vestibular placing reaction

### Decorticate Animal

The following reflexes and reactions are absent in the decorticate animal, indicating that the cerebral cortex is the centre for them.

*Optical righting reflexes*: Visual cues about the position of the body in relation to the environment help correct the head. An animal can right itself after bilateral dennervation of the labyrinth, but not if it is blindfolded. These reflexes are integrated in the visual cortex and are particularly important in man.

*Hopping reaction*: When a standing animal is pushed laterally, it prevents the fall by hopping, that is, shifting its base towards the direction of fall.

*Placing reaction*: If a blindfolded animal is suspended in the air near a table and its snout touches the table, it immediately places both its forepaws on the table to support its body weight.

## EQUILIBRIUM

The maintenance of the erect posture when the body is moving is known as equilibrium. Equilibrium is a dynamic process. The movements of the body make it susceptible to destabilization. However, owing to elaborate arrangements for fighting destabilization, man can maintain a stable equilibrium.

Various factors help in the process of equilibrium. First, the vestibular apparatus, with its gravity receptors, faithfully relays information about the position of the body in space in relation to the effective line of the gravitational pull in any position at any moment.

The eyes, by comparing the picture of the environment with the position of the body, send useful information. Proprioceptive inputs promptly relay information regarding any unusual movement (of any part of the body) which may result from a tendency for destabilization.

The above information is then analysed by the vestibular nuclei and cerebellum. The necessary decisions are taken to cause contraction of the appropriate muscles, but ordinarily, equilibrium is maintained by some reflex corrections of position, such as the vestibulospinal reflex and visuospinal reflex.

## Vestibular apparatus

The vestibular apparatus is a part of the internal ear. It is located in a complex, bony cavity called the bony labyrinth, in the petrous part of the temporal bone, along with the cochlea.

The vestibular apparatus consists of a system of thin-walled ducts and sacs to called the membranous labyrinth, the shape of which is identical with that of the bony labyrinth outside. It consists of three semicircular canals and two sacs, the utricle and the saccule. The cochlear duct connects the saccule with the cochlea (Fig. 62.9).

Outside the membranous labyrinth, that is, between the bony and the membranous walls, there is a fluid called the perilymph. Inside the membranous labyrinth, there is a fluid called the endolymph. Both fluids have a composition similar to that of tissue fluid, but the perilymph is rich in $Na^+$ and the endolymph is rich in $K^+$. There is no communication between the two.

### Semicircular Canals

There are three semicircular canals on each side of the body. These are the lateral (horizontal), superior (anterior) and posterior canals. They are oriented in the three planes of the space, at right angles to one another. The lateral canals attain the horizontal plane only when the head is bent forward by 30°. At the end, near its origin from the utricle, each canal has a dilated part called the ampulla. This contains the receptor organs, known as the crista ampullaris. The nondilated ends of the superior and posterior canals have a common opening in the utricle. Thus, the three semicircular canals open into the utricle through five apertures instead of six.

The crista is a ridge of tissue whose upper surface contains tall, columnar hair cells. The hair extends upwards, into a firm gelatinous structure called the cupula. The latter extends across the entire lumen of the ampulla and forms a movable partition. The movements of the endolymph, which are produced by the movement of the head, deflect the cupula sideways, thereby bending the

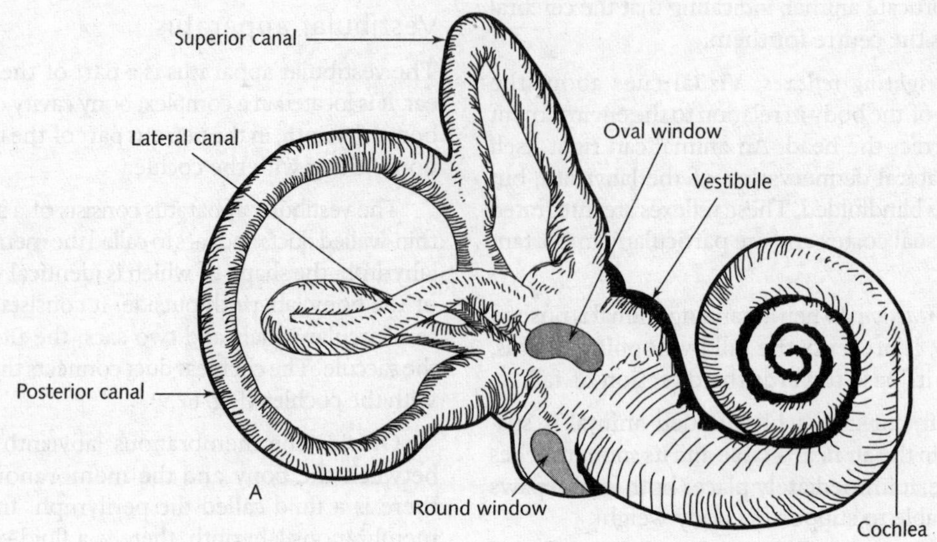


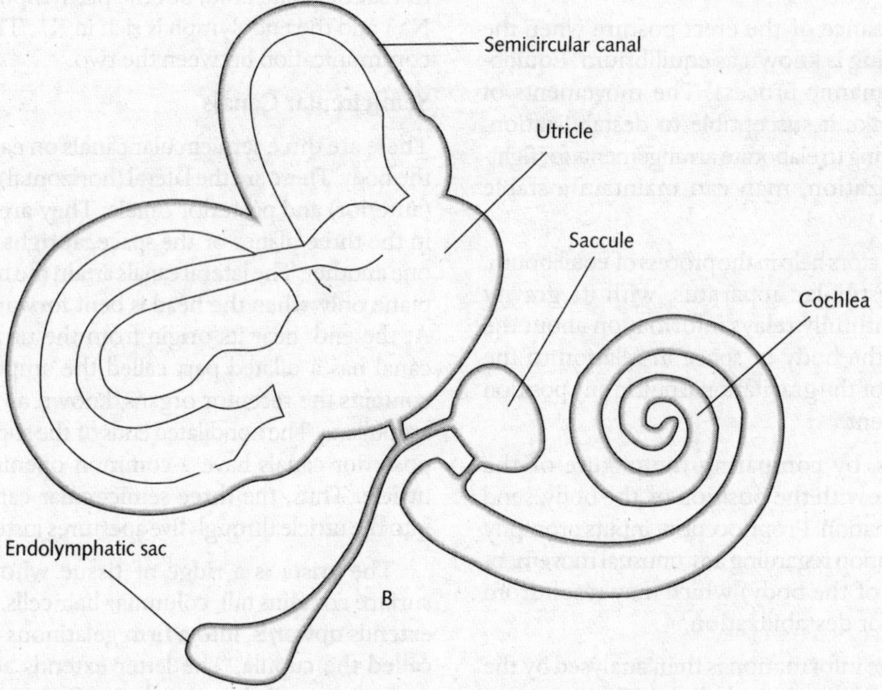


**Fig. 62.9:** Vestibular apparatus: A. Bony labyrinth, B. Membranous labyrinth

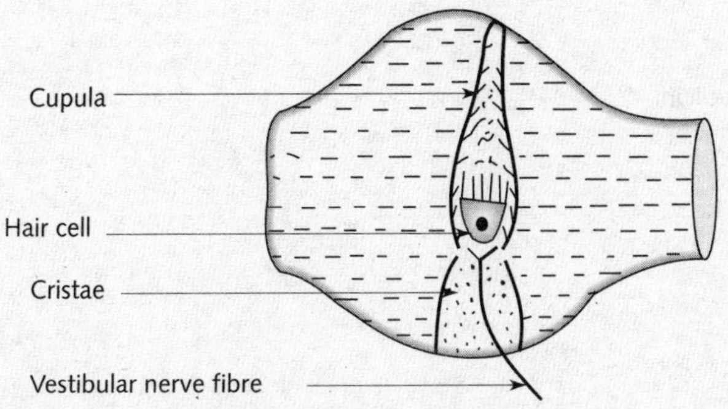


**Fig. 62.10:** Ampulla of a semicircular canal

hair cells. The bases of the hair cells synapse with the sensory axons of the vestibular nerve (Fig. 62.10).

### The Utricles and Saccules

The utricle and saccule each contain a receptor organ called the macula, which is covered by a columnar epithelium, like the crista. The hair cells are embedded in a thin, gelatinous layer which covers the epithelium. Many chalky particles ($CaCO_3$), called otoliths, are embedded in the gelatinous layer. Hence, the utricle and saccule are also known as otolith organs (Fig. 62.11).

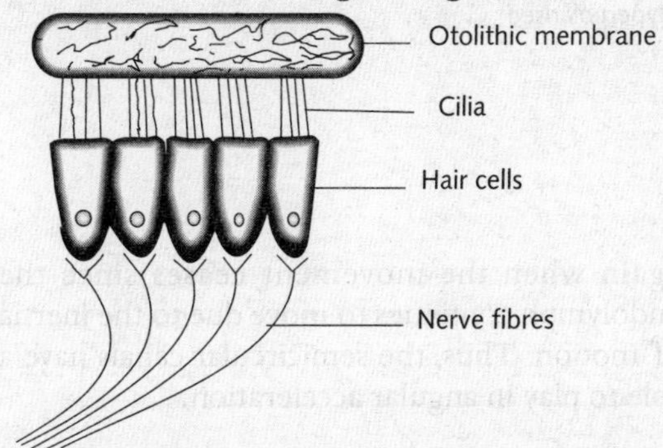


**Fig. 62.11:** Maculae of otolith organs (utricle and saccule)

When the head is in the normal vertical position, the macula of each utricle is in the horizontal plane, while the macula of each saccule lies in the vertical plane (Fig. 62.12).

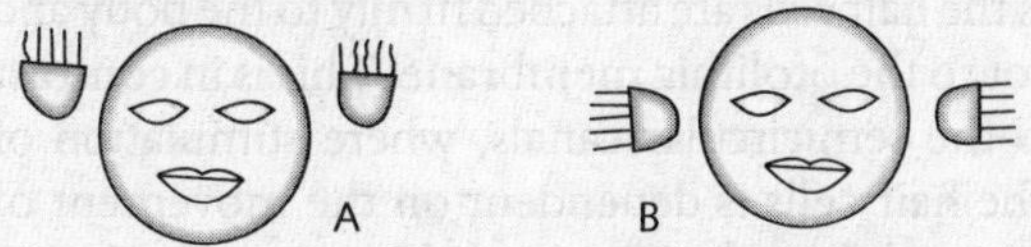


**Fig. 62.12:** Direction of cilia: A. Utricle—upward, B. Saccule—sideward

### Hair Cells

The columnar epithelium of the crista and macula consists of the true receptor cells, called the hair cells, and some supporting cells called sustentacular cells. The hair cells are innervated by the afferent fibres of the vestibular division of the vestibulocochlear (eighth cranial) nerve. A number of hairs, called stereocilia, projects from the apical surface of each hair cell and there is a large process, called the kinocilium, at one edge of the apical surface. The length of the stereocilia goes on increasing towards the kinocilium.

The RMP of hair cells is about –60 mV. When the stereocilia bend towards the kinocilium, the cell membrane gets depolarized and the discharge rate in the vestibular afferents increases. When the stereocilia bend away from the kinocilium, the discharge rate in the vestibular afferents decreases. The degree of depolarization and hyperpolarization is proportionate to the degree of displacement of the stereocilia (Fig. 62.13).

### Connections of Vestibular Apparatus

The cell bodies of the vestibular afferent nerve are situated in the vestibular ganglion. The central axons of the vestibular nerve enter the medulla, to end in the vestibular nuclei from here, the fibres go to the following areas:

1. The cerebellum, for the adjustment of posture.
2. The thalamus and cerebral cortex to the opposite side, for awareness of movement and the position of the body in space.
3. The third cranial nerve nuclei, to keep the eyes fixed on the same point when the head moves.
4. The reticular formation, for general alertness.
5. The spinal cord via the vestibulospinal tract, for the adjustment of posture.

Some fibres of the vestibular nerve pass directly to the cerebellum, and the vestibular nuclei receive fibres from the cerebellum as well. The close association between the two is important for the regulation of posture.

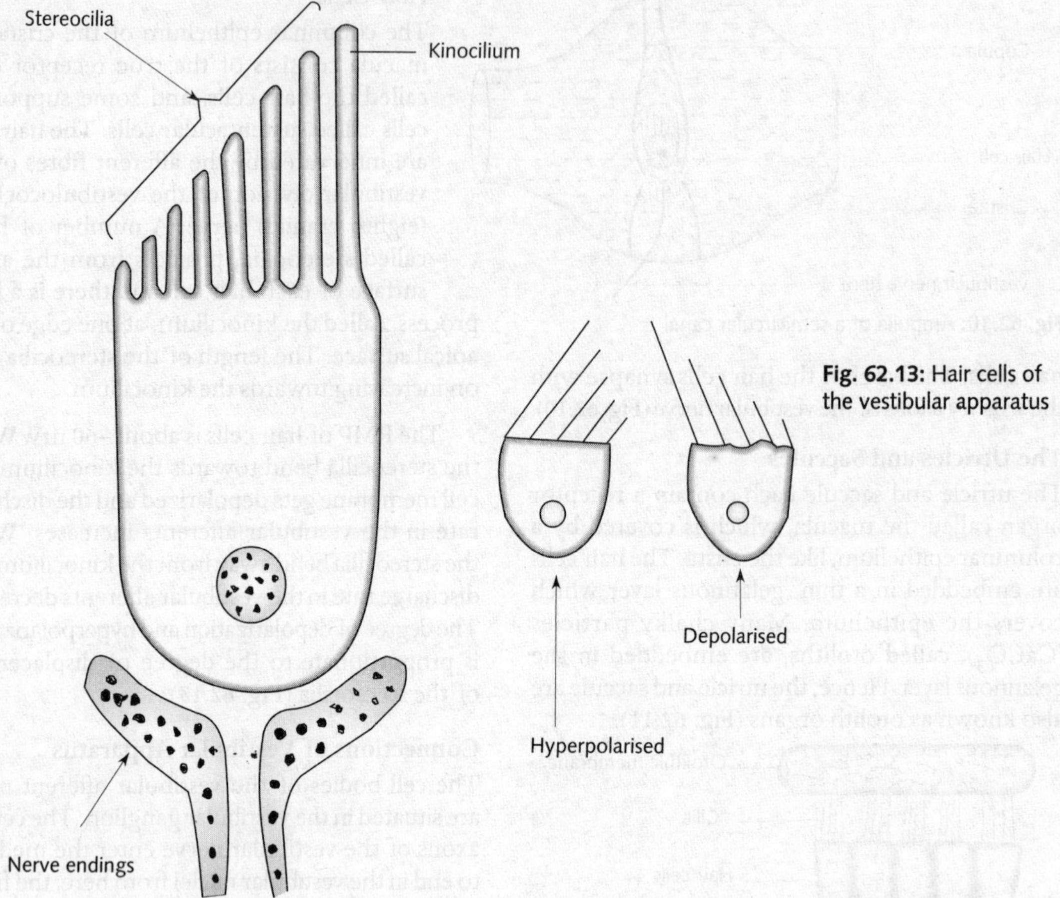


**Fig. 62.13:** Hair cells of the vestibular apparatus

## Mode of action of semicircular canals

When the head rotates in any plane, the respective canals, with the cristae and cupulae, move. However, the endolymph in the cannula fails to move immediately due to inertia. So the stationary endolymph causes the cupula to bend in the direction opposite to the movement of the head (Fig. 62.14). Since this makes the cilia bend, the activities of the hair cells get accelerated.

In this manner, if the head moves in any plane, the appropriate hair cells will be affected and the impulse carries the message to the brain. The brain then acts accordingly to stabilize the head and the body. If the movement continues at the same speed, the hair cells are not stimulated as the endolymph also moves. However, the hair cells become active again when the movement ceases since the endolymph continues to move due to the inertia of motion. Thus, the semicircular canals have a role to play in angular acceleration.

## Mode of action of otolith organs

Due to the presence of calcium carbonate crystals, the specific gravity of the otolithic membrane of the macula is greater. Hence, the pull of gravity deforms the hair cells even under resting conditions, as the hair cells are attached firmly to the body and not to the otolithic membrane. This is in contrast to the semicircular canals, where stimulation of the hair cells is dependent on the movement of the endolymph. The otolith organs discharge continuously for a given position of the head,

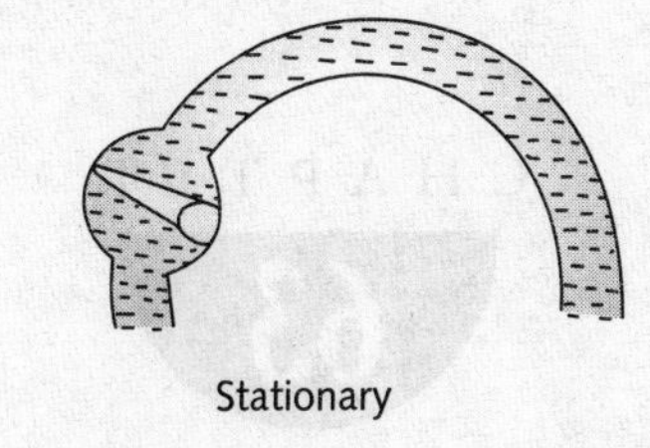


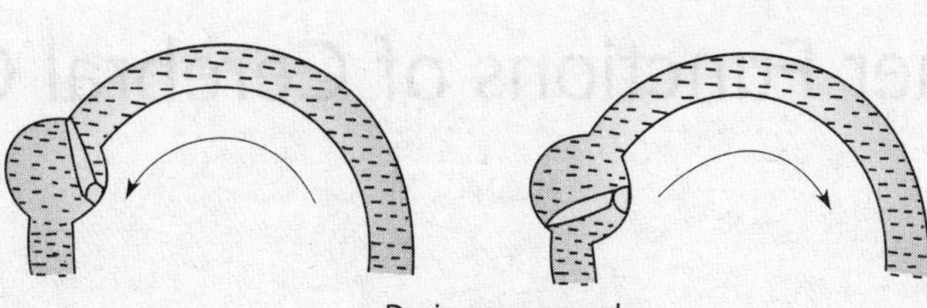


**Fig. 62.14:** Movement of crista ampularis during movement of head—arrows indicate movement of the head—cilia bend in opposite direction

providing information about the orientation of the head in space. The discharge rate from the otolith organs increases when the head is tilted in any direction and they help keep the head in the normal upright position. Hence, they are also called gravity receptors.

Stimulation of utricles and saccules in different movements of the head is as follows:

When the head is in the erect posture but motionless, the saccules get stimulated as the otolith membrane is pulled down by gravity, but the utricles are not stimulated. When the head is in the supine position but motionless, both the saccules and utricles are stimulated as the otolithic membrane hangs down because of the action of gravity.

During up and down movements of the head (such as while travelling in a lift), there is stimulation of the saccules, but not the utricles. Anterior-posterior movement of the head stimulates both the saccules and the utricles. During side-to-side movements, only the utricles are stimulated. Thus, the otolith organs play a role in static equilibrium. They are also involved in linear acceleration (not linear motion) when the body is suddenly thrust forward. For example, while running, the otolith organs fall backwards on the hair cells due to their weight and inertia. The reflex postural response consists of leaning forward to prevent a fall backwards.

## Role of Ves'tibular Apparatus

The vestibular apparatus plays a key role in the maintenance of muscle tone and posture. It is essential for static as well as dynamic equilibrium. As far as dynamic equilibrium is concerned, the vestibular apparatus is responsible for linear acceleration, angular acceleration and righting reflexes.

Further, the connections of the vestibular apparatus with the third, fourth and sixth cranial nerve nuclei help keep the eyes fixed on moving objects through the vestibulo-ocular reflex.

*Applied physiology*: Severe overstimulation of the vestibular apparatus may be produced when the body is in motion, causing nausea and vomiting.

Repetitive short, jerky movements of the eyeball, slow in one direction and quick in the opposite direction, occur in patients with a damaged vestibular apparatus and cerebellar disease. This symptom is known as nystagmus.

CHAPTER

63

# Higher Functions of Cerebral Cortex

The higher functions of the cerebral cortex include speech, intellectual functions, learning and memory.

## SPEECH

Speech is the expression of thoughts and ideas through articulate sounds or written symbols, and is important for communication. It has two components, sensory and motor. The sensory component, which involves the ears and eyes, is concerned with the ability to understand others' thoughts and ideas. The motor component involves vocalization, which means the ability to express one's own ideas and thoughts to others.

Thus, the secondary sensory (association) areas of the cerebral cortex are involved. These are concerned with the interpretation of sensory experiences, sensory motor coordination and motor activities of the highest order. The areas of the cerebral cortex that are involved in speech are (i) the sensory area, called Wernicke's area (ii) the motor areas, called Broca's area and the hand-skill area, and (iii) the arcuate fasciculus, which connects the sensory and motor areas (Fig. 63.1).

All these areas are better developed in one cerebral hemisphere (usually the left) than in the other. This is why the left hemisphere is called 'dominant'. Since the sensory and motor areas in the left cerebral cortex receive sensations and control the motor activities respectively of right side of body, majority of the people (about 90%) are right handed.

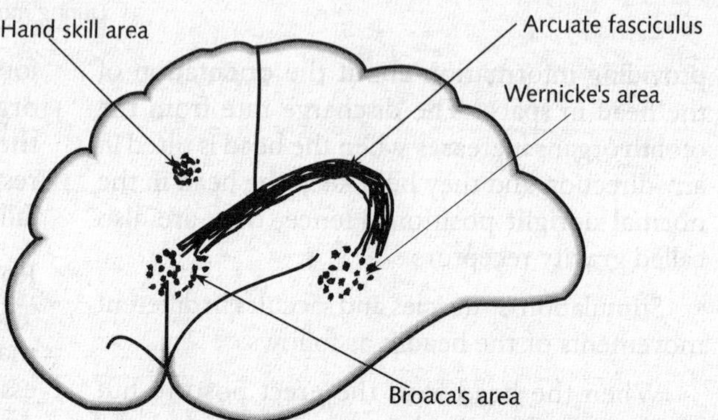


**Fig. 63.1:** Areas of cerebral cortex involved in speech

### Wernicke's Area

The posterior end of the superior temporal gyrus is called Wernicke's area. This is the site of the integration of the secondary somato sensory, auditory and visual areas. These areas are located close to the primary sensory areas, and extend 1 to 5 cm from them (Fig. 63.2).

Wernicke's area helps in the understanding of spoken or written words. In other words, it is involved in the interpretation of visual and auditory information for conversion into speech. Other sensory modalities also project on to it. The formulation of ideas and selection of words is done by Wernicke's area.

### Broca's area

This area is in the frontal lobe, in front of the lower end of the precentral gyrus, and is connected to the latter. It is responsible for the processing of the information received from Wernicke's area into the motor pattern of speech. This motor pattern is then transferred from Broca's area and the hand-skill area (near Broca's area) to the primary cortex. The latter is concerned with the control of the larynx, lips and tongue for spoken speech (vocalization and articulation), as well as of the fingers for written speech. The cerebellum and basal ganglia plan the sequencing and smooth progression of movements.

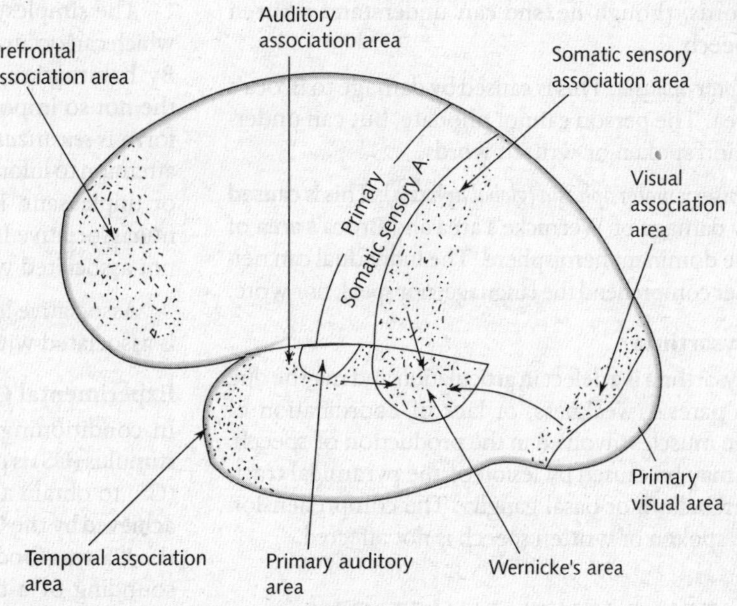


**Fig. 63.2:** Association areas of cerebral cortex

The mechanism of speech can be represented as shown below:

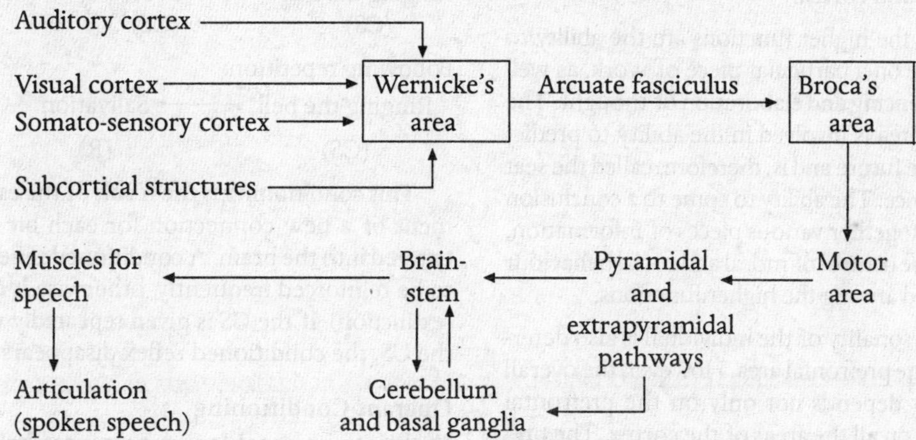


## Applied physiology

Speech defects may be classified into two main groups, aphasia and dysarthria.

### Aphasia

Aphasia is an inability to speak and may be due to damage to the sensory or motor component, or both. It is, therefore, of three types: sensory, motor and sensory-motor.

*Sensory aphasia*: A person with sensory aphasia may have word blindness (dyslexia) or word deafness. The former is caused by damage of the visual association area. The person is unable to understand written symbols, but can understand spoken speech. Word deafness is due to damage of the auditory association area. The person is unable to understand spoken words, though he/she can understand written speech.

*Motor aphasia*: This is caused by damage to Broca's area. The person cannot phonate, but can understand spoken or written words.

*Sensory-motor aphasia (global aphasia)*: This is caused by damage of Wernicke's area and Broca's area of the dominant hemisphere. The individual can neither comprehend the language, nor speak nor write.

### Dysarthria

Dysarthria is a defect in articulation and may be due to paresis (weakness) or lack of coordination of the muscles involved in the production of speech. It may be caused by lesion of the pyramidal tract, cerebellum or basal ganglia. The comprehension of spoken or written speech is not affected.

## INTELLECTUAL FUNCTIONS

The portion of the frontal lobe in front of the motor cortex is known as the prefrontal area. This area is better developed in man than in any other species. It is concerned with the higher functions of the cerebral cortex.

Among the higher functions are the ability to concentrate on a particular piece of work, as well as the sequencing and elaboration of thought. The prefrontal area is involved in the ability to predict and plan the future and is, therefore, called the seat of intelligence. The ability to come to a conclusion by putting together various pieces of information, as well as the control of moral and social behaviour are included among the higher functions.

The personality of the individual is also determined by the prefrontal area. However, the overall personality depends not only on the prefrontal cortex, but on all the areas of the cortex. The prefrontal area is considered to be highly associative and is capable of synthesizing sensory information into complex patterns.

## LEARNING

Learning is defined as the ability to alter one's behaviour on the basis of past experiences.

The simplest form of learning is *habituation*, which can occur at all levels of the nervous system. By habituation, the organism learns to ignore the not so important information. The opposite form is *sensitization*, by which the organism pays attention to information which is distinctly pleasant or unpleasant. Both these processes are part of nonassociative learning, which is learning that is not associated with any stimulus.

Associative learning, also called conditioning, is associated with another stimulus.

### Experimental Conditioning

In conditioning a response, the unconditioned stimulus (US) is paired with a conditioned stimulus (CS) to obtain a response (R), which is normally achieved by the US. In Pavlov's classic experiment, the US was food. This was paired with a CS, the sounding of a bell, just before food was given. The response was salivation. The process was repeated. It was noted that after some time, the CS alone could lead to salivation. Thus, the nervous system of an experimental animal learns to salivate at the sound of a bell.

Ringing the bell (CS) ⟶ Food (US) ⟶ Salivation (R)

Following repetition:

Ringing the bell (CS) ⟶ Salivation (R)

This conditioning is the result of the establishment of a new connection for each bit of data entered into the brain. A conditioned reflex needs to be reinforced frequently, otherwise it dies out (extinction). If the CS is given repeatedly without the US, the conditioned reflex disappears.

### Operant Conditioning

In this, the animal learns to repeat behaviour which is rewarding, or to avoid behaviour associated with punishment. Reward and punishment help reinforce the process of learning. Motivation and attention significantly expedite the process. Reward and punishment give rise to motivation and attention through positive or negative reinforcements.

## MEMORY

Memory is closely related to learning. It is the ability to recall past experiences, at the conscious or unconscious level.

The memory of an event may last for only a few seconds, while that of another may last for months or years. Accordingly, memory is of two types: primary or short-term memory (STM), and secondary or long-term memory (LTM).

### Short-term Memory (STM)

This is the memory of events that have occurred in the immediate past that is, a few minutes to hours or days earlier. An example is recalling a telephone number soon after seeing it in the directory.

STM may be due to the entry of a sensory signal into the reverberating circuits in the sensory cortex, or between the sensory cortex and the thalamus. Unless the stimulation is strong enough, the reverberating signals are wiped out by newer signals.

### Long-term Memory (LTM)

This is the memory of experiences in the distant past, and is permanent. The amount of information stored has no limit. The information can be recalled immediately.

The transfer of STM into LTM is called *consolidation*. The greater the number of rehearsals, the better the consolidation. Information which is interesting and studied in detail is consolidated more easily than information that is studied superficially. Consolidation is better when the person is awake or alert.

Secondary memory seems to result from almost permanent anatomical and biochemical changes in the cerebral synapses. Electron microscopy has shown certain anatomical changes, such as an increase in the number of synaptic connections, chemical transmitter vesicles and receptor proteins, and a decrease in the synaptic cleft.

### Parts of the Brain Involved

The parts of the brain involved in memory are the thalamus, hippocampus and amygdala, and the neocortex. The thalamus is important in the matter of searching through the memory stores. The hippocampus and amygdala are concerned with STM.

Different sensory areas in the neocortex store the LTM. Prolonged and intense sensory stimulation produces excessive thickening of the primary sensory cortex.

### Applied Physiology

Loss of memory is known as amnesia, which can be of two types: anterograde and retrograde. A person with anterograde amnesia is unable to learn anything new and cannot store more. The LTM is not affected, but there is a loss of STM. This is due to damage of the hippocampus and amygdala. Persons with retrograde amnesia suffer a loss of LTM. This has been observed after brain injury. Normally, in old age, there is progressive loss of memory.

CHAPTER

64

# The Limbic System and the Hypothalamus

## LIMBIC SYSTEM

The limbic system is the seat of emotion in the brain. It is responsible for the outward expression of the internal state of an individual, and involves both the mind and body.

The lymbic system consists of the cingulate gyrus, which is a rim of cortical tissue around the corpus callosum, and subcortical structures like the amygdala, hippocampus and septal nuclei. Phylogenetically, the limbic system is an older part of the cerebral cortex (allocortex) and histologically, it shows a primitive pattern (Fig. 64.1).

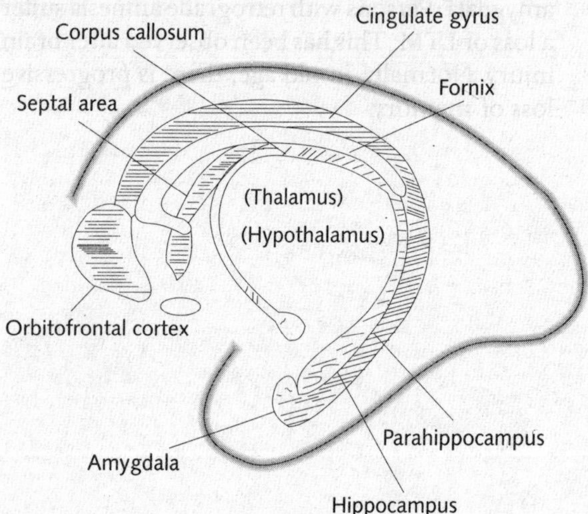


**Fig. 64.1:** The limbic system

The connections of the limbic system have two characteristic features. First, the limbic system has little connection with the neocortex. Hence, emotional behaviour is partly under voluntary control. Second, the anatomically closed circuit between the subcortical structures and the limbic cortex tends to produce prolonged emotional effect, long after the end of a sensory experience. This is due to reverberation. The reaction can also amplify.

### Functions

Most functions of the limbic system are intimately related to the functions of the hypothalamus. The functions are described below.

**Emotions**

Emotions have both psychological and physical components. Psychological changes such as feelings of fear, joy, love and anger are called internal emotions. Changes such as laughing, crying and running away are called external emotions or emotional behaviour.

The parts of the nervous system that are involved in emotions are the limbic system, ANS and somatic motor system. The amygdala and orbital surface of the frontal lobe are probably responsible for changes in the mind. The physical changes are organized by the hypothalamus, through the ANS and somatic motor system. Stimulation of the lateral hypothalamus leads to certain physical changes, seen in 'flight or fight' reaction.

### Fear, Rage and Placidity

Fear and rage are emotions that are provoked by exposure to a hostile environment. Fear is characterized by sweating, pupillary dilatation, side-to-side movement of the head and jumping to safety. Rage is characterized by growling, pilo-erection, pupillary dilatation, biting and clawing (in cats). Fear leads to avoidance or fleeing reactions, while rage gives rise to attacking or fighting reactions.

Both reactions thus involve the autonomic response and form the basis of the fundamental protective response. The hypothalamus plays an important role in both cases. The amygdala is responsible for fear and rage.

Placidity is the reverse of rage. A balance between rage and placidity is maintained with the help of the neocortex. The neocortex suppresses rage, while hypothalamic stimulation gives rise to rage.

### Autonomic Responses

Autonomic responses, such as changes in the blood pressure and respiration, are produced by the stimulation of many parts of the limbic system. Such changes are seen during emotional states.

### Feeding, Sexual and Maternal Behaviour

Stimulation of the amygdala produces the movements of chewing and licking, while a lesion produces hyperphagia (overeating). In the latter, there may be indiscriminate ingestion of edible or nonedible materials.

In male animals, lesions of certain regions of the limbic system produce hypersexuality. In man, mating is a basic instinct which is dominated by strong neocortical control.

The cingulate gyrus is concerned with maternal behaviour.

### Reward and Punishment

Experimentally, electrodes can be implanted in specific parts of the brain of an animal and connected to an electrical system and a bar in the cage. The parts of the brain which, when stimulated, produce repeated pressing of the bar are called reward centres. The punishment centres are those areas whose stimulation discourages bar-pressing. In human beings, stimulation of the reward centres produces a sensation of pleasure or relief of tension. Stimulation of the punishment centres produces fear or terror.

Reward and punishment are two important factors that control our behaviour. We feel motivated to repeat activities which give us a feeling of pleasure and avoid those which give us a feeling of punishment.

*Applied physiology*: The limbic system is connected with the autonomic centres. Hence, emotions produce a strong effect on the ANS. Prolonged emotional disturbances may lead to somatic disorders, such as peptic ulcer and ulcerative colitis. These are known as psychosomatic disorders.

## HYPOTHALAMUS

The hypothalamus is the area of the brain which forms the floor and part of the lateral wall of the third ventricle. It is a very important part of the CNS as it is the key region for the maintenance of homeostasis. It acts as the head ganglion of the ANS and also controls the secretions from various endocrine glands. Hence, the activities of both the autonomic and somatic nervous systems merge in the hypothalamus, emotional expression being an example (Fig. 64.2).

### Nuclei of hypothalamus

Various areas of the hypothalamus contain a large number of well-defined masses of grey matter or nuclei. The areas and the nuclei they contain are listed below.

1. Anterior hypothalamus
   - (i) Supraoptic nucleus
   - (ii) Preoptic nucleus
   - (iii) Anterior nucleus
   - (iv) Paraventricular nucleus
2. Medial hypothalamus
   - (i) Dorsomedial nucleus

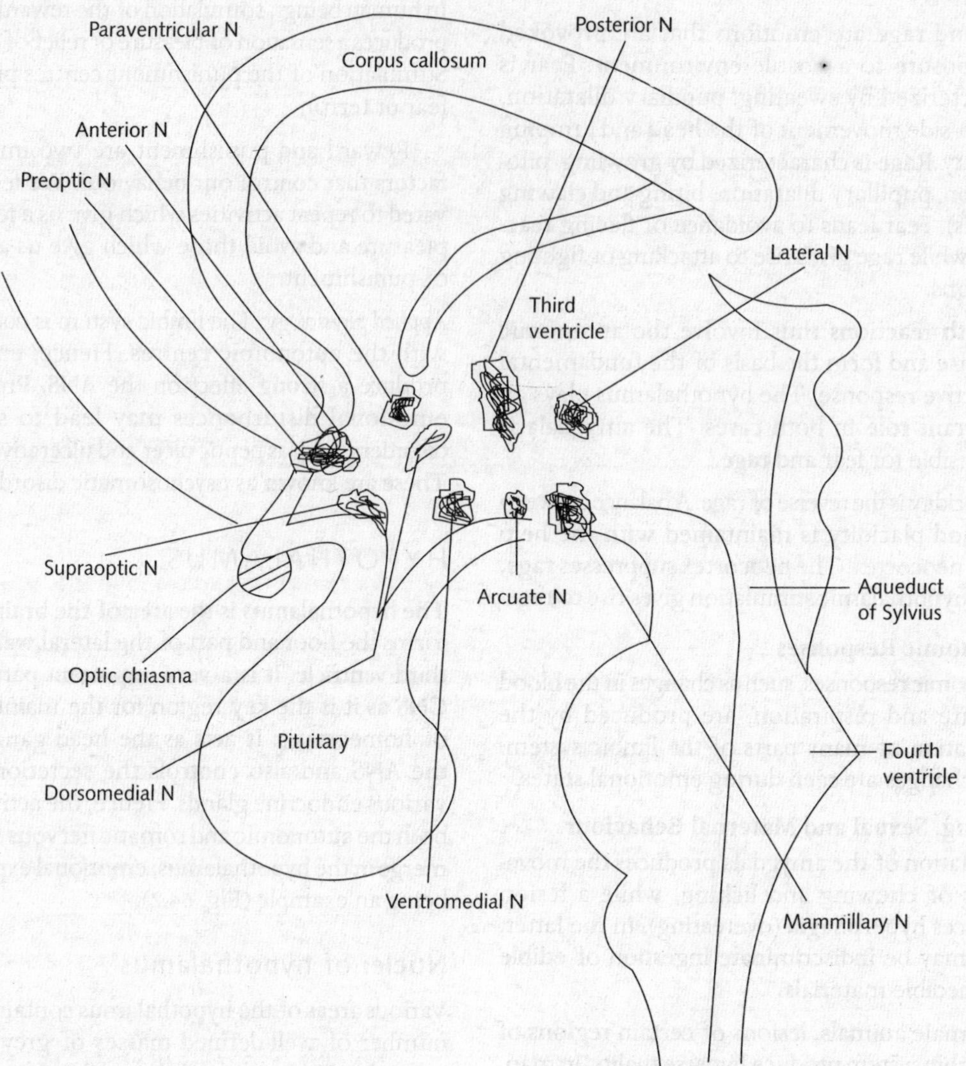


**Fig. 64.2:** Hypothalamus and its nuclei (N=nucleus)

(ii) Ventromedial nucleus
(iii) Arcuate nucleus

3. Lateral hypothalamus
   Lateral hypothalamic nucleus
4. Posterior hypothalamus
   (i) Posterior nucleus
   (ii) Mammillary nucleus

## Connections of hypothalamus

The hypothalamus is connected to several parts of the CNS, particularly to the areas related to autonomic activity, emotions and so on. It also receives various sensory inputs.

**Afferent Connections**

Among the afferent connections of the hypothalamus is the limbic system. Afferent fibres reach the hypothalamus from different parts of the limbic system, such as the hippocampus and amygdala. From the midbrain tegmentum, noradrenergic and serotonergic fibres project on to the mammillary nuclei, and then to the hypothalamus. The ascending sensory pathways project on to the hypothalamus through the reticular activating system.

The hypothalamus also has a minor neocortical projection (cortico-hypothalamic fibres), indirectly, through the limbic cortex.

#### Efferent Connections

The efferent fibres connect hypothalamus to structures:

1. Limbic system: i.e., limbic cortex and hippocampus.
2. Thalamus: Via mammillo-thalamic tract.
3. Midbrain reticular formation: From lateral hypothalamus to tegmental reticular formation and then to various brainstem centres (e.g., cardiovascular, respiratory) and lateral horn cells to spinal cord.
4. Posterior pituitary gland: Via hypothalamo-hypophyseal tract.

### Functions

#### Autonomic Function

The hypothalamus acts as a head ganglion of the ANS. Stimulation of the anterior hypothalamus produces changes similar to those seen in parasympathetic stimulation. Some examples are vasodilatation, fall in blood pressure and contraction of the urinary bladder. Stimulation of the posterior and lateral parts of the hypothalamus produces changes similar to those seen in sympathetic stimulation. A few examples are vasoconstriction and rise in the heart rate and blood pressure.

#### Endocrine Regulation

The hypothalamus itself secretes hormones, such as ADH and oxytocin, which are stored in the posterior pituitary, then released to act on the target cells. It also secretes various releasing and inhibitory hormones, which act through the anterior pituitary, to control the metabolic activities and gonadal function. This function is regulated by hormonal feedback at the hypothalamic level. The hypothalamo-hypophyseal portal circulation facilitates the process.

#### Control of Food Intake

The term 'hunger' means craving for food, 'appetite' means a desire to eat, 'feeding' means the act of eating, and 'satiety' means the absence of hunger and cessation of feeding (i.e., the feeling of fulfilment after the intake of food).

Hunger is often associated with contractions of the stomach (hunger pangs) and a desire to eat. However, these contractions are not the main cause for the craving for food. The feeding and satiety centres located in the lateral hypothalamus and ventromedial nucleus (VMN) of the hypothalamus, respectively, control feeding behaviour.

The feeding centre is continuously active, but its activity is periodically inhibited by the satiety centre, which is activated by the intake of food. The VMN acts as a satiety centre by monitoring the blood glucose level and its cells act as a glucostat. A low level of glucose in the blood reduces their activity. Thus, the feeding centre becomes active, producing hunger, which promotes the intake of food. The consequent rise in the blood glucose level increases the activity of the satiety centre, leading to inhibition of the feeding centre. The transport of glucose in the cells of the VMN is insulin-dependent. This explains why patients with diabetes mellitus have large appetites in spite of the fact that they have hyperglycaemia.

The hypothalamus thus acts as a centre for the control of the food intake and consequently, the regulation of body weight.

#### Regulation of Thirst

Thirst is the desire for drinking. It helps correct the deficit of water in the body. The hypothalamus contains a centre for the regulation of thirst. This centre is situated slightly anteriorly to the supraoptic nucleus. It is stimulated by the osmolality of body fluids, as well as the volume of ECF.

*Osmolality of body fluids*: This is a very important stimulus for thirst. The osmoreceptors of the 'drinking centre' sense increases in osmolality. This results in an increase in the ingestion of water. This process is similar to the sensing of changes in osmolality by the osmoreceptors of the supraoptic nucleus to regulate the secretion of ADH.

*Volume of ECF*: This is another important stimulus. A reduction in the ECF volume causes hypotension and the release of renin. This results in the production of angiotensin II, which initiates thirst (Fig. 64.3).

Dryness of the mouth leads to the sensation of thirst. The motor act of drinking plays a role in the satiety of thirst.

Thus, although the basic craving for water is regulated by the hypothalamus, the stomach and pharynx may also help regulate the intake of water, at least on a short-term basis.

### Role in Emotions

The hypothalamus lies in the efferent pathway of the limbic system, with which it is intimately connected. It is important for the expression of rage, and also contains reward and punishment centres.

### Regulation of Body Temperature

The role of the hypothalamus in the regulation of the body temperature has been discussed in the next section.

## REGULATION OF BODY TEMPERATURE

Human beings are called homeotherms as normally, they can regulate their body temperature within a particular narrow range, in spite of wide variations in the environmental temperature.

The normal body temperature varies between 37 and 39°C or 97 and 99°F (the average being

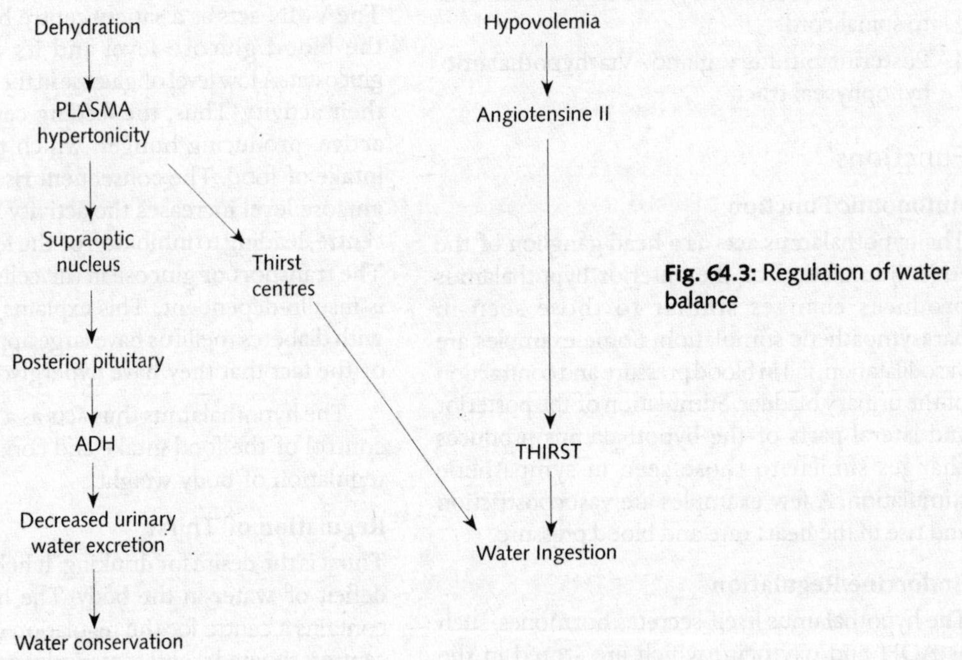


**Fig. 64.3:** Regulation of water balance

98.4°F). The average normal body temperature in different places is as follows:

1. Axillary 36.5°C
2. Oral 37°C
3. Rectal 37.5°C

The body temperature should always be measured at a single site in identical conditions. The rectal temperature is the least variable. It represents the temperature of the body core (pelvic and abdominal viscera) and needs to be regulated.

**Physiological Variations**

The body temperature shows diurnal variation and is the lowest in the morning and the highest in the evening. It increases after exercise. In females, the body temperature rises by 0.5°C following ovulation, due to the thermogenic effect of progesterone.

The regulation of the body temperature in infants is not very effective. In old age, it remains subnormal due to decreased activity. The ingestion of a hot or cold drink raises or lowers the oral temperature, respectively.

## Maintenance of body temperature

The body temperature is maintained by a balance between heat gain and heat loss. The sources of heat gain are metabolism, muscular activity and the environment. Those of heat loss are the skin (95 per cent), lungs (2 per cent), and urine and faeces (2 per cent).

**Mechanisms of Heat Gain**

The mechanisms of heat gain are described below.

*Metabolism*: The oxidation of food produces heat in the body. Specific dynamic action of protein increases the production of heat. In infants, brown fat, which is present in the interscapular region and behind the sternum, has a very high metabolic rate and, therefore, is an important source of heat production. Hormones such as thyroxine and epinephrine stimulate metabolism and hence, the production of heat.

*Muscular activity*: Muscular exercise and shivering increase heat production.

*Environment*: Heat is gained from the environment by radiation and conduction when the environmental temperature is higher than the body temperature.

**Mechanisms of Heat Loss**

Heat is lost from the body in the following ways.

*Skin*: Heat is lost from the skin by radiation, conduction, convection and the evaporation of sweat when the body temperature is higher than the environmental temperature. The amount of blood flowing to the skin determines the amount of heat that reaches the surface from the deeper tissues. The amount increases through vasodilatation, which causes greater heat loss from the surface of the skin. The subcutaneous layer of fat acts as an insulator against the loss of heat.

*Lungs*: Heat is lost from the mucous membrane of the respiratory tract even in a cold environment, by insensible perspiration and the warming of expired air.

*Urine and faeces*: Heat is lost through the urine and faeces, which are excreted at body temperature.

## Role of hypothalamus in regulation of body temperature

The body temperature is regulated by a centre in the hypothalamus called the hypothalamic thermostat. The thermostat acts in such a way as to bring the body temperature to a set point (i.e., to the normal body temperature of 37°C) in normal conditions.

The hypothalamus integrates the autonomic and somatic mechanisms of the regulation of body temperature. In response to the stimulation of the cold receptors, the posterior hypothalamus produces cutaneous vasoconstriction and piloerection, as well as abolition of sweating (autonomic effects). It also causes shivering (somatic effect), the secretion of thyroxine and epinephrine (hormonal effect), and the need for measures to block out the cold, such as wearing warm clothes (behavioural effects). In response to the stimulation of the warmth receptors, the anterior hypothalamus produces cutaneous vasodilatation and sweating.

*Afferents*: The skin contains more cold than heat receptors. There are cold receptors in the internal organs as well. Thus, it is mainly peripheral signals that activate the hypothalamic response to cold. In contrast, receptors for heat seem to be located centrally, especially in the preoptic area of the hypothalamus, and cutaneous warmth receptors play a secondary role in the regulation of temperature.

*Efferents*: The autonomic nerves, somatic motor nerves and endocrine glands bring about responses which bring the body temperature back to normal.

## Mechanisms activated by heat

### Measures to Increase Heat Loss

These include cutaneous vasodilatation and sweating.

*Cutaneous vasodilatation*: The inhibition of sympathetic discharge to the cutaneous vessels causes vasodilatation and opening of arterio-venous (A-V) anastomosis in the skin. By this mechanism, warm blood from the deeper tissues is brought to the surface and the loss of heat is facilitated by radiation, conduction, convection and evaporation.

*Sweating*: Sweating is the most important mechanism of heat loss. It is the only mechanism of heat loss when a person is exposed to an environmental temperature that is higher than the body temperature. The rate of sweating may go up to 10 l a day in heat stress.

### Measures to Decrease Heat Production

The production of heat may be decreased by anorexia, behavioural responses and hormonal responses.

*Anorexia*: A degree of anorexia, or loss of appetite, occurs in heat stress. The resulting decrease in the intake of food brings down the production of heat as there is a decrease in the specific dynamic action of food and metabolism.

*Behavioural responses:* The behavioural responses to excessive heat include moving into the shade or to a cooler place. In addition, a certain degree of lethargy occurs. This lowers muscular activity, which means that the body is producing less heat.

*Hormonal responses:* The hormonal responses to heat include a decreased secretion of thyroxine and epinephrine. This brings down the metabolic rate and hence the production of heat.

## Mechanisms activated by cold

### Measures to Increase Heat Production

The measures taken by the body to increase the production of heat are discussed below.

*Shivering*: An increase in the muscle tone and contraction of the skeletal muscles increases the production of heat by 4 to 5 times.

*Larger appetite*: A large appetite results in an increase in the intake of food. This, in turn, makes the body produce more heat as it increases the specific dynamic action of food and metabolism.

*Increased metabolism of brown fat*: In infants, brown fat is the most important source of heat production. When the metabolism of brown fat goes up, more heat is produced in response to the increase in sympathetic discharge.

*Hormonal responses*: A rise in the secretion of thyroxine and epinephrine raises the rate of cellular metabolism, thereby increasing the production of heat. The action of thyroxine starts several weeks after exposure to cold.

*Behavioural responses*: These responses include moving into an open and sunny or warmer place, as well as greater muscular activity, which increases the production of heat.

### Measures to Decrease Heat Loss

These consist of cutaneous vasoconstriction, a decrease in sweating and piloerection.

*Cutaneous vasoconstriction*: A rise in sympathetic discharge to the cutaneous vessels causes extreme vasoconstriction. The cutaneous blood flow becomes low and less heat is lost from the surface of the skin.

*Decreased sweating*: If a person sweats less, there is a decrease in the evaporative heat loss from the skin.

*Piloerection*: When the hair stands on end due to exposure to the cold, it traps air, which forms an insulating layer that prevents the loss of heat from the skin.

The following flowchart summarizes the mechanisms by which the body temperature is regulated.

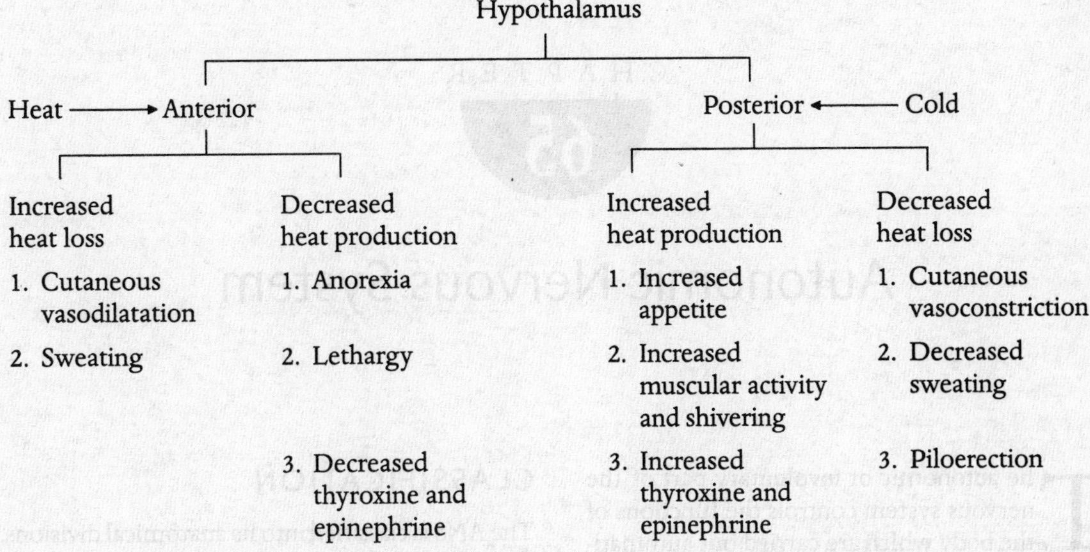


## Abnormalities in regulation

*Fever*: When the body temperature rises above the normal range, it is known as fever (pyrexia). Most often, fever is caused by an infection, which may be bacterial, viral or protozoal. Tissue damage can also produce fever. In fever, various chemicals (pyrogens) increase the hypothalamic setting to a higher level so that the production of heat continues for a longer time.

Fever is beneficial to the body in the sense that it fights infection. A higher temperature inhibits the growth of bacteria and antibody production increases. However, an abnormally high body temperature produces dehydration, a negative nitrogen balance and alkalosis. Very high body temperature (above 41°C) may produce brain damage.

*Heat stroke*: Prolonged exposure to heat may lead to dehydration, salt deficiency and even circulatory shock. In such conditions, the cutaneous heat loss mechanisms stop operating and the body temperature rises sharply. Convulsions and even death may occur when the body temperature exceeds 41°C. These changes are known as heat stroke.

Sponging the body with cold water is a simple and very effective measure against heat stroke.

*Hypothermia*: Prolonged exposure to extreme cold brings down the body temperature, which may decrease to 33°C without any ill effects. However, below 30°C, glucose metabolism is retarded, and the heart and respiration rates become slow. Below 25°C, death occurs.

Severe hypothermia (at a temperature ranging from 21 to 24°C) is produced artificially for a short time during heart or brain surgery. Hypothermia helps prevent hypoxic tissue damage by lowering the requirement for oxygen.

# CHAPTER 65

# Autonomic Nervous System

The autonomic or involuntary part of the nervous system controls the functions of the body which are carried out automatically (visceral functions). One is not conscious of these functions under normal conditions.

The autonomic nervous system (ANS) acts hand in hand with the endocrine system. The two systems are interdependent. Autonomic influences from the hypothalamus go to the pituitary and regulate the function of the endocrine glands. The actions of the ANS are potentiated by hormones. The ANS and endocrine system are involved in the maintenance of homeostasis.

The ANS acts on its own, but is not independent of the somatic nervous system. Both systems interact with each other to support the body by effecting various adaptations.

The ANS acts through a set-up which is similar to that of the somatic nervous system. It has receptors, afferent neurons, a centre, efferent neurons and target organs, and the visceral reflexes take place through the integrated action of these. The afferent nerves of the ANS travel with the somatic nerves of the respective segment, enter the spinal cord through the posterior root and follow the sensory pathways. The cranial components follow the sensory components of the cranial nerves. There are no separate sensory autonomic tracts. These afferents bring about visceral reflexes and also, relay information from the viscera to the CNS.

## CLASSIFICATION

The ANS is classified into its anatomical divisions, physiological divisions and chemical divisions. It is divided into two anatomical divisions according to the outflow of efferent neurons.

The first is the craniosacral division, which consists of the third, seventh, ninth and tenth cranial nerves and the efferent neurons coming out of the lateral horn cells of the $S_2$, $S_3$, $S_4$ segments of the spinal cord.

The second anatomical division is the thoracolumbar division, which consists of the efferent neurons coming out of the $T_{1-2}$ and $L_{1-3}$ segments of the spinal cord.

The ANS is divided into physiological divisions according to function. One is the parasympathetic (craniosacral) division and the other is the sympathetic (thoracolumbar) division.

The two chemical divisions have been done according to the chemical transmitter liberated at the nerve endings. The first is the adrenergic division. Adrenaline or noradrenaline is liberated at the nerve endings. This division consists of all the post-ganglionic sympathetic fibres except those supplying the sweat glands and skeletal muscle blood vessels.

The second chemical division is the cholinergic division. Acetylcholine is liberated at the nerve endings. This division includes the (i) complete parasympathetic nervous system (i.e., the preganglionic fibres), (ii) preganglionic sympathetic nerve endings, (iii) postganglionic sympathetic fibres supplying the sweat glands and skeletal muscle blood vessels, and (iv) peripheral autonomic ganglia, both sympathetic and parasympathetic.

## ORGANIZATION

The ANS is sometimes called the efferent nervous system or visceral motor system. It is basically a two-neuron efferent pathway, consisting of a preganglionic and a postganglionic neuron.

A comparison of a visceral reflex arc and a typical spinal somatic reflex arc helps understand the organization of the ANS (Fig. 65.1). A somatic reflex arc consists of an afferent neuron, the cell of which is in the dorsal root ganglion, an interneuron situated in the grey matter of the spinal cord and an efferent neuron, the cell body of which is situated in the anterior horn cells of the spinal cord. The axon leaves via the ventral root to innervate the skeletal muscle.

The afferent neuron in a visceral reflex arc is located similarly. It synapses with the preganglionic neuron lying in the lateral horn cells of the spinal cord, or with certain cranial nerve nuclei in the brainstem. The preganglionic neuron leaves the spinal cord as a thin myelinated fibre that synapses with the neuron in the peripheral autonomic ganglia. Nonmyelinated postganglionic nerve fibres leave the ganglia to innervate the effector organs, such as cardiac muscle, smooth muscle or glands.

The peripheral autonomic ganglia are masses of grey matter which contains cell bodies. The postganglionic nerve fibres arise from the latter.

The following are some important differences between the organization of the sympathetic and parasympathetic divisions:

1. In the sympathetic system, the ganglia are situated near the spinal cord, that is, far from the organ innervated. Hence, the postganglionic fibres are long. In the parasympathetic system, on the other hand, the ganglia are located very close to the organ innervated and hence, the length of the postganglionic fibres is very short.
2. In the sympathetic system, one preganglionic

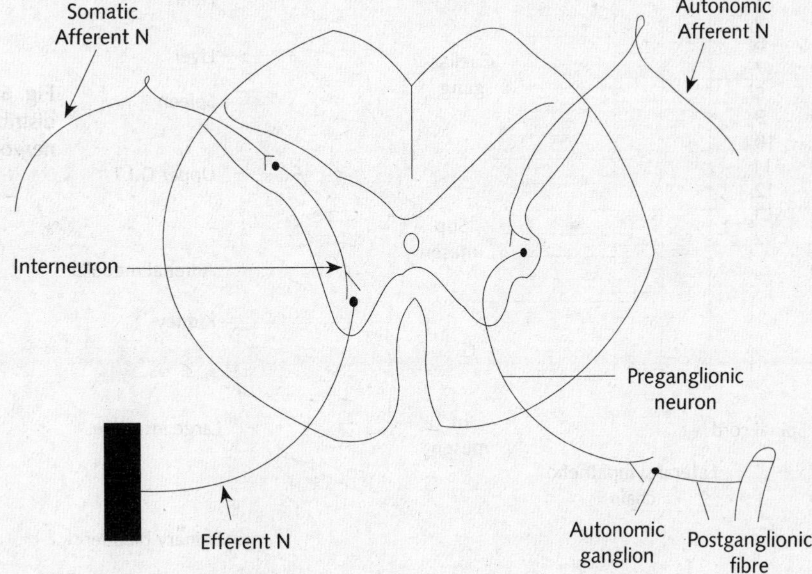


**Fig. 65.1:** Comparison of a somatic reflex arc with an autonomic reflex arc

neuron synapses with as many as thirty postganglionic neurons, that is, there is divergence. In the parasympathetic system, one preganglionic neuron usually synapses with one postganglionic neuron. Hence, sympathetic activity is widespread or generalized, whereas parasympathetic activity is more localized or discrete.

3. Sympathetic and parasympathetic actions are the opposite of each other.
4. The sympathetic system is more widely distributed, while the parasympathetic system is restricted in distribution.
5. Most organs in the body receive a dual innervation, that is, both from the sympathetic and parasympathetic nervous systems. A few examples are the eyes, salivary glands, heart, digestive system and pelvic viscera. However, sweat glands, the adrenal medulla and most of the blood vessels receive only sympathetic innervation.

The anatomical distribution of the sympathetic and parasympathetic nervous systems is shown in Figs 65.2 and 65.3, respectively.

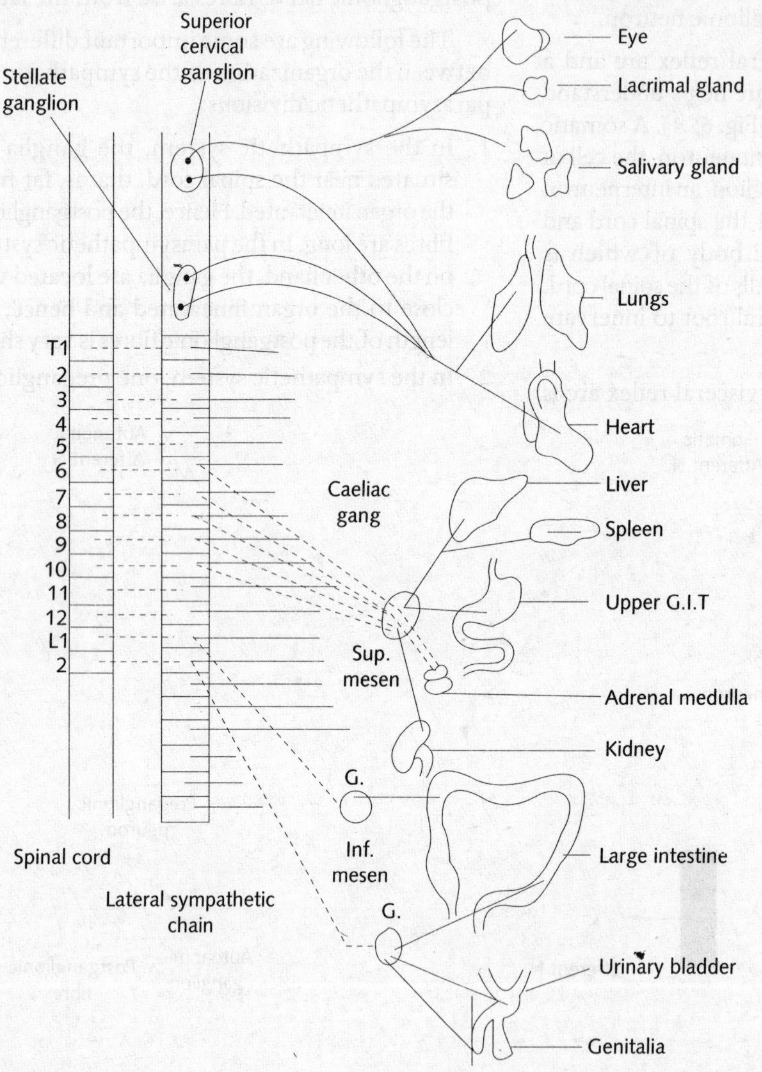


**Fig. 65.2:** Anatomical distribution of sympathetic nervous system

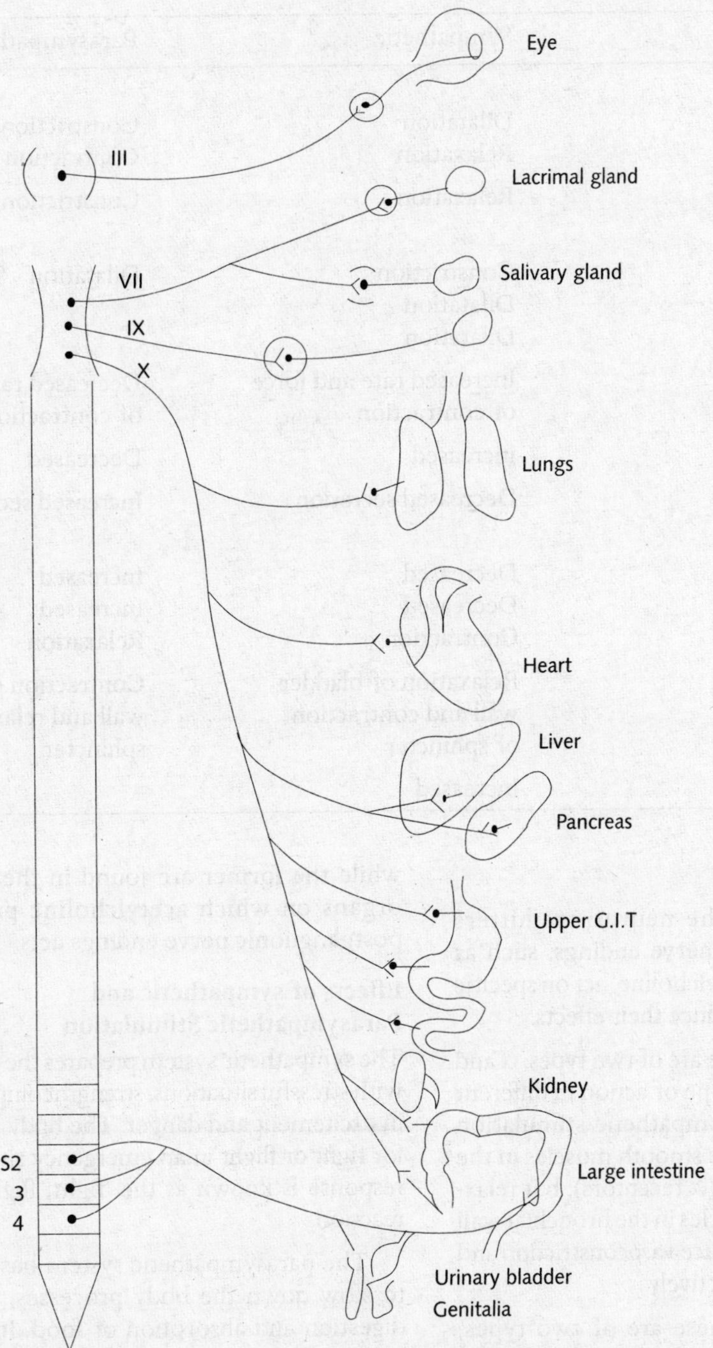


**Fig. 65.3: Anatomical distribution of parasympathetic nervous system**

**Table 65.1:** Effects of stimulation of autonomic nervous system

| Organ | Sympathetic | Parasympathetic |
|---|---|---|
| 1. Eye | | |
| (i) pupil | Dilatation | Constriction |
| (ii) ciliary muscle | Relaxation | Contraction |
| 2. Bronchial muscle | Relaxation | Constriction |
| 3. Blood vessels | | |
| (i) skin | Constriction | Dilatation |
| (ii) skeletal muscle | Dilatation | – |
| (iii) coronary | Dilatation | – |
| 4. Heart muscle | Increased rate and force of contraction | Decreased rate and force of contraction |
| 5. Blood Pressure | Increased | Decreased |
| 6. Glands | Decreased secretion | Increased secretion |
| 7. GI tract | | |
| (i) secretion | Decreased | Increased |
| (ii) motility | Decreased | Increased |
| (iii) sphincters | Contraction | Relaxation |
| 8. Urinary bladder | Relaxation of bladder wall and contraction of sphincter | Contraction of bladder wall and relaxation of sphincter |
| 9. BMR | Increased | – |

## Receptors

*Autonomic receptors*: The neurotransmitters released by autonomic nerve endings, such as norepinephrine and acetylcholine, act on specific protein receptors to produce their effects.

*Adrenergic receptors*: These are of two types, α and β. They determine the type of action in different tissues. For example, sympathetic stimulation causes contraction of the smooth muscles in the cutaneous blood vessels (α receptors), but relaxation of the smooth muscles in the bronchial wall (β receptors). These produce vasoconstriction and bronchodilatation, respectively.

*Cholinergic receptors*: These are of two types, cholinergic receptors—muscarinic and nicotinic. The latter are located in the autonomic ganglia, while the former are found in the tissues and organs on which acetylcholine produced by postganglionic nerve endings acts.

### Effects of sympathetic and Parasympathetic Stimulation

The sympathetic system prepares the body to deal with stressful situations, strengthening its defences in excitement and danger. The body is mobilized for fight or flight in an emergency situation. This response is known as the 'fight, flight or fright' reaction.

The parasympathetic system has a tendency to slow down the body processes, barring the digestion and absorption of food. It works as a peacemaker, allowing the restorative processes to occur quietly and peacefully.

The two systems function simultaneously and a delicate balance is maintained between their actions for the purpose of homeostasis.

*Applied physiology*: The ANS is involved in the regulation of various vital functions as well as important body processes. Abnormalities result in diseases. Various drugs are used to manipulate the activities of the ANS in order to tackle the related diseases. Some drugs act on the ganglia, some on the nerve endings, and some on the receptors.

# Special Senses

# CHAPTER 66

# Taste and Smell

## TASTE (GUSTATION)

Taste is a chemical sense and its receptor organ is the tongue. The mucous membrane covering the upper surface of the tongue has a velvety appearance and is covered with papillae (Fig. 66.1). The papillae are of the following three types:

1. Circumvallate: These are at the back of the tongue. They are large and arranged in a 'V' shape.
2. Fungiform: These are found at the tip of the tongue. They are small and more numerous than the circumvallate papillae.
3. Filiform: These are found at the sides and all over the tongue.

The end organs of taste, that is, the taste buds, are located in the walls of the papillae and also in the mucous membrane of the soft palate, pharynx and epiglottis. The taste buds are flask-shaped structures, made of many cells, and have an opening, called the taste pore, at the tip. Each taste bud has two types of cells—the receptor cells and the supporting cells. The free border of the receptor cell has hair-like projections or microvilli which project towards the tiny pores in the epithelium, making contact with the saliva. The base of the receptor cell is in contact with the afferent nerve endings. The taste nerve fibres arborize extensively before coming in close contact with the basal border of the receptor cells. Human beings have a total of about 10,000 taste buds (Fig. 66.2).

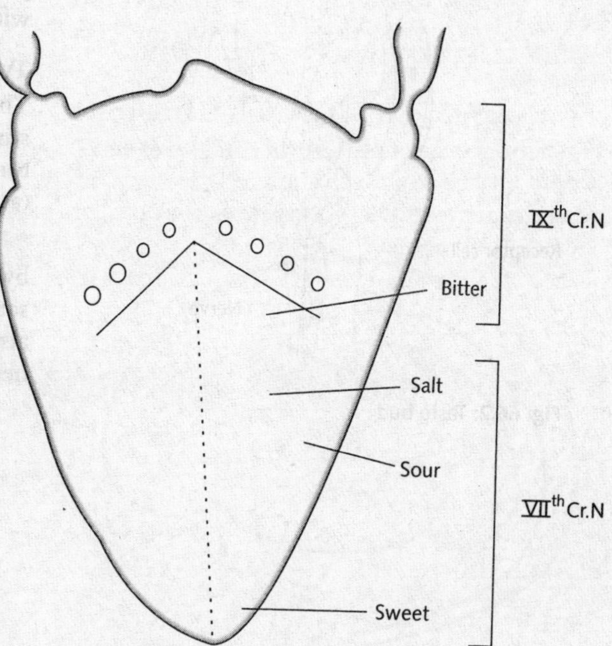


**Fig. 66.1:** Dorsum of tongue showing the areas for primary taste sensations and the nerves carrying sensation of taste

### Taste Pathway

The afferent fibres for the sensation of taste from the anterior two-thirds of the tongue are carried by the chorda tympani branch of the facial (seventh cranial) nerve. The taste fibres from the posterior one-third of the tongue are carried by the glossopharyngeal (ninth cranial) nerve, and those from the epiglottis, palate and pharynx by the vagus (tenth cranial) nerve.

The taste fibres in all these nerves are of the slow-conducting, thin and myelinated type. They enter the medulla and end in the nucleus of the tractus solitarius. Next, the axons of the second-order neurons cross to the opposite side, to join the medial lemniscus, and end in the thalamic nucleus. From here, the third-order neurons proceed to terminate in the 'face' area, in the lower part of the post-central gyrus (somato-sensory cortex), buried within the lateral sulcus (Fig. 66.3).

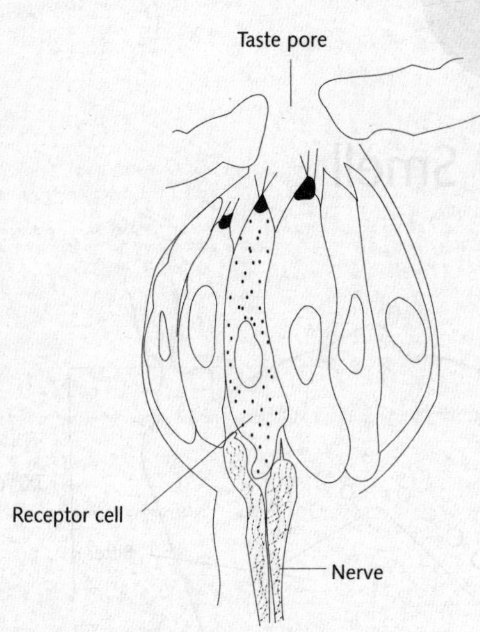


Fig. 66.2: Taste bud

### Types 'of Taste

There are four primary sensations of taste, which stimulate the taste buds in specific parts of the tongue. These are sweet (mainly at the tip), bitter (at the back), sour (at the sides), and salty (all over).

Hundreds of types of tastes are caused not only by the stimulation of the four primary taste sensations in different quantitative combinations, but also by the addition of the sensations of olfaction, heat, cold and texture, among others. The complex

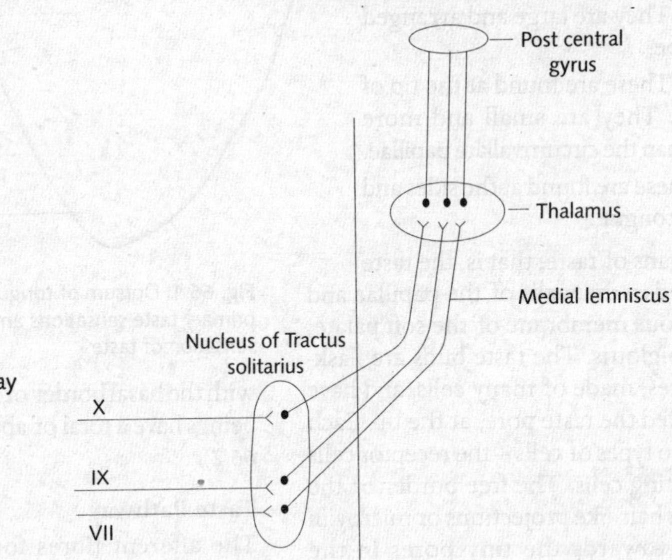


Fig. 66.3: Taste pathway

sensation arising from the combination of all these sensations is called flavour.

The sour taste is caused by agents which liberate $H^+$, for example, acids. The salty taste is produced by ionized salts, particularly sodium chloride, while the sweet taste is caused by a number of different organic chemicals, for example, sugars and saccharine. Alkaloids like quinine cause the bitter taste. The taste buds are particularly sensitive to the bitter taste. They also show adaptation. For example, if a person has sweets before taking tea with a normal quantity of sugar, the tea tastes less sweet.

*Mechanism of taste sensation*: For a substance to be tasted, it must be in solution, for example, dissolved in the saliva. The dissolved substance probably attaches itself to the microvilli of the specific taste receptor cells. This causes a change in the membrane potential of the receptor cells and it is converted to action potentials in the afferent nerves.

*Applied physiology*: The sense of taste is delicate and is diminished by cold in the head (sinusitis) or diseases of the GI tract.

## SMELL (OLFACTION)

Olfaction is also a chemical sense, the receptor organ for which is the nose. The end organs of smell are special cells located in the mucous membrane at the roof of the nasal cavity (Fig. 66.4).

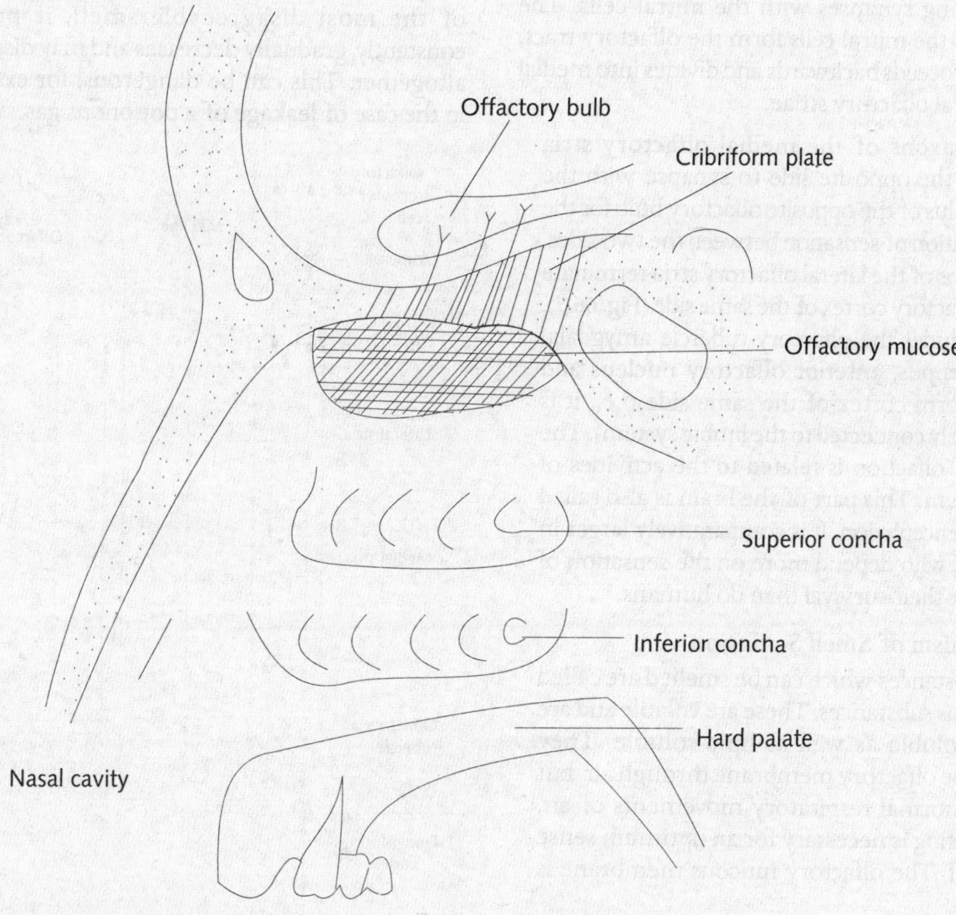


**Fig. 66.4:** Olfactory mucosa in nose

The olfactory mucous membrane is a small area which is yellow. It consists of 10 to 20 million olfactory cells, lying between the supporting cells. The surface of the supporting cells has microvilli, which secrete mucus. Mucus is also secreted by the Bowman's glands lying just under the basement membrane. Fine cilia project from the surface of the olfactory cells into the layer of mucus.

### Olfactory Pathway

The olfactory neurons, that is, the receptor cells, are the primary sensory neurons. The axons of these neurons, called olfactory (first cranial) nerves, directly enter the brain, without relaying in the thalamus. The olfactory nerves pass through the holes in the cribriform plate of the ethmoid bone. The axons form glomeruli in the olfactory bulbs by forming synapses with the mitral cells. The axons of the mitral cells form the olfactory tract, which proceeds backwards and divides into medial and lateral olfactory striae.

The axons of the medial olfactory stria cross to the opposite side to synapse with the glomerulus of the opposite olfactory bulb for the coordination of sensation between the two sides. The axons of the lateral olfactory stria terminate in the olfactory cortex of the same side (Fig. 66.5). This includes the olfactory tubercle amygdala, hippocampus, anterior olfactory nucleus and prepyriform cortex of the same side (i.e., it is extensively connected to the limbic system). The sense of olfaction is related to the activities of this system. This part of the brain is also called the rhinencephalon. It is comparatively larger in animals, who depend more on the sensation of smell for their survival than do humans.

### Mechanism of Smell Sensation

The substances which can be smelled are called odourous substances. These are volatile and are water-soluble as well as lipid-soluble. They reach the olfactory membrane through air, but not by normal respiratory movements of air, and sniffing is necessary for an optimum sense of smell. The olfactory mucous membrane is highly vascular and hence warm. This warmth produces convection air currents, which help carry the odour to the proper site.

There are fifty primary smell sensations. The odoriferous molecules dissolve in the mucus secreted by the nasal mucosa, and then bind with the cilia of the olfactory receptors. This results in receptor potential and action potential that is carried by the olfactory pathway.

The olfactory receptors are extremely sensitive to the smell of garlic. They adapt very rapidly. A pleasant smell improves the appetite.

*Applied physiology*: The sense of smell is delicate. It decreases when there is cold in the head (sinusitis) and when the olfactory system has been exposed to a particular smell for a long time. The perception of the most disagreeable smell, if present constantly, gradually decreases and may disappear altogether. This can be dangerous, for example, in the case of leakage of a poisonous gas.

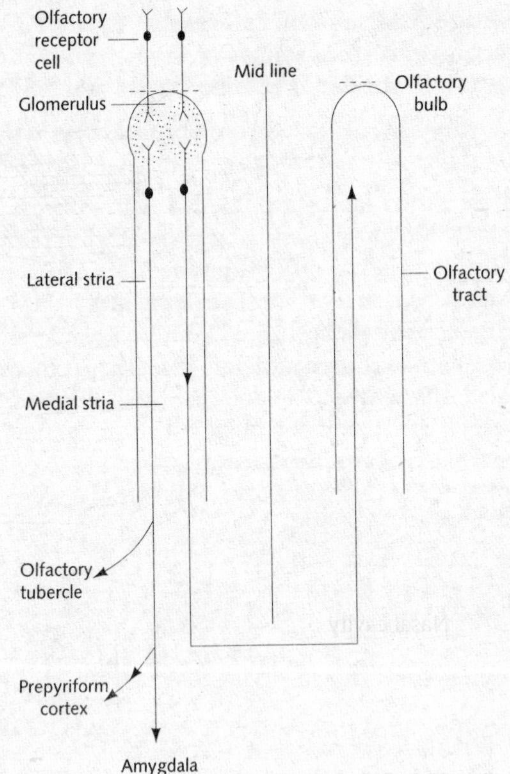


**Fig. 66.5:** Olfactory pathway

CHAPTER

67

# Vision

Vision is the most important special sense. Its receptor organ is the eye, which responds to light energy.

## FUNCTIONAL ANATOMY OF THE EYE

The human eyeball is spherical and has three coats. From the outside inwards, these are the sclera, choroid and retina (Fig. 67.1).

### Sclera

The sclera is an opaque, white, fibrous layer of the eyeball which is anteriorly replaced by the transparent cornea. There are no blood vessels in the cornea. Free nerve endings in the cornea act as receptors for pain, touch and temperature.

The sclera gives support and protection to the delicate structures in the eyeball. Its weak posterior part allows the entry of the retinal blood vessels and the exit of the optic nerve.

The cornea is a light-gathering device. It is curved anteriorly, allowing the free entry of light into the eyeball. It serves as a maximally refractory medium due to its high refractory power. The cornea is the most easily damageable structure in the eye and can be grafted.

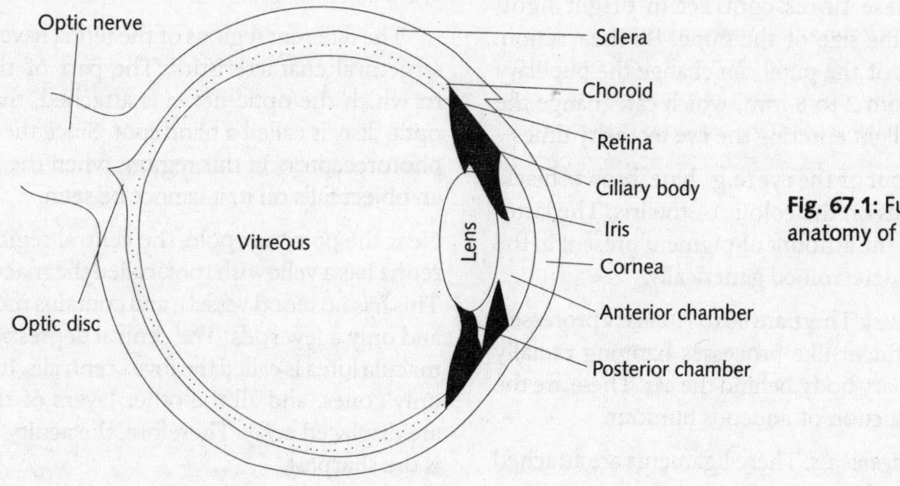


**Fig. 67.1:** Functional anatomy of the eye

## Choroid

The choroid is the pigmented, vascular layer of the eyeball. It continues anteriorly at the sclerocorneal junction as a ciliary body, containing inner circular and outer longitudinal layers of smooth muscle fibres. The latter take part in accommodation.

The choroid prevents scattering of light inside the eyeball as it contains melanin, which is a dark brown pigment. This helps in the formation of a sharp image or acuity of vision. A person with a congenital absence of melanin in the body (albino) has blurred vision and has to keep his/her eyes partially closed to avoid bright light (glare). The choroid is made of blood vessels and provides nutrition to the retina. Detachment of the retina from the choroid, therefore, leads to blindness.

The ciliary body forms a ring around the sclerocorneal junction. The following structures are attached to the latter.

*Iris*: This is a circular diaphragm, attached peripherally to the ciliary body. It is situated behind the cornea and in front of the lens. It has a central hole called the pupil. The radial muscle fibres of the pupil (dilator pupillae) are supplied by sympathetic nerves. These fibres contract in the dark, thereby increasing the size of the pupil.

The concentric muscle fibres of the pupil (constrictor pupillae) are supplied by parasympathetic nerves. These fibres contract in bright light, decreasing the size of the pupil. By their action, the muscles of the pupil can change the pupillary diameter from 2 to 8 mm, which can change the amount of light entering the eye by thirty times.

The colour of the eye (e.g., blue, brown, black, etc.) depends on the colour of the iris. The latter depends on the amount of pigment present in the iris. This is determined genetically.

*Ciliary processes*: There are 60 to 70 ciliary processes. These are finger-like processes hanging radially from the ciliary body, behind the iris. These are the site of production of aqueous humour.

*Suspensory ligaments*: These ligaments are attached radially to the lens, all around it. They suspend the lens (Fig. 67.2).

## Retina

The retina is the nervous layer of the eyeball. It consists of several layers, of which the pigment layer is the outermost. The pigment layer is next to the choroid. Next, there are three layers of neurons. From the outside inwards, these are the layers of rods and cones, bipolar cells and ganglion cells. The axons of the ganglion cells form the innermost layer, which is called the layer of optic nerve fibres (Fig. 67.3). The most important layer is that of the rods and cones. The latter are photosensitive receptors.

The rays of light have to pass through all the layers to reach the photosensitive zone. The pigment layer of the retina absorbs light to produce light and dark spots, which is essential for acuity of vision. It also stores large quantities of vitamin A, the important precursor of photosensitive pigments in the rods and cones.

The retinal vessels pass through the optic nerve and supply the inner side of the retina. The outer side of the retina (i.e., the rods and cones) receive nutrition from the choroid. The retinal vessels are the only vessels of the body which can be seen easily, through an ophthalmoscope. Hence, ophthalmoscopy is important in the diagnosis of certain systemic diseases involving the blood vessels, for example, hypertension and diabetes mellitus (Fig. 67.4).

The different regions of the retina have different structural characteristics. The part of the retina to which the optic nerve is attached, that is, the optic disc, is called a blind spot. Since there are no photoreceptors in this region, when the image of an object falls on it, it cannot be seen.

Near the posterior pole, the central region of the retina has a yellowish spot, called the macula lutea. This has no blood vessels, and contains more cones and only a few rods. The central depression in the macula lutea is called the fovea centralis. It contains only cones, and all the other layers of the retina are displaced away. Therefore, the acuity of vision is the sharpest.

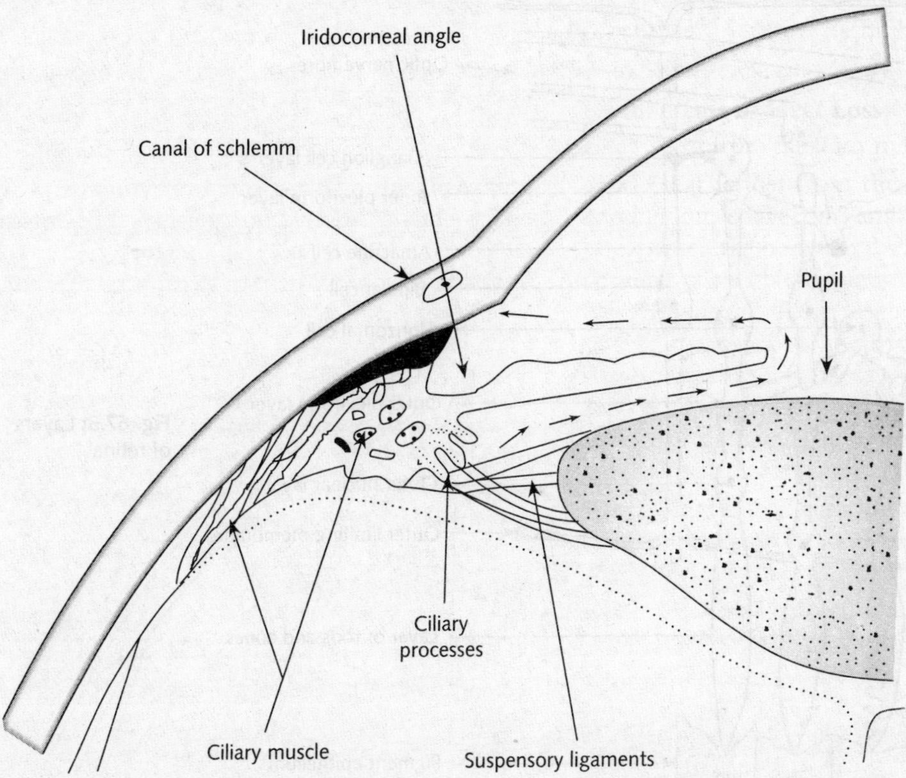


**Fig. 67.2:** Sclerocorneal junction with the ciliary body. Arrows indicate the movement of aqueous humour

The peripheral parts of the retina have more rods than cones and the acuity of vision is the lowest here.

## CONTENTS OF THE EYEBALL

The most important structure in the eyeball is the lens, which divides the interior of the eyeball into anterior and posterior segments. The anterior segment contains aqueous humour and is subdivided into anterior and posterior chambers by the iris (Fig. 67.2). The posterior segment contains a transparent gelatinous substance called the vitreous humour.

The aqueous humour is a watery fluid secreted by the ciliary processes into the posterior chamber. From here, it enters the anterior chamber through the pupil. It is absorbed into the canal of Schlemm in the sclerocorneal junction and ultimately, into the venous blood.

The aqueous humour maintains the intraocular pressure and the shape of the eyeball. It supplies nutrition to the avascular parts of the eyeball, for example, the cornea and lens. It also acts as a medium of refraction.

The normal intraocular tension is about 20 mmHg, the range being 16 to 22 mmHg. It is maintained by the balance between the formation and reabsorption of the aqueous humour. Abnormally high intraocular tension causes a serious disorder called glaucoma, which leads to blindness. Such high tension is commonly due to a defect in the drainage of the aqueous humour, caused by the closure of the iridocorneal angle.

## MECHANISM OF VISION

### Refracting media

In the human eye, an image of the outside world is formed on the retina. The rays of light entering

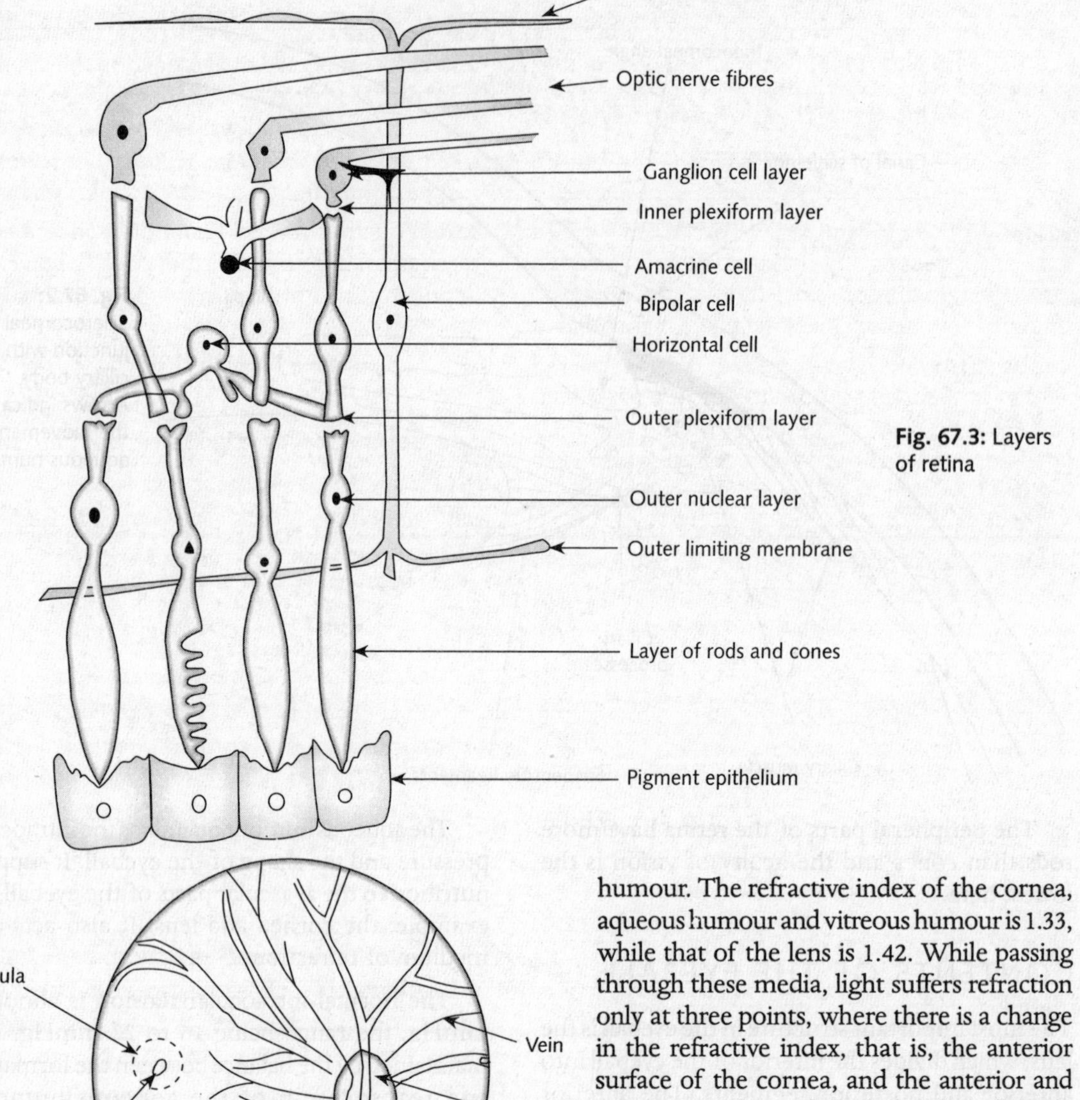


**Fig. 67.3:** Layers of retina

**Fig. 67.4:** Retinal blood vessels

the eyeball pass successively through various media of refraction to strike the retina. These media are the cornea, aqueous humour, lens and vitreous humour. The refractive index of the cornea, aqueous humour and vitreous humour is 1.33, while that of the lens is 1.42. While passing through these media, light suffers refraction only at three points, where there is a change in the refractive index, that is, the anterior surface of the cornea, and the anterior and posterior surfaces of the lens. The refractive index of air is 1. Hence, the maximum refraction occurs at the anterior surface of the cornea (air–corneal interface). The refraction is less at the lens (aqueous–lens interface) since the difference in the refractive indices at the former is greater than at the latter.

The refractive power of a lens is expressed in terms of dioptres.

$$\text{Dioptre (D)} = \frac{1}{\text{Focal length in metre (F)}}$$

In other words, 1 dioptre is the refractive power of a lens with a focal distance of 1 metre. A normal human eye has a dioptric power of 59 D, of which 43 D is contributed by the cornea and 15 D by the lens.

The lens is made of transparent collagen fibres which are enclosed in an elastic capsule. The suspensory ligaments are attached to the latter. The lens is biconvex, its posterior surface being more convex than the anterior one. When the lens becomes opaque, the condition is called cataract. Cataract may form as a result of old age, and diabetes mellitus increases the chances of cataract formation.

As a result of refraction, an inverted image of the object is formed on the retina. During the transmission of nerve impulses in the visual tracts, the image is changed in such a way that the visual cortex perceives it upright.

The importance of the lens lies in the fact that its curvature and, therefore, its refractive power can vary. Hence, objects at varying distances from the eye can be brought into sharp focus at the retina. This phenomenon is called accommodation.

## Accommodation

The ability of the eye to focus an object at varying distances is known as accommodation. However, by convention, it means a near response, that is, an adjustment of the visual apparatus from distant to near vision.

To allow this adjustment to take place, three changes, known as the accommodation reaction, occur. These are an increase in the anterior curvature of the lens, a constriction of the pupils, and convergence of the eyeballs.

*Increased anterior curvature of the lens*: The anterior curvature of the lens increases as a result of the bulging of its anterior surface. The tension in the suspensory ligaments keeps the lens in a relatively flat shape during distant vision. In near vision, the suspensory ligaments become loose due to a constriction of the ciliary ring caused by the contraction of the circular fibres in it, as well as a forward pull on the ciliary body by the contraction of the meridional fibres of the ciliary muscle (Fig. 67.5).

As a result of the combined action of the two types of fibres of the ciliary muscle, the pull exerted by the suspensory ligaments on the lens capsule becomes weaker. The elasticity of the lens capsule allows the lens to assume a more spherical shape, particularly on its anterior surface. The higher curvature of the lens increases its refractory power from 15 D (when the ciliary muscle is completely relaxed) to 29 D (when the ciliary muscle contracts). The ciliary muscle then becomes able to focus the divergent rays of a near object on the retina (Fig. 67.6).

*Constriction of pupils and convergence of eyeballs*: The constriction of the pupils, caused by the contraction of the sphincter pupillae, allows only the central part of the lens to be used and also sharpens the image.

When the eyeballs converge due to a contraction of the medial recti, the corresponding retinal points come into focus.

The accommodation reaction helps us see the details of objects that are close by, for example, reading a book.

### Pathway for accommodation

To bring about accommodation reaction, visual impulses take the following path:

Retina → occipital cortex (area 17) → association fibres → frontal eye field (area 8) → midbrain → 3rd cranial nerve nucleus of both sides → (i) medial rectus (extraocular muscle) and (ii) parasympathetic fibres to eye (sphincter pupillae and ciliary muscle).

### Far Point/Near Point

The maximum distance at which an object can be seen clearly without any adjustment of the visual apparatus is called the far point. To the normal eye, it is infinity, but for practical purposes, it is taken as 6 metres or 20 feet.

When the object is closer than 6 metres, the rays are divergent and can be brought into focus only

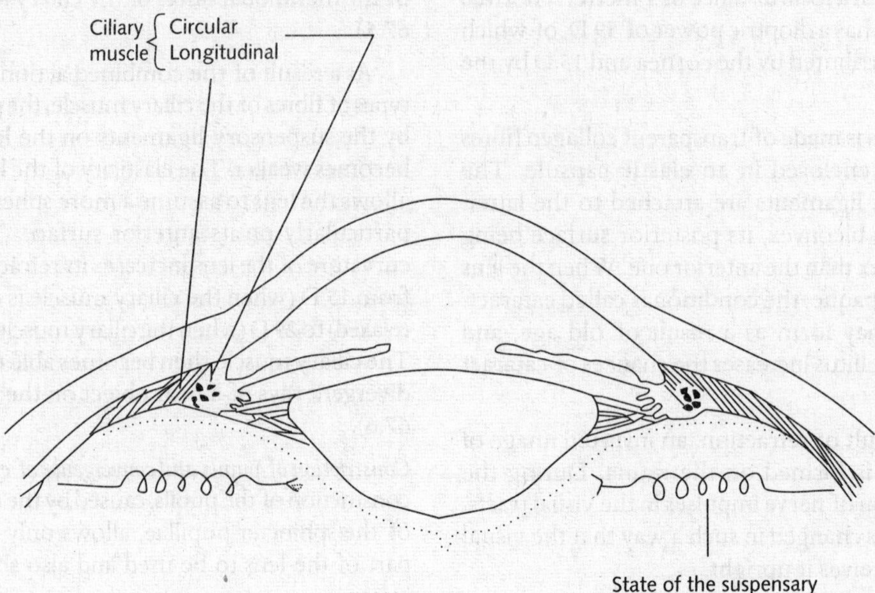


At rest the suspensory ligaments are taut and the lens is flat.

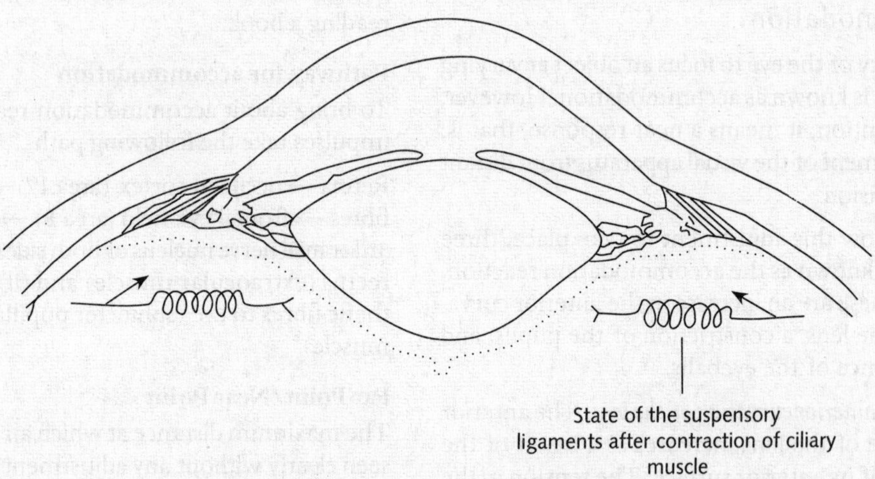


Due to contraction of the ciliary muscle the ciliary body is pulled forward and the suspensory ligaments are made loose this allows the anterior surface of the lens to bulge forward.

**Fig. 67.5:** The mechanism of increased anterior curvature of lens during accommodation

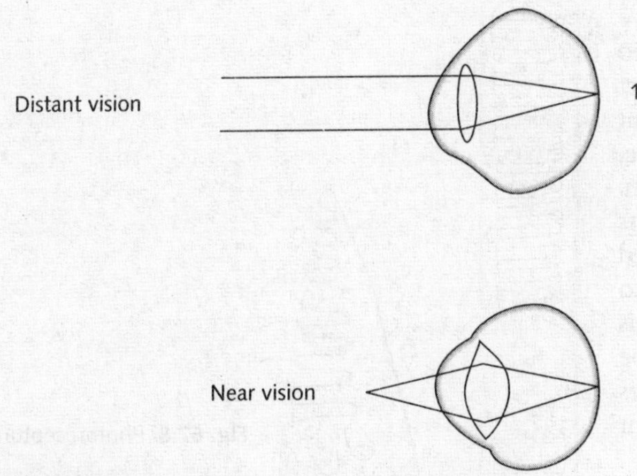


**Fig. 67.6:** Accommodation: 1. nonaccommodated eye, 2. accommodated eye

by an increase in the refractory power of the lens. The closer the object is to the eye, the more divergent are the rays of light and the greater is the refractive power required. The minimum distance from which an object can be seen clearly by the normal eye is called the near point. It is about 7 cm in young age and increases gradually with age. At the age of about 30 years, it is 14 cm, and by 40, it is 30 cm. It goes up more rapidly after the age of 40 years. The age-related decline in the power of accommodation is due to a decrease in the elasticity of the lens capsule, because of which the lens fails to become more spherical while focusing on near objects. This condition is called presbyopia and can be easily treated by the use of convex lenses for near vision.

## ERRORS OF REFRACTION

The eye is considered normal or emmetropic if the parallel rays of light are brought to a focus on the retina, when the ciliary muscle is completely relaxed. If there is a mismatch between the axial length of the eyeball and the focal length of its optical system, the image may be formed in front of or behind the retina and the object appears blurred. The errors of refraction are myopia, hypermetropia and astigmatism.

### Myopia

In this condition, the axial length of the eyeball is greater than the refractory power of its optical system. Therefore, the parallel rays of light from a distant object are brought to focus in front of the retina. The divergent rays of light can be focused on the retina only when the object is brought closer (less than 6 metres) to the eye. Thus, the eye fails to see distant objects but can see nearer objects clearly. Hence, this condition is also called short-sightedness. It can be corrected by using concave spherical lenses (Fig. 67.7). These lenses diverge the parallel rays of light so that they are focused on the retina.

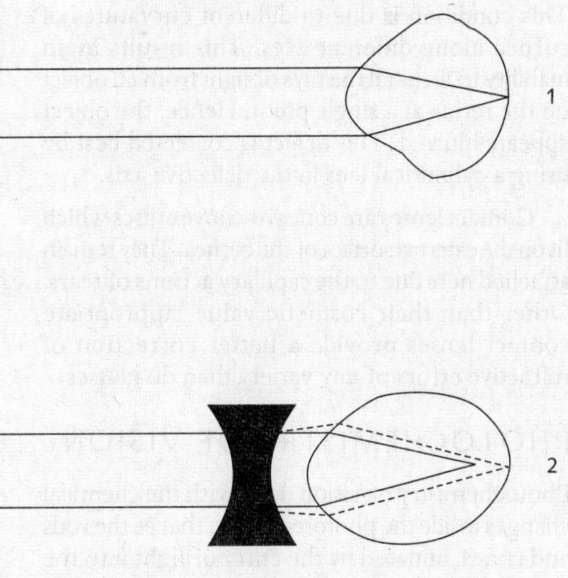


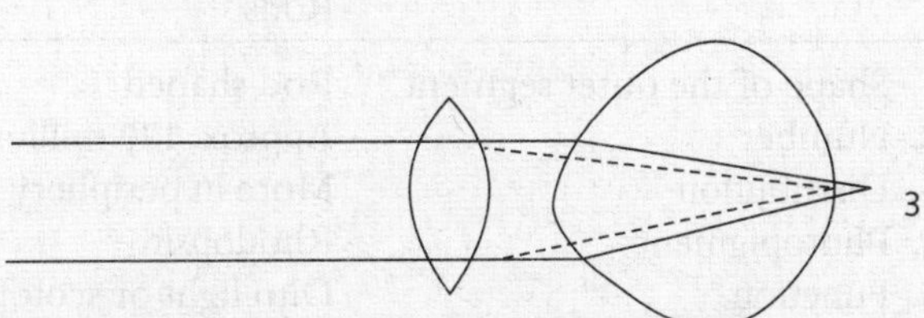


**Fig. 67.7:** Refractive errors and their correction: 1. emmetropia (normal); 2. myopia, corrected by concave glasses; 3. hypermetropia, corrected by convex glasses

### Hypermetropia

In this condition, the length of the eyeball is too short, so the parallel rays of light from a distant object are brought to focus behind the retina. Thus, distant objects cannot be seen clearly by the relaxed eye, but can be seen with the help of accommodation. There is greater difficulty in focusing on objects close by as the divergent rays from them are focused still farther behind the retina. Since the eye fails to see objects close by but can see distant objects, this condition is also called far-sightedness. It can be corrected by the use of biconvex spherical lenses (Fig. 67.7). These converge the parallel rays of light and focus them on the retina.

### Astigmatism

This condition is due to different curvatures of cornea along different axes. This results in an inability to focus all the rays of light from an object on the retina at a single point. Hence, the object appears blurred. This defect is corrected best by using a cylindrical lens in the defective axis.

Contact lenses are concavo-convex discs which fit on the external surface of the cornea. They remain attached here due to the capillary actions of tears. Other than their cosmetic value, appropriate contact lenses provide a better correction of refractive errors of any variety than do glasses.

## PHOTOCHEMISTRY OF VISION

Photochemistry of vision deals with the chemical changes inside the photoreceptors, that is, the rods and cones, initiated by the entry of light into the eye.

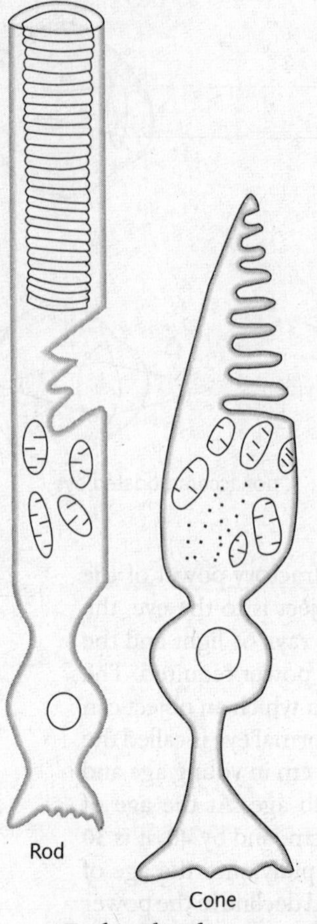

**Fig. 67.8:** Photoreceptors

Each rod and cone consists of an outer segment containing the photopigments in the discs, an inner segment, which contains the nucleus and other cytoplasmic organelles, and a synaptic zone (Fig. 67.8).

Table 67.1 lists the differences between the rods and cones.

**Table 67.1:** Comparison of rods and cones

| | Rods | Cones |
|---|---|---|
| 1. Shape of the outer segment | Rod-shaped | Cone-shaped |
| 2. Number | Approx. 120 million | Approx. 6 million |
| 3. Distribution | More in periphery | More in central region |
| 4. Photopigment | Rhodopsin | Iodopsin |
| 5. Function | Dim light or scotopic vision, as rods are more sensitive to light | (i) Bright light or photopic vision, as cones are less sensitive to light<br>(ii) Acuity of vision<br>(iii) Colour vision |

## VISUAL PIGMENTS

These substances are responsible for linking light energy to receptor activity. They are primarily of two types: the rod pigment and the cone pigment. Each pigment is made of an aldehyde form of vitamin A (retinol), called retinine (retinal), and a protein called opsin. The protein differs in different pigments. The protein in rods is scotopsin, while that in cones is photopsin. There are three types of photopsin. Both retinol and retinal can exist in 11-cis or 11-trans configuration. In rhodopsin, the retinine has 11-cis configuration.

### Rhodopsin cycle

**Decomposition**

Chemical changes occur in rhodopsin when light energy falls on it. The photoactivation of the electrons in it produces a change in the configuration of retinal from the 11-cis to the all-trans form. Its physical configuration also changes so that it cannot hold opsin and, therefore, the two (retinal and opsin) are separated. This change in configuration occurs through many intermediate stages, one of which is the production of metarhodopsin II. This is the key compound causing a change in the $Na^+$ permeability of the rods, leading to their activation.

The complete separation of opsin and retinine is called bleaching. This exhausts the pigment, so a continuous supply of pigment is necessary.

**Regeneration**

The first step in the regeneration of rhodopsin is the conversion of all-trans retinal to 11-cis retinal by the enzyme retinal isomerase. This then combines automatically with opsin to form rhodopsin (Fig. 67.9).

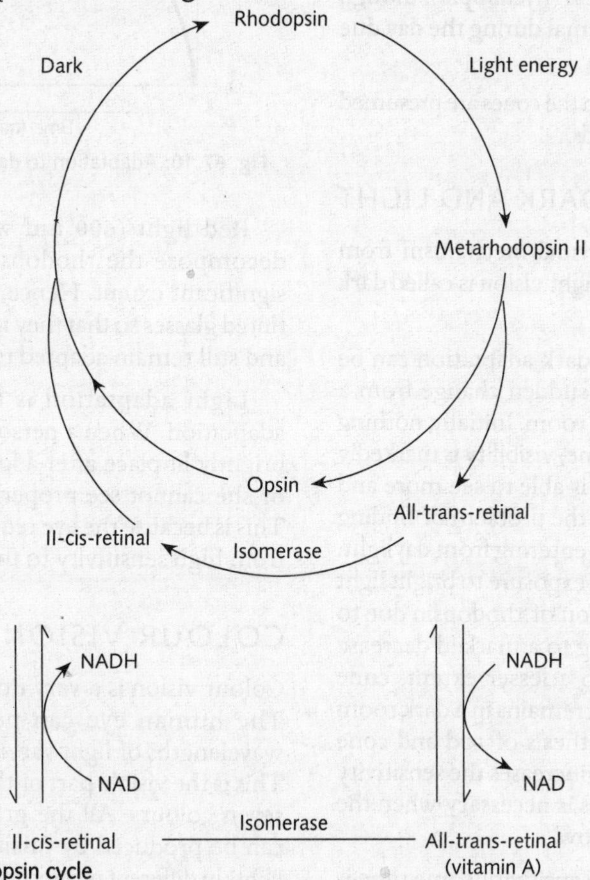


**Fig. 67.9:** The rhodopsin cycle

## Role of vitamin A

Vitamin A is present in the pigment layer of the retina and cytoplasm of the rods as all-trans retinol. All-trans retinal, which is produced by the bleaching of rhodopsin, can be reduced to all-trans retinol and stored. It can be oxidized to all-trans retinal whenever required.

All-trans retinol can be converted to 11-cis retinol, and then to 11-cis retinal, which combines with opsin to form rhodopsin. Thus, stored vitamin A acts as a continuous source of rhodopsin synthesis. Rhodopsin is bleached in the presence of light and is resynthesized in the dark. This is called the rhodopsin cycle.

A deficiency of vitamin A leads to inadequate synthesis of rhodopsin. This seriously affects rod function. A person with vitamin A deficiency suffers from night-blindness (nyctalopia), though his/her vision is fairly normal during the day due to the bright light.

The chemical changes in the cones are presumed to be the same as in the rods.

# ADAPTATION TO DARK AND LIGHT

The adjustment of the visual mechanism from bright light vision to dim light vision is called dark adaptation.

The phenomenon of dark adaptation can be easily observed during a sudden change from a brightly lit room to a dark room. Initially, nothing is visible but after some time, visibility is markedly increased and the person is able to see more and more. Take, for example, the problem of finding seats inside a theatre after entering from daylight. This is because prolonged exposure to bright light decreases the concentration of rhodopsin due to its decomposition, leading to a marked decrease in rod sensitivity and, to a lesser extent, cone sensitivity. When a person remains in a dark room for some time, the resynthesis of rod and cone photopigments gradually increases the sensitivity of the retina to light. This is necessary when the intensity of light is very low.

To change the retinal sensitivity, some time is required (Fig. 67.10). Dark adaptation is almost complete in about 20 minutes. The early part of the rise in sensitivity is due to the adaptation of the cones, and the later part is due to the adaptation of the rods.

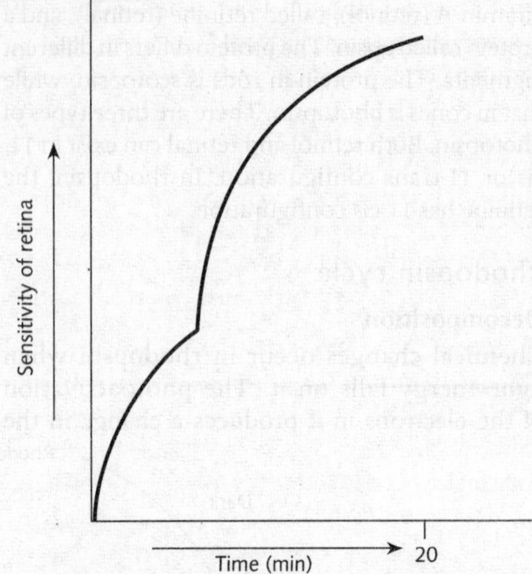


**Fig. 67.10:** Adaptation to dark

Red light (600 nm wavelength) does not decompose the rhodopsin in the rods to any significant extent. Hence, radiologists wear red-tinted glasses so that they may work in bright light and still remain adapted to the dark.

Light adaptation is the opposite of dark adaptation. When a person suddenly comes to a brightly lit place after a long stay in the dark, he or she cannot see properly and there is a glare. This is because the eye requires some time to shift from high sensitivity to the lowest.

# COLOUR VISION

Colour vision is a very important part of vision. The human eye can perceive colours with wavelengths of light varying from 400 to 700 nm. This is the visible part of the spectrum, which has seven colours. All the grades of visible colours can be produced by mixing red, green and blue lights in different proportions. These are, therefore, called the primary colours. The human eye contains three types of cones which have three types of photopigments—cyanolabe, chlorolabe and erythrolabe. These are sensitive to blue, green and red, respectively, and show the highest sensitivity to the wavelengths 430, 535 and 575 nm, respectively (Fig. 67.11).

One wavelength may stimulate more than one type of cone, as is clear from Fig. 67.11. Due to differential stimulation of the three different types of cones, we can perceive all the colours, that is, as many as 150. This trichromatic theory of colour vision is called the Young–Helmholtz theory. When all three types are stimulated maximally, the sensation of white is obtained. Black means the absence of colour.

## Abnormalities of colour vision

A normal person with the three types of normal cone pigments is called a trichromat and can detect all the colours properly. If a person needs a colour to be more bright so as to be able to distinguish it from other colours, he or she is said to be suffering from weakness in that colour. This weakness can exist in the case of any of the three primary colours. Protanomaly, deuteranomaly and tritanomaly are the terms used for weakness in red, green and blue, respectively. These individuals are trichromats, though one type of cone is defective. Red–green weakness is the most common.

When a person is unable to detect a colour or two, he/she is called colour blind. Colour blindness is of three types: protanopia, deuteranopia and tritanopia (for red, green and blue, respectively). These people lack one type of cone and are called dichromats. Tritanopia is very rare. When a person has only one type of cone (usually blue), he/she is called a monochromat. Such a person cannot see any colour, and can see only black and white, or different shades of grey.

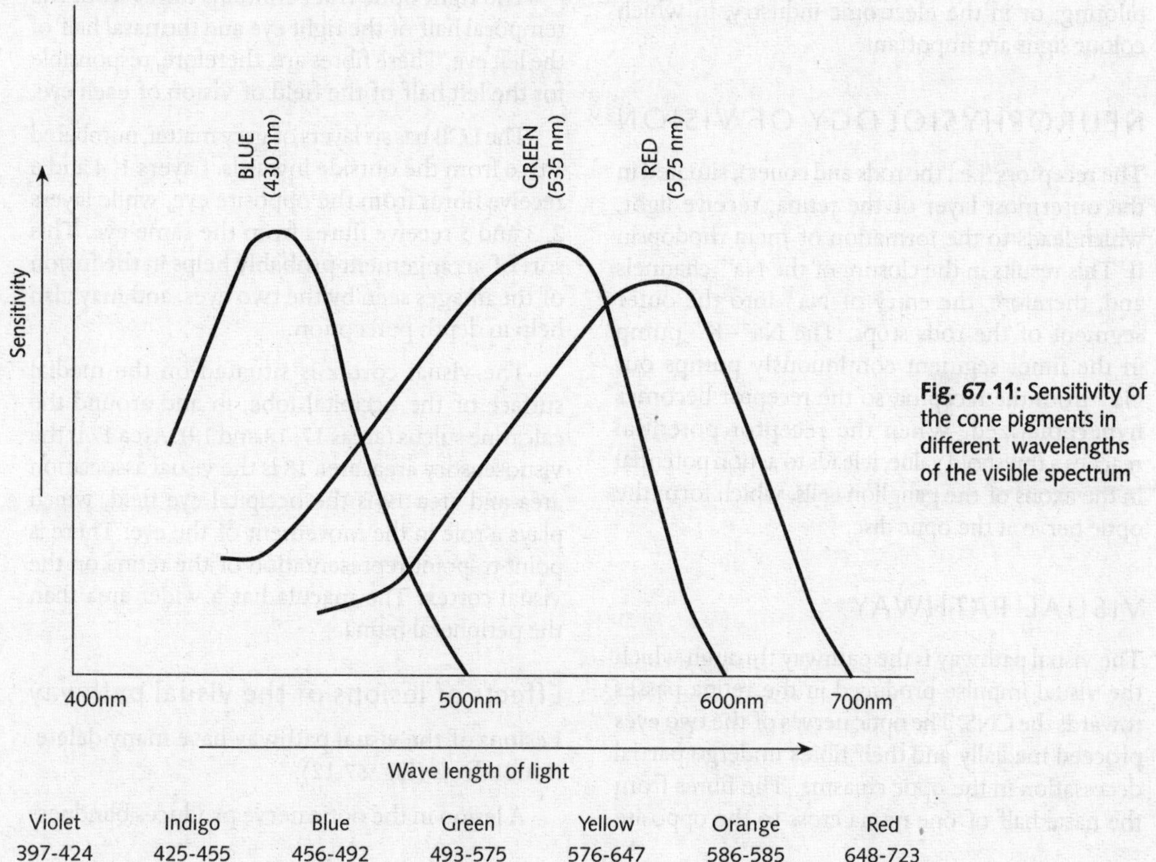


**Fig. 67.11:** Sensitivity of the cone pigments in different wavelengths of the visible spectrum

Colour blindness can be summarized as shown below.

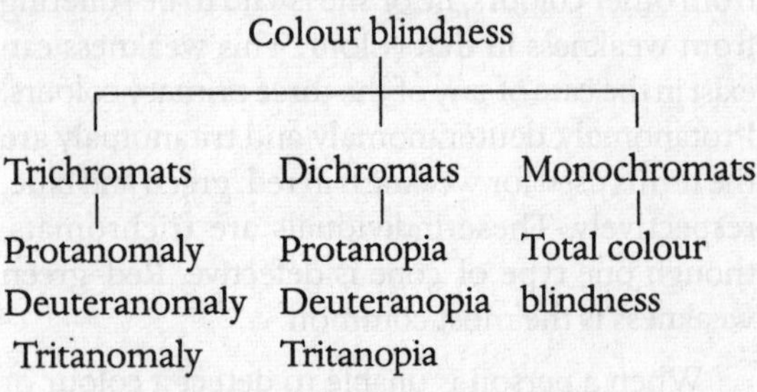


Colour blindness is a genetically inherited disorder. About 0.4 per cent of females and 8 per cent of males are colour blind. Females are the carriers of red and green defects, while males are the sufferers.

Colour vision is usually tested by Ishihara charts or the wool-matching test, among other tests. Colour blind persons are not employed in occupations such as driving cars or railway engines, piloting, or in the electronic industry, in which colour signs are important.

## NEUROPHYSIOLOGY OF VISION

The receptors (i.e., the rods and cones), situated in the outermost layer of the retina, receive light, which leads to the formation of meta-rhodopsin II. This results in the closure of the $Na^+$ channels and, therefore, the entry of $Na^+$ into the outer segment of the rods stops. The $Na^+$–$K^+$ pump in the inner segment continuously pumps out $Na^+$ from the receptor, so the receptor becomes hyperpolarized. When the receptor potential reaches a threshold value, it leads to action potential in the axons of the ganglion cells, which form the optic nerve at the optic disc.

## VISUAL PATHWAY

The visual pathway is the pathway through which the visual impulse produced in the retina passes towards the CNS. The optic nerves of the two eyes proceed medially and their fibres undergo partial decessation in the optic chiasma. The fibres from the nasal half of one retina cross to the opposite side to form optic tracts with the fibres from the temporal retina of that side. The optic tracts then proceed medially and end in the respective lateral geniculate body (LGB) of the thalamus. From the LGB, the fibres proceed to the visual cortex via the optic radiation.

A smaller number of fibres of the optic tract end in the superior colliculus (pretectal area of the midbrain). These are concerned with the light reflex (Fig. 67.12). When light is shown in one eye, its pupil contracts, and so does that of the opposite eye. Pupillary constriction is brought about by parasympathetic fibres from the third cranial nerve.

Each half of the retina receives light rays from the opposite half of the visual field. A visual field is the portion of the external world seen by each eye at a time. The field of vision in each eye can be recorded on a chart with the help of a perimeter.

The right optic tract contains fibres from the temporal half of the right eye and the nasal half of the left eye. These fibres are, therefore, responsible for the left half of the field of vision of each eye.

The LGB has six layers of grey matter, numbered 1 to 6 from the outside inwards. Layers 1, 4 and 6 receive fibres from the opposite eye, while layers 2, 3 and 5 receive fibres from the same eye. This sort of arrangement probably helps in the fusion of the images seen by the two eyes, and may also help in depth perception.

The visual cortex is situated on the medial surface of the occipital lobe, in and around the calcarine sulcus (areas 17, 18 and 19). Area 17 is the visuosensory area, area 18 is the visual association area and area 19 is the occipital eye field, which plays a role in the movement of the eye. There is point-to-point representation of the retina on the visual cortex. The macula has a wider area than the peripheral retina.

### Effects of lesions of the visual pathway

Lesions of the visual pathway have many deleterious effects (Fig. 67.12).

A lesion in the optic nerve produces blindness

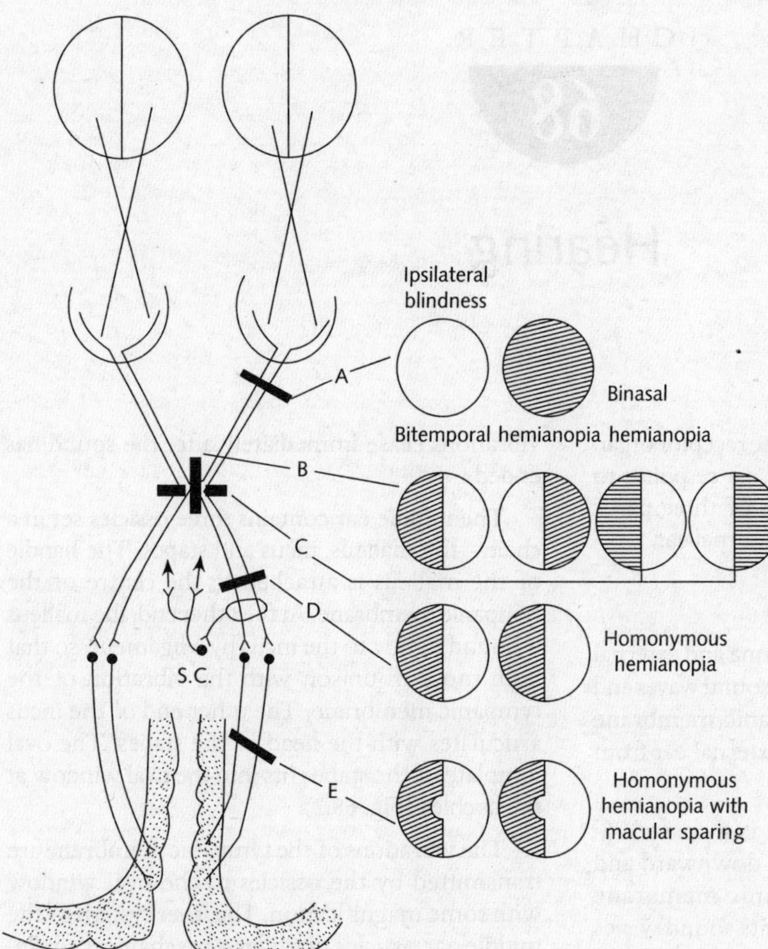


**Fig. 67.12:** Lesion at different points of the visual pathway and the corresponding defects in visual field: A. optic nerve, B. optic chiasma (nasal fibres), C. optic chiasma (temporal fibres), D. optic tract, E. optic radiation

of the eye concerned. A lesion at the crossing of the optic chiasma damages the nasal fibres from the retina and produces bitemporal hemianopia (loss of vision from one half of the visual field of each eye). A lesion on the lateral sides of the optic chiasma damages the temporal fibres from the retina and produces binasal hemianopia.

A lesion on the optic tract damages the nasal fibres from the opposite retina and the temporal fibres from the same retina. Hence, half of the field of vision on the same side of the eyes is lost. For example, left-sided homonymous hemianopia is produced if there is a lesion on the right optic tract.

A lesion in the optic radiation produces homonymous hemianopia. This is similar to lesions of the optic tract on the same side, but the macular field is usually not affected (macular sparing). A lesion in the occipital cortex results in scotoma of the opposite side. Since the fibres are widespread, only some of them are affected.

CHAPTER

68

# Hearing

Hearing is a special sense, the receptor organ for which is the ear. The ear responds to sound energy. It consists of three parts: the external ear, middle ear and internal ear.

## The external ear

The external ear consists of the pinna and external auditory canal. The pinna collects sound waves and directs them towards the tympanic membrane (eardrum), which separates the external ear from the middle ear.

The external auditory canal is a curved (S-shaped) canal, which is directed downward and forward. It protects the tympanic membrane from external injury and transmits sound waves from the air to the middle ear. It contains ceruminous and sebaceous glands, which secrete wax. The wax lubricates the skin and traps dust particles, preventing them from entering inside.

## The middle ear

The middle ear is a box-like structure filled with air. Its lateral wall is formed by the tympanic membrane. The medial wall, which separates it from the internal ear, has an oval and round window.

The tympanic membrane is oval and makes an angle of 45° with the floor of the external auditory canal (Fig. 68.1). The sound waves strike the tympanic membrane and set it vibrating. The vibrations cease immediately after the sound has ended.

The middle ear contains three ossicles set in a chain—the malleus, incus and stapes. The handle of the malleus is attached to the centre of the tympanic membrane. At the other end, the malleus is bound tightly to the incus by a ligament, so that both move in unison with the vibration of the tympanic membrane. The other end of the incus articulates with the head of the stapes. The oval footplate of the stapes fits into the oval window at the cochlea (Fig. 68.2).

The vibrations of the tympanic membrane are transmitted by the ossicles to the oval window with some magnification. The lever system of the middle ear ossicles provides a mechanical advantage, thereby increasing the force of movement by 1.3 times. In addition, the surface area of the tympanic membrane is approximately 50 $mm^2$, while that of the oval window is only 3 $mm^2$. The difference between the two surface areas increases the pressure on the oval window seventeen-fold. Thus, the total pressure exerted by the sound waves on the oval window is 22 times ($17 \times 1.3$) the pressure exerted on the tympanic membrane. This matches the independence resulting from the transmission of sound waves from the air to a fluid medium. Without this, even loud sounds are heard as whispers.

The middle ear contains two striated muscles,

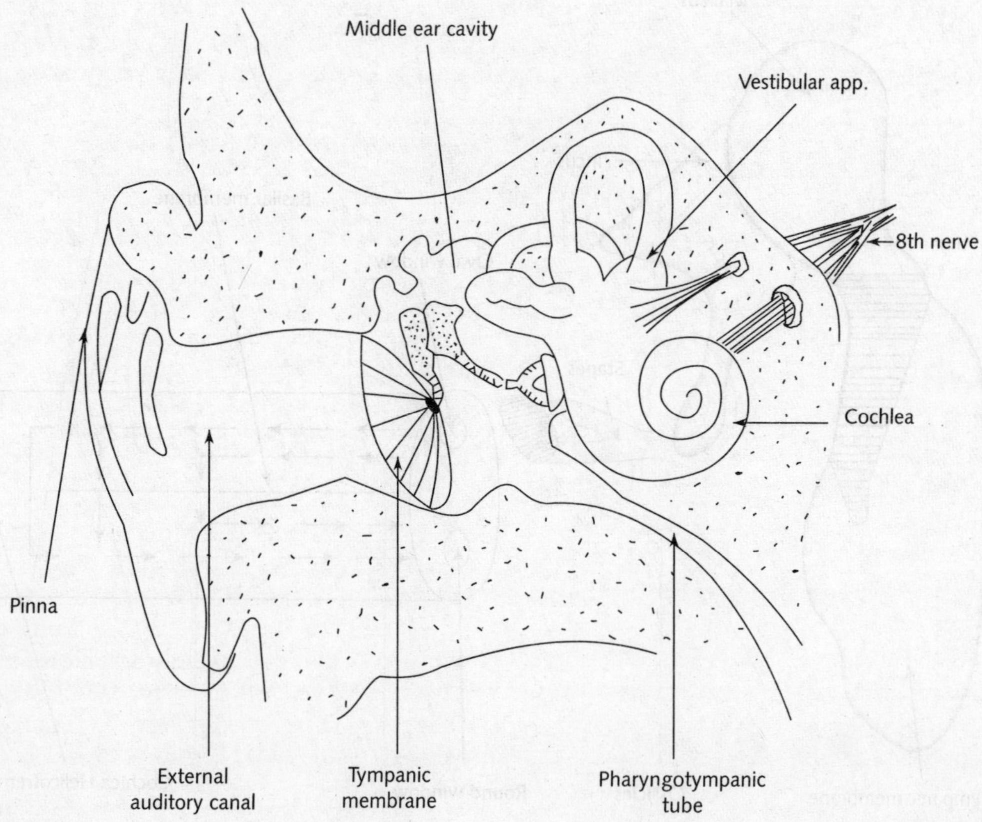


**Fig. 68.1:** Ear

the tensor tympani and the stapedius. The former is attached to the malleus and keeps the tympanic membrane taut. A contraction of the tensor tympani tends to pull the handle of the malleus inwards, whereas that of the stapedius pulls the stapes outwards, thereby making the ossicular chain ineffective in function. Both these muscles are reflexly activated by loud sounds (of 70-decibel intensity) and offer the cochlea some protection against excessively loud sounds. This is called the attenuation reflex. Its latent period is about 40 to 60 milliseconds and, therefore, it does not protect the cochlea against a sudden loud sound. The muscles of the middle ear are also activated just before speaking (i.e., vocalization). This reduces the sensitivity of the ear to one's own voice (masking).

The Eustachian tube connects the middle ear with the pharynx. It is normally closed, but opens during swallowing and keeps the middle ear pressure equal to that of the atmosphere. Thus, when open, it serves to equalize the pressures on either side of the tympanic membrane. Blockage of the Eustachian tube as a result of throat infection leads to inward retraction of the drum due to partial absorption of the air trapped in the middle ear. It also causes pain and hearing gets impaired temporarily.

## The internal ear

The internal ear consists of the cochlea and a vestibular apparatus, which is involved in the maintenance of posture as well as equilibrium. The cochlea is a coiled tube made of $2^{3/4}$ turns around a bony pillar, called the modiolus. A thin bony lamina projects from the side of the modiolus into the tube. Throughout its length, two membranes, the Reissner's membrane and the basilar membrane, divide the lumen of the

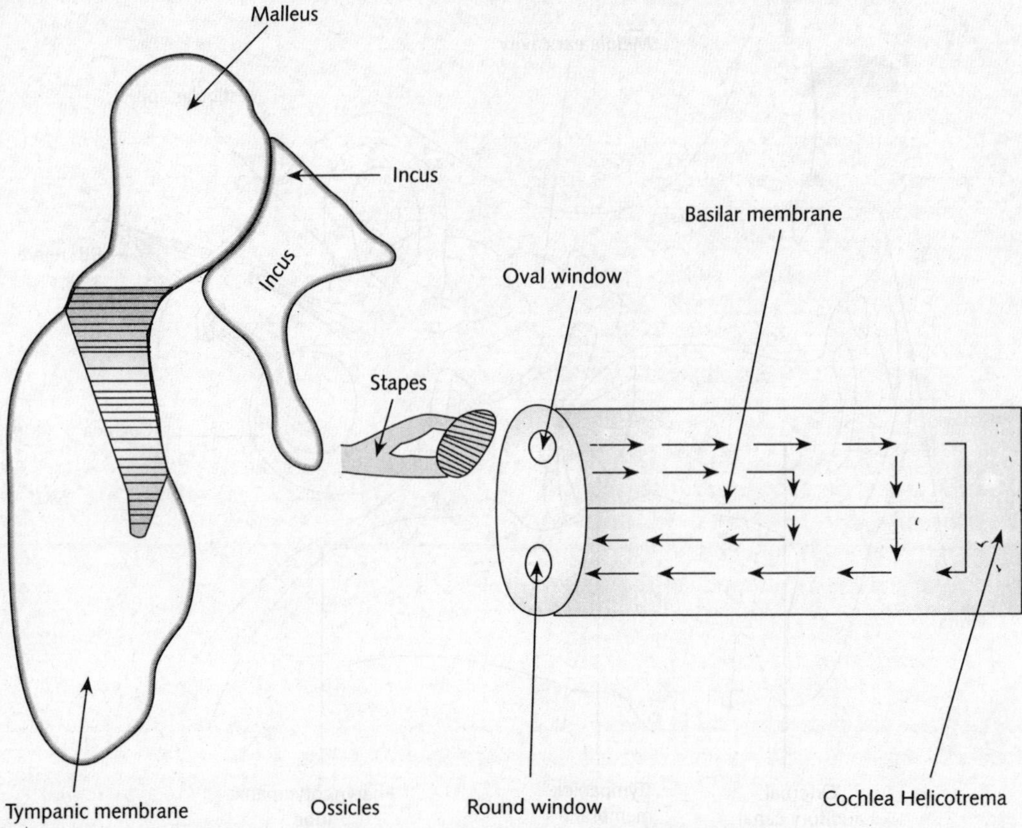


**Fig. 68.2:** Diagrammatic representation of the tympanic membrane, ossicles and cochlea

tube into three chambers, called the scala vestibuli, scala media and scala tympani (Fig. 68.3).

The Reissner's membrane separates the scala vestibuli from the scala media, while the basilar membrane separates the scala media from the scala tympani. The scala vestibuli and the scala tympani contain a fluid called perilymph, and the scala media contains endolymph. The perilymph has a high $Na^+$ and low $K^+$ content, while the endolymph has a high $K^+$ and low $Na^+$ content. The scala vestibuli and scala tympani communicate with each other through a small opening, called the helicotrema, at the apex of the cochlea. At the base, the cochlea opens into the middle ear by two openings, the oval window and the round window. The oval window is covered by the footplate of the stapes, to which it is loosely attached by the annular ligament. The round window is covered by a flexible secondary tympanic membrane.

## Organ of Corti

The organ of Corti, the sensory organ of hearing, receives sound energy and converts it into nerve impulse. It is situated in the scala media, over the basilar membrane, and extends along the whole length of the cochlea. The basilar membrane is made of transversely arranged, stiff, elastic fibres that project from the spiral lamina to the spiral ligament on the opposite wall. The length of the basilar membrane fibres increases progressively from 0.15 mm near the oval window to 0.5 mm at the helicotrema. The stiff, short fibres near the base vibrate at high frequency, while the lax, long fibres at the apex vibrate at low frequency.

The organ of Corti is made of hair cells. These are located on either side of the tunnel of Corti and are the receptors for the sensation of hearing. The tunnel of Corti is formed by the rods of Corti and is filled with perilymph from the scala tympani

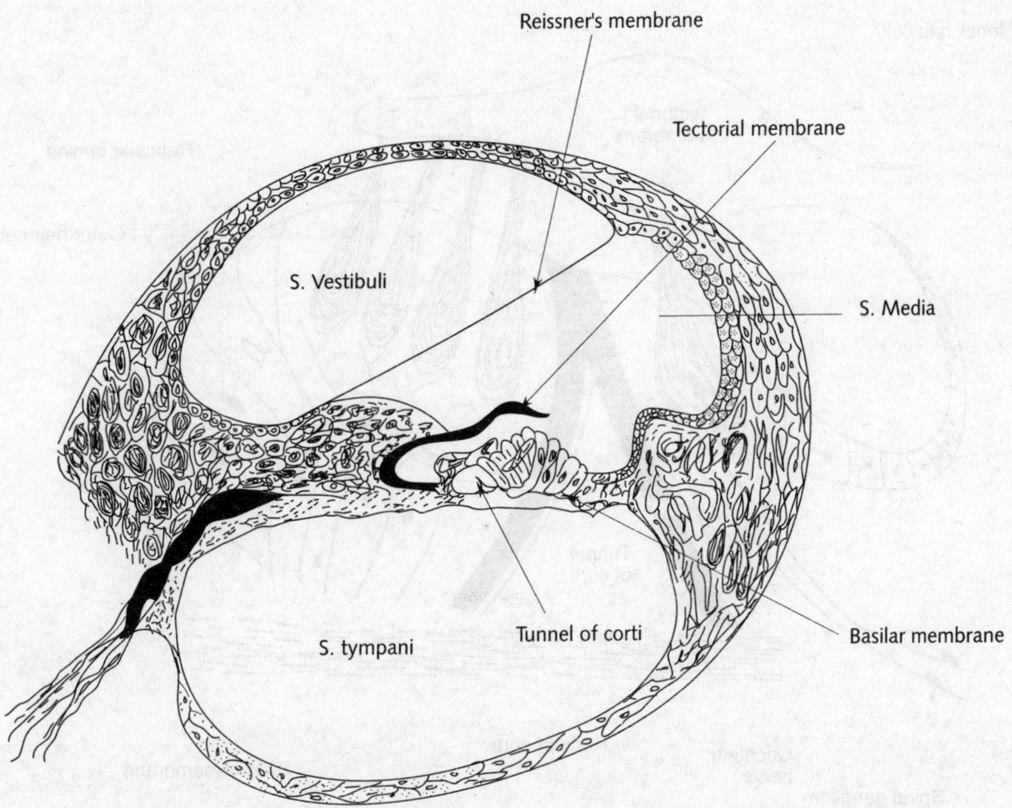


**Fig. 68.3:** Showing the three chambers of cochlea

below. The hair cells are of two types (in relation to the rods of Corti)—a single row of inner hair cells, internal to the inner rod, and 3 to 4 rows of outer hair cells, external to the outer rod. There are about 3500 inner hair cells and 20,000 outer hair cells. The minute hair or cilia project out of the upper surface, pierce through a tough membrane called the reticular lamina, to be embedded in a thin, viscous and elastic tectorial membrane present in the scala media (Fig. 68.4).

The cochlear (eight cranial) nerve afferents innervate the bases of the hair cells. About 90 per cent of them innervate the inner hair cells and 10 per cent innervate a large number of outer hair cells. These nerve fibres converge on the cell bodies of spiral ganglion. The spiral ganglion containing the cell bodies of the cochlear nerve is located within the modiolus.

The cochlear nerve also contains inhibitory efferent fibres from the superior olivary nucleus (olivo-cochlear). These innervate the hair cells, particularly the outer ones. These seem to provide a mechanism that helps improve hearing.

## TRANSMISSION OF SOUND

Sound waves enter the external ear and hit the tympanic membrane, which then vibrates accordingly. This moves the ossicular chain. The vibration is then transferred to the cochlea through the oval window by movements of the footplate of the stapes. The sound pressure is magnified in the middle ear, overcoming the inertia of the ossicles and the impedance caused by the change in the medium for the transmission of sound (i.e., air to fluid). Movements of the footplate of the stapes transmit the sound pressure to the scala vestibuli and waves are produced in the perilymph. The pressure then passes down to the scala media.

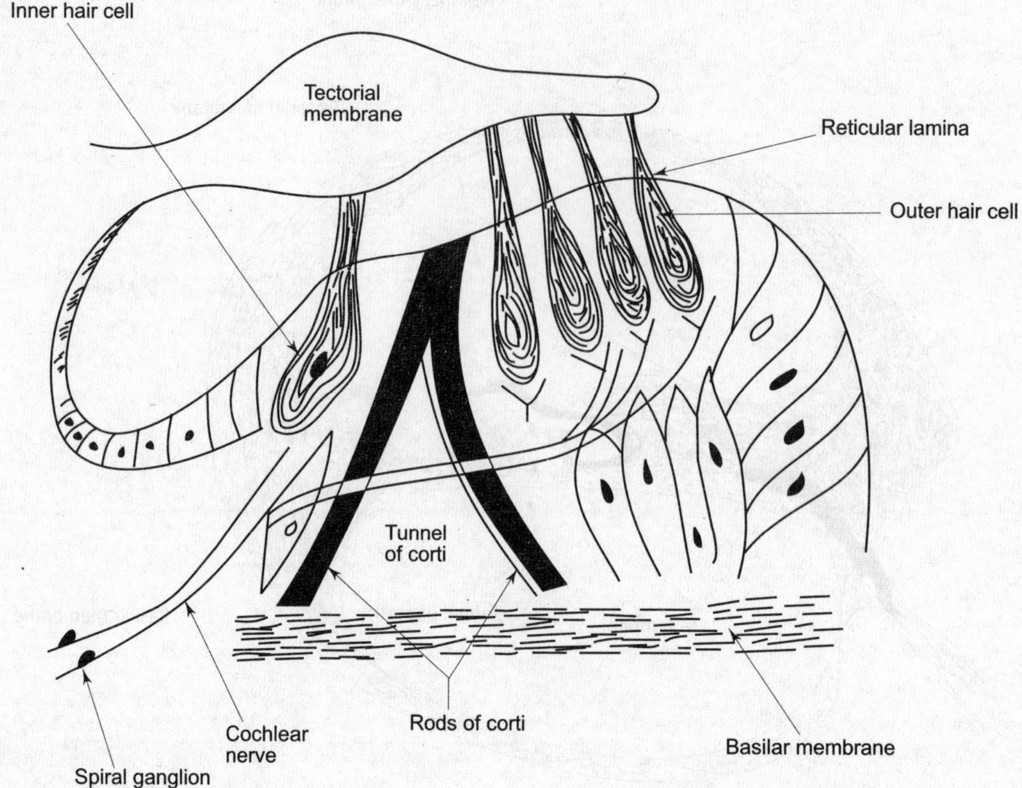


**Fig. 68.4:** The organ of Corti

This moves the basilar membrane up and down. The pressure is then transmitted to the scala tympani and is ultimately released due to the bulging of the secondary tympanic membrane covering the round window (Fig. 68.2).

**Mechanism of Stimulation of Hair Cells**

When there is a movement of the basilar membrane along with the organ of Corti (which is on the membrane) due to the passage of a sound, a sheer force is produced by the relative lateral displacement of the basilar and tectorial membranes (Fig. 68.5).

The hair cells thus move in relation to the tectorial membrane, and this makes the cilia bend. If the cells move towards the longest cilia, they (hair cells) are depolarized and hyperpolarized due to the bending of the cilia in the opposite direction. The changes in the membrane potential of the hair cells seem to excite the cochlear nerve endings.

Ultimately, the sensation of sound is transmitted as action potentials in the auditory pathway.

## Auditory pathway

The auditory pathway is a bit more complicated than the other sensory pathways. Fibres from each cochlea reach both sides of the cortex and the second-order neurons of this pathway end at different levels.

All the fibres arising from the spiral ganglion of the organ of Corti enter the dorsal or ventral cochlear nuclei, located in the upper part of the medulla. The second-, third- and fourth-order neurons ascend and relay successively in the superior olivary nucleus, inferior colliculus and medial geniculate body of the thalamus. Finally, they terminate in the primary auditory area of the cerebral cortex, via auditory radiation.

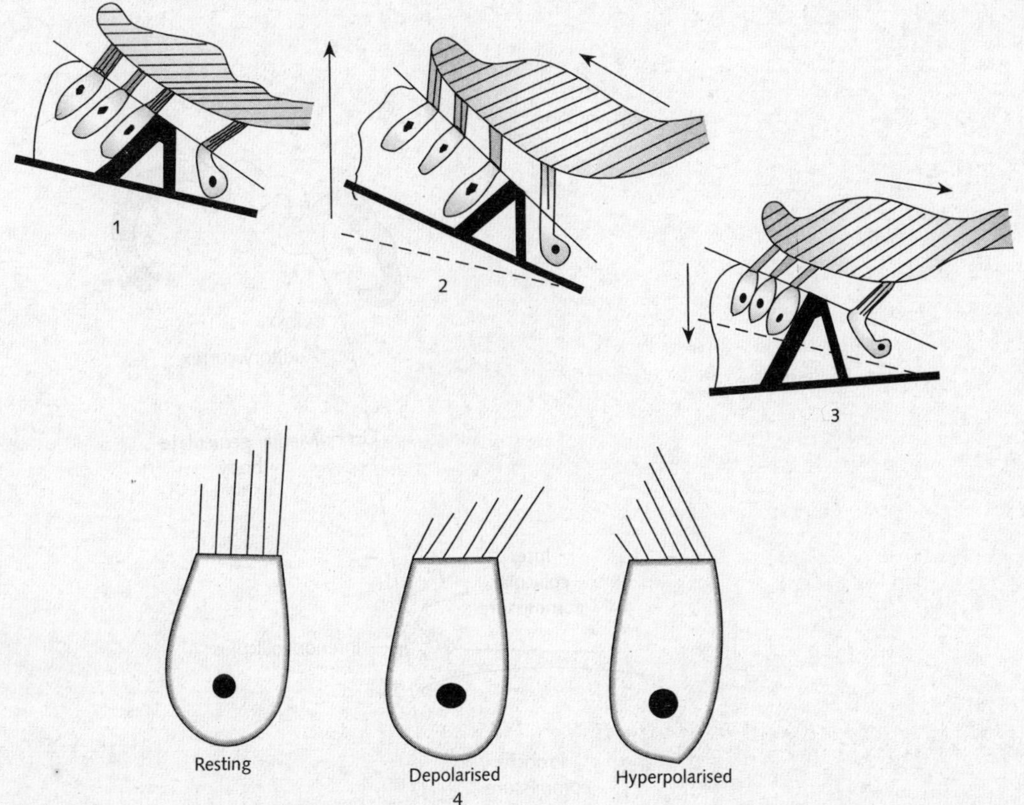


**Fig. 68.5:** Mechanism of stimulation of hair cells: 1. stationary, 2. upward movement, 3. downward movement, 4. hair cells

The trapezoid bodies and the nuclei of the lateral lemniscus are additional relay stations for some of the fibres arising from the ventral cochlear nuclei. The fibres from the dorsal cochlear nuclei reach the inferior colliculus without any relay in between (Fig. 68.6).

The superior olivary nucleus and the inferior colliculus act as centres for the integration of the ascending afferent and descending efferent auditory fibres from the auditory cortex. The fibres are given to the superior olivary nucleus for the extrapyramidal function, to the reticular formation for arousal and alertness, to the inferior colliculi for auditospinal reflexes (e.g., turning the head towards the source of the sound), and to the cerebellum. The integration of visual and auditory information occurs because of the interconnection between the superior and inferior colliculi.

The primary auditory cortex (Brodmann's area 41) is situated in the depth of the lateral cerebral fissure. The apical region of the cochlea is located anteriorly and the basal region posteriorly. The auditory association area is located around the primary auditory cortex and extends to the lateral surface of the superior temporal gyrus.

## MECHANISM OF HEARING

Sound consists of waves of alternating condensation and rarefaction of an elastic medium, such as air or water. Hearing is the subjective experience of exposure to sound waves. We not only hear and interpret a large variety of sounds, but can also discriminate their loudness, pitch and tone. The localization and understanding of the meaning of a sound are also necessary and important.

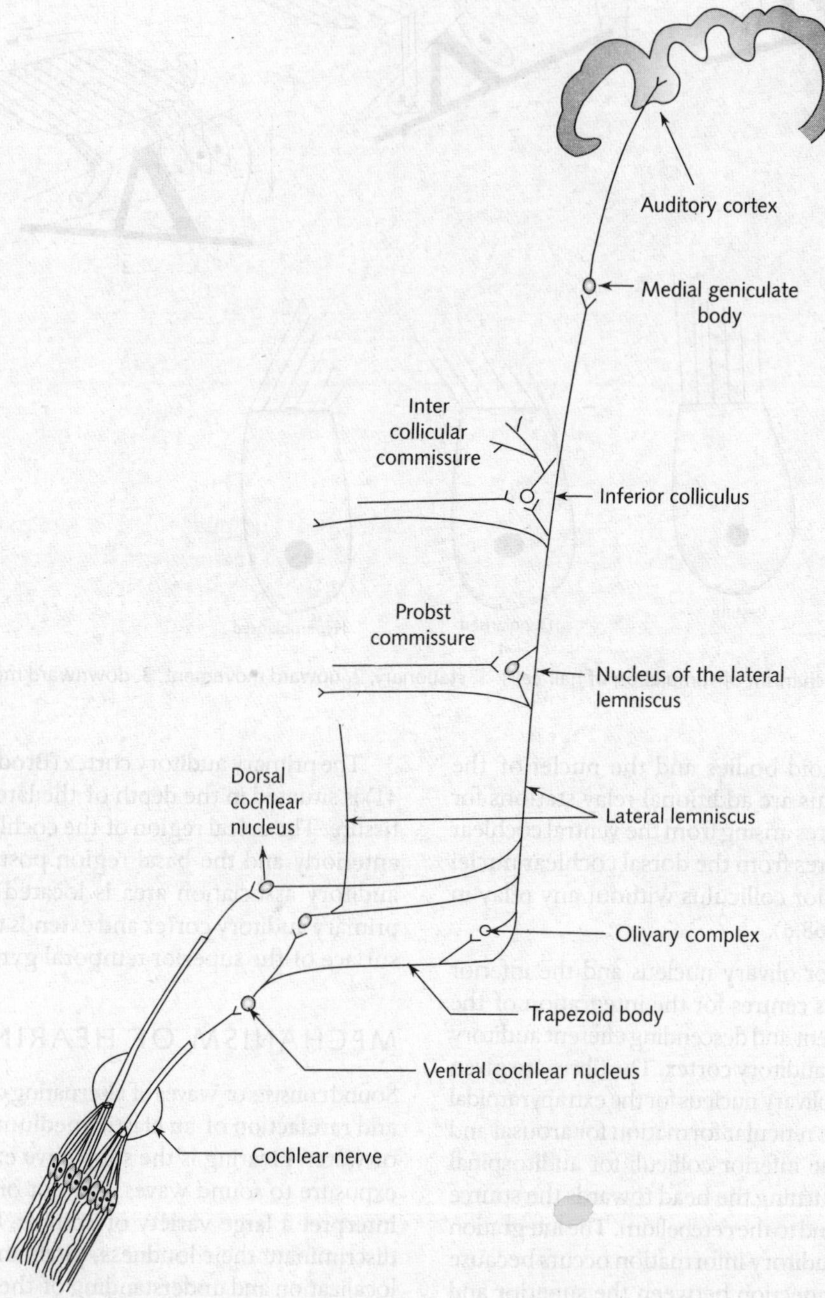


Fig. 68.6: Auditory pathways

The normal human ear can hear sound waves of frequencies ranging from 20 to 20,000 cycles/second (Hertz), though it can hear best between 1000 to 3000 Hz and can detect small changes in frequency. Within this range, the minimum sound pressure that can be detected by the human ear is 0.0002 dynes/$cm^2$. Normally, the sound pressure is expressed in decibles (one-tenth of a bel). It is a logarithmic scale and 0.0002 dynes/$cm^2$ is taken as 0 decibel. This is the intensity of sound that is just perceptible to a normal human ear (threshold of hearing). The human ear can appreciate a change of approximately 1 decibel in the intensity of sound. The intensities of common sounds are as follows:

| *Sound* | *Intensity (decibel)* |
|---|---|
| Hearing threshold | 0 |
| Whisper | 20–30 |
| Normal conversation | 40–60 |
| Heavy traffic | 80 |
| Loud music | 100–120 |
| Jet plane | 160 |

A sound of more than 100 decibels causes discomfort and above this level, there is pain and a risk of deafness.

### Determination of Hearing

The loudness of sound is a function of the amplitude of sound waves in the basilar membrane. The greater the intensity of sound, the higher the amplitude of the sound waves and the higher the frequency of action potentials in the cochlear nerve. The number of afferent nerve fibres stimulated is also correspondingly high.

### Determination of Pitch

The pitch of a sound depends on the frequency of its waves. The basilar membrane acts as a peripheral analyser of pitch. A high-pitched sound sets the lower (basal) part of the basilar membrane into vibration, whereas low-frequency sounds make the apical part of the membrane vibrate. Thus, depending on the pitch of a sound, the hair cells of different regions of the basilar membrane are stimulated. This is known as the 'place principle'. Correspondingly afferent nerve fibres from different regions of the basilar membrane are stimulated in response to sounds of different frequencies. The spinal organization of afferent nerve fibres is carried all along the auditory pathway.

### Localization of Sound

A person can detect the direction from which a sound is coming fairly accurately, but both ears are required for this. The detection depends on two cues. One is the time lag between the entry of the sound waves in the two ears. For example, if a sound originates from the right side of a person, it reaches the right ear earlier. The other cue is the difference between the intensity of the sound in the two ears. For example, the ear which is distant from the source of the sound will receive a sound of lower intensity.

## DEAFNESS

Deafness is an impairment of hearing. It may be partial or complete. There are two types of deafness—conduction deafness and nerve deafness.

### Conduction Deafness

Conduction deafness results when the conduction of sounds to the internal ear is affected. This may be caused by a foreign body or wax in the external ear, or by perforation of the tympanic membrane. Temporary deafness may also be the result of a decrease in the air pressure in the middle ear, due to the absorption of air in it when the Eustachian tube is closed for some time, as in throat infection. Fixation of the stapes in the oval window (otosclerosis) also leads to conduction deafness.

### Nerve Deafness

This may be caused by damage to the cochlea (i.e., the organ of Corti) by exposure to loud sounds and so on. Damage to the auditory nerve, for example, due to injections of streptomycin in the treatment of tuberculosis, also results in nerve deafness.

Usually, two simple tests, Weber's test and Rinne's test, are done to distinguish unilateral conduction deafness from nerve deafness. In these, a tuning fork with a frequency of 250 Hz is used.

These tests are based on a comparison between the perception of sound when conducted through the bone and of that conducted through the air. Normally, air conduction is better than bone conduction. In conduction deafness, however, bone conduction becomes better than air conduction. In nerve deafness, both air conduction and bone conduction are less than normal.

A comparison of air and bone conduction can be made more accurately by audiometry in a soundproof room. Each ear is tested separately for various frequencies of sound and the threshold of hearing is determined and plotted on a graph. This helps determine the degree of deafness and the frequency range worst affected. This is very important in prescribing an appropriate hearing aid.

# Index